Essential Maths

Book 7H

David Rayner, Michael White

Elmwood Press

First published 2008 by
Elmwood Press
80 Attimore Road
Welwyn Garden City
Herts. AL8 6LP
Tel. 01707 333232

ISBN 9781 902 214 733

Numerical answers are published in a separate book

Typeset and illustrated by Domex e-Data Pvt. Ltd.
Printed and bound by Mateu Cromo

PREFACE

Essential Maths Book 7H has been written for pupils who are working towards National Curriculum Level 6. Level 5 work is consolidated and then developed further.

Although there is no set path through the books, the topics appear in the order suggested in the National Numeracy Strategy guide. Broadly speaking, the book is split into 6 units. Each unit of work can be used during one half-term with appropriate revision material at the end of the unit. Many topics are reviewed later in the book, in line with the NNS guide.

Puzzle activities and mental arithmetic tasks can be found between the units, to be used whenever appropriate. Investigations appear regularly throughout the book. Ideas for discussing and exploring themes from the 'history of mathematics' are included between each pair of units.

The authors believe that children learn mathematics most effectively by *doing* mathematics. Many youngsters who find mathematics difficult derive much more pleasure and enjoyment from the subject when they are doing questions which help them build up their confidence. Pupils feel a greater sense of satisfaction when they work in a systematic way and when they can appreciate the purpose and the power of the mathematics they are studying.

No textbook will have the 'right' amount of material for every class. The authors believe that it is preferable to have too much material rather than too little. Opportunities for functional maths are incorporated into activities throughout the book.

Most work is broken down into two parts. 'M' exercises are aimed at all children at this level. 'E' exercises provide extension work. Pupils may move naturally onto this work after an 'M' exercise or teachers may judge that a number of students should *only* tackle 'E' exercise.

Pupil self-assessment is a very important part of assessment for learning. Regular 'check yourself' sections appear throughout the book. Answers to these parts only are provided at the back of the book for immediate feedback.

David Rayner and Michael White

CONTENTS

UNIT 1

1.1 Whole number arithmetic

In section 1.1 you will learn how to:

- use place value of digits in whole numbers
- add, subtract and multiply with whole numbers
- divide a whole number by a single digit number

Place value

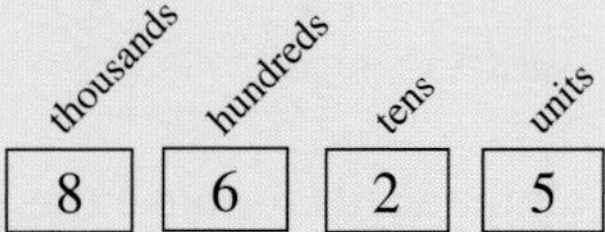

- Whole numbers are made up from units, tens, hundreds, thousands and so on.
- For the number 8625 we write 'eight thousand, six hundred and twenty-five'.

Exercise 1M

1 The figure 2 in this number 7 3 2 9 6 stands for 2 hundreds or 200.
What do these figures stand for?
(a) the 3 (b) the 9 (c) the 7

2 Starting with the number 8 5 6 0 7, write down the number you get when you
(a) add 100 (b) add 1000 (c) add 10
(d) add 10 000 (e) add 1 (f) add 100 000

3 Write down the number which is
(a) 1 less than 300 (b) 1 less than 6700 (c) 10 less than 4500
(d) 10 less than 500 (e) 100 less than 7000 (f) 1 less than 6500

4 Here are four number cards:

(a) Use all the cards to make the largest possible number.
(b) Use all the cards to make the smallest possible number.

5 Here are five number cards:

4 5 0 9 6

(a) Use all the cards to make the largest possible number.
(b) Use all the cards to make the smallest possible number.
Do not use 0 as the first card.

6 Read this news item which appeared in a newspaper.
When the cheese was cut and used to make sandwichs there were 675 100 visits to the website.
(a) Write this number in words.
(b) Try to think of a website which might appeal to the same sort of people.

Cheese web frenzy

More than 400,000 cheese-lovers have visited the website www.cheddarvision.tv to watch the maturing process of a round of Cheddar cheese. Viewing is expected to reach a frenzy tomorrow as the 441b (20kg) cheese is subjected to its first quality check. The project is based at a farm in Shepton Mallet, Somerset.

7 Here are five number cards:

6 3 4 8 9

(a) Use all the cards to make the largest possible *odd* number.
(b) Use all the cards to make the smallest possible *even* number.

8 (a) Lisa puts a 2 digit whole number into her calculator.
She multiplies the number by 10.
Fill in *one* other digit which you know must now be on the calculator.
(b) Lisa starts again with the same 2 digit number and this time she multiplies it by 1000.
Fill in all five digits on the calculator this time.

4 ☐ ☐.

☐ 6 ☐ ☐ ☐.

9 Find a number $\boxed{p}$ so that $6 \times \boxed{p} + 8 = 68$.

10 Find a pair of numbers $\boxed{a}$ and $\boxed{b}$ for which $8 \times \boxed{a} + \boxed{b} = 807$.

11 Find a pair of numbers $\boxed{p}$ and $\boxed{q}$ for which $7 \times \boxed{p} + 5 \times \boxed{q} = 7050$.

12 Show how you can use the numbers **63, 100, 2000** and **2** to make the number 2035 by adding and subtracting.

13 Here are five number cards: 4 2 7 5 8

(a) Use all the cards to make the smallest number divisible by five.
(b) Use two of the cards to make a prime number ☐ ☐.
(c) Use three of the cards to make a number which is 426 less than 1000.
(d) Use three of the cards to make a number which is divisible by three.

14 Find three numbers c, d and e for which
$(8 \times c) + (3 \times d) + (6 \times e) = 8360$

15 Find three numbers m, n and x for which
$7 \times m + 5 \times n + x = 7504$

16 The 4th of February 2008 is written 4 – 2 – 08. This is a special date because $4 \times 2 = 8$
(a) How many such dates are there in 2010?
(b) How many such dates are there in 2095?
Give the actual dates in each case.

Arithmetic

Here are some examples to remind you of non-calculator methods.

(a)
$$\begin{array}{r} 308 \\ +\ 4865 \\ \hline 5173 \\ \hline {\scriptstyle 1\ \ 1} \end{array}$$

(b)
$$\begin{array}{r} 27^{7}\not{8}^{1}4 \\ -\ \ 635 \\ \hline 2149 \\ \hline \end{array}$$

(c) $19 \times 100 = 1900$

(d)
$$\begin{array}{r} 247 \\ \times\ \ \ 5 \\ \hline 1235 \\ \hline {\scriptstyle 2\ 3\ \ } \end{array}$$

(e)
$$\begin{aligned} 115 \times 40 &= (115 \times 4) \times 10 \\ &= 460 \times 10 \\ &= 4600 \end{aligned}$$

Exercise 2M

Work out, without a calculator.

1 $624 + 88$

2 $318 + 327$

3 $85 + 517 + 407$

4 $3255 + 274$

5 $6816 + 2803$

6 $4186 + 25\,804$

7 $653 - 242$

8 $414 - 205$

9 $887 - 48$

10 $1024 - 837$

11 $524 - 176$

12 $29 + 416 - 240$

13 47×6

14 124×6

15 2061×7

16 207×10

17 2023×5

18 13×100

19 23×30

20 214×200

21 Here are five number cards: [5] [3] [9] [7] [4]
(a) Use three cards to make the number which is closest to 500.
(b) Use four cards to make two prime numbers which add up to 100. $\square\square + \square\square = 100$
(c) Use four cards so that $\square \times \square + \square + \square = 74$

Exercise 2E

Copy and complete the cross number puzzle.

Clues across

1. 413 – 61
3. 17 × 4
5. 3 × 3 × 3 × 3
6. 9 × 16
7. Half of 980
8. 1003 – 985
10. 472 + 256
11. 712 – 618
12. 4006 – 2994

Clues down

1. 5 × 11 × 7
2. 17 × 3
3. 7 + 17 + 117 + 499
4. 173 – 89
6. 9 × 12 – 89
7. 5002 – 121
8. 28 + 29 + 31 + 32
9. 9 × 49
10. (16 × 5) – 9

1	2			3	4
5			6		
		7			
	8				9
10				11	
12					

Exercise 3M

1 A man died in 2008 aged 63 years. In what year was he born?

2 How many £10 notes are there in £760 000?

3 The numbers 3, 4 and 7 can make 19 as follows 7 + 3 × 4 = 19
Fill in the boxes with either +, –, × or ÷ below
(a) 9 □ 3 □ 4 = 21
(b) 6 □ 12 □ 3 = 10
(c) 9 □ 10 □ 5 = 7
(d) 6 □ 3 □ 2 □ 4 = 8
(e) 8 □ 4 □ 4 □ 4 = 18

4 How many spots are there on nine ordinary dice?

5 The length of this rectangle is twice the width.
The perimeter is 42 cm. Calculate the area of the rectangle.

6 Eight racks of CDs each contained 95 CDs.
How many CDs were there altogether?

7 Answer true or false:
(a) 7 + 8 + 9 + 10 + 11 = 5 × 9
(b) 1 + 2 + 3 + ... + 14 + 15 = 15 × 8
(c) $\frac{(100 - 75) \times 4}{10} = (20000 - 19000) \div 100$

8 A determined frog is climbing a greasy rope. It takes $8\frac{1}{2}$ seconds to climb up and then half a second to slide down.

How many complete up and down journeys can he make in three minutes?

9 Micheline has the same number of 10p and 50p coins. The total value of the coins is £9. How many of each coin does she have?

10 I am a two digit number. The sum of my digits is 13. The product of my digits is 36. What number am I?

11 One subtraction using the digits 2, 3, 4, 5, 6 is [642 – 35]

(a) Which subtraction using all the digits 2, 3, 4, 5, 6 gives the answer 481?

(b) Which subtraction using all the digits has the smallest positive answer?

12 Work out the missing numbers.

(a) 927 + □ = 1001 (b) 542 – □ = 231 (c) □ × 7 = 1645

(d) □ ÷ 9 = 24 (e) □ – 950 = 1222 (f) 2000 ÷ □ = 50

13 Mike knows that 221 × 31 = 6851. Explain how he can use this information to work out 222 × 31.

14 Given that 357 × 101 = 36 057, work out 358 × 101 without multiplying.

15 Use each of the digits 1 to 6. Put one digit in each box to make the statement true.

[5] □ × □ = [1] □ □

16 Find two numbers which multiply together to give 54 and which add up to 21.

□ × □ = 54, □ + □ = 21

17 Find three numbers which multiply together to give 216 and which add up to 19.

□ × □ × □ = 216 □ + □ + □ = 19

18 A Toyota car uses 9 litres of petrol for every 80 km travelled. Petrol costs 95p per litre. Calculate the cost in £s of travelling 400 km.

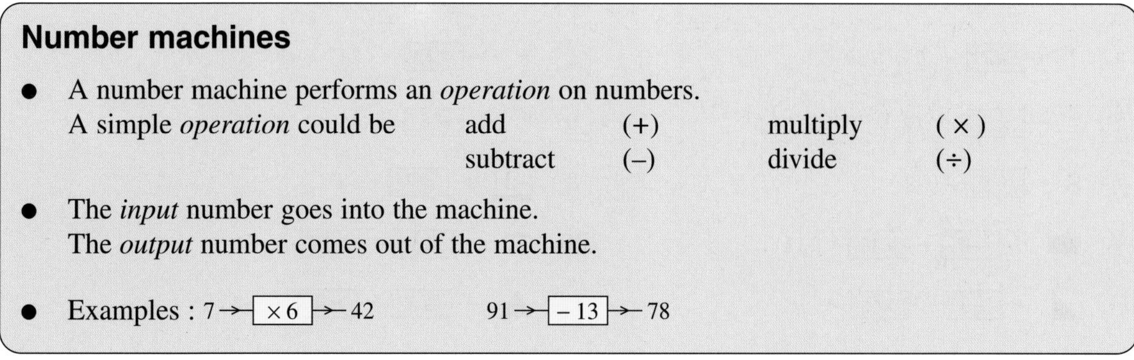

Number machines

- A number machine performs an *operation* on numbers.
  A simple *operation* could be add (+), subtract (–), multiply (×), divide (÷)
- The *input* number goes into the machine.
  The *output* number comes out of the machine.
- Examples : 7 → [× 6] → 42 91 → [– 13] → 78

Exercise 4M

Find the outputs from these number machines.

1. 4 → [+ 5] → ?
2. 7 → [+ 11] → ?
3. 10 → [− 3] → ?
4. 14 → [− 9] → ?
5. 6 → [× 7] → ▩
6. 8 → [× 2] → 🐟
7. 20 → [÷ 5] → [÷ 2] → ◢
8. 48 → [÷ 4] → [÷ 6] → ◤
9. 17 → [+ 71] → [− 8] → ▙
10. 34 → [+ 43] → [− 70] → 👢
11. 5 → [+ 4] → [× 3] → 🐟
12. 7 → [+ 9] → [× 0] → ☺
13. 12 → [+ 6] → [÷ 6] → ✦
14. 39 → [+ 13] → [÷ 4] → ▩
15. 89 → [− 15] → [+ 4] → ▩
16. 73 → [− 5] → [+ 9] → ▬
17. 42 → [− 38] → [× 7] → 👢
18. 100 → [− 81] → [× 3] → ▙
19. 85 → [− 58] → [÷ 9] → 🌲
20. 76 → [− 67] → [÷ 9] → ⚅

In questions 21 to 25 there are several operations.

21. 5 → [× 3] → [− 10] → [× 2] → [÷ 10] → ☂
22. 7 → [× 9] → [× 2] → [− 66] → [÷ 12] → ◎
23. 50 → [× 10] → [− 123] → [+ 13] → [÷ 10] → [÷ 13] → ↑
24. 17 → [× 5] → [+ 25] → [÷ 11] → [× 13] → [÷ 2] → [+ 7] → ⚐
25. 13 → [+ 84] → [× 0] → [+ 14] → [× 5] → [− 15] → [÷ 11] → !

Exercise 4E

Find the input to these systems

1. ? → [+ 6] → 11
2. ? → [+ 4] → 13
3. ? → [− 7] → 2
4. ? → [− 12] → 24
5. ? → [× 3] → 18
6. ? → [× 5] → 45
7. $ → [÷ 8] → 1
8. 👢 → [÷ 7] → 8
9. ▬ → [+ 7] → [− 11] → 11
10. π → [+ 1] → [− 17] → 1
11. ◢ → [+ 3] → [× 2] → 16
12. ▲ → [+ 3] → [× 4] → 52

13 🜂 → +4 → ÷5 → 3

14 fish → +7 → ÷9 → 2

15 boot → −2 → +17 → 34

16 ● → −16 → +61 → 84

17 ▦ → −11 → ×8 → 40

18 $ → −8 → ×7 → 21

19 ✦ → −1 → ÷11 → 4

20 ⚅ → −6 → ÷8 → 32

21 fish → ×9 → +2 → 65

22 hat → ×7 → +8 → 64

23 hat → ×13 → −12 → 1

24 ▬ → ×4 → −13 → 39

25 ◢ → ×5 → ÷6 → 5

26 ▦ → ×7 → ÷4 → 7

27 π → ÷8 → +4 → 10

28 boot → ÷11 → +3 → 11

29 ▲ → ÷7 → −5 → 4

30 ☺ → ÷12 → −6 → 1

31 ? → ÷13 → ×3 → 21

32 ● → ÷7 → ×2 → 26

Mystery machines

The following inputs go into a mystery machine…

3, 6, 27 and 0.

The diagram shows the outputs produced…

input	machine	output
3	?	6
6	?	9
27	?	30
0	?	3

The 'mystery' machine has added three to produce the outputs because it links *all* the inputs to the outputs in the same way.

The mystery machine was … input → +3 → output

Exercise 5M

What operation is taking place in each of these machines?

1
1 → ? → 5
2 → ? → 10
3 → ? → 15

2
63 → ? → 7
54 → ? → 6
27 → ? → 3

3
10 → ? → 8
9 → ? → 7
8 → ? → 6

4
3 → ? → 6
8 → ? → 11
47 → ? → 50

5
12 → ? → 6
2 → ? → 1
50 → ? → 25

6
19 → ? → 57
9 → ? → 27
7 → ? → 21

7
26 → ? → 11
40 → ? → 25
91 → ? → 76

8
9 → ? → 63
4 → ? → 28
8 → ? → 56

9
8 → ? → 64
1 → ? → 8
3 → ? → 24

For questions 10 to 15 copy and complete the number machines after working out the operation for each.

10
1 → ☐ → 7
7 → ☐ → 13
13 → ☐ → ?
? → ☐ → 26
27 → ☐ → ?

11
2 → ☐ → 8
3 → ☐ → 12
4 → ☐ → ?
10 → ☐ → ?
? → ☐ → 48

12
12 → ☐ → 5
7 → ☐ → 0
18 → ☐ → ?
? → ☐ → 13
? → ☐ → 26

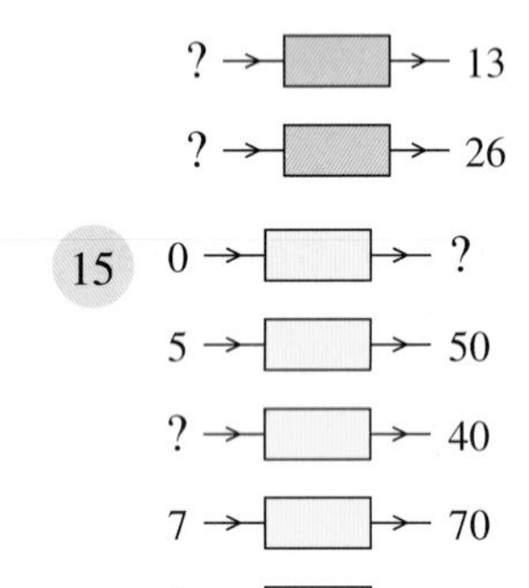

13
0 → ☐ → 11
3 → ☐ → ?
12 → ☐ → 23
? → ☐ → 31
39 → ☐ → ?

14
3 → ☐ → 1
9 → ☐ → 3
? → ☐ → 4
15 → ☐ → ?
60 → ☐ → ?

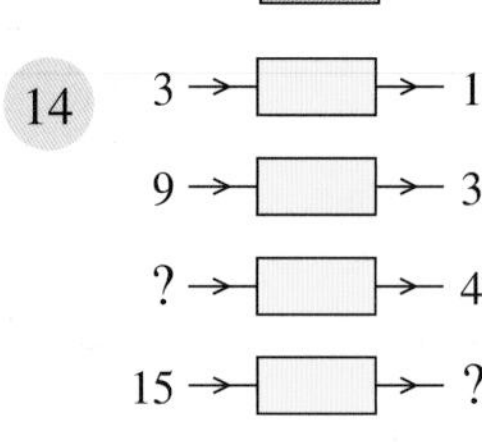

15
0 → ☐ → ?
5 → ☐ → 50
? → ☐ → 40
7 → ☐ → 70
? → ☐ → 100

Exercise 5E

1 For each chart find the *single* operation which performs the same operation as the three operations shown.

(a) In → +5 → −2 → +10 → Out

(b) → −4 → +1 → −3 →

(c) → +2 → ×2 → −4 →

2 Find the two operations which give *both* the results shown.

4 → ? → ? → 9

9 → ? → ? → 19

3 Find the two operations which give *both* the results shown.

5 → ? → ? → 14

8 → ? → ? → 23

4 Find the input number which gives the same output number for both charts below.

In → ×4 → −1 → Out

In → ×2 → +3 → Out

5 Find the input number which gives the same output number for both charts below.

In → [×3] → [−2] → Out In → [×2] → [+1] → Out

6 Find the input number which gives the same output number for both charts shown.

In → [−1] → [×4] → Out In → [×2] → [+6] → Out

Dividing by a single digit number

Division is the inverse (reverse) operation of multiplication.

When you know one × or ÷ fact, you know 3 related facts.

$9 \times 7 = 63$ $7 \times 9 = 63$

$63 \div 7 = 9$ $63 \div 9 = 7$

Exercise 6M

1 Write the answers only.

(a) $10 \div 2$ (b) $12 \div 3$ (c) $18 \div 9$ (d) $24 \div 3$
(e) $36 \div 4$ (f) $40 \div 5$ (g) $60 \div 6$ (h) $32 \div 8$
(i) $35 \div 7$ (j) $81 \div 9$ (k) $22 \div 2$ (l) $36 \div 6$
(m) $45 \div 9$ (n) $110 \div 10$ (o) $16 \div 1$ (p) $9 \div 9$
(q) $0 \div 6$ (r) $56 \div 8$ (s) $63 \div 7$ (t) $72 \div 8$

2 Copy and complete.

(a) $77 \div \square = 7$ (b) $\square \div 8 = 6$ (c) $42 \div \square = 7$
(d) $54 \div \square = 6$ (e) $24 \div \square = 12$ (f) $500 \div \square = 50$
(g) $\square \div 9 = 9$ (h) $\square \div 7 = 7$ (i) $\square \div 7 = 8$
(j) $40 \div \square = 5$ (k) $\square \div 8 = 9$ (l) $30 \div \square = 15$
(m) $\square \div 7 = 6$ (n) $200 \div \square = 5$ (o) $80 \div \square = 10$

3 For each statement write three related × or ÷ statements.

(a) $15 \div 3 = 5$ (b) $5 \times 15 = 75$ (c) $12 \times 8 = 96$ (d) $96 \div 6 = 16$

4 What number, when divided by 8 and then multiplied by 6, gives an answer of 30?

5 What number, when divided by 8 and then multiplied by 7, gives an answer of 56?

Exercise 6E

1 Copy and complete the multiplication squares. The numbers outside the square are always 2, 3, 4, 5, 6, 7, 8, 9.

(a)

×		8	2	7
5				35
		32		
3	27			
6				

(b)

×	4	7	3	8
5				
		42		
2				

(c)

×		5	8	2
	28		56	
6				
9				

(d)

×	4		3	
		45		72
		30		
7		35		

(e)

		7		9
	24		32	
				18
		42		

(f)

		5	7	
		40		32
3				
6	12			

(g)

		35	40	15
				18
	18			27

(h)

		8		
				27
		56		
		40	30	
				36

(i)

			3	
7		42		
		24		
	45			72

(j)

	18	14		
	45		20	
	54			48

(k)

			10	16
		24		48
	63			72

(l)

			40	
		18		
	18		30	42

2 In the next three squares you may have the same number at the top and along the side of the square.

(a)

				4	
			56		
					15
				36	
		14	49		
	30				25

(b)

				18	48
			49		
				9	
		45			40
	16		28		

(c)

		42	28		
		48		64	
	15			40	
					81
				24	

Dividing larger numbers

- The order in which you divide numbers *is* important. For example 12 ÷ 3 is *not* the same as 3 ÷ 12.
- Here is a 'pencil and paper' method for dividing.

(a) 625 ÷ 5

$$\begin{array}{r} 1\;2\;5 \\ 5\overline{)6^{1}2^{2}5} \end{array}$$

(b) 936 ÷ 4

$$\begin{array}{r} 2\;3\;4 \\ 4\overline{)9^{1}3^{1}6} \end{array}$$

(c) 3073 ÷ 7

$$\begin{array}{r} 0\;4\;3\;9 \\ 7\overline{)3^{3}0^{2}7^{6}3} \end{array}$$

Exercise 7M

Work out

1 $3\overline{)99}$

2 $5\overline{)65}$

3 $4\overline{)92}$

4 $7\overline{)84}$

5 $5\overline{)660}$

6 $6\overline{)72}$

7 $7\overline{)847}$

8 $9\overline{)558}$

9 $8\overline{)128}$ 10 $9\overline{)729}$ 11 $2\overline{)678}$ 12 $6\overline{)3372}$

13 $3\overline{)729}$ 14 $5\overline{)725}$ 15 $4\overline{)1028}$ 16 $8\overline{)1856}$

17 Copy and complete

(a) $\square \times 4 = 96$ (b) $\square \times 7 = 861$ (c) $9 \times \square = 1953$

(d) $\begin{array}{r} \square\,7 \\ \times\quad 5 \\ \hline 2\,3\,\square \end{array}$ (e) $\begin{array}{r} \square\,\square\,6 \\ \times\quad 7 \\ \hline 2\,2\,8\,\square \end{array}$ (f) $\begin{array}{r} \square\,\square\,3 \\ \times\quad 8 \\ \hline 5\,6\,2\,\square \end{array}$

18 Answer true or false:

(a) $3 + 4 + 5 + 6 + 7 = 5 \times 5$ (b) $77 + 78 + 79 = 3 \times 78$

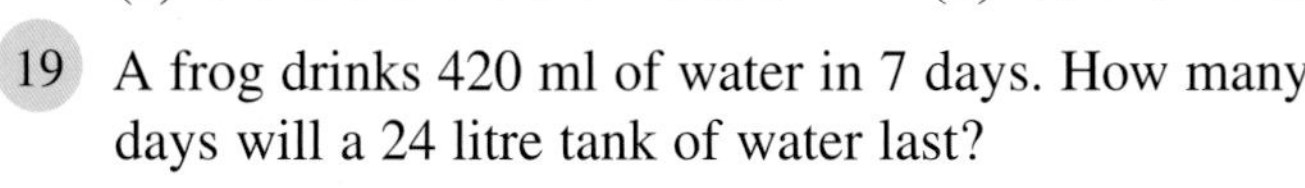

19 A frog drinks 420 ml of water in 7 days. How many days will a 24 litre tank of water last?

Exercise 7E

Work out

1 $8\overline{)2056}$ 2 $5\overline{)1025}$ 3 $6\overline{)7776}$ 4 $7\overline{)5082}$

5 $3050 \div 10$ 6 $1387 \div 1$ 7 $38\,199 \div 7$ 8 $14\,032 \div 8$

9 $31\,386 \div 6$ 10 $3490 \div 5$ 11 $28\,926 \div 9$ 12 $15\,638 \div 7$

13 Eight tins of pears weigh 3480g. How much does each tin weigh?

14 336 children are divided into eight equal teams. How many children are in each team?

15 Books are sold in boxes of 8. How many boxes are needed for 184 books?

16 Cinema tickets cost £6. How many tickets can be bought for £162?

17 Six crocodiles each laid the same number of eggs. Altogether there are 138 eggs. How many eggs did each crocodile lay?

18 Here is a number chain 5 → [× 4] → 20 → [+ 12] → 32 → [÷ 8] → 4

Find the missing numbers in these chains.

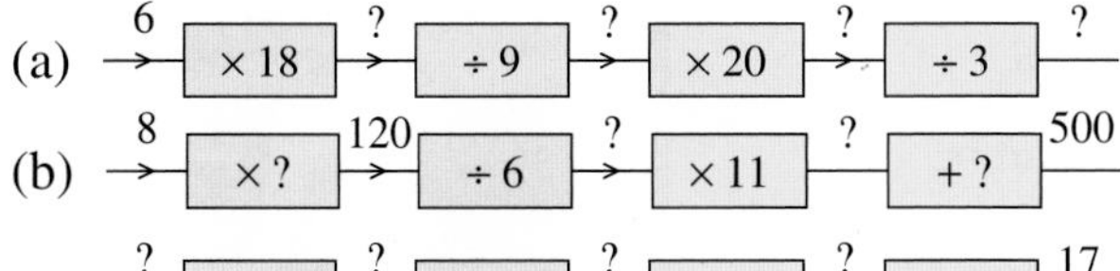

Remainders

Suppose you need to share 267 cakes between 5 people.

Work out 267 ÷ 5: $5\overline{)\,2\,6^{1}7}$ = *5 3 remainder 2*

Each person gets 53 cakes and there are 2 left over.

Exercise 8M

Write the answer with a remainder.

1 $5\overline{)432}$ 2 $4\overline{)715}$ 3 $6\overline{)895}$ 4 $3\overline{)164}$

5 $8\overline{)514}$ 6 $9\overline{)375}$ 7 $5\overline{)2642}$ 8 $2\overline{)7141}$

9 4079 ÷ 7 10 2132 ÷ 5 11 4013 ÷ 8 12 235 ÷ 6

13 657 ÷ 10 14 8327 ÷ 10 15 85 714 ÷ 6 16 4826 ÷ 9

17 2007 ÷ 7 18 9998 ÷ 9 19 6732 ÷ 11 20 84 563 ÷ 7

Rounding remainders up or down

(a) How many teams of 5 can you make from 113 people?

Work out 113 ÷ 5. $5\overline{)\,1\,1^{1}3}$ = *2 2 remainder 3*

Here we round *down*. You can make 22 teams and there will be 3 people left over.

(b) An egg box holds 6 eggs. How many boxes do you need for 231 eggs?

Work out 231 ÷ 6. $6\overline{)\,2\,3^{5}1}$ = *3 8 remainder 3*

Here we round *up* because you must use complete boxes. You need 39 boxes altogether.

Exercise 8E

In these questions you will get a remainder. Decide whether it is more sensible to round *up* or to round *down*.

1 Train tickets cost £5. How many tickets can be bought for £88?

2 A car can carry 3 children as passengers. How many cars are needed to carry 40 children?

3 There are 23 children in a class. How many teams of 4 can be made?

4 Eggs are packed six in a box. How many boxes do I need for 200 eggs?

5 Tickets cost £6 each and I have £80. How many tickets can I buy?

6 I have 204 plants and one tray takes 8 plants. How many trays do I need?

7 There are 51 children in the dining room and a table seats 6. How many tables are needed to seat all the children?

8 I have 100 cans of drink. One box holds 8 cans. How many boxes can I fill?

9 Five people can travel in one car and there are altogether 93 people to transport. How many cars are needed?

10 There are 332 children in a school. One coach holds 50 children. How many coaches are needed for a whole school trip?

11 Tins of spaghetti are packed 8 to a box. How many boxes are needed for 913 tins?

12 A prize consists of 10 000 one pound coins. The prize is shared between 7 people. How many pound coins will each person receive?

13 How many 9p stamps can I buy with a £5 note?

14 Find the missing numbers

(a) $8\overline{)5\,7\,1\,4}$ = 7 1 4 r □

(b) $7\overline{)3\,9\,\square}$ = 5 6 r 4

(c) $9\overline{)7\,3\,1\,\square}$ = 8 1 2 r 7

15 The numbers outside the multiplication square are 2, 3, 4, 5, 6, 7, 8, 9. Copy and complete the square.

	?	?	?	?
?	14			21
?			30	
?				12
?	16		48	

16 Find the missing numbers in these calculations

(a) □ 8 4 × □ = 7 0 5 6

(b) □ □ 8 × □ = 2 6 4 6

(c) □ □ 6 × □ = 3 6 4 8

(d) $\square\overline{)3\,\square\,\square\,\square}$ = 5 3 7

(e) $\square\overline{)4\,\square\,\square\,\square}$ = 5 6 4

1.2 Long multiplication and division

In section 1.2 you will learn how to:

- multiply by a two or three digit number
- divide by a two digit number
- solve mixed problems

Long multiplication

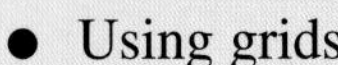

- Using grids

35×41

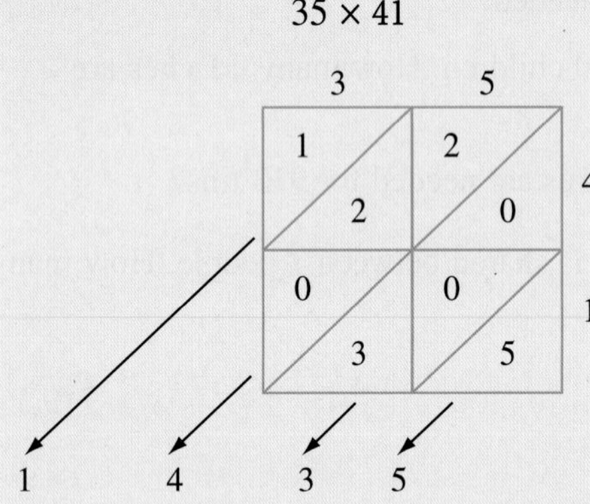

- Other method

$$\begin{array}{r l}
35 & \\
\times\ 41 & \\
\hline
35 & (35 \times 1) \\
1400 & (35 \times 40) \\
\hline
1435 &
\end{array}$$

Exercise 1M

In questions 1 to 6 copy and complete the grids and then add along the diagonals to obtain the answer (or use your own method).

1

2

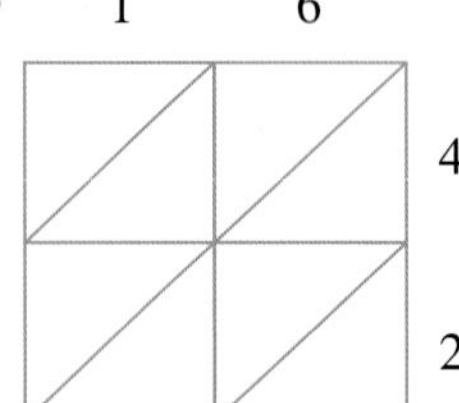

3

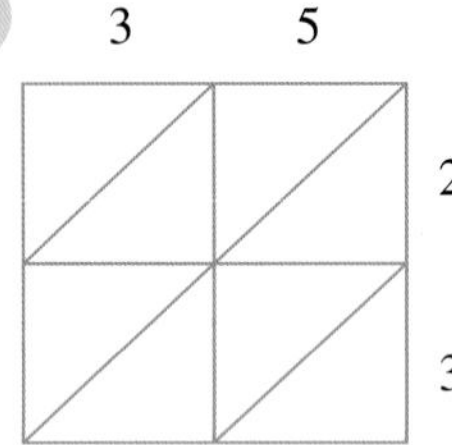

4

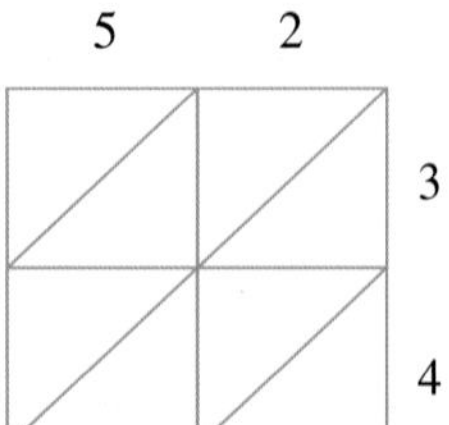

5

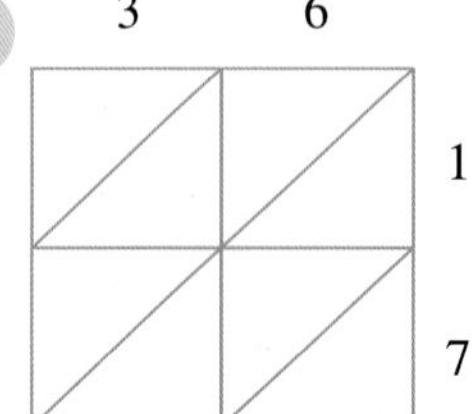

6

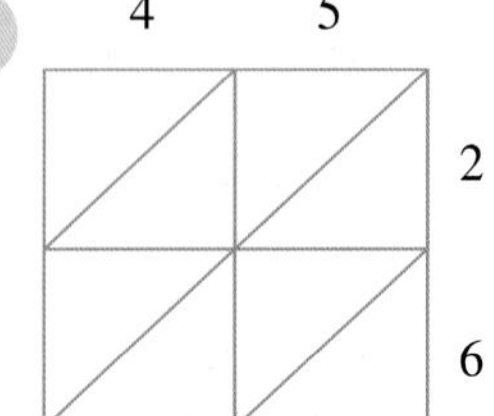

Work out

7 36×27 8 49×24 9 36×25 10 38×44

11 92×47 12 28×17 13 82×37 14 18×87

15 Each week a shop assistant earns £84. How much does he earn in 15 weeks?

16 Gold-plated trees cost €69 each. How much would 81 of these trees cost?

17 A film company hires 94 extras to film crowd scenes. They are paid £75 each. What is the total wage bill?

Exercise 1E

In questions 1 to 3 copy and complete the grids and then find the answer or use your own method.

1 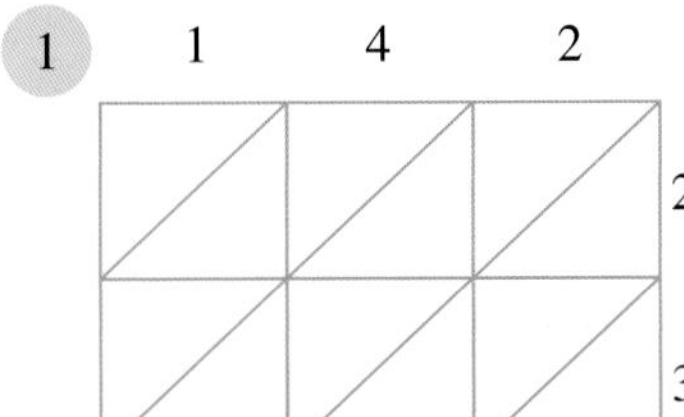

2 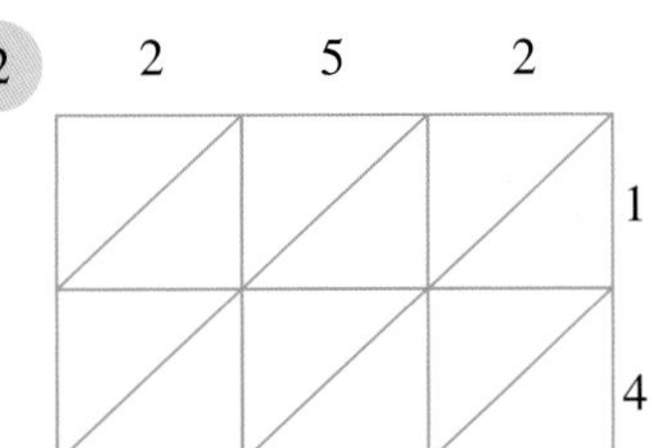

3 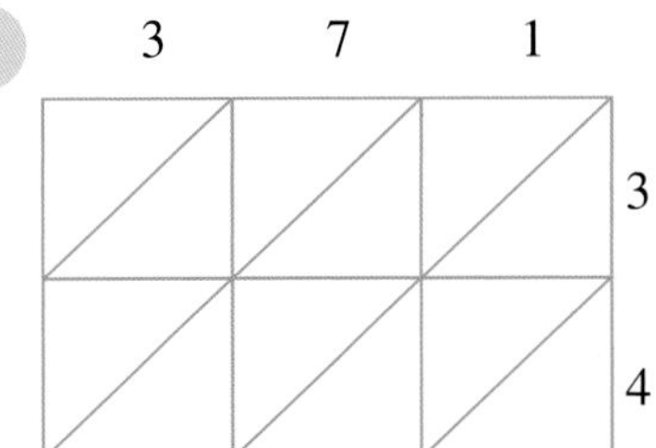

4 326×15 5 208×24 6 36×79 7 27×281

8 472×11 9 897×36 10 141×27 11 324×213

12 A delivery van uses an average of 43 litres of petrol per day. How much does the van use in 14 days?

13 An aircraft holds 174 people. The aircraft was full on every trip for three days. Look at the table opposite and work out how many people the aircraft carried in total over the three days.

Day	Number of trips
Fri	16
Sat	22
Sun	18

14 In a car park there are 25 rows of 42 cars. How many cars are in the car park?

15 How many hours are there in eleven weeks?

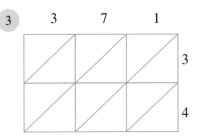

16 Fill in the boxes with the digits 2, 3, 4, 5 to make the answer correct.

```
     □ □
   × □ □
   -----
   8 4 0
```

17 Fill in the boxes with the digits 1, 2, 3, 4, 5 to make the answer correct. This is not easy but it can be done!

```
   □ □ □
   × □ □
 -------
 5 5 2 5
```

Long division

With ordinary short division, you divide and find remainders. The method for 'long' division is really the same but you set it out so that the remainders are easier to find.

Work out $864 \div 36$

```
      2 4
 36) 8 6 4      32 into 86 goes 2 times
   - 7 2 ↓      2 × 36 = 72
     1 4 4      86 – 72 = 14
   - 1 4 4      bring down 4
         0      36 into 144 goes 4 times
```

Exercise 2M

1 Work out

(a) 7)3374 (b) 13)702

Work out. There are no remainders in these questions.

2 $286 \div 13$
3 $360 \div 15$
4 $672 \div 21$
5 $621 \div 23$
6 $888 \div 24$
7 $992 \div 32$
8 $810 \div 18$
9 $644 \div 46$
10 $1224 \div 51$
11 $1035 \div 45$
12 $612 \div 36$
13 $1769 \div 29$

14 Copy and complete

(a) 32 × 17 = □□□ (b) 11 × □□□ = 3531

(c) □□ × 17 = 408 (d) 22 × 55 = □□□□

15 A box of 15 golf balls costs 975 pence. How much does each ball cost?

16 There are 23 rooms in a school and each room has 33 chairs. How many chairs are there altogether?

17 Copy and complete this multiplication square.

×	?	11	25
?	?	187	?
?	208	?	400
?	286	?	?

Exercise 2E

There are remainders in some of the divisions.

1. $450 \div 14$
2. $515 \div 15$
3. $851 \div 23$
4. $580 \div 13$
5. $775 \div 31$
6. $1128 \div 24$
7. $830 \div 36$
8. $945 \div 41$
9. A hammer costs £14. How many hammers can be bought with £355?
10. A rugby team has 15 players. How many teams can be made from 187 players?
11. How many 32 cm lengths of string can be cut from 60 metres?
12. A school hall can fit 28 chairs into one row. How many rows are needed to seat 1000 people?
13. Each box contains 25 pills. How many boxes can be filled from 6040 pills?
14. How many 23-seater coaches will be needed for a school trip for a party of 278?

Questions 15 to 21 involve either division or multiplication.

15. On average a shop sells 32 chess sets a week. How many sets are sold in a year?
16. Jars of peaches are packed 18 to a box. How many boxes do you need for 625 jars?

17. The stairs on an escalator move up at a rate of 14 cm per second. How far will the stairs go up in three quarters of a minute?
18. There are 35 offices in a building and each office has 14 phones. The phones are delivered in boxes of 15. How many boxes are needed?
19. In this multiplication the missing digits are 3, 4, 5, 6. Find the missing numbers

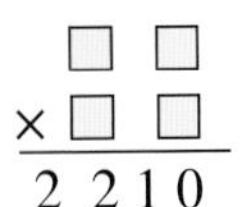

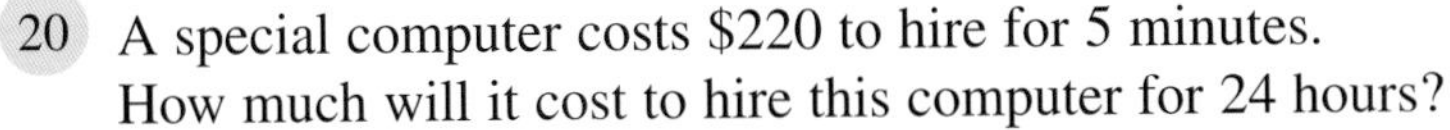

20. A special computer costs \$220 to hire for 5 minutes. How much will it cost to hire this computer for 24 hours?

CHECK YOURSELF ON SECTIONS 1.1 and 1.2

1 Using place value of digits in whole numbers

(a) Write these numbers in figures (i) Six and a half million
(ii) Four hundred and six thousand and twelve.

(b) Write down the number that is one hundred more than
(i) 6307 (ii) 2936 (iii) Five and a half thousand

2 Adding, subtracting and multiplying with whole numbers

Work out

(a) 6741 – 284 (b) 2351 plus half a million (c) 546 × 8

(d) 325 × 40 (e) 27 + 5099 – 438

3 Dividing a whole number by another whole number

Work out

(a) 2478 ÷ 7 (b) 4842 ÷ 6 (c) $8\overline{)451}$

(d) 3140 ÷ 9 (e) (3617 – 1422) ÷ 5

4 Solving mixed problems involving remainders

(a) How many 8p stamps can I buy with a £5 note?

(b) Tins of paint are packed 9 to a box.
How many boxes are needed for 673 tins?

5 Multiplying by a two or three digit number

Work out

(a) 46 × 24 (b) 63 × 37 (c) 125 × 235

6 Dividing by a two digit number

Work out

(a) 1035 ÷ 23 (b) 8466 ÷ 34

7 Solving mixed problems

(a) On average a school needs 87 exercise books a week.
How many books are needed for 38 weeks?

(b) A prize of 470 chocolate bars is shared equally between 18 winners.
How many bars does each winner get and how many are left over?

1.3 Decimals

In section 1.3 you will learn how to:

- use place value with decimals
- add and subtract decimal numbers
- multiply and divide decimal numbers

Decimal point

Decimals are a way of expressing fractions. The decimal point separates the whole number from the fractions.

The length of this feather is 3 cm and 2 tenths of a cm. As a decimal we write this as 3.2 cm.

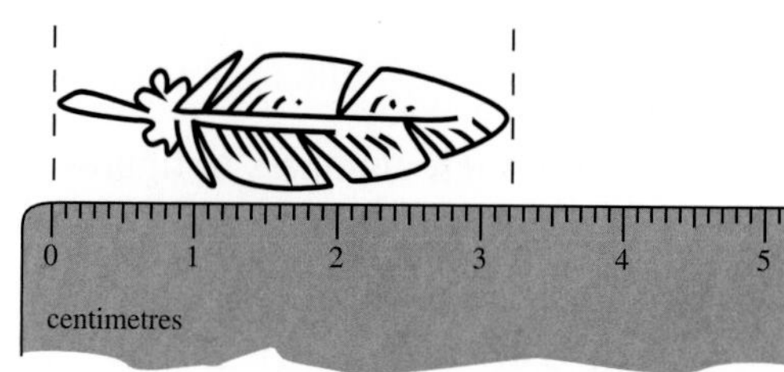

For more accurate measuring we might need hundredths or even thousandths of a cm.

The number 427.35 is $427\frac{35}{100}$.

We can write it like this.

hundreds	tens	units		tenths	hundredths
4	2	7	.	3	5

Exercise 1M

In questions 1 to 16 answer True (T) or False (F).

1. 0.7 is less than 0.71
2. 0.61 is more than 0.16.
3. 0.08 is more than 0.008
4. 0.5 is equal to 0.500
5. 0.613 is less than 0.631
6. 7.0 is equal to 0.7.
7. 6.2 is less than 6.02
8. 0.09 is more than 0.1.

Copy and complete by writing >, < or = in the box

9. 7 □ 0.71
10. 0.3 □ 0.1
11. 0.35 □ 0.53
12. 3.7 □ 3.07
13. 6 □ 6.00
14. 0.1 □ $\frac{1}{10}$
15. 0.1 + 0.01 □ 0.105
16. 0.3 – 0.01 □ 0.29
17. What does the digit 7 in 3.271 represent? And the 2? And the 1?
18. What does the digit 3 in 5.386 represent? And the 6? And the 8?
19. Write the numbers shown by each of the arrows.

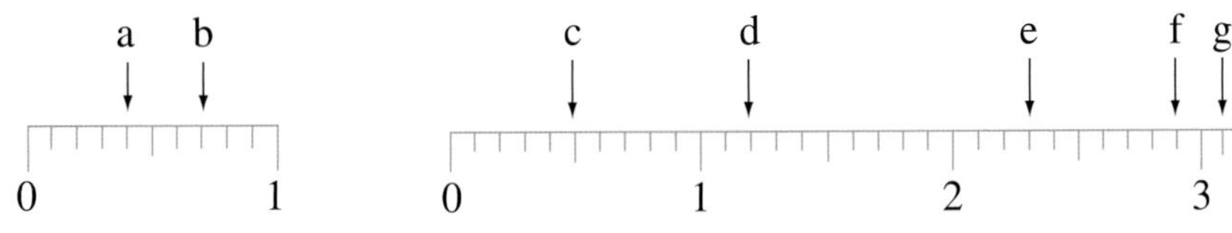

20. Give the next two terms in each sequence

(a)	0.2	0.3	0.4	0.5
(b)	0.1	0.3	0.5	0.7
(c)	0.4	0.8	1.2	
(d)	0.3	0.5	0.7	0.9
(e)	1.3	1.2	1.1	

21. Write the answer only

(a) 1.5 + 0.4	(b) 1.3 – 0.3	(c) 2.4 + 0.5	(d) 4 – 0.4
(e) 3.6 + 1.2	(f) 8 – 1.2	(g) 1.8 – 1.4	(h) 4.5 – 0.6
(i) 1.5 + 1.9	(j) 1.7 – 0.9	(k) 4.1 + 9	(l) 0.2 + 0.8

22 Write the decimal number equivalent to:
(a) three tenths
(b) seven hundredths
(c) eleven hundredths
(d) four thousandths
(e) sixteen hundredths
(f) sixteen thousandths

23 Write down the single operation needed [+, −] when you change:
(a) 5.32 to 5.72
(b) 11.042 to 11.047
(c) 0.592 to 0.392
(d) 0.683 to 0.623.
For example, to change 0.24 to 0.28, you *add 0.04.*

24 Draw a line from 0.9 to 1.1 with 20 equal divisions
[0.9 ⊔⊔⊔ … etc]
Show these numbers on your line
(a) 0.93 (b) 1.04 (c) 1.0 (d) 0.99 (e) 1.09

Ordering decimals

Consider these three decimals…

0.09, 0.101, 0.1.

Which is the correct order from lowest to highest?

> When ordering decimals it is always helpful to write them with the same number of digits after the decimal point.

0.09 ⟶ 0.090 Empty spaces can be
0.101 ⟶ 0.101 filled with zeros.
0.1 ⟶ 0.100

Now we can clearly see the correct order of these decimals from lowest to highest… 0.090, 0.1, 0.101.

Exercise 2M

In questions 1 to 20, arrange the numbers in order of size, smallest first.

1 0.21, 0.31, 0.12.

2 0.04, 0.4, 0.35.

3 0.67, 0.672, 0.7.

4 0.05, 0.045, 0.07.

5 0.1, 0.09, 0.089.

6 0.75, 0.57, 0.705.

7 0.41, 0.041, 0.14.

8 0.809, 0.81, 0.8.

9 0.006, 0.6, 0.059.

10 0.15, 0.143, 0.2.

11 0.04, 0.14, 0.2, 0.53.

12 1.2, 0.12, 0.21, 1.12.

13 2.3, 2.03, 0.75, 0.08.

14 0.62, 0.26, 0.602, 0.3.

15 0.5, 1.3, 1.03, 1.003.

16 0.79, 0.792, 0.709, 0.97.

17 5.2 m, 52 cm, 152 cm

18 £1.20, 75p, £0.8

19 200 m, 0.55 km, $\frac{1}{2}$ km

20 1.2 mm, 0.1 cm, 2 mm

21 Here are numbers with letters
(a) Put the numbers in order, smallest first. Write down just the letters.
(b) Finish the sentence using letters and numbers of your own. The numbers must increase from left to right.

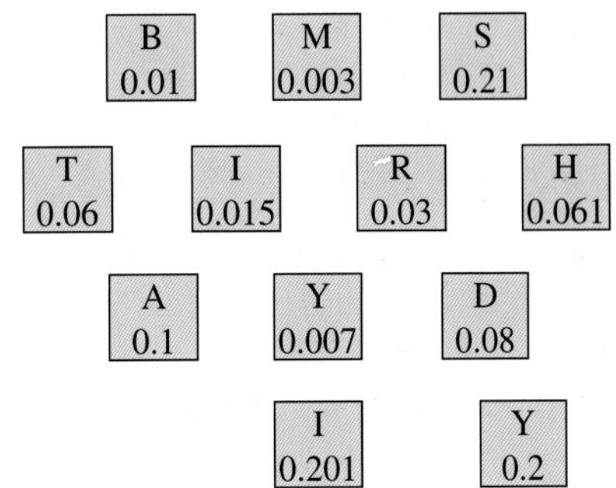

22 Increase the following numbers by $\frac{1}{10}^{\text{th}}$:

(a) 3.27 (b) 14.8 (c) 0.841

23 Increase the following numbers by $\frac{1}{100}^{\text{th}}$:

(a) 11.25 (b) 1.294 (c) 0.382

24 Increase the following numbers by $\frac{1}{1000}^{\text{th}}$:

(a) 3.142 (b) 2.7181 (c) 1.419

25 Write the following amounts in pounds:

(a) 11 pence (b) 2 pence (c) 5 pence
(d) 10 pence (e) 20 pence (f) 50 pence

Find the number which the arrow is pointing to on each of the scales.

(a)

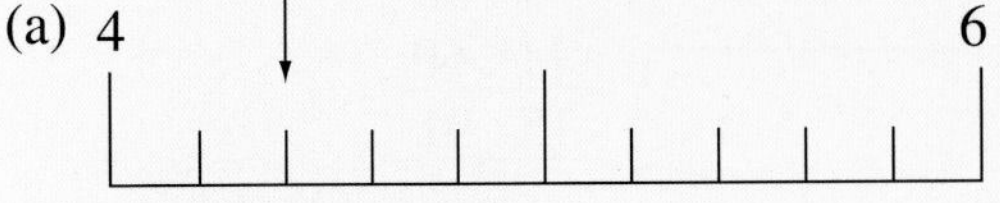

(b)

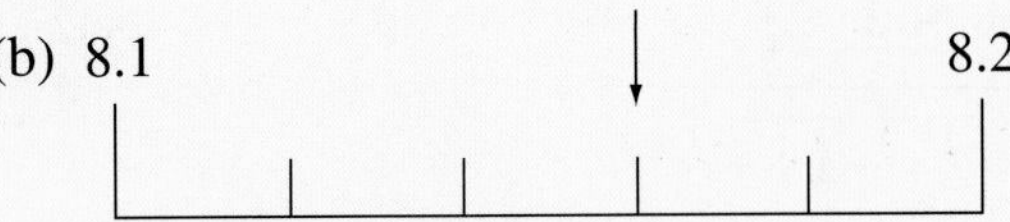

The middle number is 5.
Each division is 0.2.
The arrow points to 4.4.

Each division is 0.02.
The arrow points to 8.16.

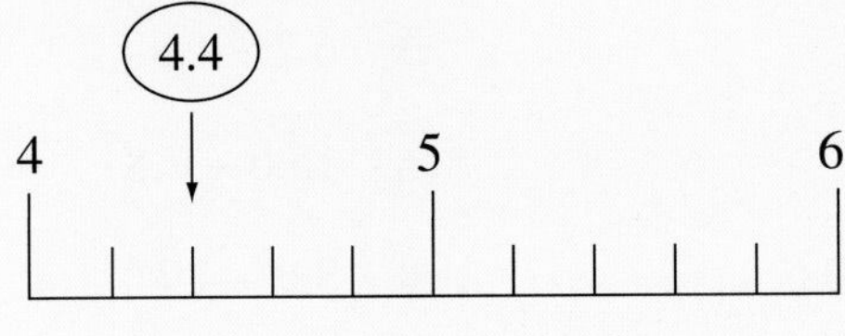

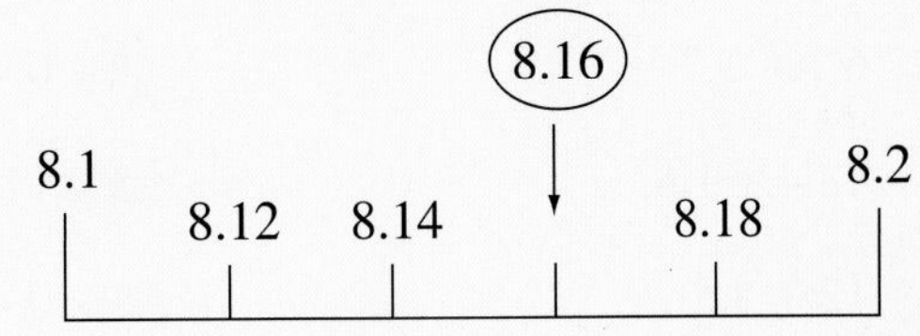

Exercise 2E

Work out the value indicated by the arrow.

1. 40 — 50
2. 2 — 3
3. 14 — 16
4. 15 — 15.5
5. 0 — 1
6. 0 — 6
7. 0 — 10
8. 5 — 6
9. 3.1 — 3.2
10. 0 — 0.1
11. 1 — 1.04
12. 0 — 1.5
13. 0.2 — 0.3
14. 100 — 200
15. 1 — 2
16. 0 — 60
17. 60 — 100
18. 4 — 4.5
19. 2.4 — 2.8
20. 3.3 — 3.7
21. 0 — 0.3
22. 70 — 80
23. 18 — 19
24. 3.1 — 3.15

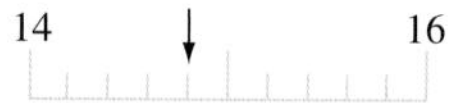

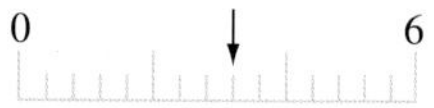

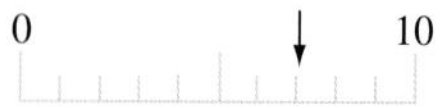

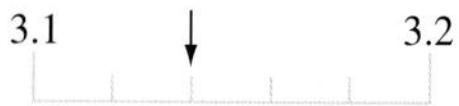

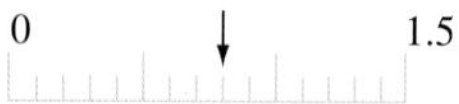

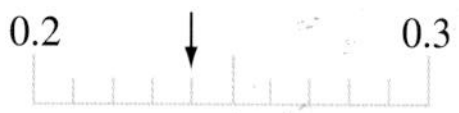

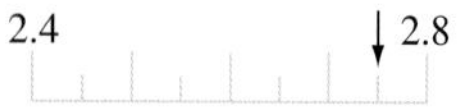

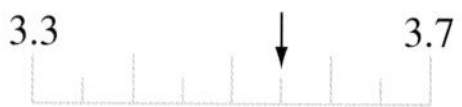

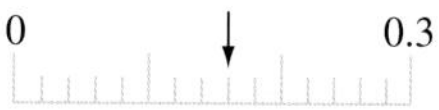

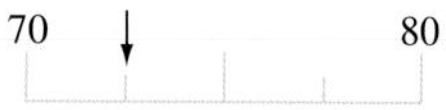

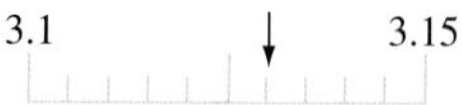

Adding and subtracting decimals

Remember:

Line up the decimal points

(a) 2.4 + 3.23

```
  2 . 40  ← put a zero
+ 3 . 23
  5 . 63
```

(line up the points)

(b) 7 − 2.3

```
 6 7̸ . 1 0
 − 2 .  3
   4 .  7
```

(write 7 as 7.0)

(c) 0.31 + 4 + 11.6

```
   0 . 31
   4 . 00
+ 11 . 60
  15 . 91
```

(write 4 as 4.00)

Exercise 3M

1. 6.1 + 1.7
2. 0.4 + 0.9
3. 6.7 + 1.8
4. 18.4 + 1.6
5. 11.9 + 3.2
6. 15.6 + 7.8
7. 12 + 4.5
8. 0.4 + 0.5 + 0.6
9. 8.9 − 4.7
10. 6.4 − 2.7
11. 15.6 − 10.9
12. 8 − 2.7

13 $5 + 0.26$

14 $2.9 + 4.37$

15 $8.6 + 7.99$

16 $0.078 + 2.05$

17 $10.04 + 3.005$

18 $13.47 + 27.084$

19 $1.97 + 19.7$

20 $4.56 + 7.890$

21 $456.7 + 8.901$

22 $16.374 + 0.947 + 27$

23 $3.142 + 2.71 + 8$

24 $0.03 + 11 + 8.74$

25 $29.6 - 14$

26 $59.2 - 34.8$

27 $81.8 - 29.9$

28 $8 - 2.7$

29 $6.7 - 4.29$

30 $47.2 - 27.42$

31 $94.63 - 5.9$

32 $2.97 - 1.414$

33 $25.52 - 1.436$

34 $3.142 - 1.414$

35 $2.718 - 1.732$

36 $12 - 3.74$

In questions 37 to 42 find the missing digits

37
$$\begin{array}{r} \square.8\square \\ +\ 1.\square 5 \\ \hline 9.27 \end{array}$$

38
$$\begin{array}{r} \square.6\square \\ +\ 0.\square 5 \\ \hline 3.90 \end{array}$$

39
$$\begin{array}{r} 5.\square 7 \\ +\ \square.5\square \\ \hline 8.91 \end{array}$$

40
$$\begin{array}{r} 8.27 \\ +\ \square.74 \\ \hline 9.\square\square \end{array}$$

41
$$\begin{array}{r} \square.8\square \\ +\ 2.\square 7 \\ \hline 9.03 \end{array}$$

42
$$\begin{array}{r} 6.95 \\ +\ \square.2\square \\ \hline 9.\square 1 \end{array}$$

Exercise 3E

1 Winston was 1.52 m tall and a year later he had grown 9 cm. How tall was he then?

2 An electrician has 8 m of cable and then cut off 45 cm. How long was the remaining cable?

3 Carlos has £3.20 and wants to buy articles costing £1.10, 66p, £1.99 and 45p. How much more money does he need?

4 Which six different coins make £1.78?

5 Jane went to a shop and bought a book for £2.95 and a CD for £10.95. She paid with a £50 note. What change did she receive?

6 Jackie bought a goldfish for £2.95, a bowl for £5.99 and a bottle of Evian water for 60p. What was the total price?

7 What must be added to £5.63 to make £18?

8 Which five different coins make a total of £1.37?

9 Prini bought her local team's replica football kit, shirt costing £10.75, shorts costing £3.99 and socks for £2.59. How much did she spend?

10 Jack spent £5.15 in the supermarket and £10.99 in the music shop. How much change did he get from £20?

In questions 11 to 16 find the missing digits

11
```
  □ . 5 □
− 4 . □ 3
  3 . 7 3
```

12
```
  4 . □ 7
+ □ . 9 □
  9 . 0 3
```

13
```
  3 . 1 7 □
− □ . 4 □ 8
  0 . □ 4 8
```

14
```
  8 . □ 8
+ □ . 8 □
  9 . 6 6
```

15
```
  □ . 9 □
− 2 . □ 6
  3 . 6 6
```

16
```
  2 . □ 5 7
+ □ . 3 4 □
  6 . 8 □ 5
```

17 I started with 6.658 and then subtracted a number. The answer was 6.648. What number did I subtract?

18 I started with 0.954 and then added a number. The answer was 0.956. What number did I add?

19 Write down the answers.

(a) 1.242 + 0.03 (b) 9.042 – 0.03 (c) 11.817 + 0.002

(d) 8.679 – 0.001 (e) 6.53 + 0.002 (f) 41.44 – 0.4

(g) 0.473 – 0.2 (h) 0.046 + 0.004 (i) 11.617 – 0.005

20 Write the numbers in order, smallest first, to make a word.

I	L	N	E	O	R	T	A
0.501	0.3	4	0.034	0.8	0.03	0.5	0.33

21 The twelfth term in the sequence 0.3, 1, 1.7... is 8

What is (a) the thirteenth term, (b) the tenth term?

22 Copy and complete the addition square.

	3.2	0.54		
			3.6	4.5
	11.8			10.4
		0.58		
8				

23 Find the missing numbers.

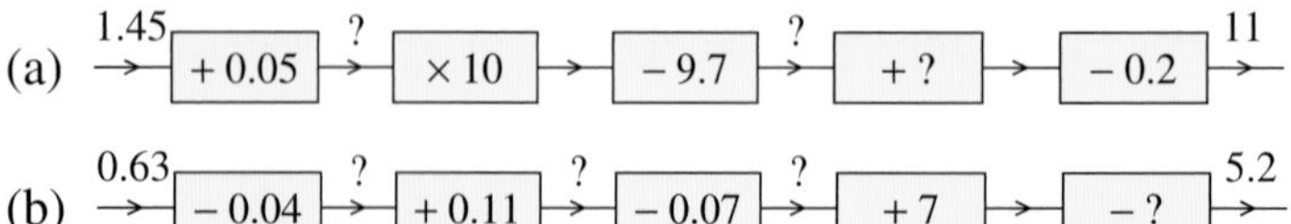

Multiplying decimals by whole numbers

Here are three numbers multiplied by 10

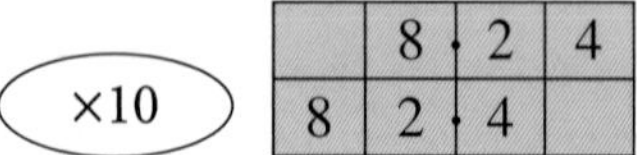

	4	3 .	1	7
4	3	1 .	7	

	1 .	4	3	5
1	4 .	3	5	

When you multiply by **10** you move the digits **one** place to the left. [Some people prefer to think of moving the decimal point one place to the right. *You* use the method that *you* prefer.]

Similarly when you multiply by **100** you move the digits **two** places to the left and when you multiply by **1000** you move the digits **three** places to the left.

$4.601 \times 100 = 460.1$ $\quad$ $0.231 \times 100 = 23.1$

$0.324 \times 1000 = 324$ $\quad$ $10.24 \times 1000 = 10240$ (add a zero)

When you divide by 10, 100, 1000 and so on the digits move to the right.

$11.7 \div 10 = 1.17$ $\quad$ $235.6 \div 100 = 2.356$

$85 \div 1000 = 0.085$ $\quad$ $25400 \div 10000 = 2.54$

Exercise 4M

Do the following calculations

1 4.23×10
2 5.63×10
3 0.427×100
4 100×4.63
5 0.075×10
6 100×0.0063
7 1.147×1000
8 10.7×1000
9 6.33×100
10 $0.00714 \times 10\,000$
11 100×6.36
12 8.142×10
13 $10\,000 \times 0.71$
14 8.9×1000
15 12×100
16 10×13
17 7×1000
18 10000×9.2
19 0.7×100
20 $0.5 \times 100\,000$

Copy and complete

21 $0.8 \times \square = 80$
22 $\square \times 1000 = 5500$
23 $\square \times 10 = 0.52$
24 $1.8 \times 100 = \square$
25 $0.81 \times \square = 810$
26 $0.4 \times 1000 = \square$
27 $7.2 \times \square = 7.2$
28 $\square \times 100 = 11.7$
29 $\square \times 100 = 0.2$
30 Answer true or false: $0.3 \times 10 = 0.03 \times 1000$

Work out

31 $57.2 \div 10$
32 $89.2 \div 10$
33 $5.3 \div 10$
34 $47.1 \div 100$
35 $141.2 \div 100$
36 $19.3 \div 10$
37 $1518 \div 100$
38 $4.7 \div 100$
39 $25.2 \div 1000$
40 $0.63 \div 10$
41 $47.2 \div 100$
42 $27.9 \div 1000$
43 $6.2 \div 1000$
44 $198.7 \div 100$
45 $47 \div 10$
46 $416 \div 1000$

Multiplying decimals by whole numbers

Method 1

- $7.93 \times 4 \approx 8 \times 4 = 32$
  (Estimate first)
  $7.93 \times 4 \quad 7.00 \times 4 = 28.00$
  $0.90 \times 4 = 3.60$
  $0.03 \times 4 = 0.12 +$
  31.72

- $3.16 \times 6 \approx 3 \times 6 = 18$
  (Estimate first)
  $3.16 \times 6 \quad 3.00 \times 6 = 18.00$
  $0.10 \times 6 = 0.60$
  $0.06 \times 6 = 0.36 +$
  18.96

Method 2

- $7.24 \times 4 \approx 7 \times 4 = 28$
  (Estimate first)
  7.24
  × 4
  28.96
  1

- $0.096 \times 9 \approx 0.1 \times 9 = 0.9$
  (Estimate first)
  0.096
  × 9
  0.864
  8 5

The answer has the same number of figures after the point as there are in the numbers being multiplied.

Exercise 5M

Work out the following. Find an estimate first.

1. 5.1 × 2
2. 2.3 × 3
3. 3.7 × 4
4. 5.6 × 5
5. 6.13 × 6
6. 10.22 × 7
7. 5.34 × 8
8. 1.29 × 9
9. 7×0.63
10. 1.452×6
11. 9×0.074
12. 11.3×5
13. 13.6×5
14. 0.074×5
15. 6×2.22
16. 8.4×11
17. Copy and complete with the missing numbers.
    (a) $0.3 \times 4 = \square$
    (b) $0.6 \times \square = 4.2$
    (c) $\square \times 5 = 2.0$
    (d) $1.5 = 6 \times \square + 0.3$
    (e) $\square \times 7 - 2 = 1.5$
    (f) $8 \times \square = 0.16$
18. Find the cost of 6 golf balls at £1.95 each.
19. What is the cost of 2 CDs at £10.95 each?
20. If one brick weighs 1.35 kg, how much do 5 weigh?

Exercise 5E

1 Work out
(a) 6.35×4 (b) 0.72×9 (c) 1.45×7
(d) $0.4 \times 3 \times 10$ (e) $1.7 \times 3 \times 100$

2 Copy and complete

(a) 1.1 —×4→ ☐ —×10→ ☐ —÷100→ ☐

(b) 0.4 —×7→ ☐ —×3→ ☐ —×10→ ☐

(c) 1.5 —×5→ ☐ —×3→ ☐ —×100→ ☐

(d) 0.04 —×8→ ☐ —×100→ ☐ —÷2→ ☐

3 What is the total cost of 6 books at £2.13 each?

4 A new car tyre costs £29.99.
What is the total cost of 4 new tyres?

5 Find the total cost of 8 batteries at £1.19 each.

6 If 1 kg of cheese costs £4.59, find the cost of 3 kg.

7 Ink cartridges cost £1.25 a packet. What is the cost of 10 packets?

8 A sack of coal costs £6.90. Find the total cost of 9 sacks.

9 If 1 litre equals 1.76 pints, how many pints is 8 litres?

10 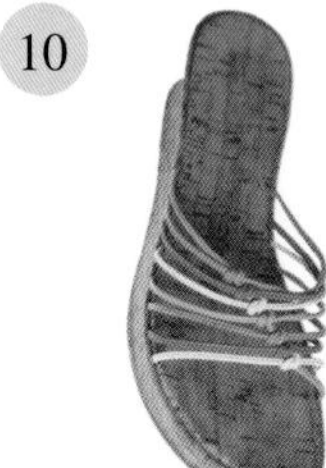

A pair of sandals costs £14.50.
A parcel contains 8 pairs of sandals.
A van contains 1000 parcels full of sandals.
(a) What is the cost of one parcel?
(b) What is the cost of the sandals on the van?

In questions 11 to 14 find the total cost.

11 2 jars at £1.75 each
4 boxes at £0.40 each
1 bottle at £1.25

12 3 tins at £0.51 each
5 packets at £1.10 each
2 pints of milk at 22p per pint.

13 4 litres of oil at 97p per litre
6 bags at £0.33 each
3 lb of meat at £2.12 per lb
1 cauliflower at 42p

14 18 eggs at 50p per dozen
$\frac{1}{2}$ lb of cheese at £1.30 per lb
3 lb of leeks at 18p per lb
2 packets at £2.30 each

15 If £1 is equivalent to \$2.05,
(a) how many dollars are equivalent to £350,
(b) how many pounds are equivalent to \$205,000?

16 A lady smokes 30 cigarettes a day and a packet of 20 costs £4.30. How much does she spend on cigarettes in four days?

17 (a) Write down the next number in the sequence 0.2, 0.6, 1.8, 5.4, . . .
(b) Work out the eighth term in the sequence.

18 Gavin spends £4.90 on two items in a shop. One item cost 40p more than the other. How much did each item cost?

19 Calculate the total surface area of the solid cuboid shown.

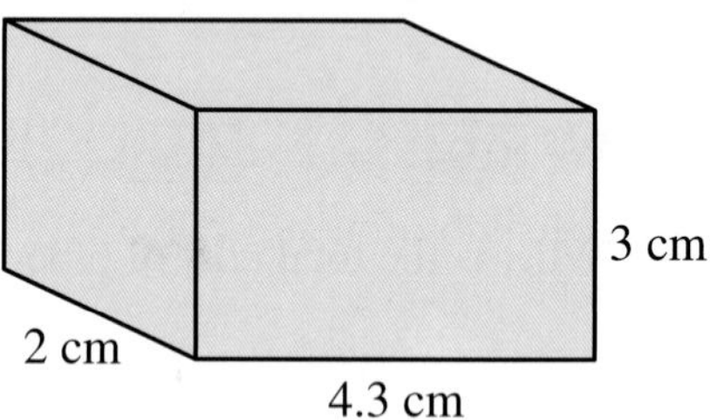

20 Answer true or false:
$40 \times 4.5 \times 5^2 = (0.314 + 0.17 + 0.016) \times 3^2 \times 1000$

Division of decimals by whole numbers

(a) $9.6 \div 3$

$$\begin{array}{r} 3.2 \\ 3\overline{)9.6} \end{array}$$

(b) $22.48 \div 4$

$$\begin{array}{r} 5.62 \\ 3\overline{)22.{}^{2}48} \end{array}$$

(c) $7.3 \div 4$

$$\begin{array}{r} 1.\,8\,2\,5 \\ 4\overline{)7.{}^{3}3{}^{1}0{}^{2}0} \end{array}$$

↑↑
Note the extra zeros.

(d) $21.28 \div 7$

$$\begin{array}{r} 3.0\,4 \\ 7\overline{)21.2{}^{2}8} \end{array}$$

(e) $3.12 \div 4$

$$\begin{array}{r} 0.7\,8 \\ 4\overline{)3.{}^{3}1{}^{3}2} \end{array}$$

Exercise 6M

1 $8.42 \div 2$

2 $205.2 \div 6$

3 $18.52 \div 4$

4 $4.984 \div 7$

5 $236.0 \div 5$

6 $18.93 \div 3$

7 $49.92 \div 8$

8 $487.26 \div 9$

9 $6.7 \div 5$

10 A father shares £4.56 between his three children.
How much does each receive?

11 Copy and complete the cross number puzzle on the next page.
There are decimal points on some lines.

1	2		3	4	5
6		7		8	
	9		10		
11			12	13	
14	15			16	17
18			19		

Clues across

1. 4×1.9
3. $6.2 \div 5$
6. $83.2 \div 4$
8. $0.42 \times 2 \times 50$
9. $348 \div 3$
12. 0.95×40
14. $928 + 45$
16. $31.8 \div 6$
18. $2004 - 1989$
19. $5.1 \div 5$

Clues down

1. $36.4 + 35.6$
2. $542 + 5 + 54$
4. $7.2 \div 3$
5. $(85 \times 5) \div 10$
7. 0.081×1000
10. $31.5 \div 5$
11. $200 - (0.9 \times 10)$
13. 0.85×1000
15. $60 \div 8$
17. $0.0032 \times 100 \times 100$

Exercise 6E

1 A length of wood measuring 39.41 cm has to be cut into seven equal lengths. How long is each piece?

2 The total bill for a meal for nine people is £76.23. How much does each person pay if they each paid the same?

3 Work out

(a) $11.2 \div 5$ (b) $9.01 \div 4$ (c) $12.1 \div 8$

(d) $0.82 \div 4$ (e) $17 \div 5$ (f) $22 \div 8$

4 If 5 bricks weigh 4.64 kg, find the weight of one brick.

5 Five people share the fuel cost of a car journey which amounts to £18.65. How much does each person pay?

6 Find the answer to the calculation in each box.
Arrange the answers in order of size, smallest first. What word do you get?

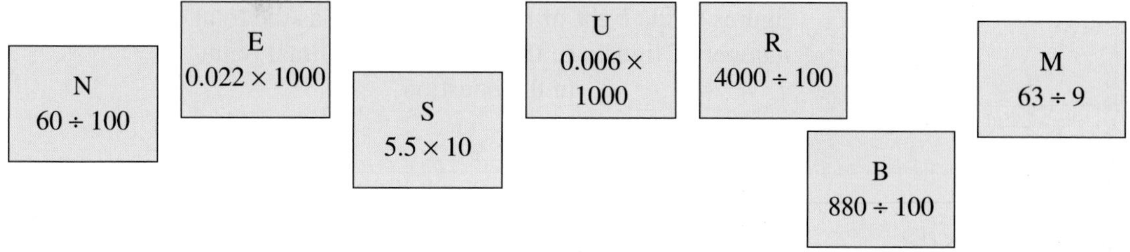

7 How many times will a 9 litre bucket have to be filled and emptied to completely empty a water drum containing 139.5 litres?

8 If nine cups of coffee cost £8.55, find the cost of 7 cups.

9 A steel rod of length 2.86 m is divided into 11 equal pieces.
How long is each piece?

10 One hundred ball bearings weigh 2.5 kg.
What is the weight of one? Give your answer in grams.

11 Copy and complete

(a) $57.8 \div 17 = \square$ (b) $108 \div 25 = \square$ (c) $\square \times 21 = 75.6$

(d) $\square \times 46 = 143.52$ (e) $244.8 \div 34 = \square$

12 The perimeter of a square is 5.6 m. Work out the area of the square.

13 Read the newspaper cutting from 'The Times'.
The spray costs £3.99 for 125 ml.
Work out the cost per litre of 'Expert Sensitive Refreshing Facial Spritz'.

> According to the can it is a "gentle facial spritz specially formulated to refresh and hydrate. Hypoallergenic and fragance-free it instantly cools and freshens skin. Lanolin free. Dermatologically tested". Just one small word gives the game away that this is a triumph of marketing over common sense: the only listed ingredient is "Aqua".
>
> Boots confirmed yesterday that it is selling water at £3.99 for little more than a cupful. Its Expert Sensitive Refreshing Facial Spritz is exactly what is says on the can: water.

Multiplying decimal numbers

- 5×0.3 is the same as $5 \times \frac{3}{10}$. Work out $(5 \times 3) \div 10 = 15 \div 10 = 1.5$

  4.2×0.2 is the same as $4.2 \times \frac{2}{10}$. Work out $(4.2 \times 2) \div 10 = 8.4 \div 10 = 0.84$

  21.4×0.05 is the same as $21.4 \times \frac{5}{100}$. Work out $(21.4 \times 5) \div 100 = 1907 \div 100 = 19.07$

- Quick method:

  When we multiply two decimal numbers together, the answer has the same number of figures to the right of the decimal point as the total number of figures to the right of the decimal point in the question.

(a) 0.3×0.4
$(3 \times 4 = 12)$

So $0.3 \times 0.4 = 0.12$

(b) 0.7×0.05
$(7 \times 5 = 35)$

So $0.7 \times 0.05 = 0.035$

Exercise 7M

1 0.4×0.2

2 0.6×0.3

3 0.8×0.2

4 0.4×0.03

5 0.7×3

6 0.7×0.02

7 0.9×0.5

8 6×0.04

9 0.04×0.05 10 0.7×0.7 11 8×0.1 12 14×0.3

13 15×0.03 14 0.4×0.04 15 0.001×0.6 16 33×0.02

17 1.2×0.3 18 3.2×0.2 19 1.4×0.4 20 2.1×0.5

21 Work out the area of each shape

(a)

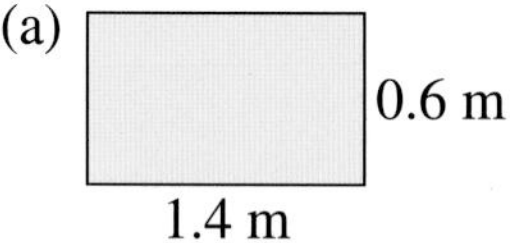

(b)

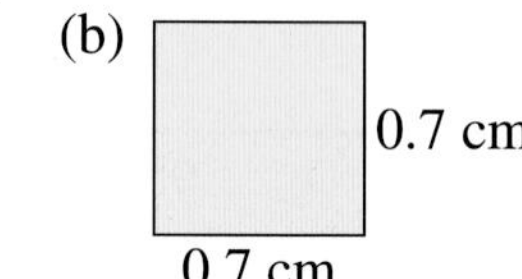

(c)

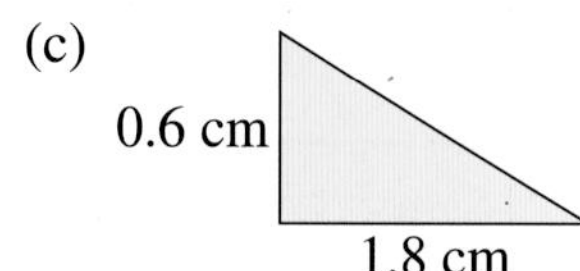

22 The length of a rectangle is 1.5 m and its perimeter is 4.2 m. Find the area of the rectangle.

Exercise 7E

1 Copy and complete

(a) $6 \times 0.2 = \square$ (b) $0.4 \times \square = 0.04$ (c) $1.5 \times \square = 150$

(d) $0.3 \times \square = 0.06$ (e) $0.1 \times \square = 0.08$ (f) $\square \times 0.013 = 1.3$

Work out the following

2 3.61×0.3 3 2.1×0.6 4 0.31×0.7 5 0.42×0.02

6 0.33×0.02 7 3.24×0.1 8 8.11×0.07 9 16.2×0.8

10 5.06×0.05 11 30.9×0.3 12 0.2^2 13 0.4^2

14 Copy and complete the multiplication square.

×	0.1	0.02		
		0.06		24
0.2			0.1	
2.1				
				80

15 Phone cable costs £0.55 per metre. Calculate the cost of 2.6 m of cable.

16 The exchange rate is 1.42 Euros to the pound. In a catalogue in England an MP3 player is priced at £35.50. What is the cost in Euros?

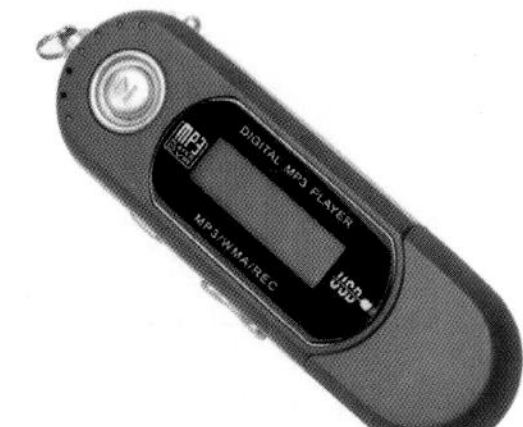

17 A square has a perimeter of 3.64 m. Calculate the area of the square.

Hidden words

(a) Start in the top left box.
(b) Work out the answer to the calculation in the box.
(c) Find the answer in the top corner of another box.
(d) Write down the letter in that box.
(e) Repeat steps (b), (c) and (d) until you arrive back at the top left box.
What is the message.

1

6.4 5×15	66 L $2^3 + 3^3$	274 N 20% of 50	985 E 15×100	12 S $756 \div 9$
422 N 10^3	75 S $150 - 67$	1.68 R 8×22	10 C $8.7 \div 10$	2.4 I $37 + 385$
3.85 U 0.16×10	176 E $421 - 147$	0.87 H $5 + 1.4$	1000 F $8.4 \div 5$	83 O $385 \div 7$
55 L $1000 - 15$	1500 I $\frac{2}{3}$ of 99	1.6 N 0.4×6	35 I 25% of 48	84 S $5.32 - 1.47$

2

612 $1.8 + 8.2$	0.8 T 5% of 400	0.77 W $2^3 \times 6$	0.2 V 5×69	0.62 T 20% of 65
32 C $50\,000 \div 200$	10 B $\frac{2}{5}$ of 450	13 R 0.6×2.6	18 E 80% of 80	250 U $0.9^2 - 0.1^2$
1.56 E $\frac{3}{8}$ of 48	0.6 R $\frac{1}{2}$ of 0.3	180 E $(0.2)^2$	0.15 S 0.32×10^2	64 S $806 - 194$
0.04 A 10% of 2	0.27 O $770 \div 1000$	20 D $0.3 - 0.03$	48 N 3.1×0.2	345 E $4.2 \div 7$

3

1.1 5.2 + 52	100.9 Y 0.1% of 40 000	1.55 D 0.5 × 11	5.14 O $\frac{1}{3}$ of 19.5	1 I 0 ÷ 0.07
1000 E 26.6 ÷ 7	84 E $\frac{1}{100}$ of 170	6.5 R 999 + 998	57.2 C 77 ÷ 100	5100 D 2.1 × 40
0.2 U half of 199	3.5 H $10^5 \times 0.01$	6.4 D 5.1 × 1000	0.08 S 100 × 0.011	3.8 H 0.6 × 0.7
0.77 A 2.1 × 9	14.7 W 46.26 ÷ 9	1997 D 0.4 × 0.2	5.5 T 4.2 – 0.7	40 O 100 × 0.002
0.42 I 25.1 – 18.7	0 N 0.15 + 1.4	99.5 F 100 × 0.1 × 0.1	1.7 N 6 + 8.7	18.9 N 111 – 10.1

4

45 $\frac{1}{2} + \frac{1}{4}$	4 H 2^4	371 C 10 ÷ 1000	21 A 5 ÷ 8	0.51 S 21 – 5 × 4
896 M $1^2 + 2^2 + 3^3$	0.06 E 51 ÷ 100	0.05 L 1% of 250	0.01 E $5 \times (5-2)^2$	34 Y 5.1 × 100
0.625 T $\frac{2}{3} \times \frac{1}{5}$	1 O 6000 ÷ 20	$\frac{3}{4}$ M 4 + 5 × 6	$\frac{3}{8}$ S 0.3 × 0.2	32 I 53 × 7
510 C $\frac{3}{5}$ of 35	16 A $\frac{1}{2} - \frac{1}{8}$	2.5 Y $9 \times 10^2 - 2^2$	300 N $\frac{1}{4} - 0.2$	$\frac{2}{15}$ C 20 ÷ (12 – 7)

1.4 Using a calculator

In section 1.4 you will learn about:

- the order of operations (+, –, ×, ÷)
- using a calculator with simple expressions
- using the 'brackets' and memory keys on a calculator

Order of operations

Consider the possible answers to this question:
'Work out 5 + 7 × 3'

On some calculators, we get: 5 + 7 × 3
= 12 × 3 (adding first)
= 36

On other calculators, we get: 5 + 7 × 3
= 5 + 21 (multiplying first)
= 26

Both answers seem sensible but if we could get different answers to the same question people around the world would argue over who is correct. Another question comes when there are brackets in a calculation, for example 6 × (8 – 3).

The rule we use is

> 'work out the brackets first and then multiply or divide before you add or subtract'

The correct answers to the calculations above are

5 + 7 × 3 = 26
6 × (8 – 3) = 30

Later we will work with indices like 5^2 or 4^3 and when they are involved the complete rule is shown in the table below.

B rackets	( )	do first	'B'
I ndices	x^y	do next	'I'
D ivision M ultiplication	÷ ×	do this pair next	'D' 'M'
A ddition S ubtraction	+ –	do this pair next	'A' 'S'

Remember the word 'B I D M A S'.

(a) $40 \div 5 \times 2$
$= 8 \times 2$
$= 16$

(b) $9 + 8 - 7$
$= 17 - 7$
$= 10$

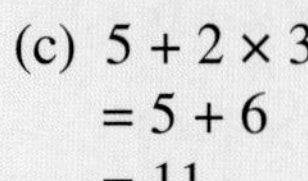

(c) $5 + 2 \times 3$
$= 5 + 6$
$= 11$

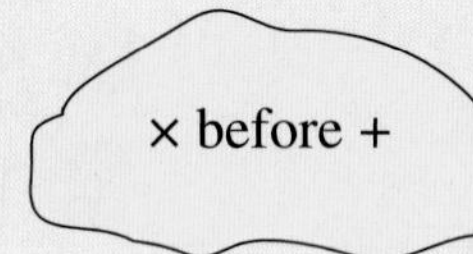

(d) $10 - 8 \div 2$
$= 10 - 4$
$= 6$

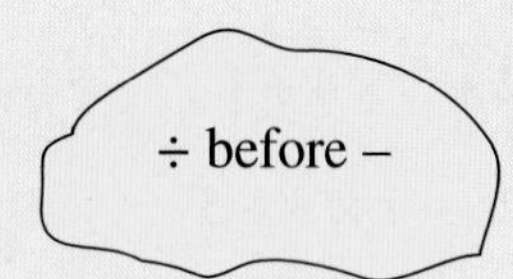

Exercise 1M

Work out the following. Show every step in your working.

1. $5 + 3 \times 2$
2. $4 - 1 \times 3$
3. $7 - 4 \times 3$
4. $2 + 2 \times 5$
5. $9 + 2 \times 6$
6. $13 - 11 \times 1$
7. $7 \times 2 + 3$
8. $9 \times 4 - 12$
9. $2 \times 8 - 7$
10. $4 \times 7 + 2$
11. $13 \times 2 + 4$
12. $8 \times 5 - 15$
13. $6 + 10 \div 5$
14. $7 - 16 \div 8$
15. $8 - 14 \div 7$
16. $5 + 18 \div 6$
17. $5 + 18 \div 6$
18. $6 - 12 \div 4$
19. $20 \div 4 + 2$
20. $15 \div 3 - 7$
21. $24 \div 6 - 8$
22. $30 \div 6 + 9$
23. $8 \div 2 + 9$
24. $28 \div 7 - 4$
25. $13 + 3 \times 13$
26. $9 + 26 \div 13$
27. $10 \times 8 - 70$
28. $96 \div 4 - 4$
29. $36 \div 9 + 1$
30. $1 \times 2 + 3$
31. Copy each calculation and write in the missing number.

(a) $4 \times \square - 7 = 9$
(b) $20 - 3 \times \square = 5$
(c) $24 \div \square - 4 = 4$
(d) $(10 - \square) \times 4 = 36$
(e) $26 - (10 - \square) = 19$
(f) $36 \div (7 - \square) = 6$
(g) $(\square + 7) \times 5 = 65$
(h) $11 - \square \div 2 = 5$
(i) $\square + 7 \times 3 = 30$
(j) $44 + (24 \div \square) = 56$
(k) $(\square \times 7) - 21 = 0$
(l) $48 \div \square + 11 = 17$

(a) $8 + 3 \times 4 - 6$
$= 8 + (3 \times 4) - 6$
$= 8 + 12 - 6$
$= 14$

× and ÷ before + and –

(b) $3 \times 2 - 8 \div 4$
$= (3 \times 2) - (8 \div 4)$
$= 6 - 2$
$= 4$

(c) $\frac{8 + 6}{2} = \frac{14}{2}$
$= 7$

A horizontal line acts as a bracket.

Notice that we have put brackets in to make the working easier.

Exercise 1E

Evaluate the following. Show every step in your working.

1 $2 + 3 \times 4 + 1$
2 $4 + 8 \times 2 - 10$
3 $7 + 2 \times 2 - 6$
4 $25 - 7 \times 3 + 5$
5 $17 - 3 \times 5 + 9$
6 $11 - 9 \times 1 - 1$
7 $1 + 6 \div 2 + 3$
8 $6 - 28 \div 7 - 2$
9 $8 + 15 \div 3 - 5$
10 $5 - 36 \div 9 + 3$
11 $6 - 24 \div 4 + 0$
12 $8 - 30 \div 6 - 2$
13 $3 \times 4 + 1 \times 6$
14 $4 \times 4 + 14 \div 7$
15 $2 \times 5 + 8 \div 4$
16 $21 \div 3 + 5 \times 4$
17 $10 \div 2 + 1 \times 3$
18 $15 \div 5 + 18 \div 6$
19 $5 \times 5 - 6 \times 4$
20 $2 \times 12 - 4 \div 2$
21 $7 \times 2 - 10 \div 2$
22 $35 \div 7 - 5 \times 1$
23 $36 \div 3 - 1 \times 7$
24 $42 \div 6 - 56 \div 8$
25 $72 \div 9 + 132 \div 11$
26 $19 + 35 \div 5 - 16$
27 $50 - 6 \times 7 + 8$
28 $30 - 9 \times 2 + 40$
29 $4 \times 11 - 28 \div 7$
30 $13 \times 11 - 4 \times 8$

In questions 31 to 54 remember to perform the operation in the brackets first.

31 $3 + (6 \times 8)$
32 $(3 \times 8) + 6$
33 $(8 \div 4) + 9$
34 $3 \times (9 \div 3)$
35 $(5 \times 9) - 17$
36 $10 + (12 \times 8)$
37 $(16 - 7) \times 6$
38 $48 \div (14 - 2)$
39 $64 \div (4 \times 4)$
40 $81 + (9 \times 8)$
41 $67 - (24 \div 3)$
42 $(12 \times 8) + 69$
43 $(6 \times 6) + (7 \times 7)$
44 $(12 \div 3) \times (18 \div 6)$
45 $(5 \times 12) - (3 \times 9)$
46 $(20 - 12) \times (17 - 9)$
47 $100 - (99 \div 3)$
48 $1001 + (57 \times 3)$
49 $(3 \times 4 \times 5) - (72 \div 9)$
50 $(2 \times 5 \times 3) \div (11 - 5)$
51 $\dfrac{15 - 7}{2}$
52 $\dfrac{160}{7 + 3}$
53 $\dfrac{19 + 13}{6 - 2}$
54 $\dfrac{5 \times 7 - 9}{13}$

Indices

Remember BIDMAS:
B rackets
I ndex
D ivide
M ultiply
A dd
S ubtract

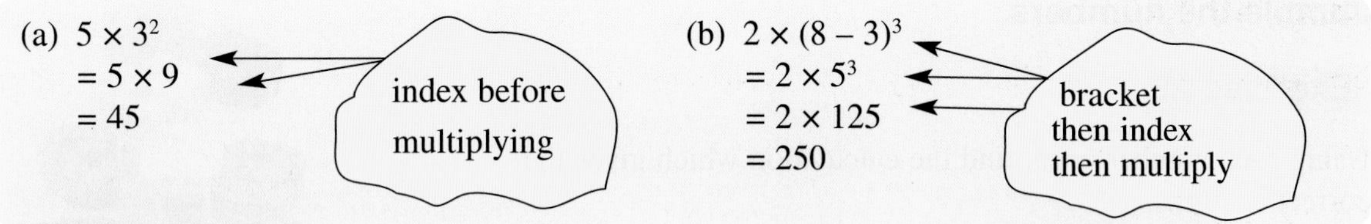
(a) 5×3^2
$= 5 \times 9$
$= 45$
index before multiplying
(b) $2 \times (8 - 3)^3$
$= 2 \times 5^3$
$= 2 \times 125$
$= 250$
bracket then index then multiply

Exercise 2M

Part A

Evaluate the following, showing all your working.

1 2^4
2 3^3
3 0^5
4 $10 + 3^3$
5 $4^2 - 8$
6 $32 - 5^2$
7 $3 + 3^2$
8 8^2
9 5×4^2
10 $3^2 \times 2$
11 62×2^3
12 $5^3 \times 1$
13 $1^4 \times 3^4$
14 $(1 + 1)^3$
15 $(1 + 2)^3$
16 $(5 - 4)^3$
17 $4 \times (3 + 1)^2$
18 $(9 - 5)^4 \div 4$
19 $2 \times (3^2 - 1)$
20 $(5^2 + 5^2) \div 5$
21 $2 \times (6 - 3)^2$
22 $5 \times (2 \times 1)^3$
23 3×2^3
24 $20 - 4^2$

Part B

Copy each question and write brackets so that each calculation gives the correct answer.

1 $3 + 4 \times 5 = 35$
2 $6 + 9 \times 7 = 69$
3 $7 \times 2 + 3 = 17$
4 $9 + 12 \times 5 = 105$
5 $6 \times 8 - 2 = 36$
6 $3 \times 8 - 6 = 18$
7 $19 - 6 \times 3 = 39$
8 $27 - 9 \div 3 = 24$
9 $51 \div 3 + 4 = 21$
10 $7 \times 24 - 5 = 133$
11 $6 + 14 \div 2 = 10$
12 $11 + 6 \times 4 = 68$
13 $12 \times 8 - 9 \times 7 = 33$
14 $8 \times 9 - 4 \times 7 = 44$
15 $5 \times 6 - 4 \div 2 = 13$
16 $81 \div 9 \times 12 - 4 = 72$
17 $3 + 5 \times 9 - 7 = 16$
18 $16 - 10 \div 18 \div 6 = 2$
19 $6 + 7 - 1 \div 2 = 6$
20 $5 + 7 \div 3 \times 0 = 0$

Jumble the numbers

Exercise 2E

Using each number once, find the calculation which gives the correct answer.

For example:

Numbers	Answer	Calculation
5, 3, 6	3	$(6-5) \times 3 = 3$

	Numbers			Answer	Calculation		Numbers			Answer	Calculation
1.	2	4	8	6		**2.**	2	3	5	21	
3.	7	2	3	3		**4.**	9	2	4	7	
5.	8	4	5	20		**6.**	20	2	3	6	
7.	7	2	4	30		**8.**	7	22	6	20	
9.	6	4	3	8		**10.**	8	40	3	8	
11.	8	36	4	5		**12.**	7	49	2	14	
13.	21	14	11	24		**14.**	16	3	9	57	
15.	12	4	16	7		**16.**	24	42	6	24	
17.	18	5	13	25		**18.**	40	6	16	4	
19.	7	8	6	50		**20.**	13	8	4	44	
21.	4	3	9	12		**22.**	7	9	3	21	
23.	45	4	3	11		**24.**	121	11	7	77	

25 Make up your own question to try on a friend.
You may use as many numbers as you like.

Using a calculator

Division can be written with a horizontal line

$8 \div 2 = \frac{8}{2}$ $\quad (4+6) \div 2 = \frac{4+6}{2}$ $\quad 4 + 6 \div 2 = 4 + \frac{6}{2}$

$12 \div (4+2) = \frac{12}{4+2}$ $\quad (8-3) \div (11+2) = \frac{8-3}{11+2}$

Exercise 3M

1 Write the following expressions with a horizontal line

(a) $8 + 6 \div 2$ (b) $10 \div 2 + 4$ (c) $12 - (8 \div 2)$
(d) $10 \div (3+1)$ (e) $(12-7) \div 2$ (f) $10 \div 5 - 1$

2 Work out without a calculator

(a) $\frac{8-2}{3}$ (b) $12 - \frac{8}{2}$ (c) $\frac{14-8}{2}$ (d) $\frac{8}{4} + 1$
(e) $\frac{8}{3+1}$ (f) $\frac{12-8}{2}$ (g) $\frac{16}{1+3}$ (h) $15 + \frac{12}{3}$

In questions **3** to **14** use a calculator to find the answer.

3 2.5×1.67	**4** $19.6 - 3.73$	**5** $0.795 \div 0.25$
6 $0.13 + 8.9 - 3.71$	**7** $2.4 \times 2.4 - 3.45$	**8** $5.3 \times 1.7 + 3.7$
9 $0.71 \times 0.92 - 0.15$	**10** $\dfrac{15.48}{1.72}$	**11** $\dfrac{8.448}{1.32}$
12 $8.2 \times 0.4 - 3$	**13** 4.65×101	**14** $8.17 - 1.56 + 7.4$

In questions **15** to **32** remember the correct order of operations.

15 $2.5 + 3.1 \times 2.4$	**16** $7.81 + 0.7 \times 1.82$	**17** $8.73 + 3.45 \div 0.5$
18 $11.7 \div 9 - 0.74$	**19** $4.48 \div 0.32 + 1.15$	**20** $2.6 + 5.2 \times 1.7$
21 $2.9 + \dfrac{6.039}{1.83}$	**22** $1.6 \times 1.7 + 2.62$	**23** $5.2 + \dfrac{4.995}{1.85}$
24 $9.64 + \dfrac{10.92}{0.42}$	**25** $1.27 + 3.1 \times 4.4$	**26** $\dfrac{1.5 \times 1.5}{25}$
27 $0.15 + 1.4 \times 9.2$	**28** $1.7 \times 1.7 \times 1.7$	**29** $8.2 + 3.2 \times 3.3$
30 $3.2 + \dfrac{9.408}{6.72}$	**31** $\dfrac{1.9 + 2.953}{2.3}$	**32** $\dfrac{8.7 - 5.622}{1.14}$

Using brackets

For the calculation 14 – (8 ÷ 2) you press

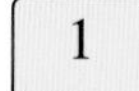

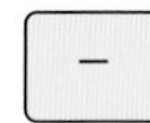

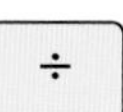

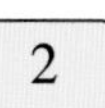

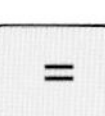

When the right hand bracket button is pressed you will see that the calculation inside the brackets has been performed. Try it.

Don't forget to press the [=] button at the end to give the final answer.

(a) $8.72 - (1.4 \times 1.7)$

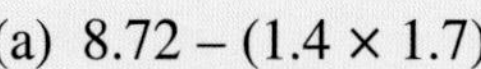

[8.72] [–] [( ] [1.4] [×] [1.7] [ )] [=]

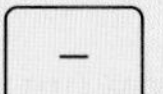

Answer = 6.34

(b) $\dfrac{6.405}{(1.94 - 0.72)}$

[6.405] [÷] [( ] [1.94] [–] [0.72] [ )] [=]

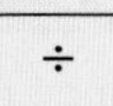

Answer = 5.25

Exercise 3E

1 Work out what answer you would get when the buttons are pressed.

(a) (8 + 7) ÷ 3 = (b) 1 8 − (5 × 2) =

(c) 1 2 ÷ (6 − 3) = (d) 9 ÷ (6 ÷ 2) =

2 Write down the sequence of buttons you would press to work out the following calculations.

(a) $17 - (4.2 \times 3)$ (b) $\dfrac{28}{2.41 + 4.59}$

Work out

3 $18.41 - (7.2 \times 1.3)$

4 $11.01 + (2.45 \div 7)$

5 $(2.38 + 5.6) \div 1.4$

6 $9.6 + (11.2 \div 4)$

7 $(8.73 \div 3) - 1.4$

8 $11.7 - (2.6 \times 2.7)$

9 $7.41 - \left(\dfrac{6.44}{1.4}\right)$

10 $\left(\dfrac{11.39}{1.7}\right) - 2.63$

11 $\dfrac{28.65}{(1.7 + 0.21)}$

12 $(1.56 + 4.32) \div 2.45$

13 $3.2 \times (1.9 - 0.74)$

14 $4.956 \div (1.3 - 0.71)$

15 $(7.77 \div 1.4) \times 1.49$

16 $(2.67 + 1.2 + 5) \times 1.1$

17 $23 - (9.2 \times 1.85)$

18 $\dfrac{(8.41 + 0.704)}{1.47}$

19 $\dfrac{132.43}{8.2 \times 0.95}$

20 $\dfrac{43.87 - 8.17}{17}$

21 Find three pairs of equivalent expressions

A $\dfrac{24}{3} - 2$ B $\dfrac{24 - 2}{3}$ C $24 - 2 \div 3$ D $(24 - 2) \div 3$

E $24 - \dfrac{2}{3}$ F $\dfrac{24}{3 - 2}$ G $24 \div (3 - 2)$

22 Write down the sequence of buttons you would press to evaluate the following.

(a) $\dfrac{9 - 3}{4 + 8}$ (b) $\dfrac{30}{8 - 3} + 4 \times 7$

In questions 23 to 44 use the x^2 button where needed and write down all the numbers on your calculator display.

23 $2.6^2 - 1.4$

24 $8.3^2 \times 1.17$

25 $7.2^2 \div 6.67$

26 $(1.4 + 2.67)^2$

27 $(8.41 - 5.7)^2$

28 $(2.7 \times 1.31)^2$

29 $8.2^2 - (1.4 + 1.73)$

30 $\frac{2.6^2}{(1.3 + 2.99)}$

31 $4.1^2 - \left(\frac{8.7}{3.2}\right)$

32 $\frac{(2.7 + 6.04)}{(1.4 + 2.11)}$

33 $\frac{(8.71 - 1.6)}{(2.4 + 9.73)}$

34 $\left(\frac{2.3}{1.4}\right)^2$

35 $9.72^2 - (2.9 \times 2.7)$

36 $(3.3 + 1.3^2) \times 9$

37 $(2.7^2 - 2.1) \div 5$

38 $\left(\frac{2.84}{7}\right) + \left(\frac{7}{11.2}\right)$

39 $\frac{(2.7 \times 8.1)}{(12 - 8.51)}$

40 $\left(\frac{2.3}{1.5}\right) - \left(\frac{6.3}{8.9}\right)$

41 $(1.31 + 2.705) - 1.3^2$

42 $(2.71 - 0.951) \times 5.62$

43 $\frac{(8.5 \times 1.952)}{(7.2 - 5.96)}$

44 $\left(\frac{80.7}{30.3}\right) - \left(\frac{11.7}{10.2}\right)$

Using the memory

We will use the following memory keys: [Min] Puts a number into the memory.

[MR] Recalls a number from the memory.

To *clear* the memory we will press [0] [Min].

Some calculators have a [STO] button which works like the [Min] button.

Also the [ANS] button can be used as a 'short term memory'.
It holds the answer from the previous calculation.

The [Min] key is very useful because it *automatically* clears any number already in the memory when it puts in the new number.

So if you pressed [13.2] [Min] [6.5] [Min], the number in the memory would be 6.5. The 13.2 is effectively 'lost'.

Work out

(a) $\frac{2.25}{1.6 - 0.975}$

Work out the bottom line first.

[1.6] [–] [0.975] [=] [Min]

[2.25] [÷] [MR] [=]

Answer = 3.6

(b) $8.51 - \left(\frac{3.24}{1.73}\right)$

Work out the brackets first.

[3.24] [÷] [1.7] [=] [Min]

[8.51] [–] [MR] [=]

Answer = 6.63716763...

A very common error occurs when people forget to press the [=] button at the end of the calculation.

Exercise 4M

Work out and write down all the numbers in your calculator display.

1 $\dfrac{5.63}{2.8 - 1.71}$

2 $\dfrac{11.5}{5.24 + 1.57}$

3 $\dfrac{8.27}{2.9 \times 1.35}$

4 $\dfrac{3.7 - 2.41}{1.9 + 0.72}$

5 $\dfrac{8.5 + 9.3}{12.9 - 8.72}$

6 $\dfrac{0.97 \times 3.85}{1.24 + 4.63}$

7 $14.5 - \left(\dfrac{1.9}{0.7}\right)$

8 $8.41 - 3.2 \times 1.76$

9 $11.62 - \dfrac{6.3}{9.8}$

10 $\dfrac{9.84 \times 0.751}{6.3 \times 0.95}$

11 $5.62 + 1.98 + \dfrac{1.2}{4.5}$

12 $8.5 - \dfrac{8.9}{11.6}$

13 $\dfrac{6.3}{4.2} + \dfrac{8.2}{11.9}$

14 $\dfrac{8.43 + 1.99}{9.6 - 1.73}$

15 $\dfrac{17.6}{8.4} - \dfrac{1.92}{8.41}$

16 $25.1 - 4.2^2$

17 $(9.8 - 4.43)^2$

18 $18.7 - 2.33^2$

19 $8.21^2 + 1.67^2$

20 $9.23^2 - 7.42^2$

21 $16.1 - 1.1^2$

22 $\dfrac{16.1}{4.7} - 1.8^2$

23 $\left(\dfrac{17.2}{9.8} - 1.2\right)^2$

24 $9.9 - 8.3 \times 0.075$

25 $1.21 - \dfrac{9}{14^2}$

26 $3.7^2 + \dfrac{11.4}{1.7}$

27 $\dfrac{11.7 - 3.73}{2.45^2}$

28 $\dfrac{8.94}{4.8 + 1.7^2}$

29 $\dfrac{3.21^2}{8.2 - 4.11}$

30 $\dfrac{116.7}{8.1^2 + 32}$

31 $8.7 + \dfrac{8.2}{9.7} + \dfrac{4.1}{5.6}$

32 $8.5 - (1.6^2 + 1.9^2)$

33 $8.3 + \dfrac{1.9}{8.4} - \dfrac{1.7}{6.5}$

34 $3.2 + \left(3.2 + \dfrac{1.4}{5}\right)^2$

35 $\dfrac{3.4}{1.6} + \left(\dfrac{2.1}{1.3}\right)^2$

36 $\left(8.2 - \dfrac{1}{8.2}\right) \times 8.2$

37 You can buy euros at the rate of 1.4523 euros to the pound.
(a) How many euros will you get for £265?
(b) How many pounds will you get for €700?
Give your answers to the nearest whole number.

38 A rectangular field measures 115 m by 215 m.
Work out the area of the field
(a) in m^2 (b) in hectares (1 hectare = 10 000 m^2)

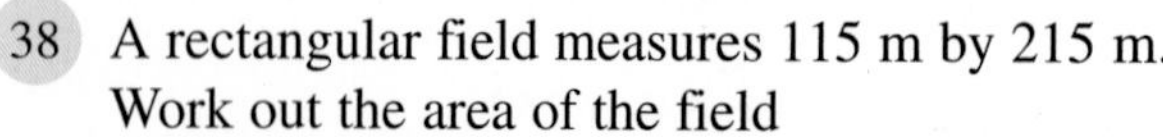

39 A man's heart beats at 70 beats/min. How many times will his heart beat between 03.30 and 23.30 on the same day?

40 The year 2000 is clearly not a prime number but it is a thousand times a prime number. Which, if any, of the years from 2000 to 2010 are prime numbers?

Calculator words

- When you hold a calculator display upside down some numbers appear to form words: 4506 spells "Gosh"

  0.710 spells "Old" (ignoring the decimal point)

Exercise 4E

Translate this passage using a calculator and the clues below:

"(1)___!" shouted Olag out of the window of his (2)___. "I need some (3)___ / (4)___ for my dinner. Do you (5)___ them?"
"(6)___ did" (7)___ / (8)___ "I even took off the (9)___ for free. (10)___ / (11)___ / (12)___ they were. The problem is that all the (13)___ were eaten in the (14)___, mostly by (15)___ . (16)___ / (17)___ such a (18)___ / (19)___ lately. (20)___ and (21)___ are always (22)___ because of the amount of (23)___ they drink every night"
"(24)___ well, he is the (25)___ I suppose" Olag grumbled "Roast (26)___ again tonight then…"

Clues to passage

1. $(2.37 + 2.53) \div 0.7^2$
2. $(3 \div 40) + 0.0011$
3. $\frac{3}{8} - (39.2 \div 10^4)$
4. $5 \times 12 \times 100 - 7$
5. $(90 \times 80) + (107 \times 5)$
6. $\sqrt{0.01} \times 10$
7. $(68 + 1.23) \div 200$
8. $101^2 - (5 \times 13) - 2$
9. $750^2 + (296\,900 \div 20)$
10. $2^3 \times 5^2 \times 3 + 16.3 + 1.7$
11. $(70\,000 \div 2) + (3 \times 2)$
12. $11\,986 \div 2$
13. $(600^2 - 6640) \div 10$
14. $200^2 - 685$
15. $(0.5^2 \times 0.6)$
16. $\sqrt{289} \times 2$
17. $836.4 \div 17 + 1.8$
18. $30^2 + 18$
19. $5^3 \times 64.6$
20. $(63\,508 \times 5) - 3$
21. $\sqrt{(1160 - 4)}$
22. 1.3803×0.25
23. $(32 \times 10^3) + 8$
24. $2^3 \times 5$
25. $(5^3 \times 2^2 \times 11) + 8$
26. $7 \times 10^7 - 9\,563\,966$

CHECK YOURSELF ON UNITS 1.3 and 1.4

1 Using place value with decimals

(a) Arrange the numbers in order of size, smallest first

(i) 0.007, 0.08, 0.081, 0.0065
(ii) 0.2, 0.221, 0.202, 0.022

(b) Increase the following numbers by $\frac{1}{100}^{\text{th}}$

(i) 7.162 (ii) 3.7082 (iii) 0.593

2 Adding and subtracting with decimals

(a) $1.362 + 0.28$
(b) $51.52 - 3.4$
(c) $(3.81 + 0.09) - 2.99$
(d) $0.3 + 0.04 + 0.005 - 0.02 - 0.003$

3 Multiplying and dividing with decimals

(a) 3.24×7
(b) $21.24 \div 6$
(c) 0.4×0.5
(d) $(8.4 - 7.6) \times 0.2$
(e) $0.2^2 + 0.01^2$

4 Order of operations

(a) $8 - 24 \div 4$
(b) $8 \times 3 - 10 \div 2$
(c) $17 - (60 \div 6)$
(d) $(2 + 7 \times 4) \times (21 - 17)$
(e) $\dfrac{6 \times 5 - 6}{8}$
(f) $5 \times (4 - 1)^2$

5 Using a calculator with simple expressions

(a) $78.2 + 4.6 \times 2.5$
(b) $1.72 - 0.456 \times 2$
(c) $8.15 - \dfrac{6.72}{3.2}$
(d) $\dfrac{4.771 - 1.711}{0.85}$

6 Using the brackets and memory keys

(a) $23.78 - (6.7 \times 1.9)$
(b) $11.4 + \left(\dfrac{3.57}{1.7}\right)$
(c) $\dfrac{19 - 1.32}{5.6 - 2.35}$
(d) $\dfrac{25.92}{1.6} - 3.5^2$

1.5 Sequences

In section 1.5 you will learn how to:

- find the next term in a sequence
- find and use a rule for a sequence
- solve problems involving harder sequences

Here is sequence 3 7 11 15 19

- A number sequence is a set of numbers in a given order.
- Each number in a sequence is called a *term.*
- Here are three sequences. Try to find the next term.

(a) 5, 8, 12, 17, ?

(b) $\frac{1}{2}$, 1, 2, 4, ?

(c) 15, 14, 16, 13, 17, ?

Exercise 1M

1 The numbers in boxes make a sequence. Find the next term.

(a) | 9 | 7 | 5 | 3 | |

(b) | 4 | 9 | 14 | 19 | |

(c) | 2 | 9 | 16 | 23 | |

(d) | 2 | 3 | 5 | 8 | 12 | |

In questions 2 to 17 write down the sequence and find the next term.

2 21, 17, 13, 9

3 60, 54, 48, 42

4 1, 2, 4, 8, 16

5 $\frac{1}{2}$, 1, $1\frac{1}{2}$, 2

6 3, $4\frac{1}{2}$, 6, $7\frac{1}{2}$

7 60, 59, 57, 54, 50

8 5, 7, 10, 14

9 3, 30, 300, 3000

10 1.7, 1.9, 2.1, 2.3

11 1, 3, 9, 27

12 8, 4, 0, –4, –8

13 7, 5, 3, 1, –1

14 1, 2, 4, 7, 11

15 –2, –1, 0, 1

16 200, 100, 50, 25

Exercise 1E

1 Write down each sequence and find the next term.
(a) 2, 5, 8, 11 (b) 2, 8, 14, 20 (c) –2, 0, 2, 4
(d) 0.9, 1, 1.1, 1.2 (e) 22, 17, 12, 7 (f) 0.2, 0.5, 0.8

In questions 2 to 10 you may have to add, subtract, multiply or divide to find the next term.

2 21, 15, 9

3 0.2, 2, 20, 200

4 0.8, 1, 1.2

5 80, 40, 20, 10

6 11, 8, 5, 2

7 10000, 1000, 100

8 1.5, 1.1, 0.7

9 540, 180, 60

10 7, 30, 53

11 Write down the sequence and find the missing numbers.

(a) | | 6 | 12 | 24 | |

(b) | 4 | | 10 | 13 | |

(c) | | 16 | 8 | 4 | |

(d) | | 6 | 3 | 0 | –3 | |

The next four questions are more difficult. Find the next term.

12 1, 2, 6, 24, 120

13 $2 \times 4^2,\ 3 \times 5^2,\ 4 \times 6^2$

14 $\frac{1}{3}, \frac{2}{5}, \frac{3}{7}, \frac{4}{9}$

15 2, 2, 4, 12, 48, 240

16 Golf balls can be stacked in a 'solid' pyramid.
The picture shows the view from above a pyramid with **1** ball at the top, **4** balls on the next layer and **9** balls on the next layer after that.
(a) How many balls will be on the next layer?
(b) How many balls will there be altogether in the first five layers?

Sequence rules

- For the sequence 10, 13, 16, 19, 22, …. the first term is 10 and the term-to-term rule is 'add 3'.
  For the sequence 3, 6, 12, 24, 48, …. the term-to-term rule is 'double' or 'multiply by 2'.

Exercise 2M

1 The first term of a sequence is 20 and the term-to-term rule is 'add 5'. Write down the first five terms of the sequence.

2 You are given the first term and the rule of several sequences.
Write down the first five terms of each sequence.

	First term	Rule
(a)	8	add 2
(b)	100	subtract 4
(c)	10	double
(d)	64	divide by 2

3 Write down the rule for each of these sequences.

(a) 3, 10, 17, 24
(b) 100, 89, 78, 67
(c) 0.7, 0.9, 1.1, 1.3
(d) 1, 2, 4, 8, 16

4 The rule for the number sequences below is

'double and add 1'

Find the missing numbers
(a) $2 \rightarrow 5 \rightarrow 11 \rightarrow 23 \rightarrow \square$
(b) $\square \rightarrow 7 \rightarrow 15 \rightarrow 13$
(c) $\square \rightarrow 51 \rightarrow \square \rightarrow \square$

5 The rule for the number sequences below is

'multiply by 3 and take away 2'

Find the missing numbers
(a) $2 \rightarrow 4 \rightarrow 10 \rightarrow \square$
(b) $\square \rightarrow 7 \rightarrow 19 \rightarrow 55$
(c) $1 \rightarrow \square \rightarrow \square \rightarrow \square$

6 Write down the rule for each of these sequences.

(a) 2, $2\frac{1}{2}$, 3, $3\frac{1}{2}$, 4, ...
(b) 5, 10, 20, 40, 80, ...
(c) 1.5, 1.6, 1.7, 1.8, ...
(d) 81, 27, 9, 3, 1, ...
(e) 1.5, 1.35, 1.2, 1.05
(f) 76, 38, 19, 9.5
(g) 1, 4, 10, 22, 46
(h) 3, 10, 31, 94

7 Write down the first six terms of these sequences

(a) the first term is 3
the rule is 'subtract 0.3'
(b) the first term is 864
the rule is 'divide by 6'
(c) the fourth term is 60
the rule is 'add 11'
(d) the third term is 6
the rule is 'divide by 10'
(e) the first two terms are 1, 4
the rule is 'add the two previous terms'
(f) the first two terms are 0, 2
the rule is 'add the two previous terms'
(g) the first term is 3
the rule is 'multiply by 2 and then add 3'
(h) the first term is 5
the rule is 'write down the next prime number'

8 In the sequences of squares the number of matches is shown.

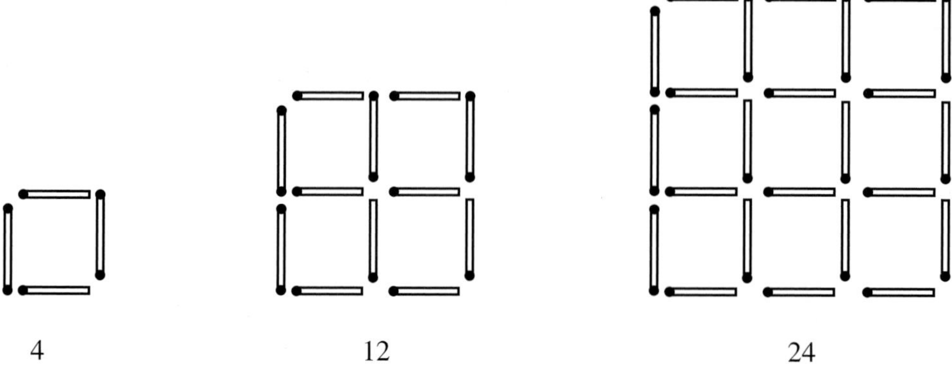

(a) Draw the next square in the sequence and write down the number of matches in the square.
(b) Copy and complete the number pattern below.

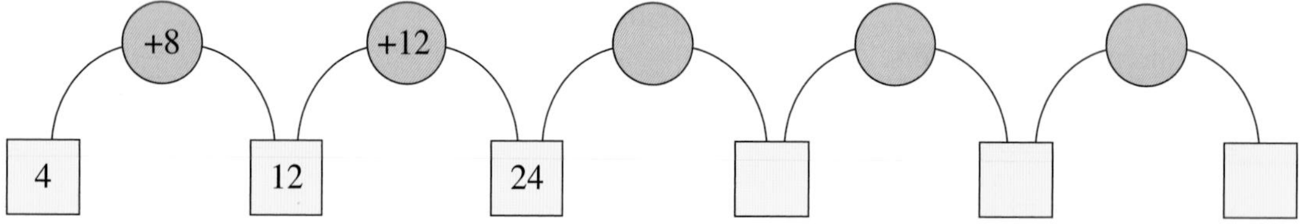

9 The first number in a sequence is 5. Write down a possible rule so that all the terms in the sequence are odd numbers.

10 The rule for a sequence is 'add 3'. The first three terms of the sequence are negative numbers. Find what numbers the first term of the sequence could be.

11 The tenth number in the sequence 1, 3, 9, 27 ... is 19 683.
What is (a) the ninth number,
(b) the twelfth number?

Exercise 2E

1 In this question the rule for several *different* sequences is 'add 5'.
(a) Find a sequence for which all the terms are divisible by 5.
(b) Find a sequence for which none of the terms is a whole number.
(c) Can you find a sequence with the 'add 5' rule in which all the terms are odd numbers?

2 Find the first five terms of each sequence.

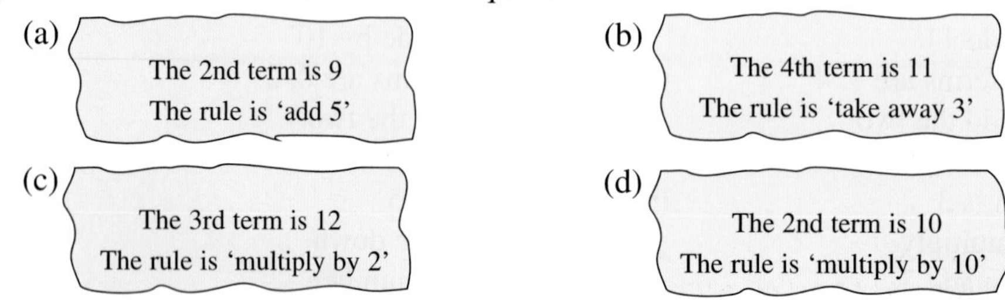

(a)
The 2nd term is 9
The rule is 'add 5'
(b)
The 4th term is 11
The rule is 'take away 3'
(c)
The 3rd term is 12
The rule is 'multiply by 2'
(d)
The 2nd term is 10
The rule is 'multiply by 10'

3 In a *linear* sequence the terms go up or go down in equal steps.
For example 7, 10, 13, 16, ... or 20, 18, 16, 14, ...
Fill in the missing numbers in these linear sequences

(a) 2, □, 8, □, □, 17 (b) 10, □, 18, □, 26, 30, □

(c) □, 37, □, □, 28, 25

4 The following are linear sequences.

(a) The 2nd term is 9
The 3rd term is 13
What is the 6th term?

(b) The 4th term is 11
The 12th term is 27
What is the 9th term?

(c) The first term is –2
The 3rd term is the smallest 2 digit multiple of 4
What is the 6th term?

(d) The 2nd term is 9
The 5th term is six times as large as the 1st term.
What is the 6th term?

5 (a) Copy this pattern and write down the next three lines. Do not use a calculator!

$1 \times 999 = 999$
$2 \times 999 = 1998$
$3 \times 999 = 2997$
$4 \times 999 = 3996$

(b) Copy this pattern and write down the next two lines.

$3 \times 5 = 15$
$33 \times 5 = 165$
$333 \times 5 = 1665$
$3333 \times 5 = 16665$

(c) Copy and complete $333\,333\,333 \times 5 =$

6 (a) Look at the pattern below and then continue it for a further three rows.

$2^2 + 2 + 3 = 9$
$3^2 + 3 + 4 = 16$
$4^2 + 4 + 5 = 25$
. . . .
. . . .
. . . .

(b) Write down the line which starts
$12^2 + \ldots$

7 (a) Copy this pattern and write down the next line.

$1 \times 9 = 9$
$21 \times 9 = 189$
$321 \times 9 = 2889$
$4321 \times 9 = 38\,889$
$54321 \times 9 = 488\,889$

(b) Complete this line $87\,654\,321 \times 9 =$

8 (a) Copy this pattern and write down the next line.

$1 + 9 \times 0 = 1$
$2 + 9 \times 1 = 11$
$3 + 9 \times 12 = 111$
$4 + 9 \times 123 = 1111$

(b) Find the missing numbers

$\square + 9 \times \square = 1111111$

9 (a) Copy this pattern and write down the next line.

$3 \times 4 = 3 + 3 \times 3$
$4 \times 5 = 4 + 4 \times 4$
$5 \times 6 = 5 + 5 \times 5$

(b) Copy and complete

$10 \times 11 =$
$11 \times 12 =$
$100 \times 101 =$

10 The odd numbers can be added in groups to give an interesting sequence.

1	=	1	=	1^3	$(1 \times 1 \times 1)$
3 + 5	=	8	=	2^3	$(2 \times 2 \times 2)$
7 + 9 + 11	=	27	=	3^3	$(3 \times 3 \times 3)$

The numbers 1, 8, 27 are called *cube* numbers. Another cube number is 5^3 (we say '5 cubed')

$5^3 = 5 \times 5 \times 5 = 125$

Write down the next three rows of the sequence to see if the sum of each row always gives a cube number.

11 A famous sequence in mathematics is Pascal's triangle.

(a) Look carefully at how the triangle is made. Write down the next row. It starts: 1 7 ...
(b) Look at the diagonal marked A. Predict the next three numbers in the sequence 1, 3, 6, 10, 15, ...
(c) Work out the *sum* of the numbers in each row of Pascal's triangle. What do you notice?
(d) Without writing down all the numbers, work out the sum of the numbers in the 10th row of the triangle.

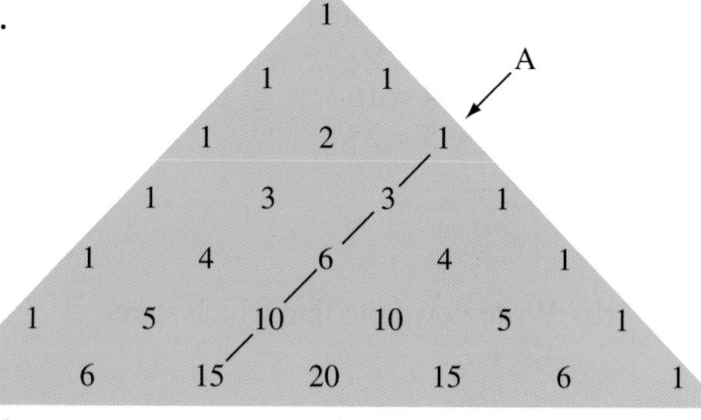

12 (a) What is the sum of all the numbers in the triangle down to and including (i) the 3rd row,
(ii) the 6th row?
(b) Predict the sum of all the numbers in the triangle down to and including the 10th row.

1.6 Perimeter and area

In section 1.6 you will learn how to:

- find perimeters
- find areas involving rectangles
- find areas involving triangles

Perimeter

The perimeter of a shape is the distance around its edges. It is a length and is measured in units of length such as metres or centimetres.

Area

The area of a shape is the amount of surface it covers. It is measured in squares, usually square metres (m^2) or square centimetres (cm^2).

Exercise 1M

1 Copy and complete this table showing the measurements of rectangles.

length	9 cm	8 cm	6 cm	8 cm	6.7 cm	
width	7 cm	3 cm			2.9 cm	4.5 cm
perimeter			26 cm	34 cm		37 cm

2 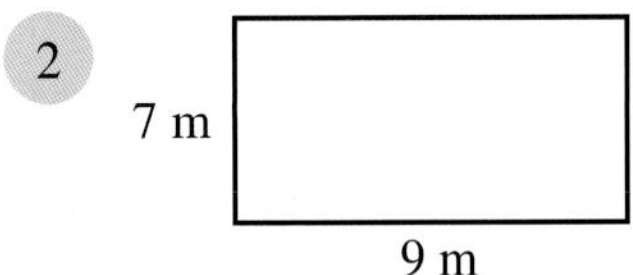

(a) Find the perimeter of this garden.
(b) Ed wants to put fence panels around the entire edge of the garden. Each fence panel is 2 m long. How many fence panels will Ed need?

The shapes in questions 3 to 10 consist of rectangles joined together. Find the missing lengths and then work out the perimeter of each shape. The lengths are in cm.

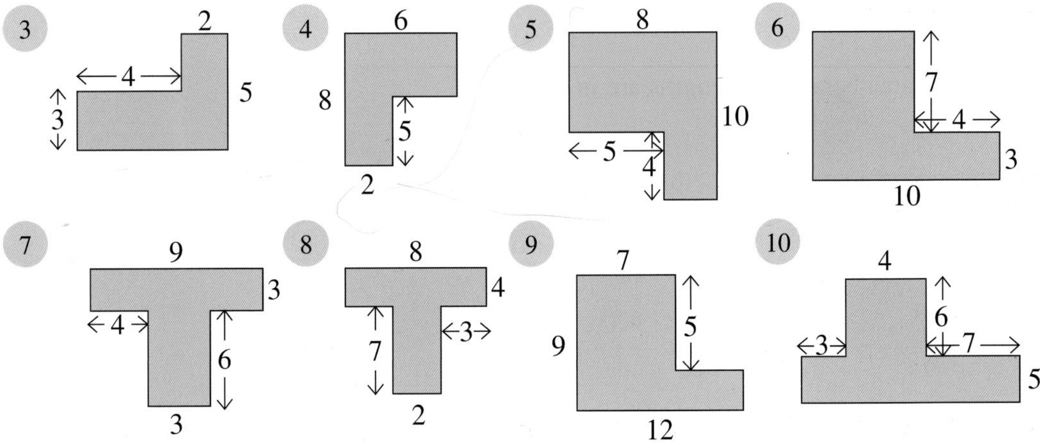

11 The perimeter of a rectangular lawn is 50 m.
The shortest side is 8 m. How long is the longest side?

12 A picture frame has its length twice its height. The total length of wood used in the frame is 108 cm. Work out the length of the frame.

13 Here are four shapes made with centimetre squares.

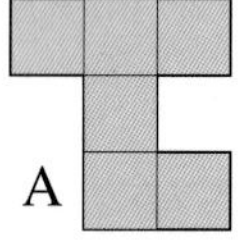

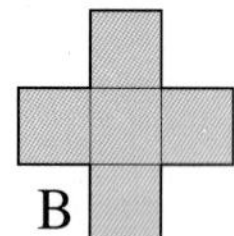

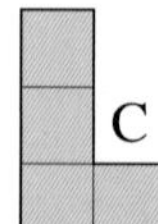

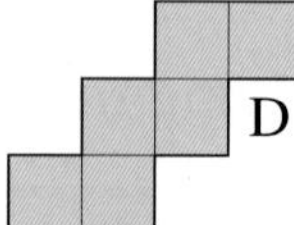

(a) Which shape has an area of 5 cm^2?
(b) Which two shapes have the same perimeter?

14 Each of the shapes here has an area of 2 cm^2?

(a) On square dotty paper draw three more shapes with area 2 cm^2.
(b) Draw three shapes with area 3 cm^2.
(c) Draw one shape with area 4 cm^2 and perimeter 10 cm.

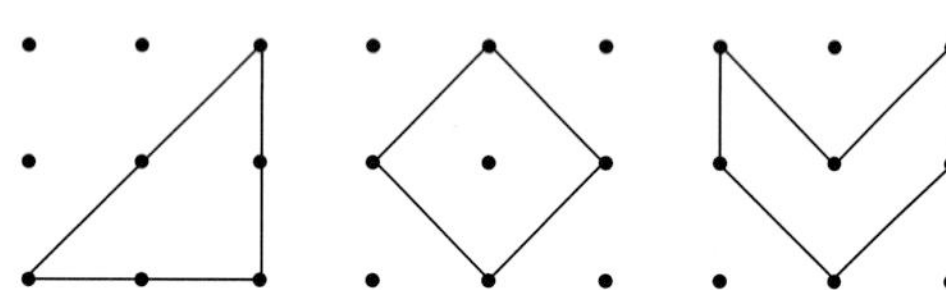

15 Here are five shapes made from equilateral triangles of side 1 cm.

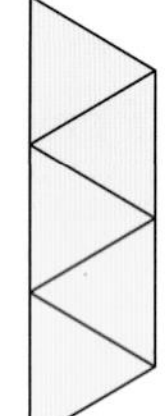

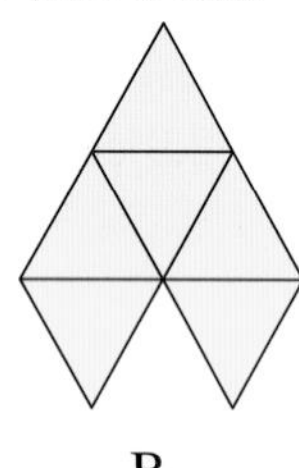

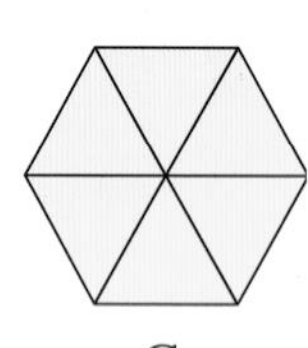

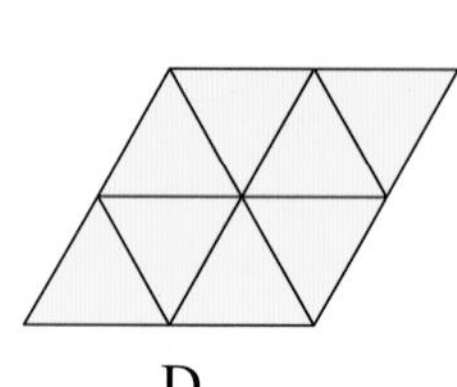

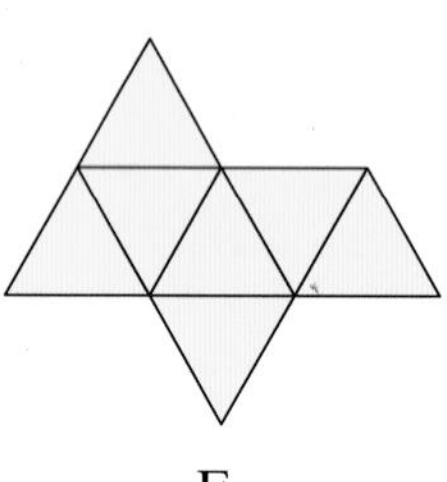

(a) Which shape has the longest perimeter?
(b) Which shape has the smallest area?
(c) Which shape has the same perimeter as D?

Exercise 1E

1 Find each blue area below (the lengths are in cm)

(a)
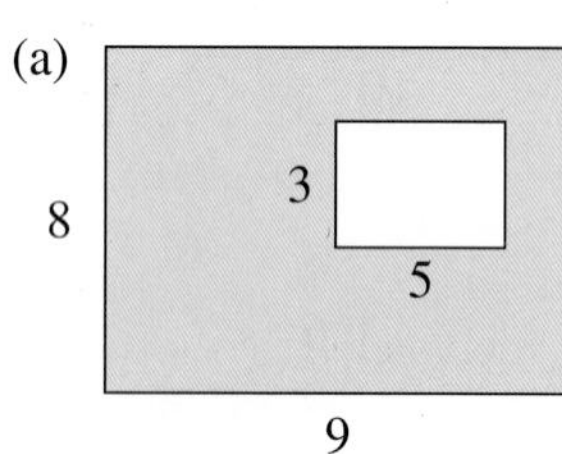

(b)
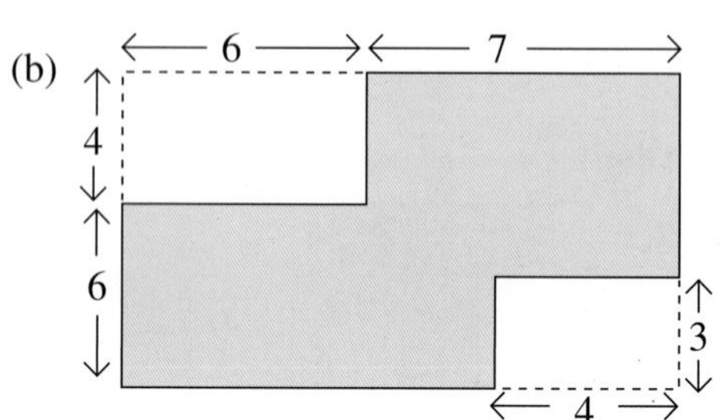

2 Find the area of each shape. The lengths are in cm.

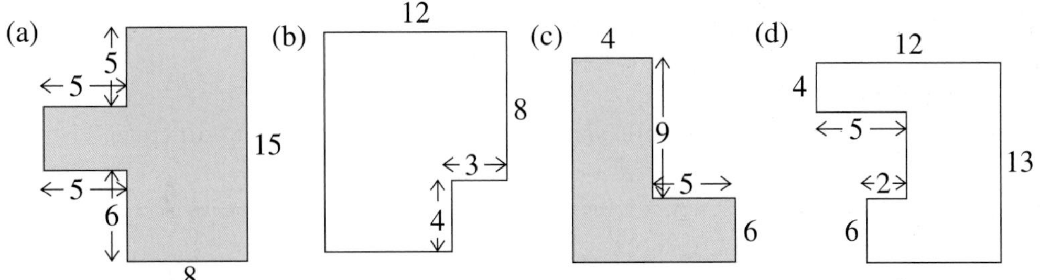

3 In the rectangles below, the area is written inside the shape. Calculate the length of the side marked x.

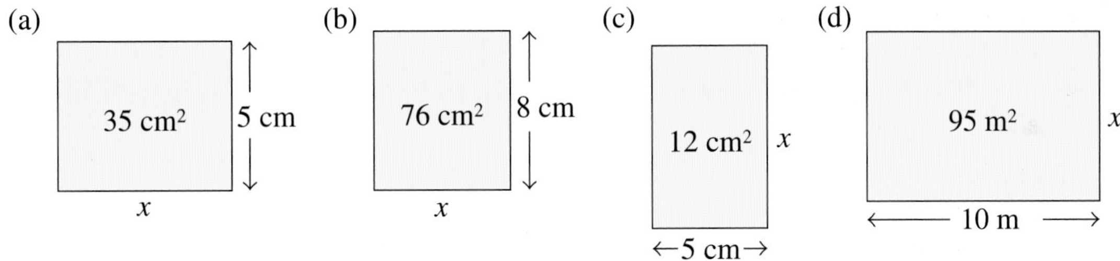

4 A square has an area of 144 cm². How long is each side of this square?

5

2 m

1.5 m

(a) Write down the length and width in cm only.

(b) This wall is to be covered with tiles. Each tile has a length of 20 cm and a width of 10 cm. How many tiles are needed to cover the entire wall?

6 A square has an area of 225 cm². Find the perimeter of this square.

7 A lawn is surrounded by a path which is 1m wide. Calculate the area of the path.

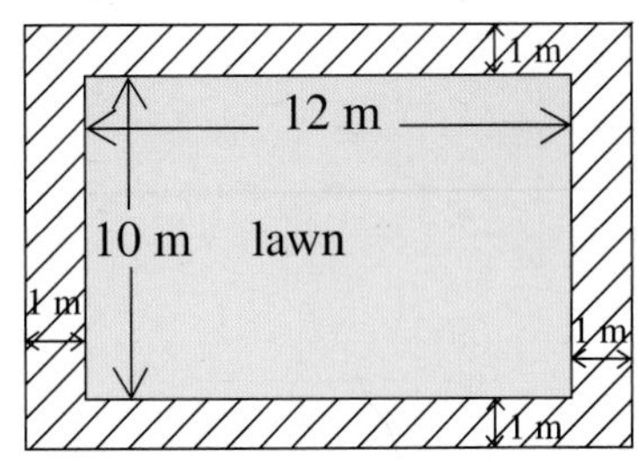

8

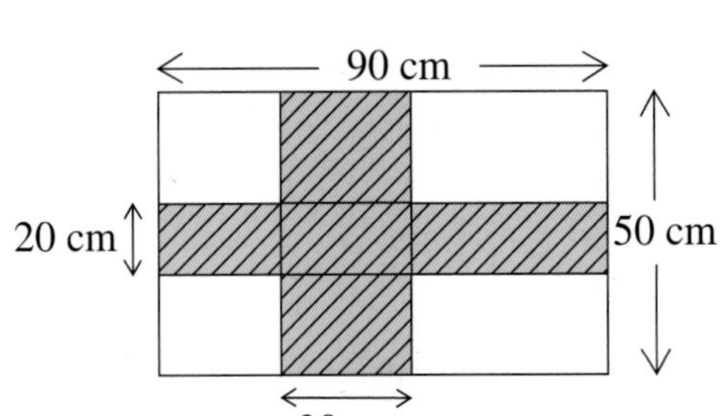

Calculate the area of the shaded cross.

9

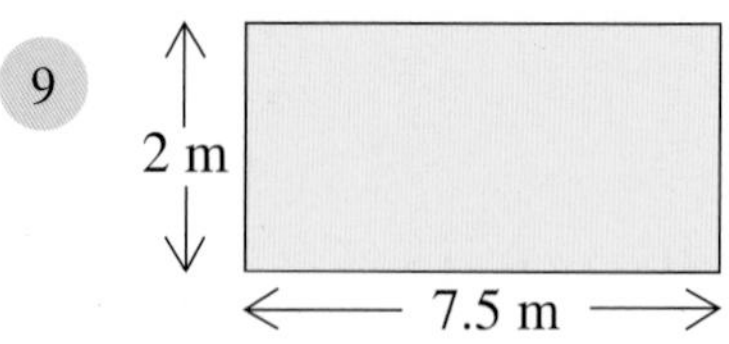

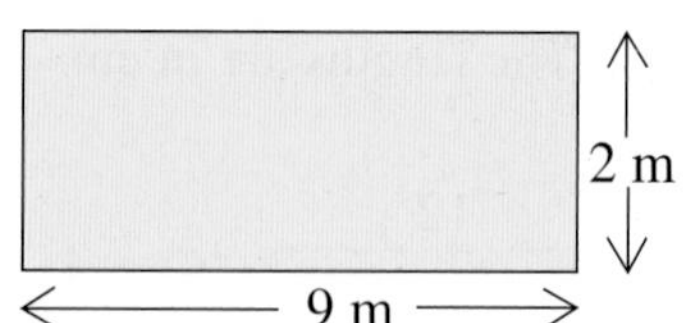

Shahanya wants to paint the two walls shown above. Each tin of paint will cover 11 m^2. How many tins of paint will she need?

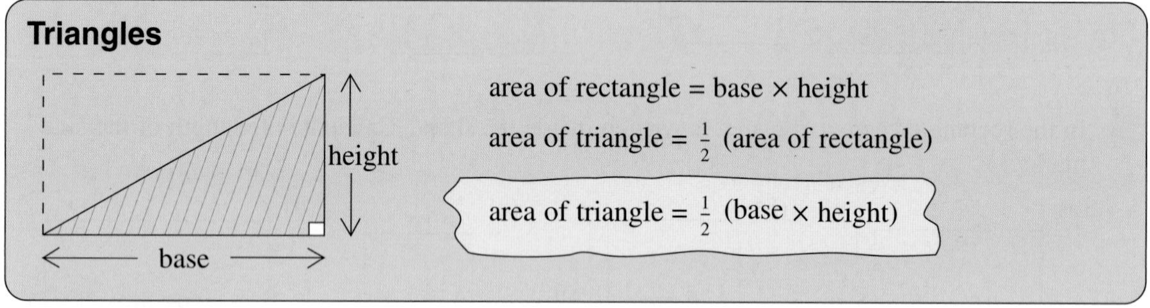

Triangles

area of rectangle = base × height

area of triangle = $\frac{1}{2}$ (area of rectangle)

area of triangle = $\frac{1}{2}$ (base × height)

Exercise 2M

1 Find the area of each triangle. Lengths are in cm.

(a)

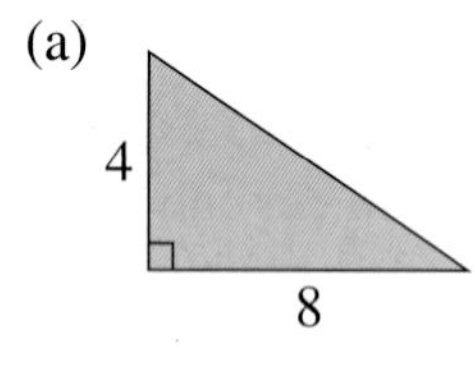

(b)

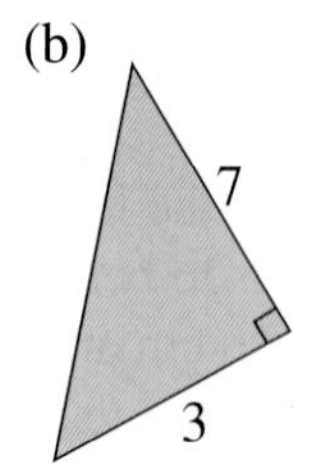

(c)

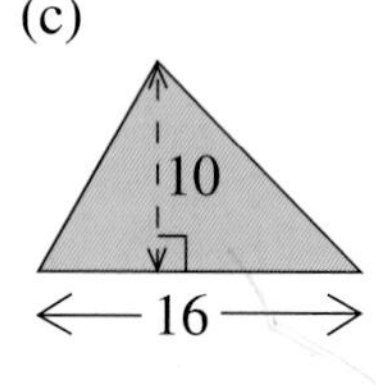

(d)

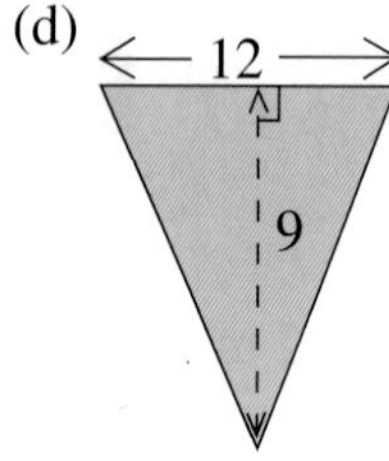

(e)

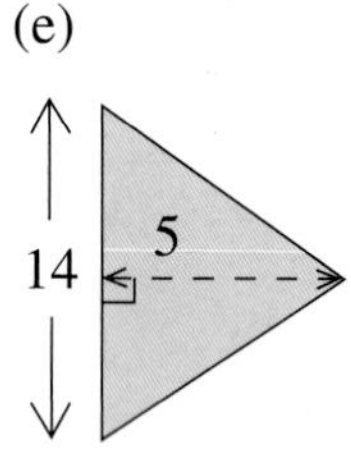

(f)

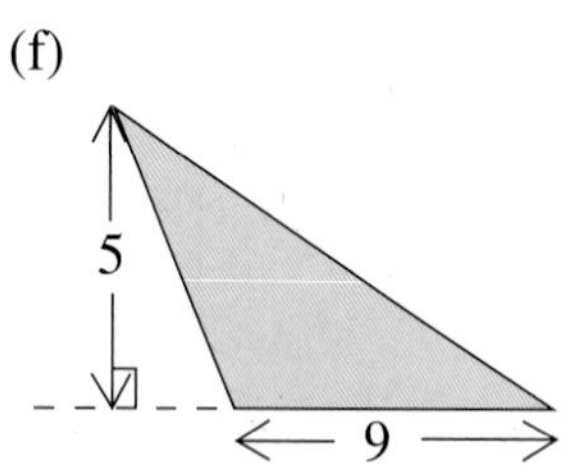

(g)

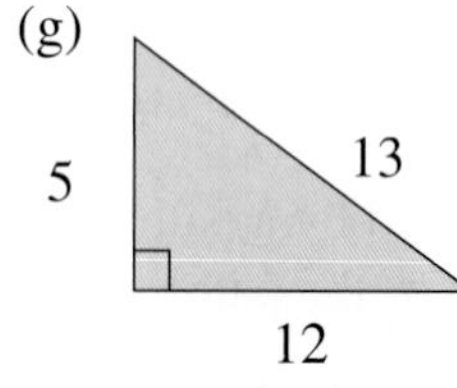

(h) 14 12 16

2 Copy and complete this table showing the measurements of triangles.

base	6 cm	8 cm	14 cm		7 cm
height	4 cm			30 cm	
area		36 cm^2	140 cm^2	90 cm^2	105 cm^2

3 Find the area of each triangle. Give each answer in square units.

(a) 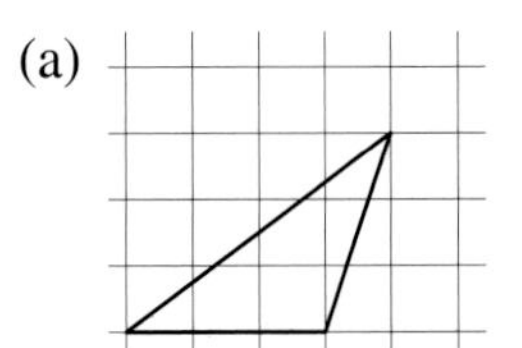

(b) 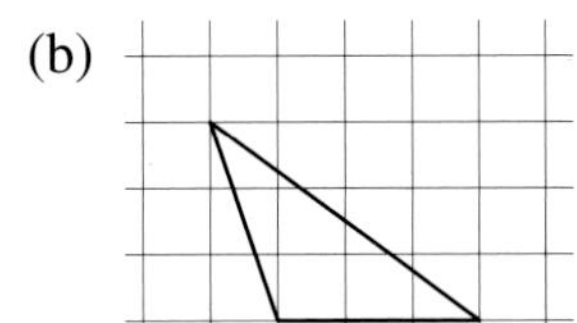

(c) 

(d) 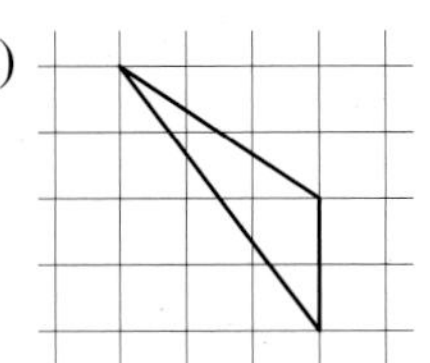

4 Find the total area of each shape. Lengths are in cm.

(a) 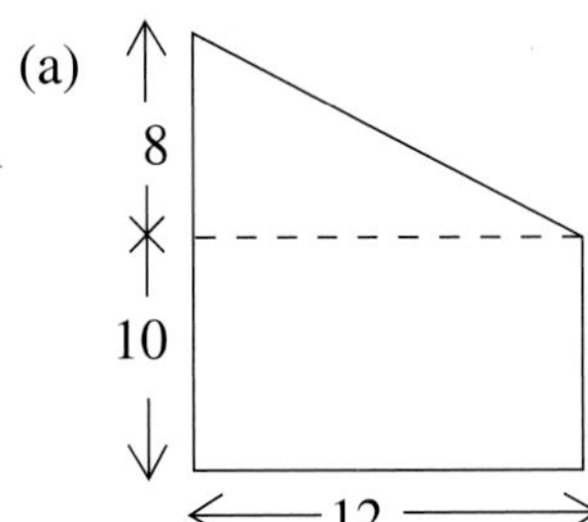

(b) 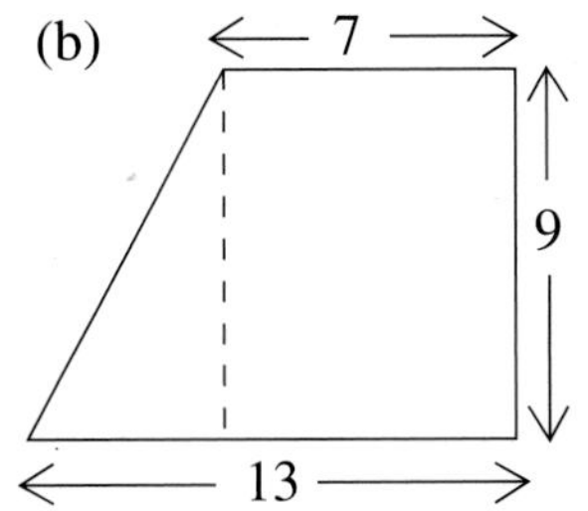

(c) 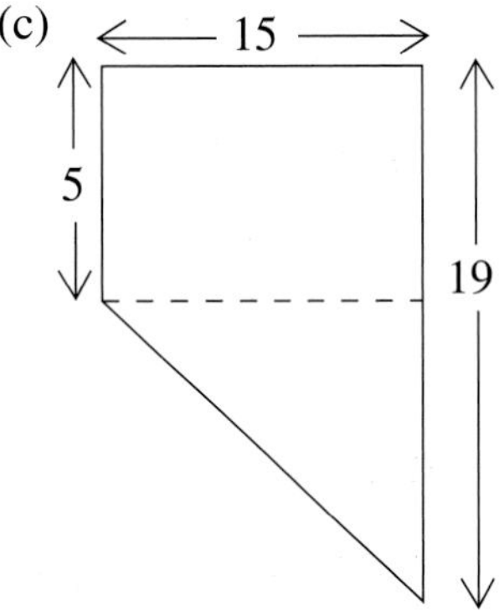

5 Find the total area of each shape. Lengths are in cm.

(a) 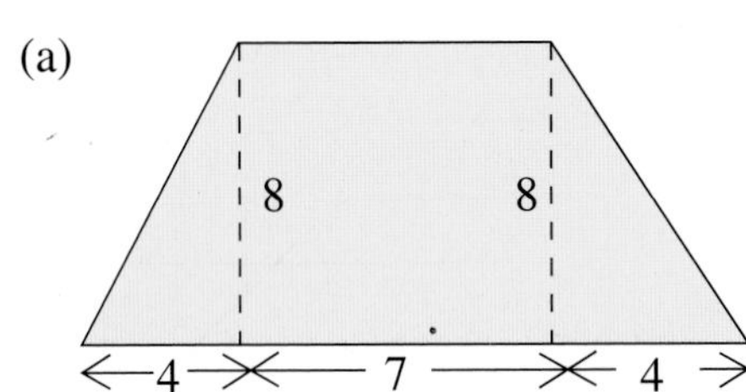

(b) 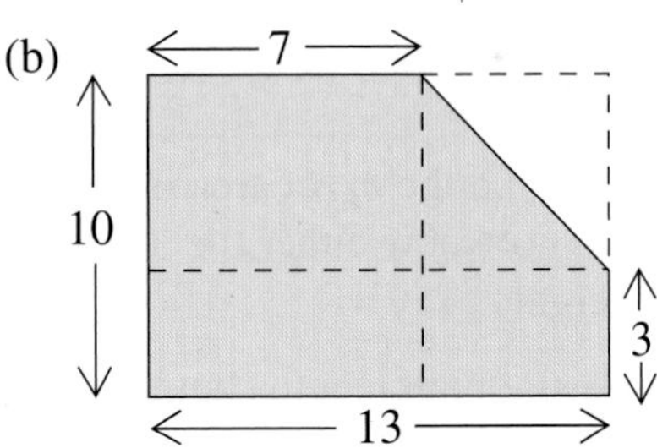

6 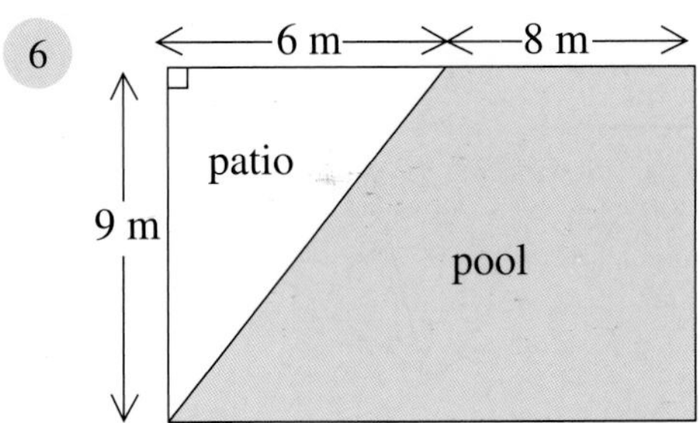

Calculate the area of the pool.

7

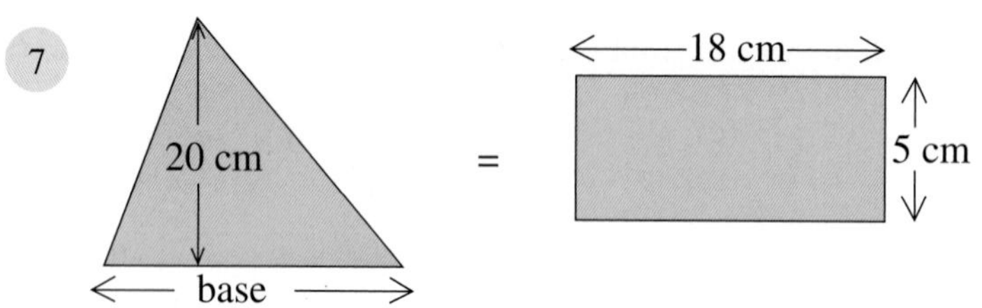

The area of the triangle is equal to the area of the rectangle. How long is the base of the triangle?

8 Calculate the length of each side marked x. The area is shown inside the triangle.

(a)

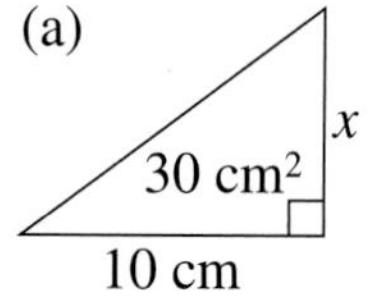

(b)

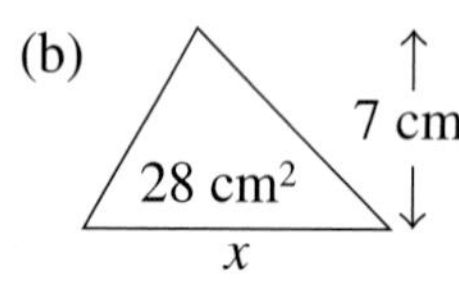

(c)

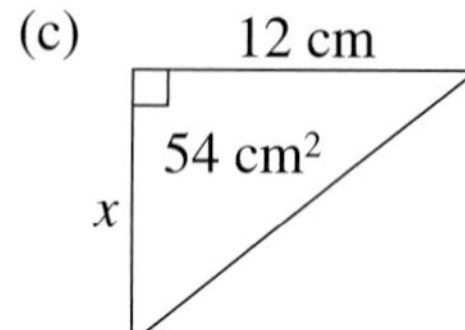

(d)

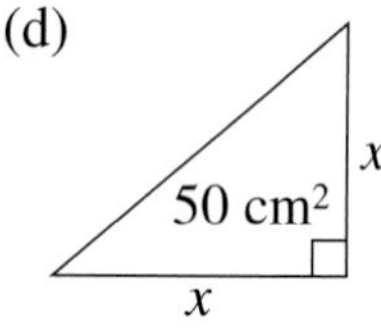

9 Find the area coloured blue. Lengths are in cm.

(a)

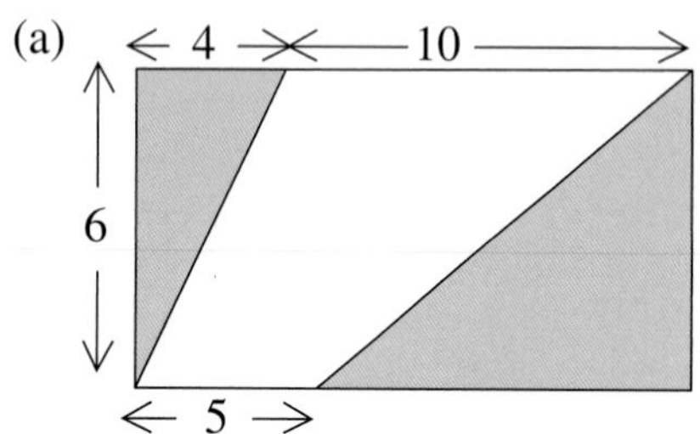

(b)

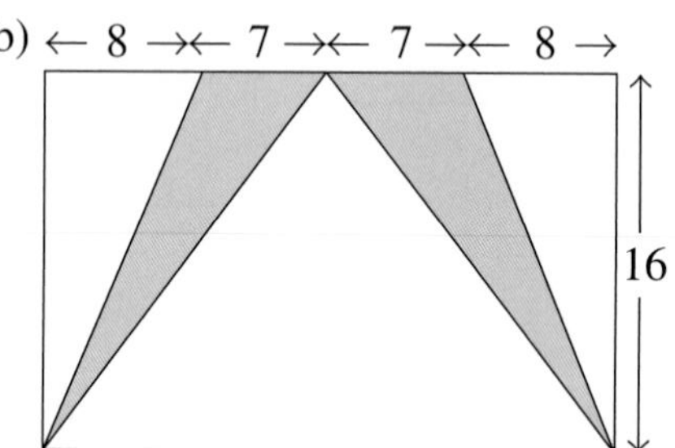

Irregular shapes

It is not easy to find the exact area of the triangle shown because we do not know either the length of the base or the height.

We could measure both lengths but this would introduce a small error due to the inevitable inaccuracy of the measuring.

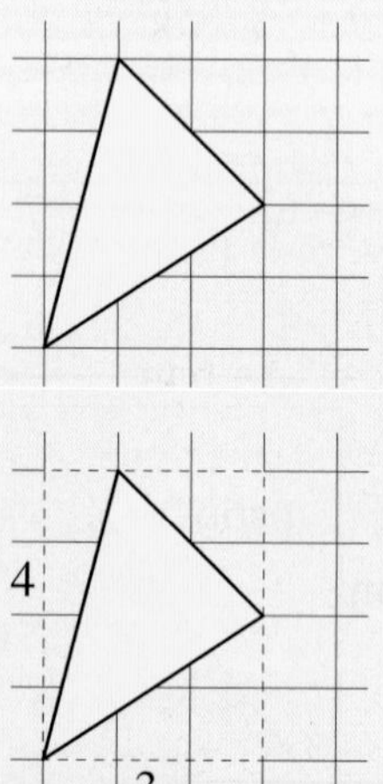

- A good method is to start by drawing a rectangle around the triangle. The corners of the triangle lie either on the sides of the rectangle or at a corner of the rectangle.
  Calculate the area of the rectangle. In this example:
  Area of rectangle = 3×4

  $= 12$ square units.

- Now find the areas of the three triangles marked A, B and C. This is easy because the triangles each have a right angle. Use the symbol 'Δ A' to mean 'triangle A'

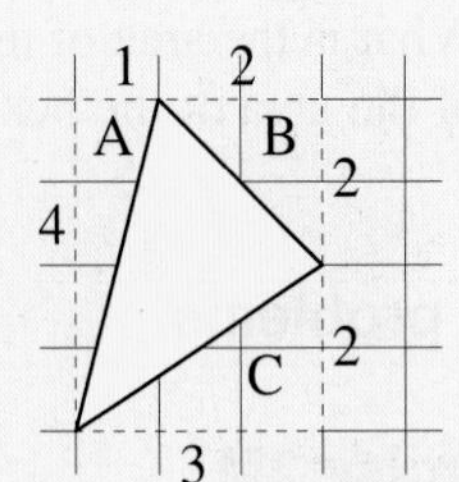

Area of Δ A = $\frac{4 \times 1}{2}$ = 2 square units

Area of Δ B = $\frac{2 \times 2}{2}$ = 2 square units

Area of Δ C = $\frac{3 \times 2}{2}$ = 3 square units

Now we can find the area of the required triangle by subtracting the areas of Δ A, Δ B and Δ C from the area of the rectangle.

Area of yellow triangle = 12 – [2 + 2 + 3]
= 5 square units.

Exercise 2E

1 Find the area of each shape.

(a)

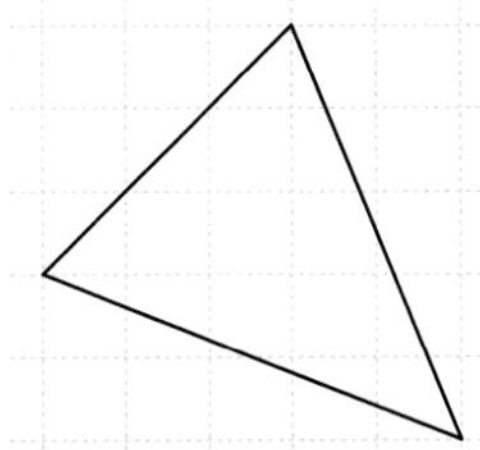

(b)

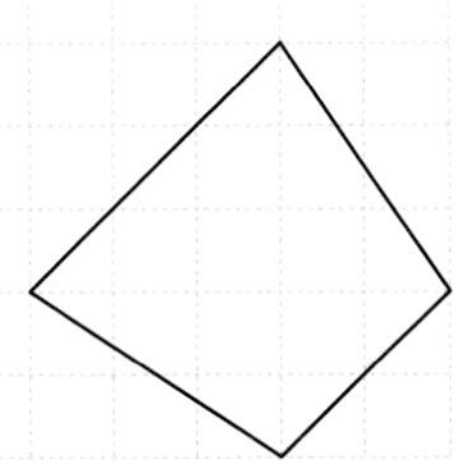

(c)

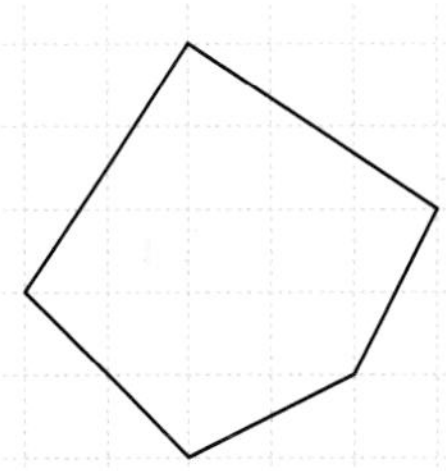

2 For each question, draw two axes from 0 to 6. Plot the points given and join them up in order. Find the area of each shape.

(a) (1, 3), (3, 4), (5, 1) (b) (5, 1), (2, 4), (4, 6), (6, 5)

3 Do the same as question 2 with the two axes drawn from 0 to 7.

(a) (1, 7), (5, 5), (5, 2), (2, 3) (b) (0, 3), (3, 7), (7, 2), (3, 2), (1, 1)

4 Do the same as question 2 with the two axes drawn from 0 to 10.

(a) (2, 1), (4, 8), (7, 8), (10, 6), (8, 2), (6, 4)
(b) (0, 2), (2, 4), (0, 8), (9, 7), (10, 2), (6, 4), (4, 1)

5 A triangle and a square are drawn on dotty paper with dots 1 cm apart. What is the area of the shaded region?

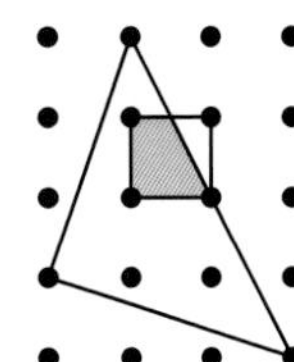

6 A triangle is drawn inside a regular hexagon. What is the area of the triangle as a fraction of the area of the hexagon?

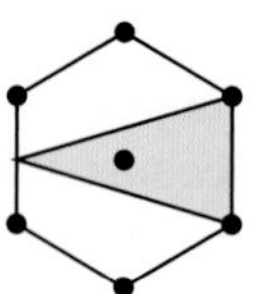

Area problems

Exercise 3M

1 Find each area shaded pink. All the lengths are in cm.

(a)

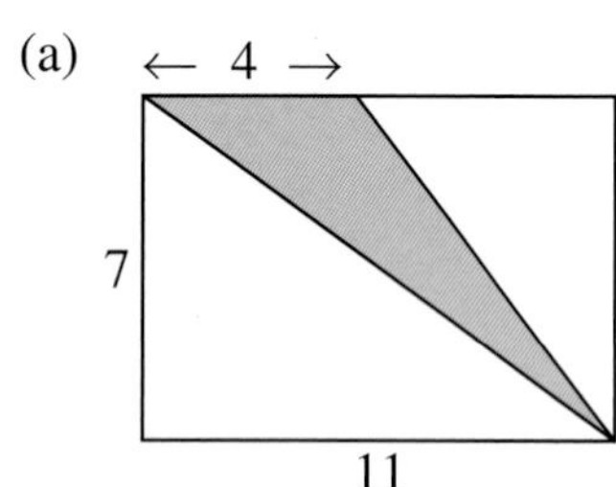

(b)

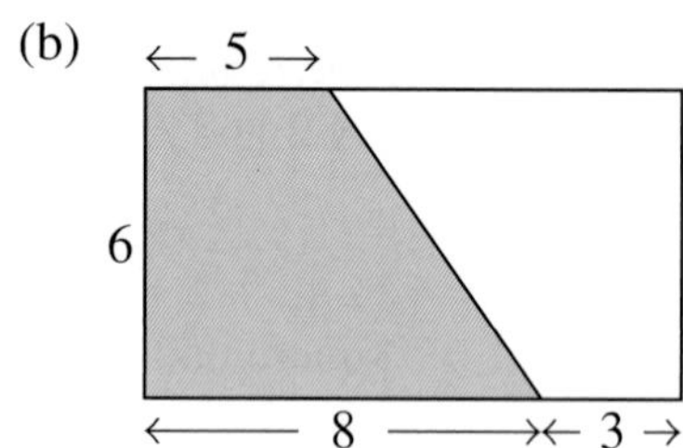

2 A rectangle has a perimeter of 34 m and a length of 7.5 m. What is its area?

3 The diagram shows the areas of 3 faces of a rectangular box. What are the measurements of the box?

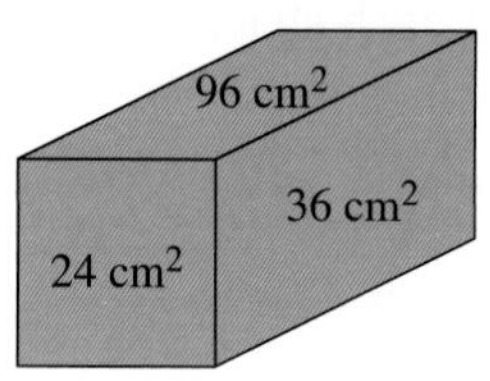

4 A floor measures 5 m by 4 m. It is to be covered by rectangular tiles measuring 80 cm by 50 cm. How many tiles are needed?

5 A picture measures 12 cm by 7 cm. It is surrounded by a border 3 cm wide. What is the area of the border?

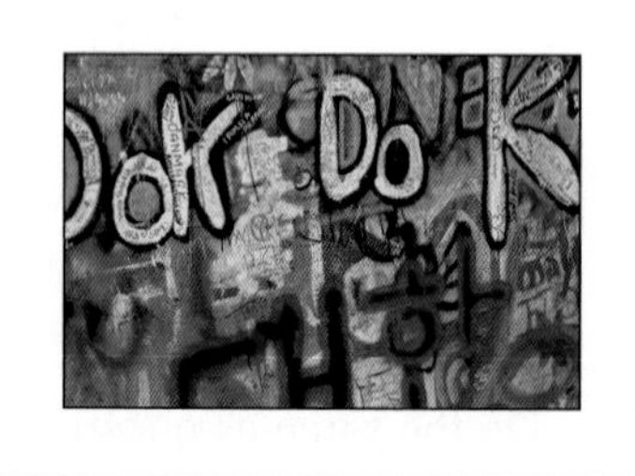

6 How many panes of glass 35 cm by 25 cm can be cut from a sheet which is 1 metre square?

7 A path passing through a garden is shown opposite. Find the area of the shaded path.

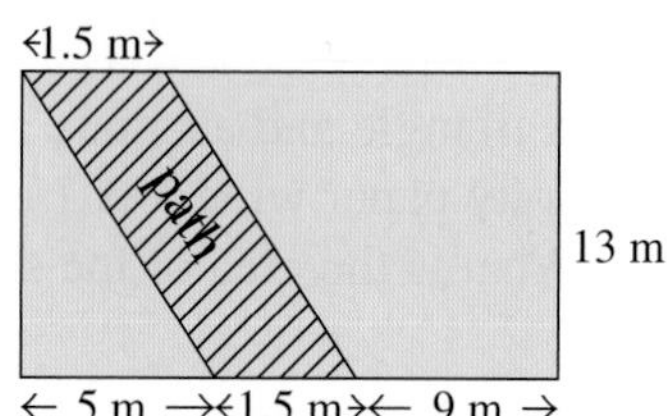

8 A line starts at A and goes along the dotted lines to B. It divides the area of the rectangle into two halves.

(a) Draw a rectangle like the one below and draw a line from C to D which divides the area of the rectangle into two halves.

(b) Draw a second rectangle and draw a line from C to D which divides the area of the rectangle into two parts so that one part has *twice* the area of the other part.

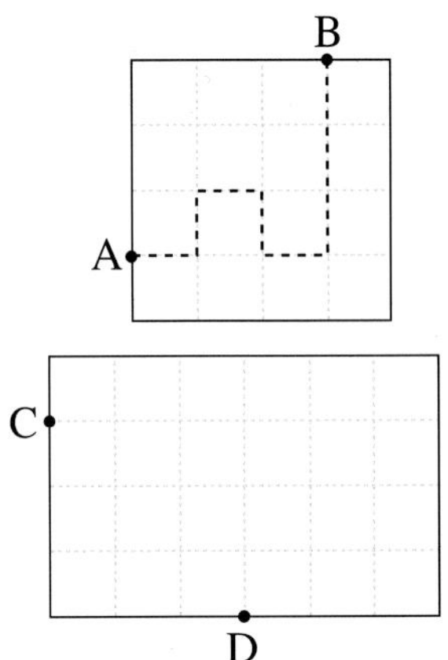

Exercise 3E

(Note that 10000 m^2 = 1 hectare)

1 A rectangular field measures 0.8 km by 500 m. Find the area of the field in hectares.

2 A rectangular field 500 m long has an area of 7 hectares. Calculate the width of the field.

3 A groundsman has enough grass seed to cover 1.5 hectares. A tennis court measures 15 m by 40 m. How many courts can he cover with seed?

4 Farmland is sold at £3500 per hectare. How much would you pay for a piece of farmland in the shape of a right angled triangle with base 500 m and height 320 m?

5 A rectangular field 280 m long has an area of 3.5 hectares. Calculate the perimeter of the field.

6 A waterproofing spray is applied to the outside of the 4 walls, including the door, and the roof of the garage shown.

(a) Calculate the total area to be sprayed.

(b) The spray comes in cans costing £3.95 and each can is enough to cover 4 m^2. How much will it cost to spray this garage? (Assume you have to buy full cans)

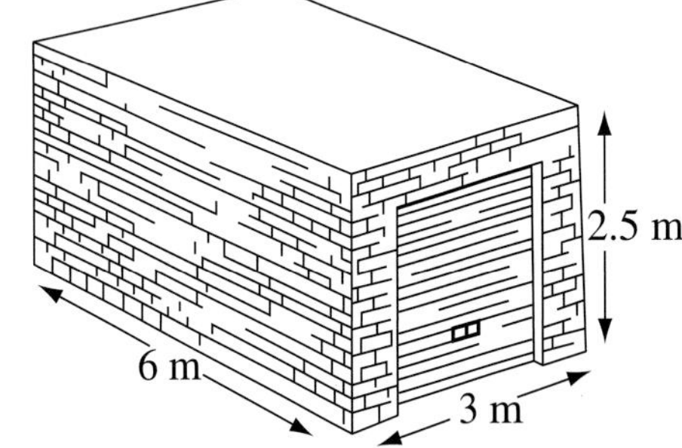

7

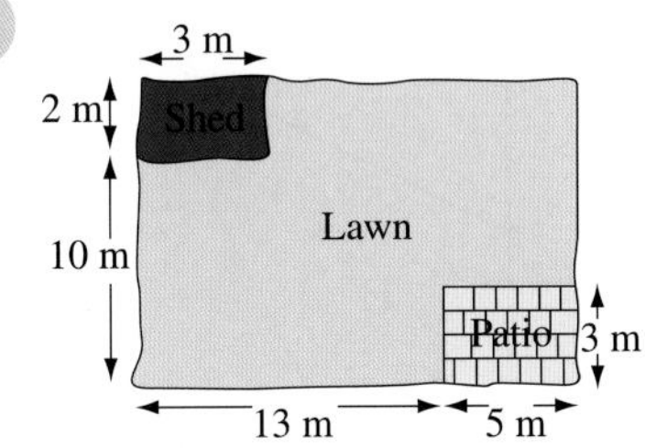

A gardener is using moss killer on his lawn. The instructions say that 4 measures of the mosskiller, in water, will treat 10 m^2 of lawn. The box contains 250 measures and costs £12.50.
Find the area of the lawn and hence the cost of the moss killer required.

8 The field shown is sold at auction for £55 250. Calculate the price *per acre* which was paid. [1 acre = 4840 square yards]

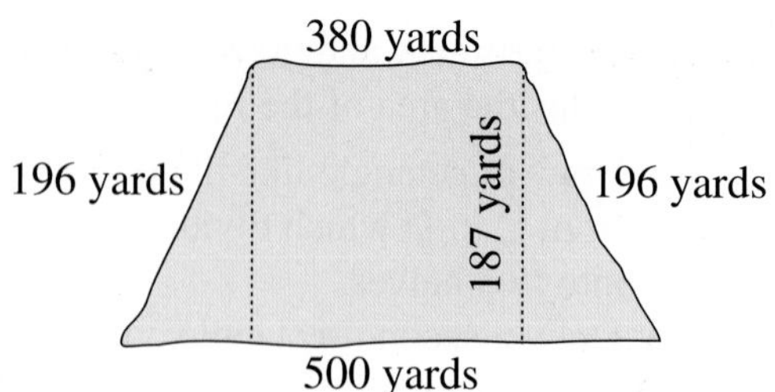

9 The pink triangle is drawn inside a rectangle with longer side 12 cm.

(a) If area of triangle (2) = 2 × (area of triangle (1)), find the length x.

(b) If area of triangle (2) = 3 × (area of triangle (1)), find the length x.

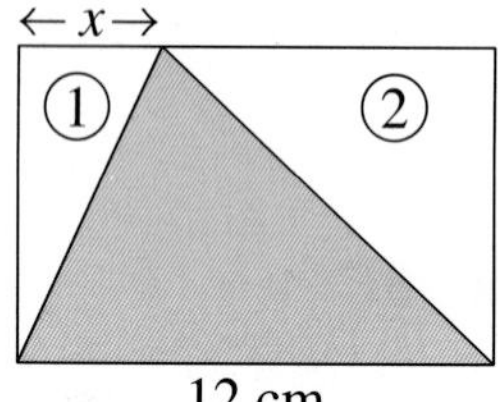

10 In a recent major survey of children's mathematical ability only 1 in 20 of fifteen year olds gave the correct answer to the following question:
'Find the length of the rectangle if the area is $\frac{1}{3}$ cm^2.'
Calculate the length.

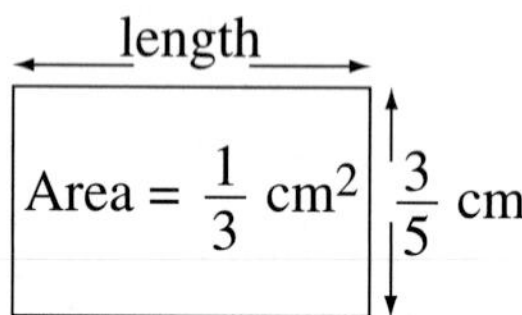

11 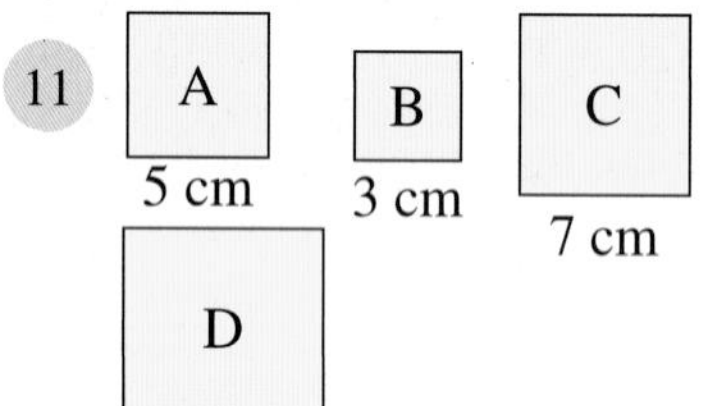

The diagrams show squares A, B, C and D. The sum of the areas of squares A, B, and C is equal to the area of square D.

Calculate the length of the side of square D.

12 Work out the areas of A, B, C, ..., I in the shapes below. The dots are 1 cm apart.

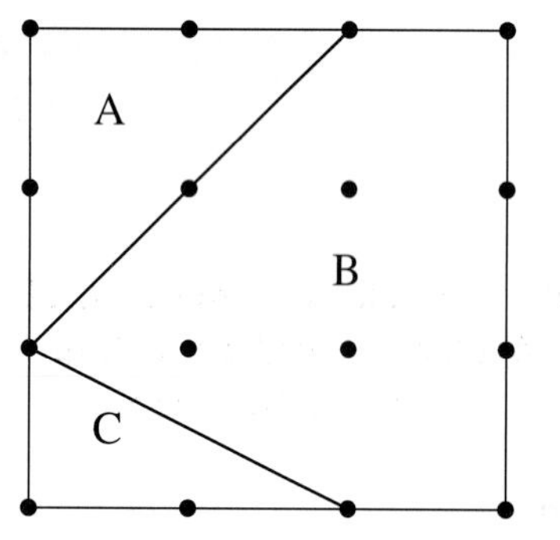

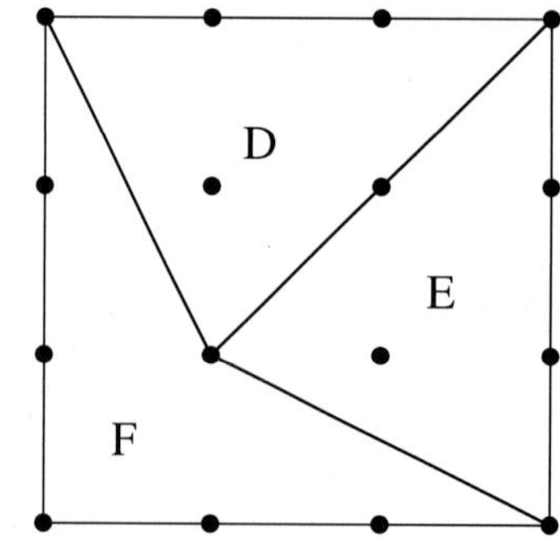

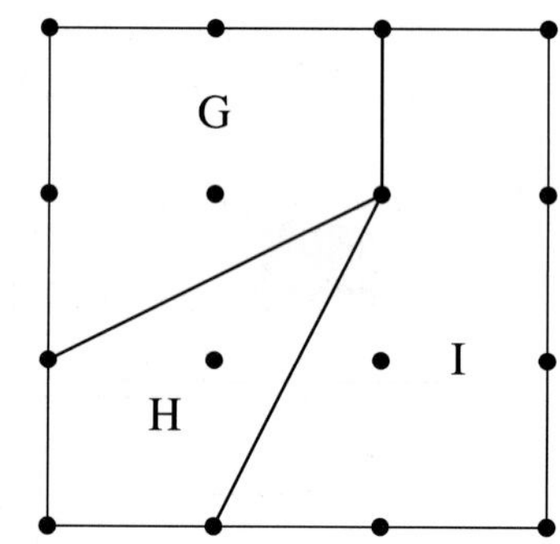

Investigation – area and perimeter

You need squared paper. Each side of the rectangles below must be a whole number.

Part A

Draw four different rectangles which all have a *perimeter* of 24 cm.

Part B

Draw three different rectangles which all have an *area* of 24 cm^2.

Part C

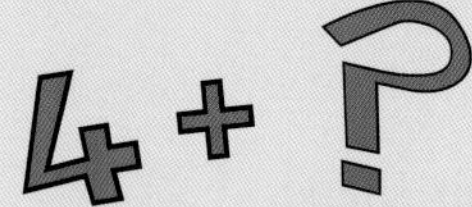

Draw at least four rectangles which have a perimeter of 20 cm.
(1) Work out the area of each rectangle.
(2) Which of your rectangles has the largest area?

Part D

The perimeter of a new rectangle is 32 cm.
(1) *Predict* what the sides of the rectangle will be so that it has the largest possible area.
(2) Check by drawing different rectangles to see if your prediction was correct.

Part E

A rectangle has a perimeter of 100 cm. What are the length and width if the rectangle is to have the largest possible area? What is the largest possible area?

CHECK YOURSELF ON SECTION 1.6

1 Finding perimeters

(a) Find the perimeter of this shape

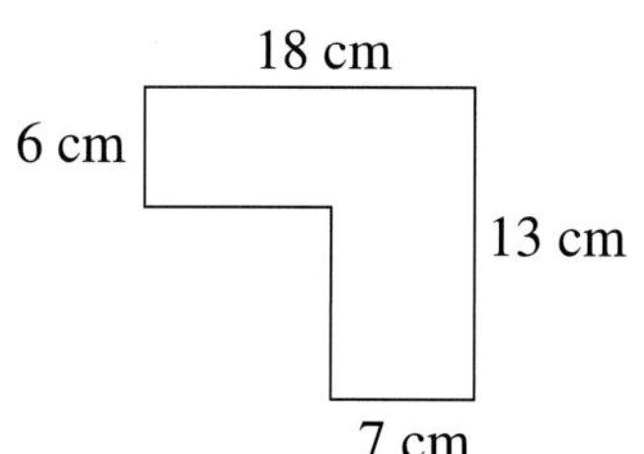

(b) A wall of perimeter 38 m surrounds a rectangular yard of length 12 m. What is the width of the yard?

2 Finding areas involving rectangles

(a) Find the area of this shape.

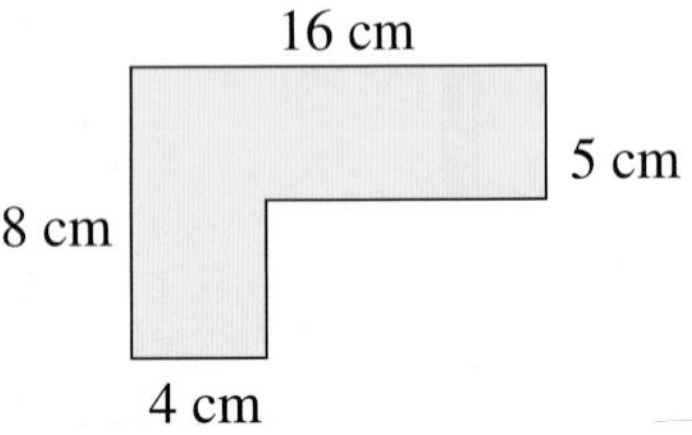

(b) Find the green area.

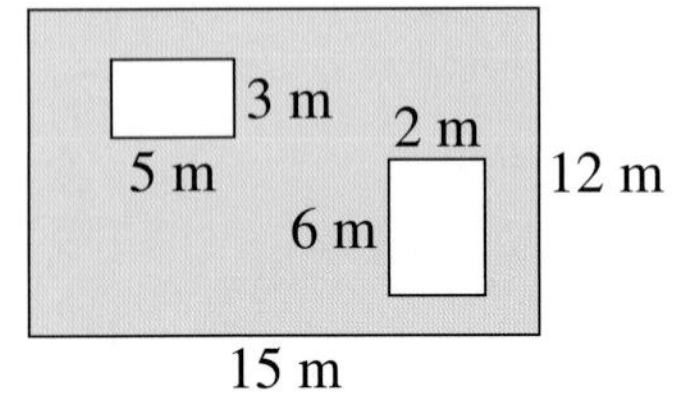

(c) Find the yellow area.

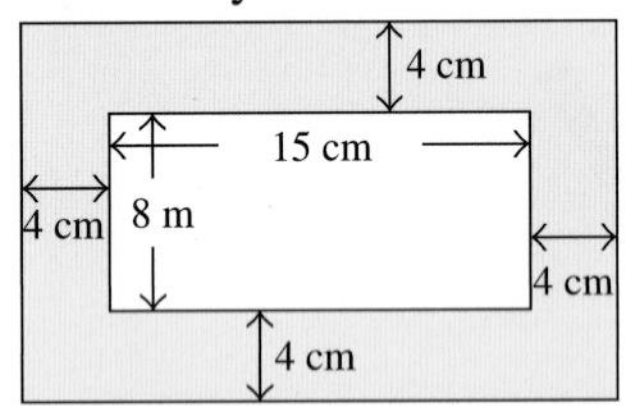

(d) A rectangular room has an area of 42 m². If the width of the room is 6 m, what is its length?

3 Finding areas involving triangles

(a) Find the area of this triangle.

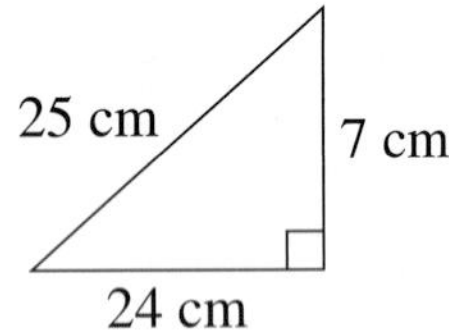

(b) Find the area of this shape.

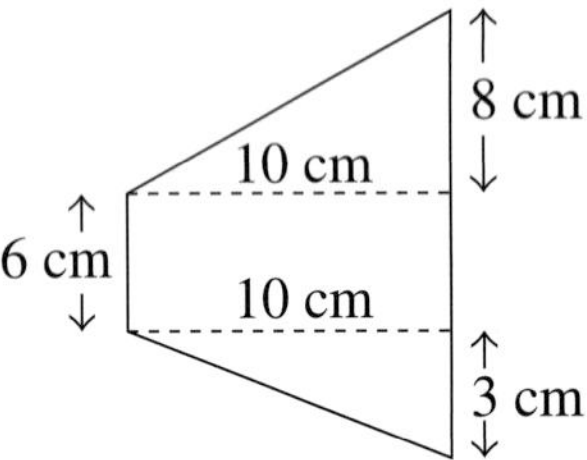

(c) The area of a triangle is 48 cm². Find the base of the triangle if the height is 8 cm.

(d) Find the area of this irregular shape.

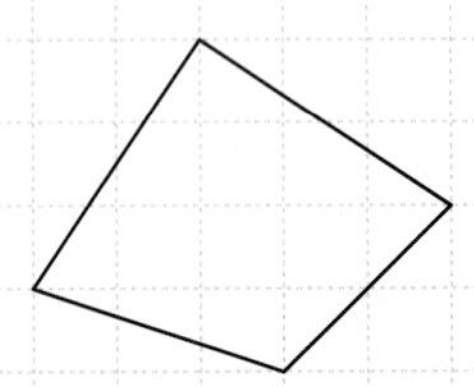

UNIT 1 MIXED REVIEW

Part one

Copy and complete by writing the missing digits in the boxes

1 (a)

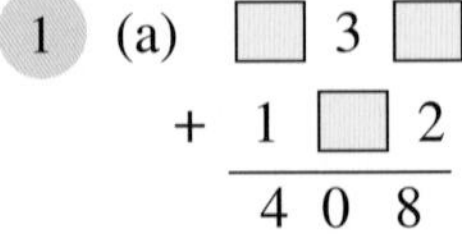

```
  □ 3 □
+ 1 □ 2
-------
  4 0 8
```

(b)

```
  3 □ 9
+ □ 0 □
-------
  5 6 3
```

(c)

```
  □ 8 □
+ 1 □ 8
-------
  7 6 3
```

(d) 3□9 + □5□ = 705

(e) □4□ + 1□8 = 414

(f) 5□9 + □9□ = 853

2 (a) □0 – 4□ = 7

(b) 4□ – □8 = 8

(c) □6 + 5□ = 138

(d) □1□ – 2□3 = 63

(e) 6□1 – □7□ = 413

(f) 4□4 – □2□ = 345

3 (a) □7 × 2 = 13□

(b) □6 × 4 = 34□

(c) □7 × 6 = 34□

(d) □9 × 3 = 11□

(e) □□9 × 6 = 143□

(f) □□3 × 4 = 213□

4 (a) 3)1□9 = 53

(b) 4)2□8 = 57

(c) 6)5□4 = 94

(d) 7)45□ = 65

(e) 7)□41 = 63

(f) 9)4□6 = 54

5 Copy and complete the cross number

Clues across	Clues down
1. 311 – 92	**1.** 38 × 7
4. 275 ÷ 5	**2.** 13^2
6. 70.01 – 3.47	**3.** 50 × 1.9
8. 0.069 × 100	**5.** 32.16 ÷ 6
9. 188 × 2	**7.** 54.5 × 8
11. 4 – 0.31	**10.** 10 003 – 2 007
12. 21^2	**11.** (366 + 254) ÷ 2
14. 67.9 ÷ 7	**12.** (9 × 8) – 25
16. 30 × 25	**13.** 36 ÷ 8
17. 1.28 × 50	**15.** 0.37 × 200

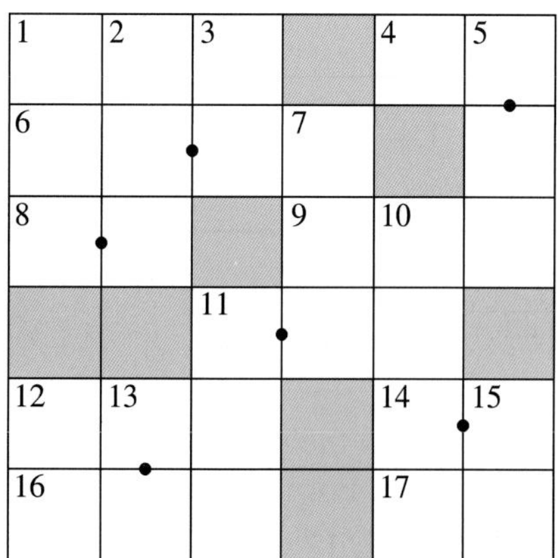

Part two

1 Which list is arranged in ascending order?
A 0.14, 0.05, 0.062, 0.09
B 0.14, 0.09, 0.062, 0.05
C 0.050, 0.062, 0.09, 0.14
D 0.050, 0.090, 0.14, 0.062

2 Copy and complete the multiplication squares

×				8
5	35			40
		8	18	
			54	48
	63			

15			18	
	63			28
10				
		40		20
	72		48	

3 The rule for the sequences here is '*multiply by 3 and add 1*'. Find the missing numbers.

(a) $1 \rightarrow 4 \rightarrow 13 \rightarrow \square$
(b) $\square \rightarrow 7 \rightarrow 22 \rightarrow \square$
(c) $\square \rightarrow 2 \rightarrow \square \rightarrow 22$

4 Copy and complete by finding the missing number.

(a) $5 \times \square - 6 = 24$
(b) $30 - 4 \times \square = 2$
(c) $36 \div \square + 7 = 11$
(d) $(12 - \square) \times 4 = 20$
(e) $32 - (12 - \square) = 28$
(f) $13 - \square \div 2 = 7$

Evaluate, using a calculator

5 $0.37 + 9.75 - 0.6$

6 19.5×3.2

7 $11 - 3.2 \times 2$

8 $4.5 + \dfrac{4.48}{1.4}$

9 $\dfrac{8.94 + 3.66}{3.6}$

10 $\dfrac{7.008 + 1.44}{1.32}$

11 $\dfrac{11.39}{1.7} - 2.63$

12 $3.2 + \dfrac{4.704}{3.36}$

13 $\dfrac{28.1 + 0.55}{1.6 + 0.31}$

14 $25 - (8.2 \times 1.75)$

15 $4.956 \div (1.5 - 091)$

16 $\dfrac{14.24}{9.17 - 4.72}$

17 Write down the rule for each sequence.
(Reminder. For the sequence 5, 8, 11, 14, ... the rule is 'add 3')

(a) 2, 7, 12, 17
(b) 1, 2, 4, 8, 16
(c) 45, 39, 33, 27
(d) 1, 0.97, 0.94
(e) 1, 3, 9, 27
(f) 1, 3, 7, 15, 31

18 At the end of Year 7 Mark said 'I have now lived for over one million hours'. Work out if Mark was right.

19 The diagram opposite shows a room which is to be carpeted.

(a) Find the area of carpet required to cover the floor.

(b) What is the perimeter of the room?

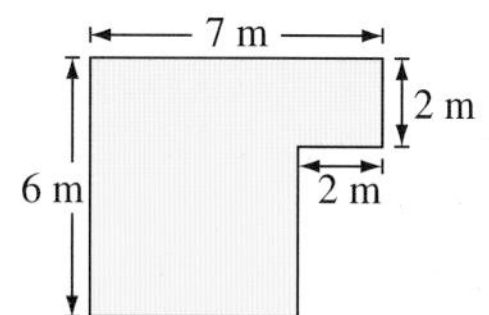

20 Work out the green area. All the lengths are in cm.

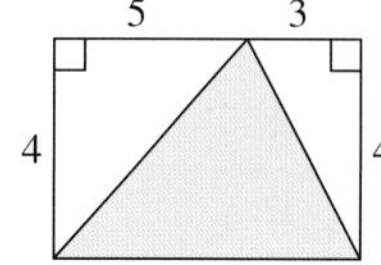

21 In one million seconds which of these would you be able to do?

(a) Take a term off school.

(b) Go without sleep for two whole days.

(c) Spend ten days on the beach in France.

(d) Go to Africa for a year.

Explain your working.

22

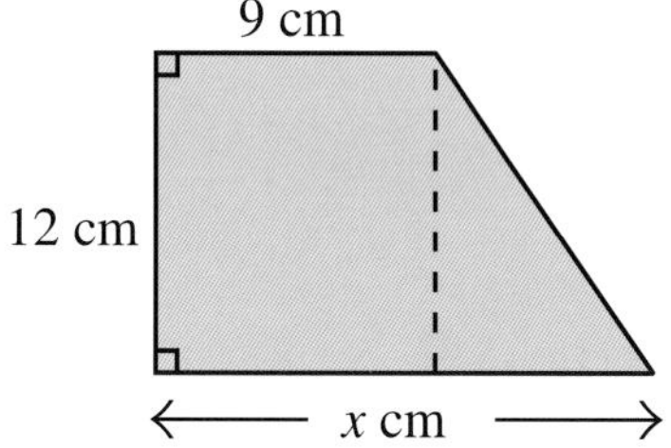

The area of this shape is 126 cm^2. Find the value of x.

23 The perimeter of a rectangular lawn is 30 m. The shortest side is 6.5 m. How long is the longest side?

24 A wheat field is a rectangle measuring 250 m by 800 m. Each hectare produces 4.7 tonnes of wheat. How much wheat is produced in this field? [1 hectare = 10 000 m^2]

25 How many panes of glass 30 cm by 20 cm can be cut from a sheet which is 1 metre square?

26 Grass seed should be sown at the rate of $\frac{3}{4}$ of an ounce per square yard. One packet of seed contains 3 lb of seed. How many packets of seed are needed for a rectangular garden measuring 60 feet by 36 feet? [3 feet = 1 yard, 16 ounces = 1lb]

Puzzles and Problems 1

1 The totals for the rows and columns are given. Unfortunately some of the totals are hidden by ink blots. Find the values of the letters.

(a)

A	A	A	A	28
A	B	C	A	27
A	C	D	B	30
D	B	B	B	
	25	30	24	

(b)

A	B	A	B	B	18
B	B	E	C	D	21
A	B	B	A	B	18
C	B	C	B	C	19
E	B	D	E	D	26
27	10	25	23	17	

(c)

A	A	A	A	24
C	A	C	D	13
A	B	B	A	18
B	B	D	C	12
	18	15	18	

This one is more difficult

(d)

A	B	B	A	22
A	A	B	B	22
A	B	A	B	22
B	B	A	B	17
27	17	22	17	

Find the missing digits.

2 (a) $\begin{array}{r} 3\ 1\ 4 \\ +\ \square\ 6\ 3 \\ \hline 7\ \square\ \square \end{array}$ (b) $\begin{array}{r} 3\ 5\ \square \\ +\ \square\ 2\ 4 \\ \hline 9\ \square\ 8 \end{array}$ (c) $\begin{array}{r} \square\ 5\ 8 \\ +\ 1\ 4\ \square \\ \hline 5\ \square\ 2 \end{array}$

3 (a) $\begin{array}{r} 5\ 3\ 6 \\ +\ 2\ \square\ 4 \\ \hline \square\ 5\ \square \end{array}$ (b) $\begin{array}{r} 2\ \square\ 6 \\ +\ 3\ 5\ 7 \\ \hline \square\ 0\ 3 \end{array}$ (c) $\begin{array}{r} 6\ 3\ 4 \\ +\ \square\ 8\ \square \\ \hline 9\ \square\ 8 \end{array}$

4 (a) $\begin{array}{r} 3\ \square \\ \times\ \ 5 \\ \hline 1\ 8\ 5 \end{array}$ (b) $\begin{array}{r} 4\ \square \\ \times\ \ 9 \\ \hline 4\ 2\ 3 \end{array}$ (c) $\begin{array}{r} \square\ \square\ 4 \\ \times\ \ 8 \\ \hline 2\ 9\ 9\ 2 \end{array}$

5 (a) $\square\ \square\ \square \div 7 = 33$ (b) $\square\ \square \times 11 = 143$

(c) $12 \times \square = 108$ (d) $\square\ \square\ \square \div 6 = 153$

6 (a) $\begin{array}{r} 8\ \square\ 6 \\ -\ 3\ 2\ \square \\ \hline \square\ 3\ 2 \end{array}$ (b) $\begin{array}{r} 8\ \square\ 2 \\ -\ \square\ 1\ \square \\ \hline 4\ 1\ 7 \end{array}$ (c) $\begin{array}{r} \square\ 4\ \square \\ -\ 2\ \square\ 8 \\ \hline 3\ 5\ 7 \end{array}$

7 (a) □ □ × 8 = 440 (b) □ □ × 11 = 231

(c) 400 ÷ □ = 50 (d) □ □ □ ÷ 6 = 163

8 (a) □ □ + 48 = 127 (b) □ □ □ − 49 = 463

(c)
```
  □ 5 3
− 4 □ 7
  1 6 □
```

(d)
```
  8 7 5
− 5 7 □
  □ □ 6
```

9 What is the largest possible number of people in a room if no two people have a birthday in the same month?

10 The letters A, B, C, D, E appear once in every row, every column and each main diagonal of the square. Copy the square and fill in the missing letters.

				B
D				
				E
A	D			

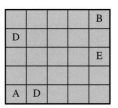

11 Two different numbers on this section of a till receipt are obscured by food stains. What are the two numbers?

tapes at £ .99 : £87.89

12 King Henry has 9 coins which look identical but in fact one of them is an underweight fake. Describe how he could discover the fake using just *two* weighings on an ordinary balance.

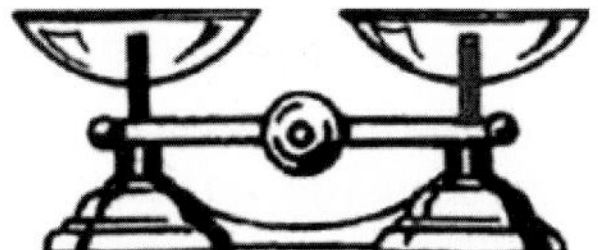

Divisibility investigation

Below is a quick way to check if a whole number is divisible by 2, 3, 4, 5, 6, 8, 9 or 10.

- number is even → divisible by 2
- sum of the digits is divisible by 3 → divisible by 3
- last two digits are divisible by 4 → divisible by 4
- last digit is 0 or 5 → divisible by 5
- number is even and also divisible by 3 → divisible by 6
- half of the number is divisible by 4 → divisible by 8
- sum of digits is divisible by 9 → divisible by 9
- last digit is 0 → divisible by 10

TASK A Copy and complete the table below, using √'s and ×'s.

Number	Divisible by						
	2	3	4	5	6	8	9
363	×	√					
224							
459							
155							
168							
865							
360							
2601							

TASK B Is there a test for divisibility by 7?

Test 18228
Find the difference between the last 3 digits and the digits at the front: 228 – 18 = 210.
This difference is divisible by 7. Does this mean that the original number is divisible by 7?
Using a calculator gives 18228 ÷ 7 = 2604 so the original number is divisible by 7.

Try the same test on these numbers:
37177, 8498, 431781, 42329, 39579, 910987.

Now choose some numbers of your own (4, 5 or 6 digit numbers). Check with a calculator. Does the test always work?

TASK C Investigate to find out whether or not a similar test works for 'divisibility by 11'.

Mental Arithmetic Practice 1

There are two sets of mental arithmetic questions in this section. Ideally a teacher will read out each question twice, with pupils' books closed. Each test of 25 questions should take about 15–20 minutes.

Test 1

1. What is forty-two divided by seven?
2. What is six hundred and forty seven to the nearest hundred?
3. Write 0.25 as a fraction.
4. Add together seven, nine and fifteen.
5. Change five and a half metres into centimetres.
6. How many thirds make up three whole ones?
7. What is four squared?
8. If seventy-three per cent of the children in a class are girls, what percentage of the class are boys?
9. The side of a square is six metres. What is the area of the square?
10. Write down a factor of 16 which is greater than 5.
11. What is eight thousand five hundred divided by ten?
12. Write down any multiple of eight.
13. What is the remainder when 50 is divided by 8?

14 What is the difference between 2.6 and 6.9?

15 Write down the number that is halfway between twelve and eighteen?

16 At midnight the temperature is minus four degrees celsius. By midday the temperature rises eighteen degrees. What is the temperature at midday?

17 How much change from five pounds would you get after spending three pounds and forty-two pence?

18 How many fourteens are there in two hundred and eighty?

19 Ten per cent of a number is twenty-eight. What is the number?

20 What is the obtuse angle between clock hands showing four o'clock?

21 Add together 11, 12 and 13.

22 True or false: 'All prime numbers are odd numbers'.

23 Write down the square root of 64.

24 Work out $\frac{1}{4}$ plus $\frac{1}{8}$.

25 Find 20% of the sum of 11 and 29.

Test 2

1 Divide 7 into 63.

2 Write the number that is sixteen less than two hundred.

3 Write three-quarters as a decimal.

4 Work out 24 divided by 10 as a decimal.

5 What four coins make 67p?

6 What is the cost of 3 calculators at £5.99 each?

7 Change fifteen centimetres into millimetres.

8 What is the product of 40 and 6?

9 One fifth of a number is 6. What is the number?

10 Subtract the sum of 5 and 9 from 70.

11 Oranges cost 87p for three. What is the cost of one orange?

12 What number is halfway between four and eleven?

13 Write 5:30 p.m. in 24 hour clock time.

14 Two angles in a triangle are seventy-four degrees and sixty degrees. How large is the third angle?

15 The area of a square is 49 cm^2. How long is each side?

16 Ali buys a pen for £1.25 and a drink for 53p. How much change will Ali receive from a twenty pound note?

17 Peaches cost 34p each. What is the cost of 6 peaches?

18 A film starts at twenty minutes to six and lasts for two hours forty-five minutes. At what time does the film finish?

19 What is three-fifths of one hundred?

20 How many millimetres are there in 4 metres?

21 Add together three and minus seven.

22 What is half of 2.5?

23 Take away 50 from 5000?

24 Which is larger: $\frac{2}{5}$ or $\frac{3}{6}$?

25 Find the sum of all the coins from 1p to 20p.

A long time ago! 1

Napier's rods

An early calculator was invented by John Napier in the sixteenth century. It was made of rods which were marked as shown below. Each rod shows the 'times table' for the number at the top.

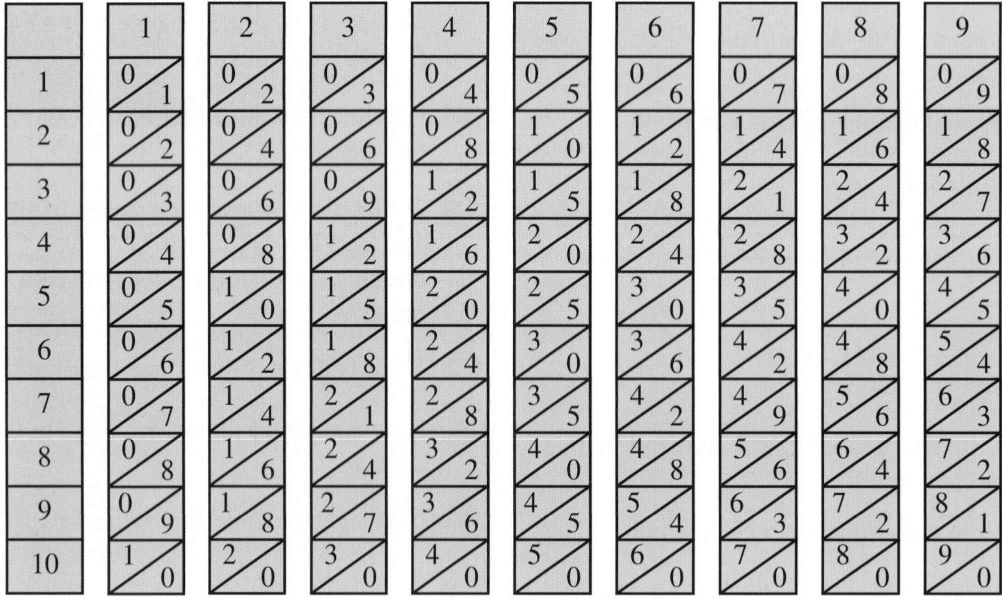

To multiply two numbers together eg. 678 × 7, place the rods together with 6, 7 and 8 at the top. Place next to the blue rod with the numbers 1 to 9.

	6	7	8
1	0/6	0/7	0/8
2	1/2	1/4	1/6
3	1/8	2/1	2/4
4	2/4	2/8	3/2
5	3/0	3/5	4/0
6	3/6	4/2	4/8
7	4/2	4/9	5/6
8	4/8	5/6	6/4
9	5/6	6/3	7/2
10	6/0	7/0	8/0

We are multiplying by 7 so look at row 7. Add the numbers diagonally moving from right to left.

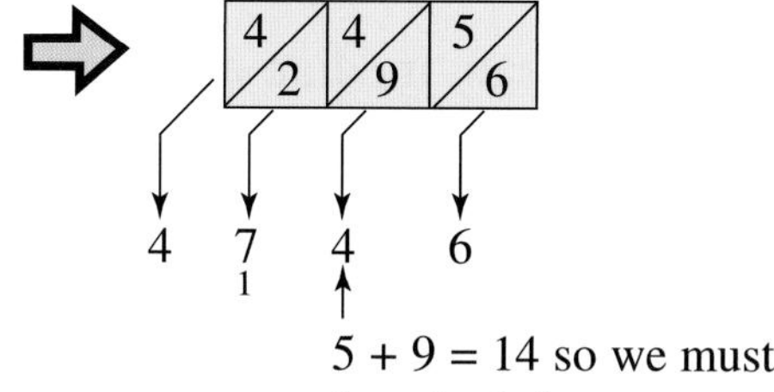

5 + 9 = 14 so we must carry the 1 to the left

$678 \times 7 = 4746$

Exercise

1 Draw and cut out a set of Napier's rods. Your teacher will tell you how long to make the rectangles.

2 Use your Napier's rods to work out the following:

(a) 368×4 (b) 427×6 (c) 592×7

(d) 4276×9 (e) 56392×4 (f) 684539×7

(g) A builder uses 4965 bricks for each of 8 houses. How many bricks does he use in total?

(h) The Army has to pay 3 shillings each to 27483 soldiers. How many shillings in total is this?

3 **RESEARCH:** Find out:

(a) When were Napier's rods most widely used?

(b) In which kinds of jobs were they used?

(c) How can Napier's rods be used to multiply by 2-digit numbers?

(d) Can Napier's rods be used for division?

UNIT 2

2.1 Averages and range

In section 2.1 you will learn how to:

- find the mean, median and mode
- find the range
- compare 2 sets of data using averages and range
- find averages from frequency tables

The mean
All the data is added and the total is divided by the number of items.

The median
When the data is arranged in order of size, the median is the one in the middle.
If there are two 'middle' numbers, the median is in the middle of these two numbers.

The mode
The number which occurs most often.
A set of data may have more than one mode.

The range
The difference between the largest value and the smallest value.
The range is a measure of how *spread* out the data is. The range is *not* an average.

The shoe sizes of 8 people were: 8, 4, 6, 10, 7, 6, 6, 9

(a) mean shoe size $= \frac{8+4+6+10+7+6+6+9}{8} = \frac{56}{8} = 7$

(b) arrange the shoe sizes in order: 4 6 6 6 7 8 9 10

the median is the $\frac{1}{2}$ – way number

median $= \frac{6+7}{2} = 6.5$

(c) mode = 6 because there are more 6s than any other number

(d) range = highest number – lowest number = 10 – 4 = 6

Exercise 1M

1 For each set of numbers, find the mode

(a) 8, 6, 3, 3, 5, 5, 6, 3, 9 (b) 7, 4, 8, 4, 3, 7, 2

2 For each set of numbers, find the mean

(a) 8, 4, 3, 7, 7, 7 (b) 3, 9, 2, 8, 3 (c) 8, 2, 9, 3, 8, 5, 6, 8, 7, 4

3 For each set of numbers, find the median

(a) 5, 3, 6, 2, 2 (b) 1, 2, 3, 4 (c) 7, 14, 13, 8, 7, 18, 17, 5, 14, 11

4 For each set of numbers, find the range

(a) 6, 9, 5, 3, 12, 13, 6 (b) 8, 4, 12, 17, 9, 23, 8, 17, 17, 3, 19

5 Carys and Nina play cricket. During one month they score the runs shown below.

(a) Find the mean score for Carys. (b) Find the mean score for Nina.

Carys			
28	15	41	38
18	3	13	51
39	14		

Nina			
2	23	9	74
46	12	34	16

(c) Who has the higher mean score and by how much?

6 Harry played a computer game nine times. His scores are below.

43000	37800	46500	48150	33800
39170	45700	49060	46350	

Find his median score.

7 The children in class 7C list how many pets they have.

2	6	3	2	0	1	8	2	1	3	5	2	2
0	3	2	0	1	8	4	2	5	6	1	6	3

(a) Which number of pets is the mode?

(b) Write down the range for these numbers.

8 The total height of 4 children is 660 cm.

Find the mean height of the children.

9 Nine dogs weigh 207 kg in total. Find the mean average weight of the dogs.

10 Lynne caught twelve fish.
Their masses were:

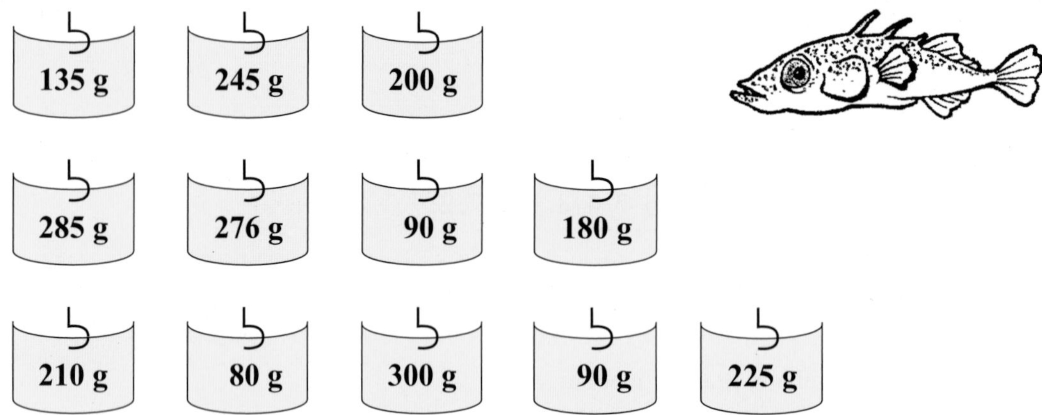

(a) Find the modal mass (the mode).

(b) Find the median mass.

(c) Find the range.

(d) Find the mean mass.

11 In a science test the marks for the boys were 13, 16, 9, 13, 18, 15 and the marks for the girls were 12, 16, 19, 17.

(a) Find the mean mark for the boys.

(b) Find the mean mark for the girls.

(c) Find the mean mark for the whole class.

12 (a) Copy and complete: 'For the set of numbers 7, 7, 8, 10, 11, 12, 12, 13, there are ☐ modes. The modes are ☐ and ☐.'

(b) Find the mode or modes for this set of numbers 2, 3, 3, 3, 5, 5, 7, 8, 8, 8, 10, 10, 11, 11, 12, 12, 12, 14, 15.

Exercise 1E

1 (a) Calculate the mean of the numbers 8, 5, 3, 8, 7, 5, 6

(b) Calculate the new mean when the lowest number is removed.

2 The range for nine numbers on a card is 56. One number is covered by a piece of blu-tac. What could that number be?

55	22	13
38	61	10
24	44	

3 Rena throws a dice ten times and wins 50p if the median score is more than 4. The dice shows 5, 6, 5, 2, 1, 4, 6, 3, 6, 2. Find the median score. Does she win 50p?

4 

The temperature in seven towns across the UK were recorded at 03:00.

Grantham	–1°	Taunton	0°
Aberdare	1°	Burnley	–5°
Loughborough	–2°	Portrush	–4°
Perth	–7°		

What was the median temperature?

5 Colin has 5 cards. The mean of the five cards is 7. The range of the five cards is 8. What numbers are on the two other cards?

7	7	7		

6 There were 5 people living in a house. The *median* age of the people was 21 and the range of their ages was 3.

Write each sentence below and write next to it whether it is *True, Possible* or *False*.

(a) Every person was either 20 or 21 years old.

(b) The oldest person in the house was 24 years old.

(c) The mean age of the people was less than 21 years.

7 Meg has 4 cards. The mean of the four cards is 5. What number is on the final card?

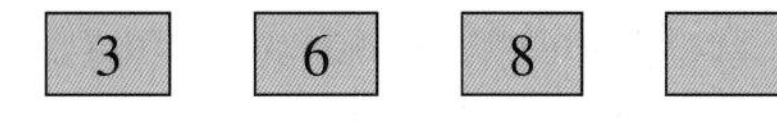

8 (a) Sid has 3 cards. Find the mean.

5	2	11

(b) Sid takes another card and the mean goes up by 2. What number is on the new card?

5	2	11	

9 Cath has 5 cards. There are two modes which are 11 and 16. The total on all five cards is 69.

(a) Write down the number on each card. (b) Write down the median.

10 Will has 4 cards. The mean for three of the cards is 7.
When the fourth card is included, the mean for all four cards is 6.
Write down the number on the fourth card.

Shoe sizes

The Freeman family:	11	5	5	10	6	
The Davidson family:	4	8	5	4	9	10

For the Freeman family: find an average, eg. mode = 5
find the range, i.e. 11 – 5 = 6
For the Davidson family: find an average, e.g. mode = 4
find the range, i.e. 10 – 4 = 6

Compare the shoe sizes of the Freeman family and the Davidson family.

Answer

The mode (modal shoe size) for the Freeman family is greater than the mode for the Davidson family but the range for the Freeman family is the same as the range for the Davidson family (i.e. they have the same spread).

Comparing sets of data

To compare 2 sets of data, always write at least 2 things:

1 Compare an average (i.e. mean, median or mode).

2 Compare the range of each set of data (this shows how spread out the data is).

Exercise 2E

1 20 children were asked how many baths or showers they had each week (10 children from Year 8 and 10 children from Year 9). The results are below:

(a) Work out the mean and range for year 8.

(b) Work out the mean and range for year 9.

(c) Write a sentence to compare the number of baths or showers taken by children in year 8 and year 9.

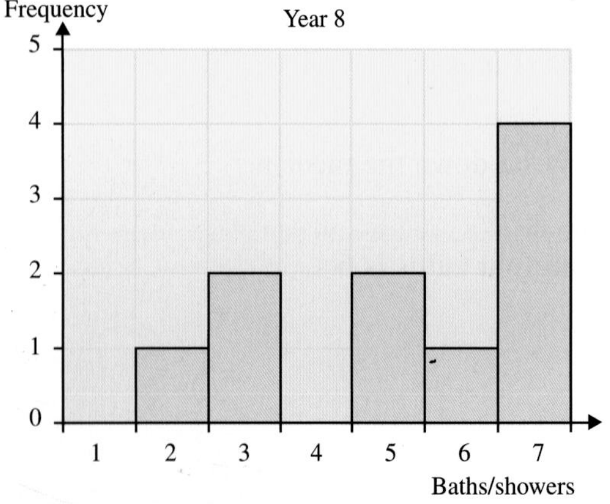

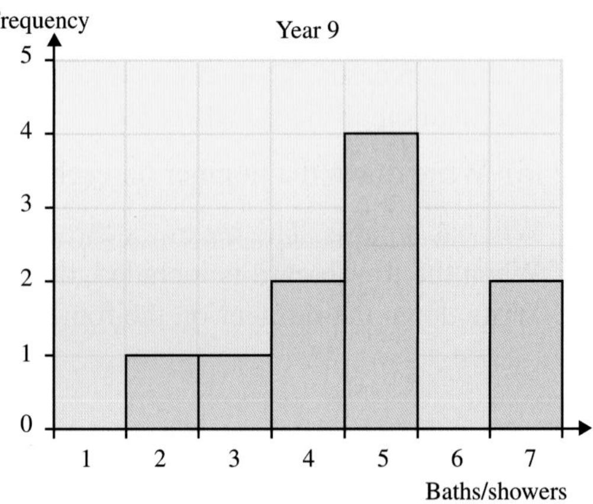

2 12 pupils in year 7 and 12 pupils in year 11 were asked how many hours of TV they watched each day. The results are recorded below:

Year 7	6	7	4	4	2	6	4	5	7	1	3	3
Year 11	2	1	1	5	3	5	6	8	4	3	1	2

(a) Work out the median and range for year 7.

(b) Work out the median and range for year 11.

(c) Write a sentence to compare the number of hours of TV watched each day by pupils in year 7 and year 11.

3 The heights (in metres) of the players in two rugby teams are shown below:

Catcott: 1.85, 1.95, 1.66, 1.98, 1.88, 1.91, 1.81, 2, 1.82, 1.93, 1.88, 1.81, 1.89, 1.95, 1.86

Tipperton: 1.87, 1.99, 1.93, 1.85, 1.94, 1.86, 1.87, 1.96, 1.92, 1.93, 1.85, 1.99, 1.97, 1.89, 1.96

(a) Find the median height for Catcott.

(b) Find the range for Catcott.

(c) Find the median height for Tipperton.

(d) Find the range for Tipperton.

(e) Which team generally has taller players? Give reasons for your answers.

4 18 children were asked how often they ate meat each week (10 children from Year 9 and 8 children from Year 11). The results are below:

(a) Work out the mean and range for Year 9.

(b) Work out the mean and range for Year 11.

(c) Write a sentence to compare the number of times meat is eaten each week by children in Year 9 and Year 11.

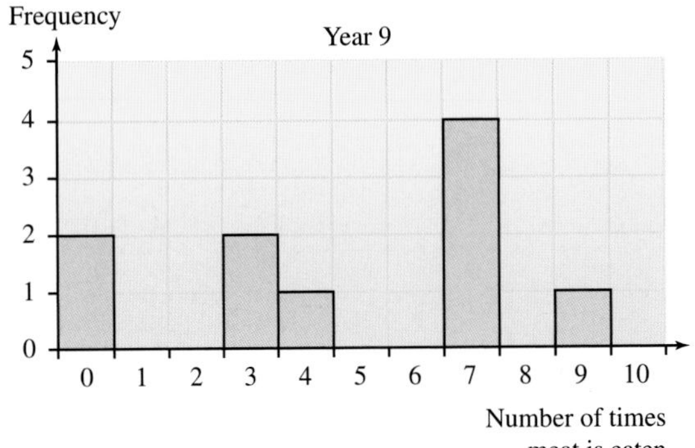

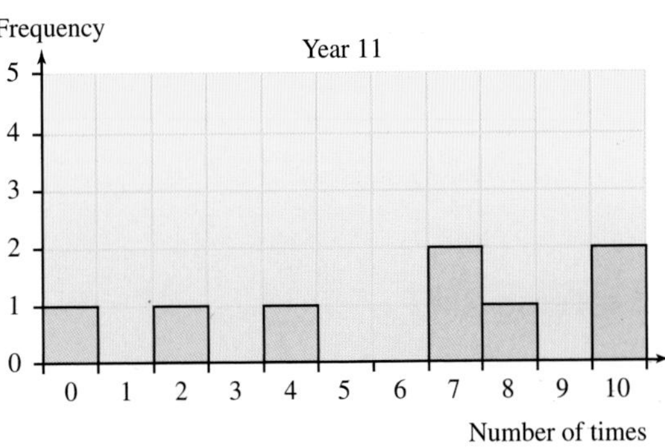

5 

Helen and Nadia record their best ten times for a swimming race. The times (in seconds) are shown below:

Helen: 75, 70, 69, 70, 74, 69, 73, 69, 67, 74

Nadia: 78, 81, 80, 76, 80, 79, 69, 79, 80, 78

(a) Find the mean time for Helen.

(b) Find the range for Helen.

(c) Find the mean time for Nadia.

(d) Find the range for Nadia.

(e) Who is generally quicker? Give reasons for your answers.

Averages from frequency tables

Twenty children were asked how many computer games they had bought during one year. The results are below.

5 4 4 0 1 2 2 6 1 2

3 5 2 5 1 0 3 3 5 2

This data can be recorded in a frequency table.

number of computer games	0	1	2	3	4	5	6
frequency (number of children)	2	3	5	3	2	4	1

Use the table to work out the mean number of computer games.

$$\text{mean} = \frac{(2 \times 0) + (3 \times 1) + (5 \times 2) + (3 \times 3) + (2 \times 4) + (4 \times 5) + (1 \times 6)}{20}$$

↗ total number of children

$$\text{mean} = \frac{56}{20} = 2.8$$

Exercise 2M

1 The table below shows the number of children in each of 100 families.

number of children	0	1	2	3	4	5	6	7
frequency	4	24	22	19	15	7	7	2

Copy and complete: mean number of children $= \frac{(4 \times 0) + (24 \times 1) + (\ldots)}{10} = \frac{\square}{100} = \square$

2 The table below shows the number of cars for each house on Carter Road in Romford.

number of cars	0	1	2	3
frequency	7	12	11	10

Copy and complete: mean number of cars $= \frac{(7 \times 0) + (12 \times 1) + (\ldots) + (\ldots)}{40}$

$$= \frac{\square}{40} = \square$$

3 Work out the mean score in these two dice rolling experiments.

(a)

Score on dice	1	2	3	4	5	6
Number of throws	4	5	3	2	6	5

(b)

Score on dice	1	2	3	4	5	6
Number of throws	7	6	9	5	6	7

4 Hatton United play 20 games of football. The number of goals scored in each match is shown below:

1 3 2 4 4 2 1 0 5 0 1 1 2
0 1 1 4 2 2 1 2 0 1 3 5

(a) Record this data in a frequency table.

(b) Find the modal number of goals scored.

(c) Find the mean number of goals scored.

5 The table below shows the number of pets in each of 50 families.

number of pets	0	1	2	3	4	5	6
frequency	6	19	10	6	5	2	2

(a) Write down the modal number of pets (the mode)

(b) Write down the range for the number of pets.

(c) Find the mean number of pets.

6 The number of daily portions of fruit and vegetables eaten by 24 people is shown in the table below:

number of portions	0	1	2	3	4	5	6
frequency	2	2	2	6	2	8	2

P.T.O.

(a) Find the mean number of portions eaten each day.

(b) Danny joins the group of people. The mean number of portions increases to 3.6. How many portions does Danny eat each day?

CHECK YOURSELF ON SECTION 2.1

1 Finding the mean, median and mode

Consider 9, 13, 8, 3, 15, 4, 8, 12

(a) Find the mean (b) Find the median (c) Find the mode

2 Finding the range

Sonia has the following exam marks:

83, 69, 72, 48, 73, 58, 85, 61, 76

Write down the range for her marks.

3 Comprising 2 sets of data using averages and range

The Warriors and the Sabres are 2 basketball teams. The ages (in years) of the players in each team are listed below:

The Warriors:	24	22	17	28	22	19	31	27	21	27
The Sabres:	28	24	18	20	19	30	27	19	24	18

Use the mean and range to write a sentence to compare the ages of the players for the Warriors and the Sabres.

4 Finding averages from frequency tables

The table below shows the number of computers owned by each of 80 families.

number of computers	0	1	2	3	4	5
frequency	8	14	13	20	16	9

(a) Find the modal number of computers.

(b) Find the mean number of computers.

2.2 Fractions

In section 2.2 you will learn how to:

- find equivalent fractions
- find a fraction of a number
- add and subtract fractions (including mixed numbers)

Equivalent fractions

$\frac{\text{numerator}}{\text{denominator}}$ → the top number of a fraction
→ the bottom number of a fraction

When the numerator and denominator are both divided by the same number, we say the fraction is *cancelled down*.

(a) Cancel $\frac{9}{21}$

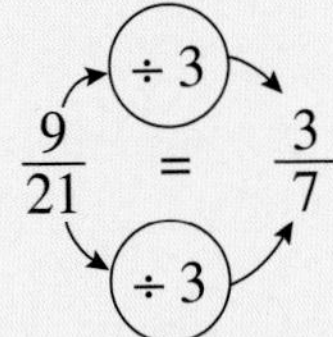

(b) Cancel $\frac{10}{15}$

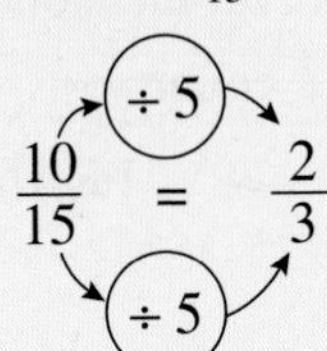

(c) Find the missing number to make these fractions equivalent

$\frac{3}{8} = \frac{\square}{32}$

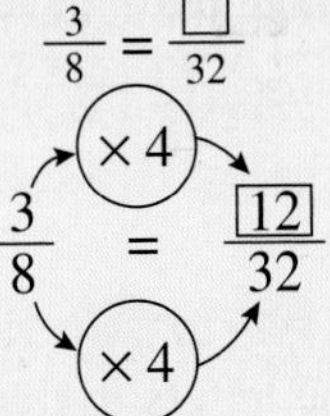

Exercise 1M

1 Find the missing number to make these fractions equivalent.

(a) $\frac{3}{4} = \frac{\square}{16}$ (b) $\frac{1}{5} = \frac{\square}{20}$ (c) $\frac{5}{6} = \frac{\square}{12}$ (d) $\frac{8}{10} = \frac{\square}{5}$

(e) $\frac{5}{9} = \frac{\square}{27}$ (f) $\frac{4}{7} = \frac{\square}{35}$ (g) $\frac{3}{8} = \frac{\square}{24}$ (h) $\frac{12}{20} = \frac{\square}{60}$

(i) $\frac{7}{10} = \frac{\square}{30}$ (j) $\frac{5}{8} = \frac{25}{\square}$ (k) $\frac{4}{11} = \frac{20}{\square}$ (l) $\frac{16}{20} = \frac{48}{\square}$

(m) $\frac{20}{25} = \frac{4}{\square}$ (n) $\frac{18}{30} = \frac{\square}{5}$ (o) $\frac{8}{18} = \frac{4}{\square}$ (p) $\frac{28}{40} = \frac{7}{\square}$

2 Cancel down each fraction to its simplest terms.

(a) $\frac{7}{35}$ (b) $\frac{24}{30}$ (c) $\frac{28}{36}$ (d) $\frac{12}{18}$ (e) $\frac{27}{45}$

(f) $\frac{18}{63}$ (g) $\frac{54}{81}$ (h) $\frac{18}{72}$ (i) $\frac{56}{72}$ (j) $\frac{32}{48}$

In the table given below, pick out all the letters above the fractions which are equivalent to one half $\left(\frac{1}{2}\right)$.

C	Q	E	A	Y	P	R	N	H	F	letters
$\frac{5}{10}$	$\frac{3}{4}$	$\frac{2}{4}$	$\frac{21}{42}$	$\frac{1}{3}$	$\frac{3}{5}$	$\frac{6}{12}$	$\frac{3}{6}$	$\frac{4}{7}$	$\frac{5}{10}$	fractions

The letters are C, E, A, R, N, F

because… $\frac{5}{10}$, $\frac{2}{4}$, $\frac{21}{42}$, $\frac{6}{12}$, $\frac{3}{6}$, $\frac{5}{10}$ are all the same as $\frac{1}{2}$.

Now rearrange the letters to make the name of a country.

C, E, A, R, N, F ⟶ FRANCE

In questions 3 to 6, find the fractions in the table which are equivalent to the given fraction. Rearrange the letters to make a word using the clue.

3 $\left(\frac{3}{5}, \text{sport}\right)$

T	G	U	F	O	Y	R	A	B	L
$\frac{18}{36}$	$\frac{36}{60}$	$\frac{27}{45}$	$\frac{30}{40}$	$\frac{20}{25}$	$\frac{12}{20}$	$\frac{9}{15}$.	$\frac{12}{18}$	$\frac{6}{10}$	$\frac{18}{21}$

4 $\left(\frac{2}{3}, \text{country}\right)$

A	N	E	R	S	B	I	Z	Q	L
$\frac{4}{6}$	$\frac{9}{12}$	$\frac{14}{22}$	$\frac{60}{90}$	$\frac{16}{25}$	$\frac{8}{12}$	$\frac{22}{33}$	$\frac{20}{30}$	$\frac{32}{49}$	$\frac{12}{18}$

5 $\left(\frac{5}{9}, \text{clothing}\right)$

T	M	S	R	K	C	E	H	O	I
$\frac{100}{180}$	$\frac{21}{70}$	$\frac{20}{36}$	$\frac{35}{63}$	$\frac{18}{21}$	$\frac{40}{70}$	$\frac{24}{45}$	$\frac{45}{81}$	$\frac{140}{160}$	$\frac{15}{27}$

6 $\left(\frac{3}{4}, \text{fruit}\right)$

B	O	P	A	E	I	H	C	R	T
$\frac{6}{7}$	$\frac{12}{16}$	$\frac{33}{44}$	$\frac{6}{8}$	$\frac{6}{9}$	$\frac{30}{40}$	$\frac{18}{25}$	$\frac{15}{20}$	$\frac{36}{48}$	$\frac{9}{12}$

7 Ask your teacher for card. Cut out 24 cards as shown. On each pair of cards write down two equivalent fractions.

Now play a game with 2, 3 or 4 players using these equivalent fraction cards.

How to play:

- Shuffle the cards, place them face down in a pattern of 6 rows by 4 columns.
- Decide who will go first.
- Each turn requires a player to turn over a pair of cards.
- If the pair of cards are equivalent such as $\frac{1}{5}$ and $\frac{2}{10}$ the player keeps the pair. If the cards are not equivalent turn the cards face down again.
- Try to remember which cards are where!
- If you find a pair you get another go, the player with the most pairs when no cards are left is the winner.

Proper and improper fractions

Proper fraction	*improper* fraction	*mixed number*
	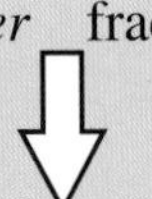	⇩
numerator is less than denominator.	numerator is larger than denominator.	contains both a whole number and a fraction.
examples: $\frac{3}{7}$, $\frac{17}{59}$	examples: $\frac{4}{3}$, $\frac{17}{5}$	examples: $4\frac{1}{2}$, $7\frac{3}{4}$

(often called 'top–heavy' fractions)

Exercise 1E

Change the following improper fractions to mixed numbers or whole numbers only.

1 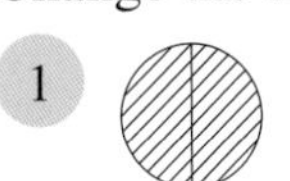  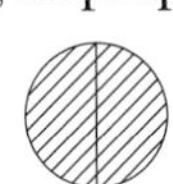 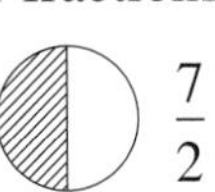 $\frac{7}{2}$

2 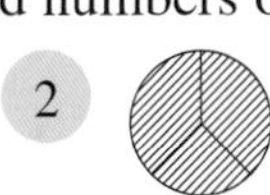 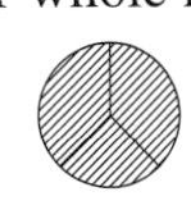 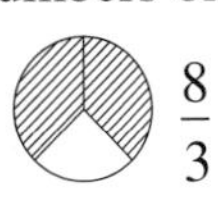 $\frac{8}{3}$

3 $\frac{5}{4}$ 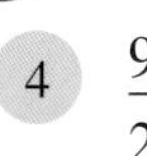 4 $\frac{9}{2}$ 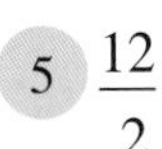 5 $\frac{12}{2}$ 6 $\frac{13}{7}$ 7 $\frac{11}{8}$ 8 $\frac{28}{7}$

9 $\frac{12}{5}$ 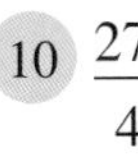 10 $\frac{27}{4}$ 11 $\frac{22}{7}$ 12 $\frac{17}{9}$ 13 $\frac{23}{6}$ 14 $\frac{73}{10}$

15 How many halves are there in $6\frac{1}{2}$?

16 How many quarters are there in $7\frac{3}{4}$?

In questions 17 to 31 change the mixed numbers to improper fractions.

17 $2\frac{1}{3}$	18 $3\frac{1}{4}$	19 $5\frac{2}{3}$	20 $6\frac{3}{4}$	21 $4\frac{2}{5}$
22 $7\frac{1}{8}$	23 $5\frac{1}{5}$	24 $4\frac{3}{7}$	25 $5\frac{1}{3}$	26 $2\frac{4}{5}$
27 $4\frac{7}{9}$	28 $6\frac{7}{10}$	29 $5\frac{3}{8}$	30 $8\frac{1}{5}$	31 $7\frac{4}{9}$

Fraction of a number

The dungeon of a castle contained 135 prisoners. $\frac{4}{5}$ of the prisoners were innocent of any crime. How many innocent prisoners were there?

Find $\frac{1}{5}$ of 135 first so $135 \div 5 = 27$

$\frac{1}{5}$ of $135 = 27$ so $\frac{4}{5}$ of $135 = 27 \times 4 = 108$

There were 108 innocent prisoners in the dungeon.

Note

$\boxed{\frac{3}{5} \text{ of } 30}$ is same as $\boxed{\frac{3}{5} \times 30}$ is same as $\boxed{30 \times \frac{3}{5}}$

Exercise 2M

1 Work out

(a) $\frac{3}{4}$ of 20 (b) $\frac{5}{8}$ of 24 (c) $\frac{7}{10}$ of 90 (d) $\frac{2}{5}$ of 55

(e) $\frac{5}{6}$ of 42 (f) $\frac{4}{9}$ of 18 (g) $\frac{2}{3}$ of 48 (h) $\frac{5}{7}$ of 56

2 Here are calculations with letters. Put the answers in order of size, smallest first. Write down the letters to make a word.

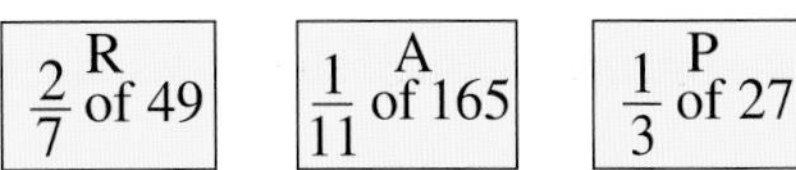
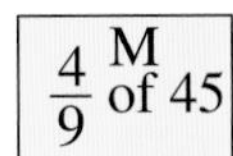

R	A	P	M	Y	D	I
$\frac{2}{7}$ of 49	$\frac{1}{11}$ of 165	$\frac{1}{3}$ of 27	$\frac{4}{9}$ of 45	$\frac{3}{4}$ of 16	$\frac{5}{6}$ of 300	$\frac{5}{8}$ of 96

3 Work out

(a) $\frac{2}{3} \times 36$ (b) $\frac{4}{5} \times 20$ (c) $18 \times \frac{5}{9}$ (d) $42 \times \frac{4}{7}$

(e) $80 \times \frac{7}{20}$ (f) $\frac{3}{8} \times 56$ (g) $140 \times \frac{7}{10}$ (h) $\frac{8}{9} \times 108$

4 Mario has an order for 60 pizzas. If $\frac{5}{12}$ of his pizzas must be vegetarian, how many will be non-vegetarian?

5 A petrol tank in a car holds 56 litres when full. How much *more* petrol can be put into the tank when it is $\frac{3}{8}$ full?

6 Work out

(a) $\frac{2}{3}$ of 45 kg (b) $\frac{4}{5}$ of 90 cm (c) $\frac{5}{9}$ of £108

(d) $\frac{4}{7}$ of £63 (e) $\frac{5}{8}$ of 240 kg (f) $\frac{3}{20}$ of 160 m

(g) $\frac{5}{12}$ of 48 cm (h) $\frac{8}{9}$ of 54 m (i) $\frac{37}{100}$ of £400

7 A 'super bouncy' ball rises to $\frac{7}{10}$ of its previous height on each bounce. One of these balls is dropped from a height of 4 m.

(a) How high will it rise after one bounce?
(b) How high will it rise after the second bounce?

8 Find each missing number below

(a) $\frac{\square}{5}$ of 30 = 18 (b) $\frac{\square}{3}$ of 15 = 10 (c) $\frac{3}{\square}$ of 40 = 12

(d) $\frac{3}{\square}$ of 28 = 21 (e) $\frac{4}{5}$ of $\square$ = 16 (f) $\frac{7}{10}$ of $\square$ = 28

9 What fraction of each shape is shaded?

(a) 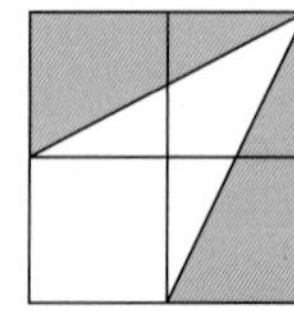

(b) 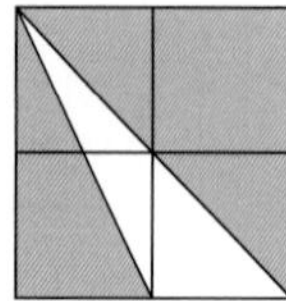

(c) 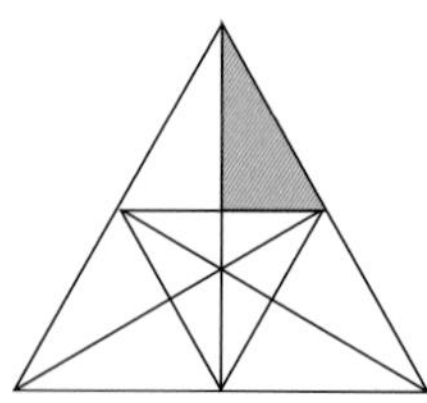

10 

Alma has a bag of 32 sweets. Alma gives $\frac{3}{8}$ of her sweets to her brother Max. Max then gives $\frac{1}{4}$ of his share to a friend and eats the rest. Alma meanwhile eats $\frac{2}{5}$ of her remaining sweets.

(a) How many sweets does Alma have left at the end?
(b) How many sweets does Max eat?

11 (a) Draw a 4 × 5 rectangle.

Use different colours to show $\frac{1}{2}$, $\frac{1}{4}$, $\frac{1}{5}$ and $\frac{1}{20}$ of the whole rectangle. Parts must not overlap.

(b) Draw a 5 × 6 rectangle. Divide it into three parts using three different fractions, each with numerator 1.

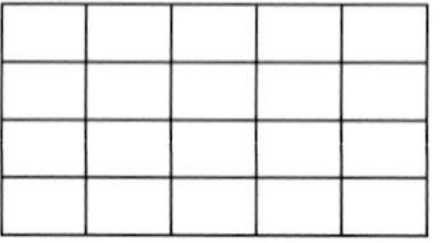

12 Work out a half of ninety-nine and a half.

Adding and subtracting fractions

If fractions do not have the same denominator, change them into *equivalent fractions* which do have the same denominator before adding or subtracting.

(a) $\frac{1}{6}+\frac{1}{3}$

$=\frac{1}{6}+\frac{2}{6}$

$=\frac{3}{6}=\frac{1}{2}$

cancel final answer if you can

(b) $\frac{7}{8}-\frac{3}{4}$

$=\frac{7}{8}-\frac{6}{8}$

$=\frac{1}{8}$

(c) $\frac{2}{5}+\frac{3}{7}$

$=\frac{14}{35}+\frac{15}{35}$

$=\frac{29}{35}$

Exercise 2E

Work out

1 $\frac{1}{7}+\frac{3}{7}$ 2 $\frac{2}{8}+\frac{3}{8}$ 3 $\frac{5}{7}-\frac{2}{7}$ 4 $\frac{1}{4}-\frac{1}{8}$ 5 $\frac{5}{8}-\frac{1}{2}$

6 $\frac{4}{5}+\frac{1}{10}$ 7 $\frac{7}{20}-\frac{1}{10}$ 8 $\frac{5}{9}-\frac{7}{18}$ 9 $\frac{5}{12}+\frac{1}{3}$ 10 $\frac{19}{40}-\frac{3}{8}$

11

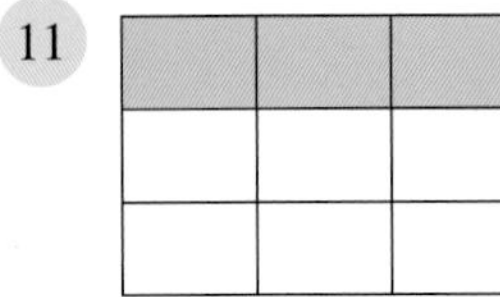

$\frac{1}{3}$ +

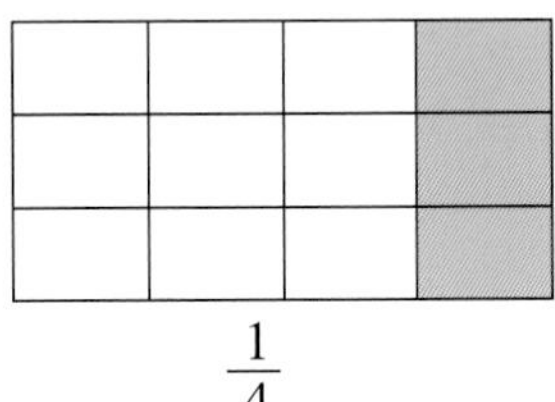

$\frac{1}{4}$

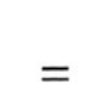

=

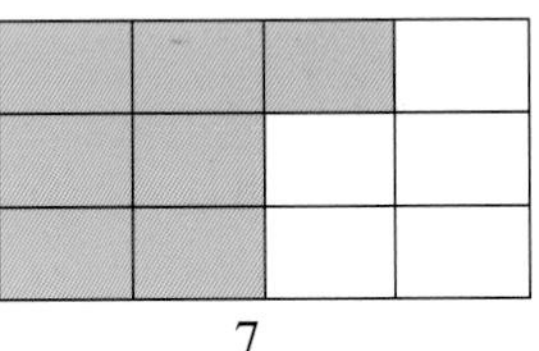

$\frac{7}{12}$

Draw similar diagrams to show that $\frac{2}{3}+\frac{1}{4}=\frac{11}{12}$.

Work out

12 $\frac{3}{5}+\frac{1}{4}$ 13 $\frac{3}{4}-\frac{1}{3}$ 14 $\frac{2}{3}-\frac{4}{7}$ 15 $\frac{3}{8}+\frac{2}{5}$ 16 $\frac{9}{10}-\frac{7}{9}$

17 $\frac{5}{6}-\frac{5}{8}$ 18 $\frac{11}{12}-\frac{1}{5}$ 19 $\frac{5}{7}+\frac{2}{9}$ 20 $\frac{4}{9}+\frac{1}{5}$ 21 $\frac{7}{10}-\frac{2}{3}$

22 Work out

(a) $\frac{1}{2}+\frac{1}{3}+\frac{1}{12}$ (b) $\frac{3}{5}+\frac{1}{4}-\frac{7}{10}$ (c) $\frac{5}{6}+\frac{1}{10}-\frac{4}{5}$

23

Ruby goes shopping. She spends $\frac{1}{3}$ of her money on shoes and $\frac{1}{5}$ of the rest of her money on shirts.

(a) What fraction of her money has she spent in total?
(b) What fraction of her money does she have left?

24 Copy and complete the following

(a) $1\frac{1}{2}+\frac{5}{8}$

$=\frac{\square}{2}+\frac{5}{8}$

$=\frac{\square}{8}+\frac{5}{8}$

$=\frac{\square}{8}$

$=\square\frac{\square}{8}$

(b) $1\frac{1}{4}+1\frac{2}{3}$

$=\frac{\square}{4}+\frac{\square}{3}$

$=\frac{\square}{12}+\frac{\square}{12}$

$=\frac{\square}{12}$

$=\square\frac{\square}{12}$

(c) $3\frac{1}{8}-1\frac{2}{5}$

$=\frac{\square}{8}-\frac{\square}{5}$

$=\frac{\square}{40}-\frac{\square}{40}$

$=\frac{\square}{40}$

$=\square\frac{\square}{40}$

Work out

25 $1\frac{3}{4}+\frac{1}{3}$

26 $1\frac{4}{5}+\frac{2}{3}$

27 $2\frac{1}{2}-\frac{7}{8}$

28 $3\frac{1}{4}-1\frac{5}{6}$

29 $2\frac{3}{5}+1\frac{3}{4}$

30 $3\frac{1}{6}-1\frac{3}{8}$

31 $4\frac{1}{2}-2\frac{4}{5}$

32 $2\frac{5}{8}+1\frac{3}{10}$

33 Find the perimeter of this rectangle.

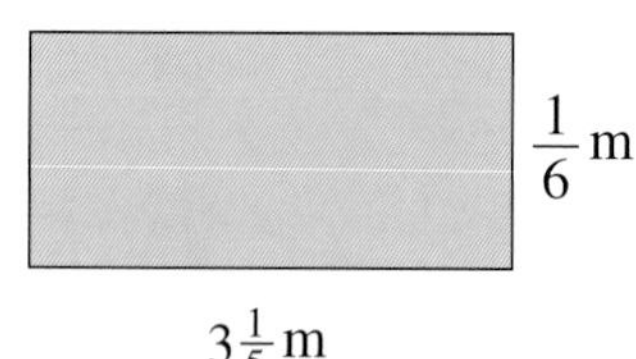

34 What is one sixth less than seven tenths?

35 The fraction sum $\frac{1}{3}+\frac{4}{6}$ is made from four different digits and the sum is 1.
Find other fraction sums using four different digits so that the sum is 1.

Questions 36, 37 and 38 are more difficult.

36 A cylinder is $\frac{1}{2}$ full of water

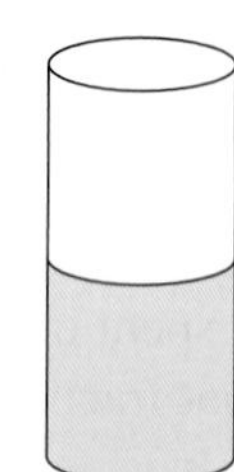

After 90 ml of water is added the cylinder is $\frac{4}{5}$ full.

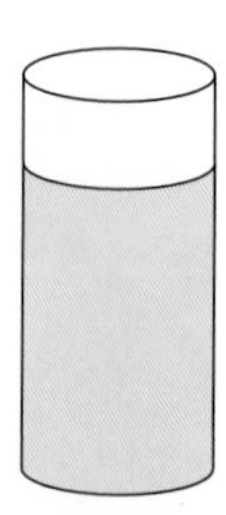

Calculate the total volume of the cylinder.

37 A pond is $\frac{1}{4}$ full. After a further 4200 gallons of water are pumped in the pool is $\frac{2}{5}$ full.

(a) What is the total volume of the pond?
(b) How many more gallons are required to fill the pond?

38 In her will Granny Sheldrake left $\frac{1}{3}$ of her money to her sister Emily, $\frac{2}{5}$ of her money to her grandson Eric and the rest to her cat, which was to be looked after by Eric. Eric immediately spent $\frac{3}{4}$ of his inheritance on a new car and put the rest in the bank. One day, while driving his new car, he ran over the cat and consequently inherited the cat's share of the money. Eric put this money in the bank. If Emily inherited £45 000, work out

(a) how much money was left to the cat.
(b) how much money Eric had in the bank after the cat's 'accident'.

2.3 Fractions, decimals, percentages

In section 2.3 you will learn how to:

- convert between fractions, decimals and percentages

Changing fractions to decimals

Convert denominator to 10, 100, etc.

$\frac{1}{5} = \frac{2}{10} = 0.2$ $\frac{1}{25} = \frac{4}{100} = 0.04$ $\frac{9}{20} = \frac{45}{100} = 0.45$

Cancelling fractions can help.

$\frac{12}{16} = \frac{3}{4} = 0.75$ $\frac{60}{240} = \frac{1}{4} = 0.25$

Exercise 1M

Copy and complete the boxes.

1 $\frac{7}{20} = \frac{35}{100} = 0\cdot\square\square$

2 $\frac{3}{20} = \frac{\square}{100} = 0\cdot\square\square$

3 $\frac{4}{5} = \frac{\square}{10} = 0\cdot\square$

4 $\frac{3}{12} = \frac{\square}{4} = 0\cdot\square\square$

5 $\frac{3}{5} = \frac{\square}{10} = 0\cdot\square$

6 $\frac{4}{25} = \frac{\square}{100} = 0\cdot\square\square$

Convert these fractions into decimals.

7 $\frac{11}{20}$ 8 $\frac{2}{5}$ 9 $\frac{7}{25}$ 10 $\frac{27}{36}$ 11 $\frac{17}{20}$

12 $\frac{23}{25}$ 13 $\frac{19}{25}$ 14 $\frac{150}{200}$ 15 $\frac{120}{200}$ 16 $\frac{18}{72}$

17 On a calculator $\frac{1}{9} = 0.1111111$
Without using a calculator, write down $\frac{1}{900}$ as a decimal.

Exercise 1E

Convert the fractions to decimals and then write the numbers in order of size, smallest first.

1 $\frac{8}{20}$, 0.3, $\frac{9}{25}$

2 $\frac{3}{4}$, $\frac{3}{5}$, 0.7

3 $\frac{12}{16}$, 0.7, $\frac{4}{5}$

4 $\frac{1}{5}$, 0.15, $\frac{1}{20}$

Convert these fractions into decimals.

5 $\frac{19}{1000}$ 6 $\frac{1}{125}$ 7 $\frac{17}{125}$ 8 $\frac{54}{72}$ 9 $\frac{150}{2000}$

10 $\frac{7}{250}$ 11 $\frac{19}{76}$ 12 $\frac{89}{500}$ 13 $\frac{36}{3000}$ 14 $\frac{173}{10000}$

Changing decimals into fractions

$0.6 = \frac{6}{10} = \frac{3}{5}$ $0.27 = \frac{27}{100}$

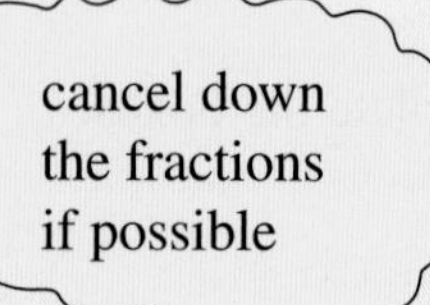
cancel down
the fractions
if possible

$0.65 = \frac{65}{100} = \frac{13}{20}$ $0.04 = \frac{4}{100} = \frac{1}{25}$

Exercise 2M

Change these decimals into fractions.

1 0.3 2 0.7 3 0.01 4 0.09 5 0.13

6 0.51	7 0.69	8 0.9	9 0.23	10 0.37
11 0.89	12 2.3	13 4.73	14 5.01	15 6.7

Exercise 2E

1 Carol and Oscar each have a bar of chocolate. Carol has eaten 0.85 of her bar and Oscar has eaten $\frac{17}{20}$ of his bar. Who has eaten the most chocolate?

Change these decimals into fractions (cancel down fractions when possible).

2 0.8	3 0.05	4 0.08	5 0.25	6 0.24
7 0.02	8 0.4	9 0.32	10 0.15	11 0.18
12 0.75	13 3.2	14 4.5	15 0.56	16 6.04
17 7.12	18 3.75	19 8.6	20 2.95	21 4.36

Changing fractions and percentages

(a) Percentage to fraction
('per cent' means 'out of 100')

$$60\% = \frac{60}{100} = \frac{3}{5}$$

$$24\% = \frac{24}{100} = \frac{6}{25}$$

$$2\% = \frac{2}{100} = \frac{1}{50}$$

(b) Fraction to percentage
(make the denominator equal to 100)

$$\frac{4}{5} = \frac{80}{100} = 80\%$$

$$\frac{3}{20} = \frac{15}{100} = 15\%$$

$$3\frac{1}{2} = \frac{350}{100} = 350\%$$

- Learn the following:

$\frac{1}{4} = 25\%$ $\quad \frac{1}{8} = 12\frac{1}{2}\%$ $\quad \frac{1}{3} = 33\frac{1}{3}\%$ $\quad \frac{2}{3} = 66\frac{2}{3}\%$

Exercise 3M

1 Change these percentages into fractions. Cancel down answers where possible.

(a) 40% (b) 7% (c) 22% (d) 80% (e) 5%
(f) 89% (g) 10% (h) 28% (i) 4% (j) 35%

2 Copy and complete the following.

(a) $\frac{2}{5} = \frac{40}{100} = \square\%$ (b) $\frac{9}{20} = \frac{45}{100} = \square\%$

(c) $\frac{3}{25} = \frac{\square}{100} = \square\%$ (d) $\frac{11}{20} = \frac{\square}{100} = \square\%$

(e) $\frac{9}{10} = \frac{\square}{100} = \square\%$ (f) $\frac{19}{50} = \frac{\square}{100} = \square\%$

3 Here are some test marks. Change them to percentages.

(a) $\frac{17}{20}$ (b) $\frac{13}{25}$ (c) $\frac{46}{50}$

4 

During one season, José won 85% of his races. What *fraction* of his races did he *not* win?

5 Megan spent 36% of her money on the first day of her holiday.
What *fraction* of her money did she have left?

6 Rosa was absent from school for $\frac{1}{25}$ of the Autumn term.
What *percentage* of the Autumn term was she absent for?

7 One in five people in Henton own a laptop computer.
What *percentage* of people in Henton do *not* own a laptop?

8 Answer true or false for each of the following statements:

(a) $\frac{2}{3} = 66\frac{2}{3}\%$ (b) $\frac{1}{8} = 18\%$ (c) $\frac{4}{25} = 16\%$

(d) $\frac{1}{3} = 35\%$ (e) $\frac{7}{50} = 14\%$ (f) $\frac{19}{20} = 95\%$

9 Write down which fractions are greater than the given percentage

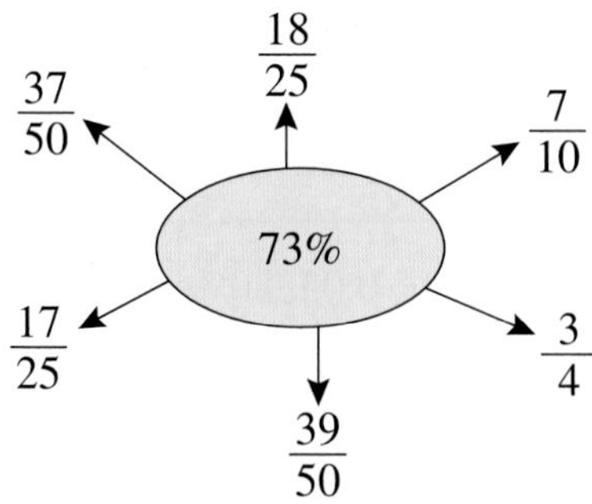

Changing decimals, fractions and percentages

Exercise 3E

1 Copy and complete to change the following decimals into percentages.

(a) $0.37 = \frac{\square}{100} = \square\ \%$ (b) $0.17 = \frac{\square}{100} = \square\ \%$

(c) $0.03 = \frac{\square}{100} = \square\ \%$ (d) $0.4 = \frac{4}{10} = \frac{\square}{100} = \square\ \%$

2 Change these percentages into decimals.

(a) 29% (b) 52% (c) 80% (d) 6%
(e) 3% (f) 13% (g) 130% (h) 240%

3 Copy and complete the table.

	fraction	decimal	percentage
(a)		0.3	
(b)			55%
(c)			12%
(d)	$\frac{1}{20}$		
(e)		0.48	

4 Each fraction, decimal or percentage has an equivalent in the list with letters. Find the letters to make a sentence.

(a) | 50%, $\frac{1}{4}$, 10%, 0.2, 0.11 | 17%, 11% | 0.75, 99%, $\frac{1}{10}$ | 20%, $\frac{1}{4}$, $\frac{1}{8}$, 0.7 |

(b) | $\frac{7}{10}$, 0.8, 45%, $\frac{17}{100}$, 0.5, $\frac{1}{4}$, $\frac{10}{25}$, 0.11 | $\frac{3}{6}$, $\frac{4}{16}$, 0.05, 80% | $\frac{22}{200}$, 0.8, 75%, 11%, $\frac{8}{10}$ |

(c) | 17% | 45%, 0.25, 75% | 0.11, $\frac{99}{100}$, $\frac{4}{10}$, $\frac{41}{50}$, $\frac{400}{500}$ | $\frac{3}{20}$, $\frac{2}{16}$, $\frac{99}{100}$, $\frac{1}{3}$, 0.4, 0.8, $\frac{10}{20}$, 11% |

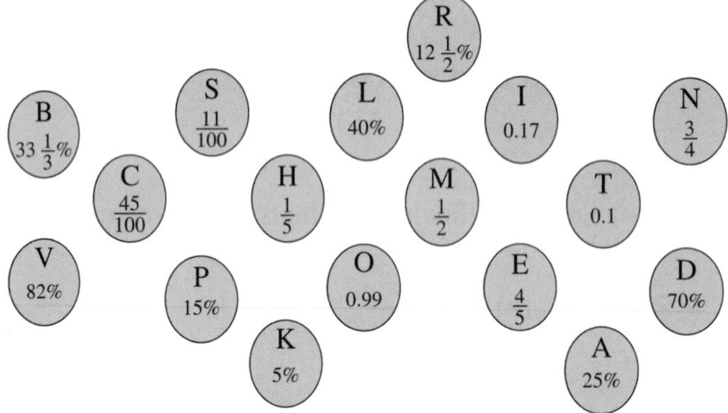

Investigation – Escape

In the town of Decford a prison has 10 cells. All the cells have one prisoner in them and all the cell doors are locked.

- A jailer walks from cell 1 to cell 10 and unlocks each door.
- The jailer returns to the start and locks every second door.
- The jailer returns to the start and changes the state of every third door (ie. cells 3, 6, 9). '*Changes the state of a door*' means '*lock if unlocked*' or '*unlock if locked*'.
- The jailer repeats the process for every fourth door then fifth door, sixth, seventh, eighth, ninth and finally tenth.

(a) How many prisoners can now escape through an unlocked door? Write down the cell numbers of those prisoners who can escape.

(b) The prison in the city of Centford has 100 cells. A jailer repeats the above process from changing the state of every door then every second door, etc to changing the state of every 100th door. How many prisoners can now escape through an unlocked door? Write down the cell numbers of those prisoners who can escape. Can you explain *why* these cell doors are unlocked at the end?

(c) If the process was repeated for 1000 cells, how many prisoners would be able to escape through the unlocked doors?

CHECK YOURSELF ON SECTIONS 2.2 AND 2.3

1 Finding equivalent fractions

Find the missing number to make these fractions equivalent.

(a) $\frac{1}{6} = \frac{\square}{42}$ (b) $\frac{7}{9} = \frac{28}{\square}$ (c) $\frac{32}{48} = \frac{2}{\square}$

(d) Write down which fractions are equivalent to $\frac{7}{8}$.

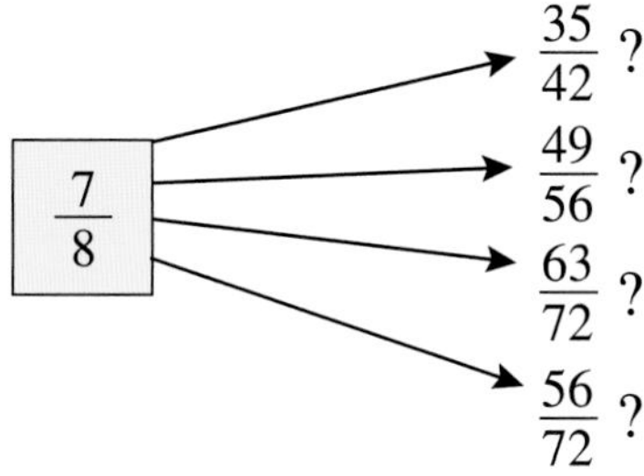

7/8
35/42 ?
49/56 ?
63/72 ?
56/72 ?

2 Finding a fraction of a number

Work out

(a) $\frac{5}{6}$ of 24 (b) $\frac{3}{5}$ of 70 (c) $63 \times \frac{7}{9}$

3 Adding and subtracting fractions (including mixed numbers)

Work out

(a) $\frac{2}{5} + \frac{3}{7}$ (b) $\frac{3}{4} - \frac{2}{3}$ (c) $3\frac{1}{5} - \frac{7}{8}$ (d) $1\frac{2}{3} + 2\frac{1}{4}$

4 Converting between fractions, decimals and percentages

There are four groups of equivalent fractions, decimals and percentages below. Write down each group (beware: there are two odd ones out). For example $\frac{1}{2}$, 0.5, 50% is a group.

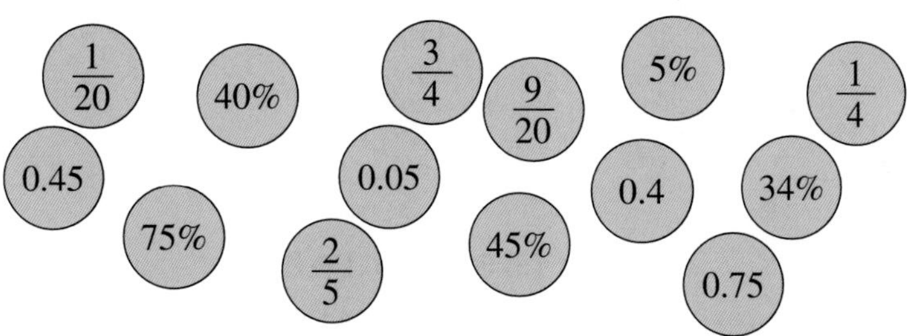

2.4 Angles

In section 2.4 you will learn how to:

- label angles
- measure and draw angles with a protractor
- calculate angles on a straight line and at a point
- calculate angles in a triangle
- calculate angles with parallel lines
- calculate angles in a quadrilateral

Labelling angles

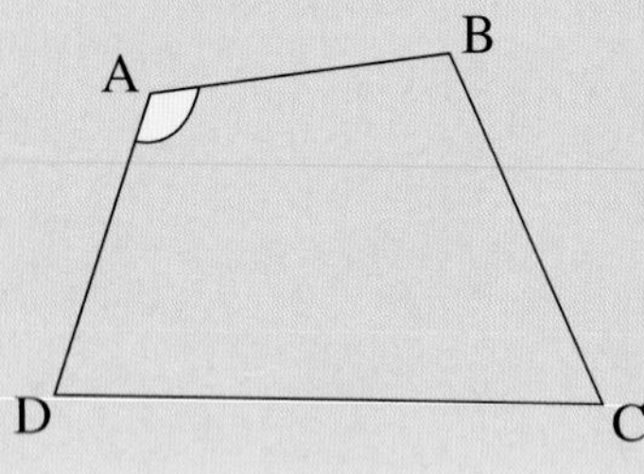

This is called angle DAB or angle BAD. We write this as DÂB or BÂD. Angles are labelled with capital letters and the middle letter wears a 'hat' to indicate an angle.

Exercise 1M

Name the shaded angles below:

1 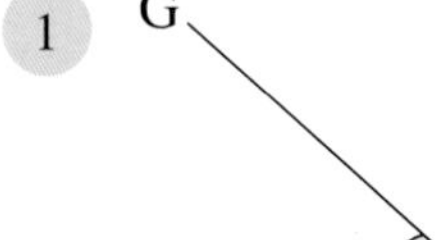

2 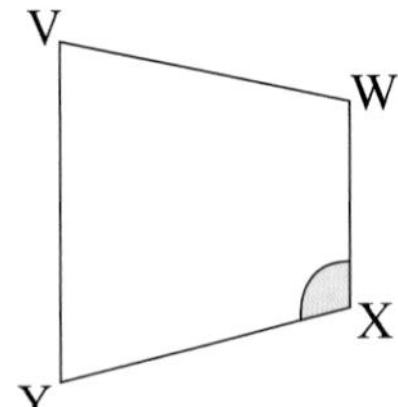

3 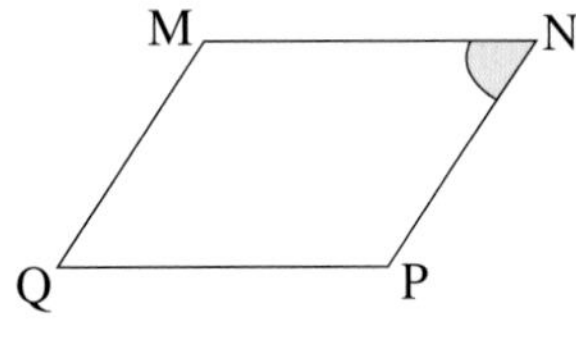

Write down the size of each angle stated below:

4 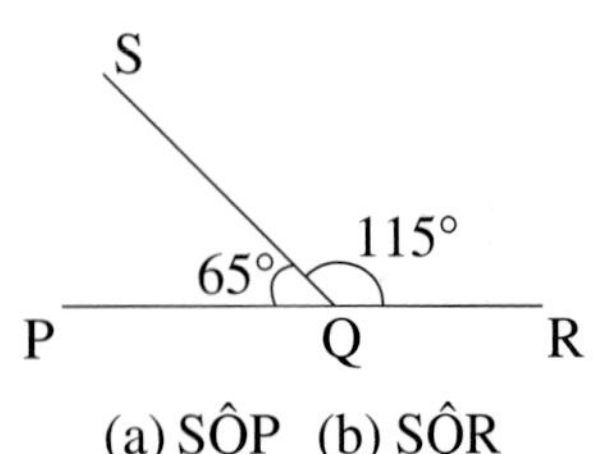

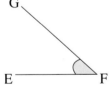

(a) SQ̂P (b) SQ̂R

5 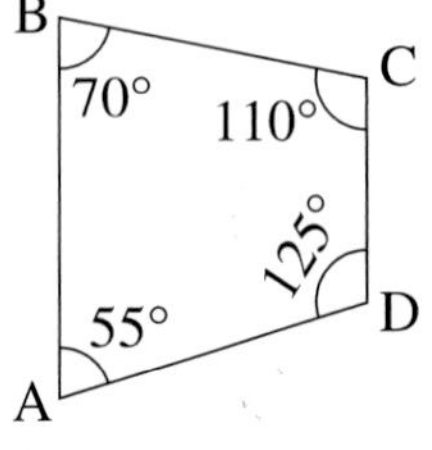

(a) BĈD (b) DÂB
(c) DĈB (d) AD̂C

6 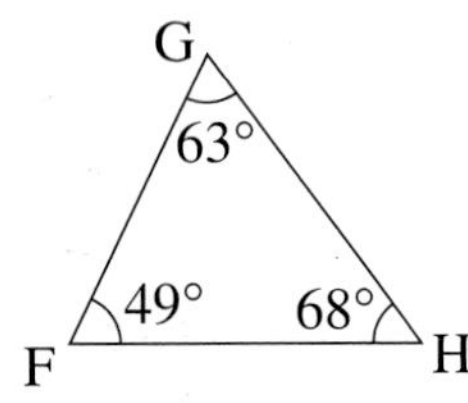

(a) FĤG (b) HĜF

7

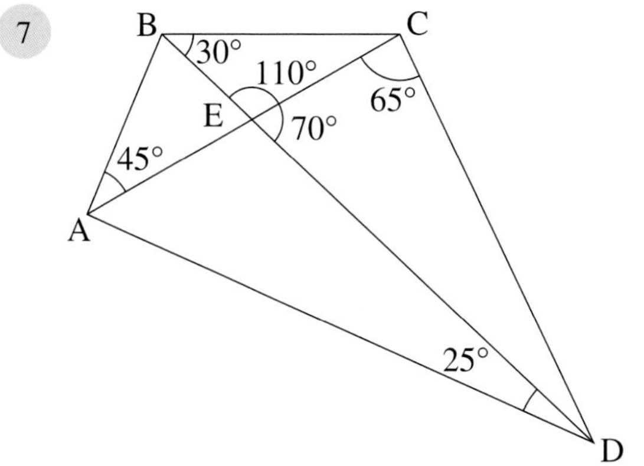

Describe each angle listed below (example: 110º is BÊC)

(a) 70º
(b) 45º
(c) 25º
(d) 65º
(e) 30º

Exercise 1E

Give the measurement of each angle listed below.
Remember to read the correct scale. Some questions are done for you, to remind you of this.

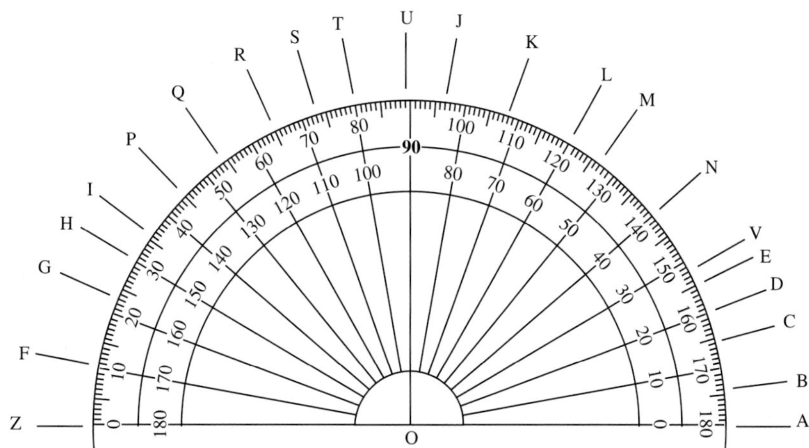

1	AÔD = 20°	2	AÔN =	3	AÔL = 60°	4	AÔK =
5	ZÔF =	6	ZÔP = 45°	7	ZÔR =	8	ZÔT = 80°
9	ZÔI =	10	ZÔG =	11	AÔC =	12	AÔV =
13	AÔQ = 126°	14	AÔP =	15	AÔF =	16	AÔB =
17	ZÔH =	18	ZÔB =	19	ZÔC =	20	ZÔD =
21	AÔG =	22	AÔH =	23	AÔI =	24	AÔM =
25	AÔR =	26	ZÔE =	27	ZÔJ =	28	ZÔK =
29	ZÔL =	30	ZÔM =	31	AÔE =	32	AÔJ =

33 AÔU = 34 AÔS = 35 ZÔN = 36 ZÔQ =

37 ZÔS = 38 ZÔU = 39 ZÔV = 40 AÔT =

Exercise 2M

Use a protractor to measure the angles indicated.

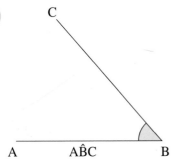

1 C A AB̂C B

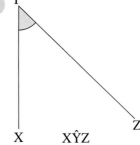

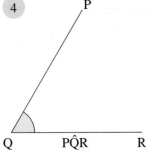

2
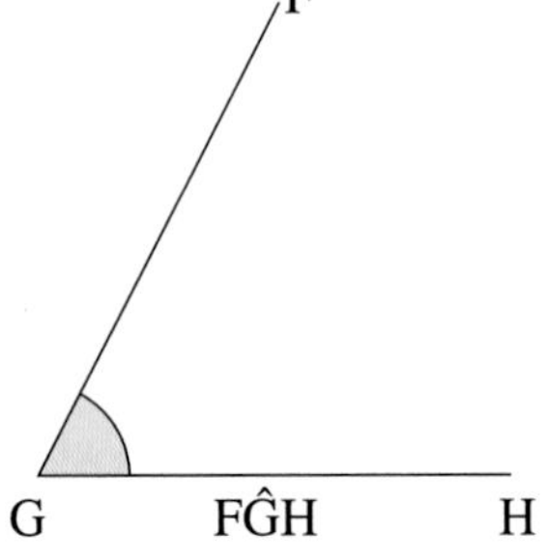

3 Y X XŶZ Z

4 P Q PQ̂R R

5
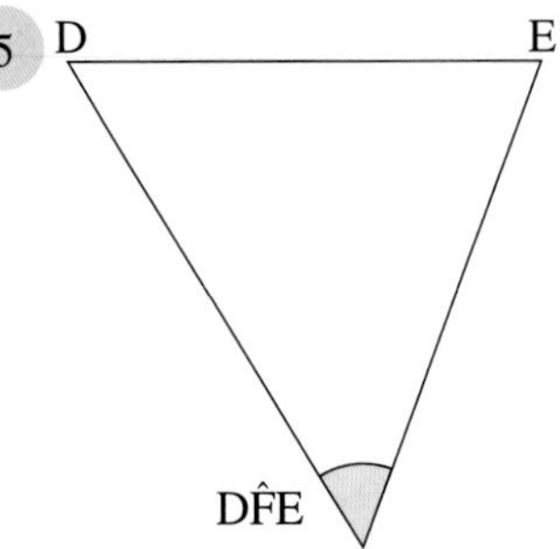

6
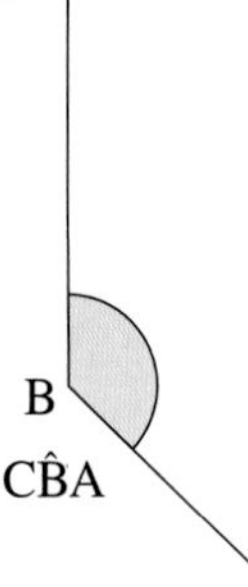

7
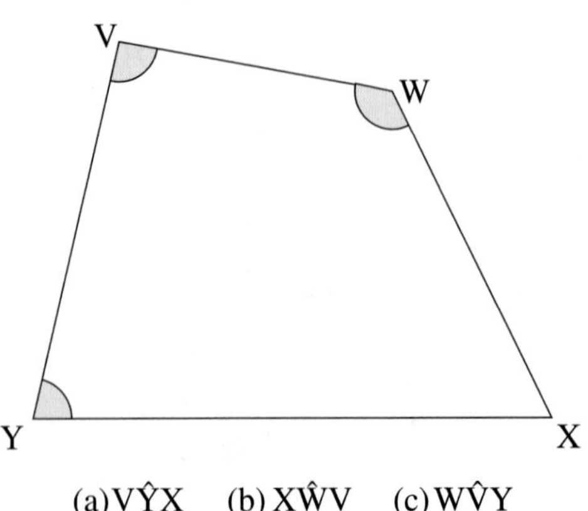

(a) VŶX (b) XŴV (c) WV̂Y

8
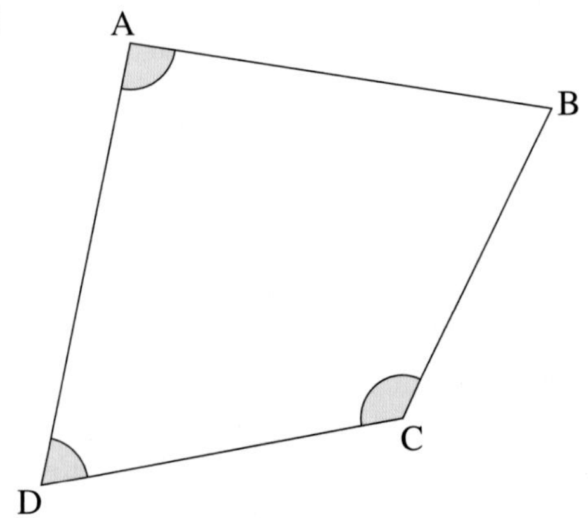

(a) AD̂C (b) BĈD (c) BÂD

9 Use a protractor to draw the following angles accurately.

(a) 85° (b) 48° (c) 130° (d) 164° (e) 18°
(f) 25° (g) 210° (h) 156° (i) 304° (j) 123°

10 For each angle in question 9, state whether it is acute, obtuse or reflex.

Exercise 2E

Measure the following angles.

1. $B\hat{A}C$
2. $R\hat{C}D$
3. $D\hat{E}R$
4. $E\hat{A}B$
5. $D\hat{R}C$
6. $B\hat{E}A$
7. $S\hat{R}B$
8. $A\hat{C}B$
9. $D\hat{T}B$
10. $C\hat{P}E$
11. $C\hat{D}E$
12. $D\hat{S}C$
13. $D\hat{C}B$
14. $E\hat{D}S$
15. $U\hat{D}Q$
16. $E\hat{C}B$

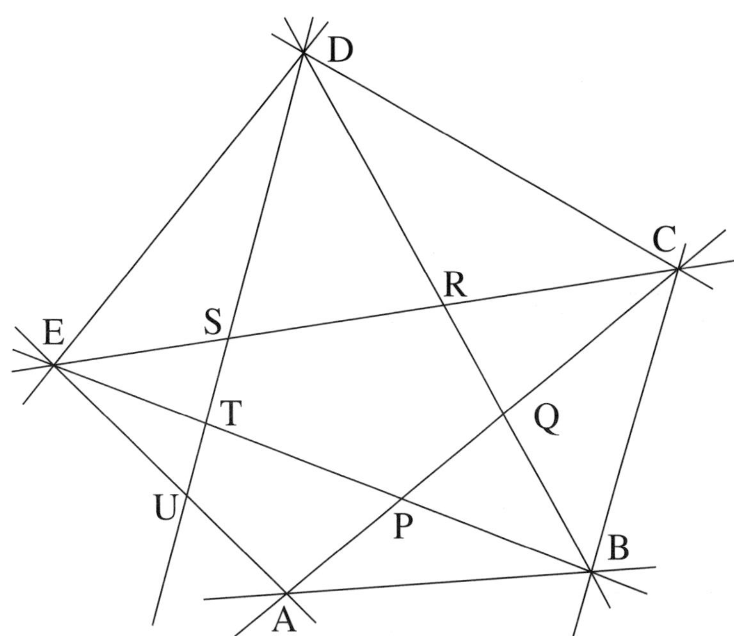

Calculating angles on a straight line and at a point

- **Angles on a straight line**

a b

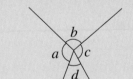

$a + b = 180°$

The angles on a straight line add up to 180°

- **Angles at a point**

b
a c
d

$a + b + c + d = 360°$

The angles at a point add up to 360°

- **Vertically opposite angles**

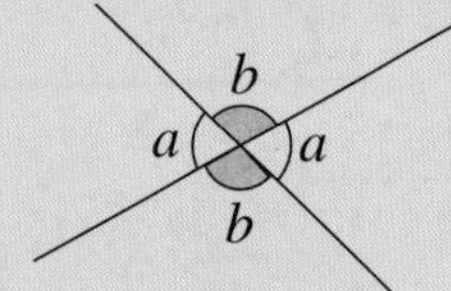

The opposite angles are equal when two lines intersect

Exercise 3M

Find the angles marked with letters.

1 140° a

2 b 129°

3 c 40° 80°

4 65° d

5 137° e

6 35° f 29° 56°

7 53° 25° g 60°

8 i 125° h

9 70° j 109° 88°

10 74° 65° 68° k

11 27° l m n

12 r p q

Exercise 3E

Find the angles marked with letters.

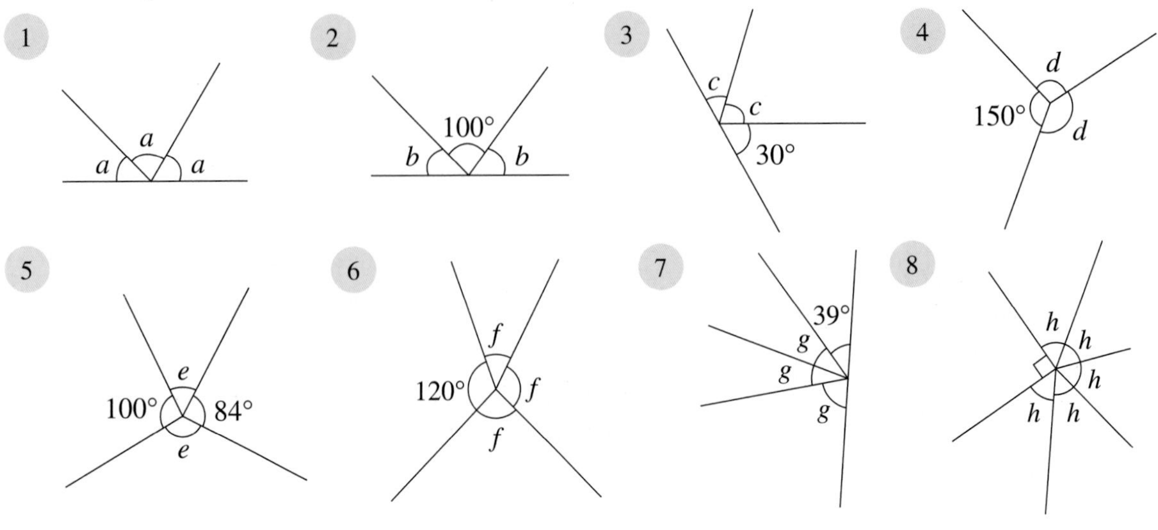

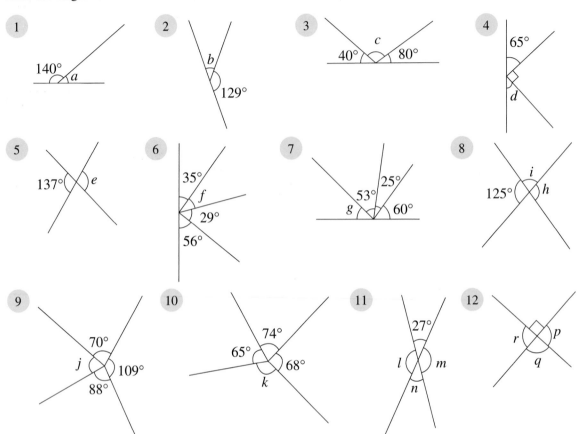

9
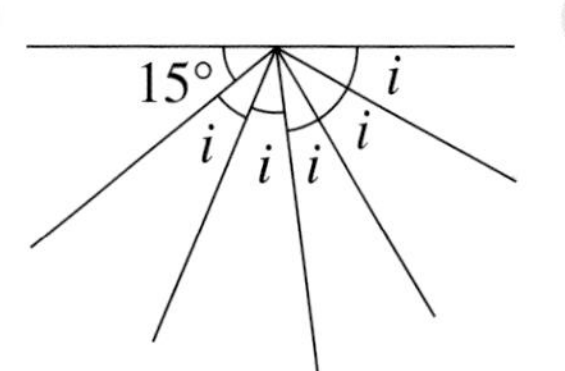

10
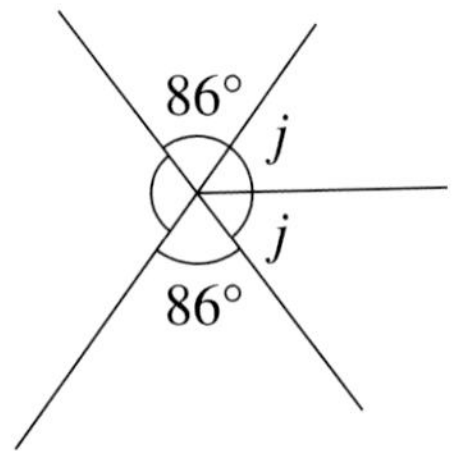

11
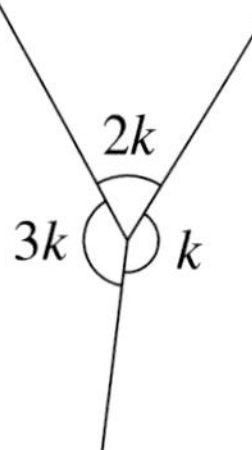

12
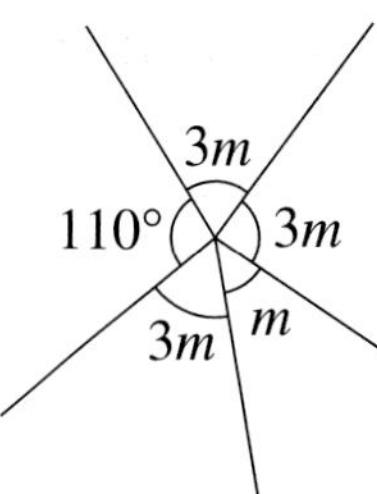

Calculating angles in a triangle

Draw a triangle of any shape on a piece of card and cut it out accurately. Now tear off the three corners as shown.

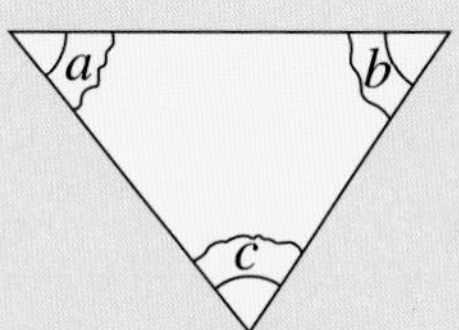

When the angles a, b and c are placed together they form a straight line.

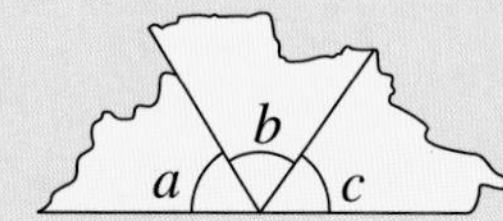

We see that:

The angles in a triangle add up to 180°

Isosceles and equilateral triangles

An *isosceles* triangle has two equal sides and two equal angles.

The sides AB and AC are equal (marked with a dash) so angles $\hat{B}$ and $\hat{C}$ are also equal.

An *equilateral* triangle has three equal sides and three equal angles (all 60°).

Find the angles marked with letters.

(a)

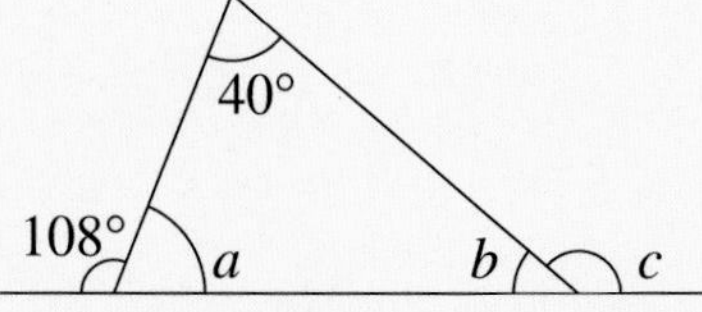

$a = 72°$ (angles on a straight line)

$b + 72° + 40° = 180°$ (angles in a triangle)

$b = 68°$

$c = 112°$ (angles on a straight line)

(b)

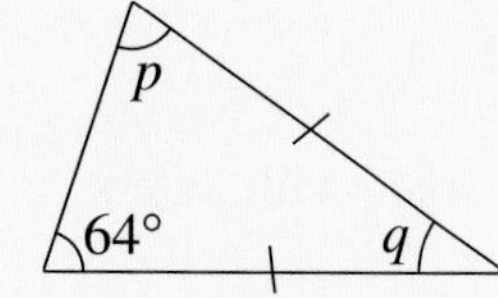

$p = 64°$ (isosceles triangle)

$q + 64° + 64° = 180°$ (angles in a triangle)

$q = 52°$

Exercise 4M

Find the angles marked with letters.

1 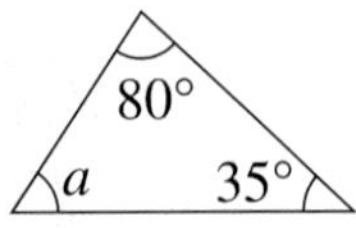

2 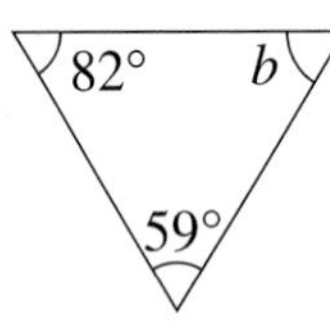

3 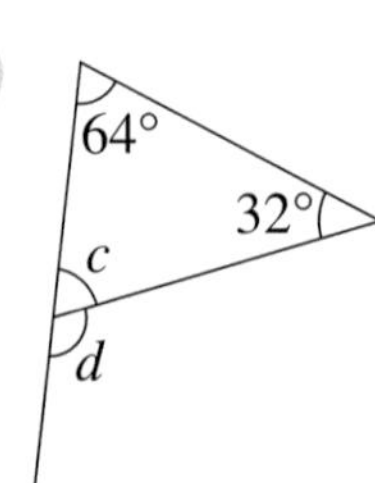

4 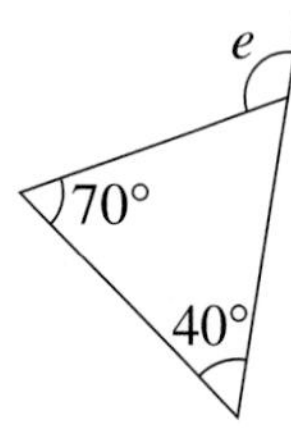

5 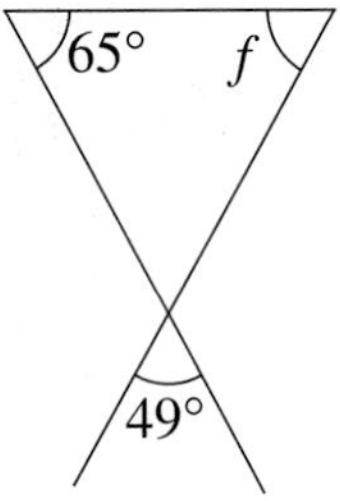

6 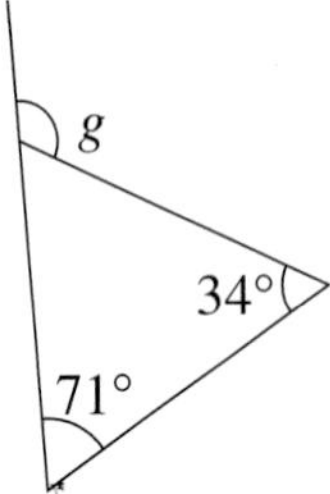

7 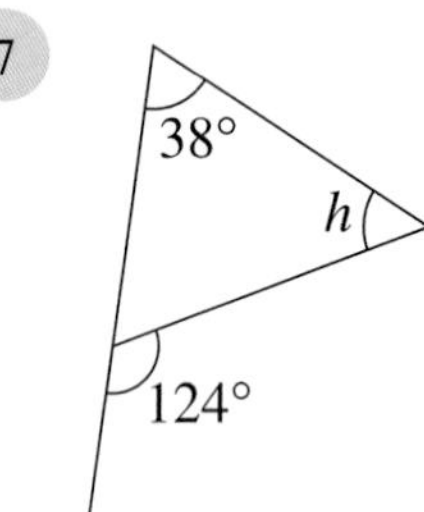

8 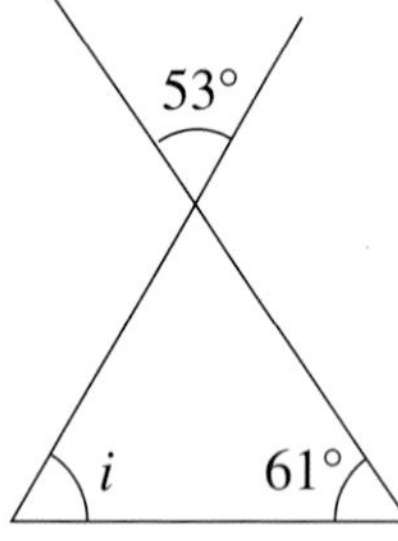

9 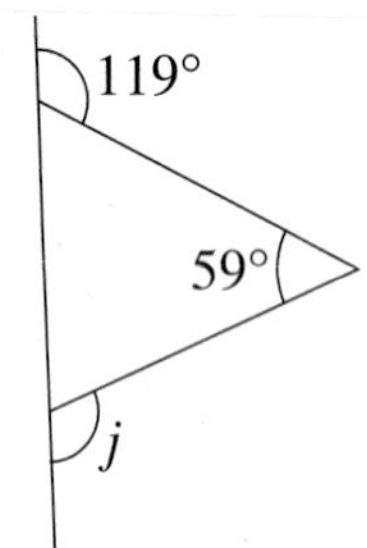

10 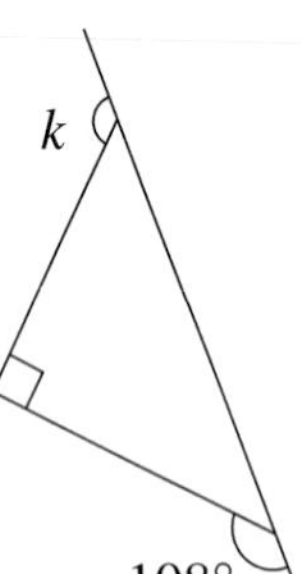

11 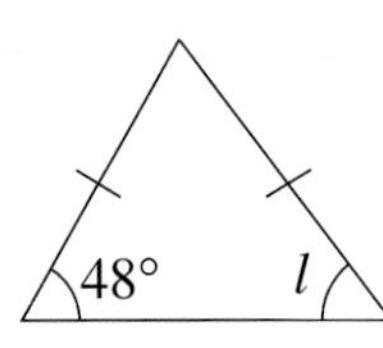

12 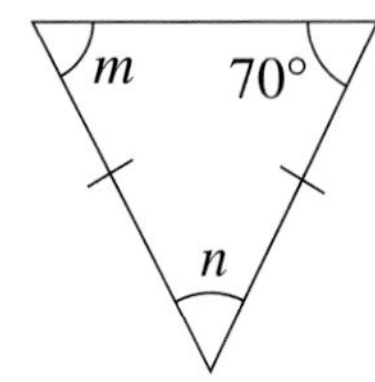

13 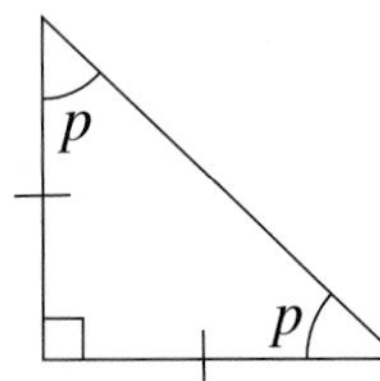

14 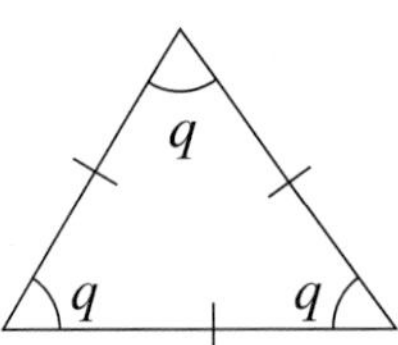

15 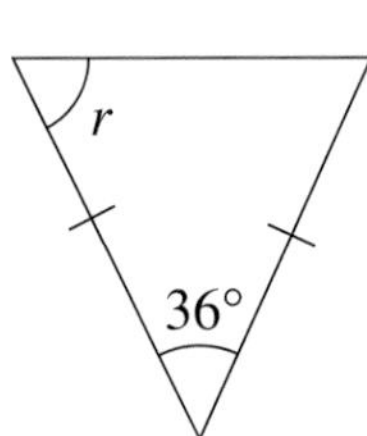

16 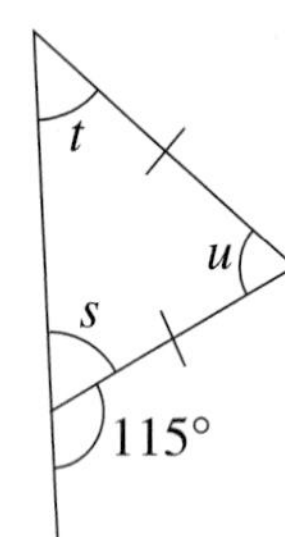

Exercise 4E

Find the angles marked with letters.

1 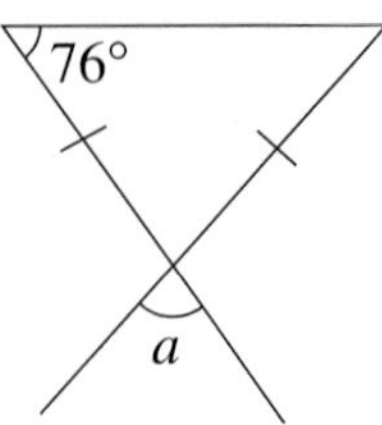

2 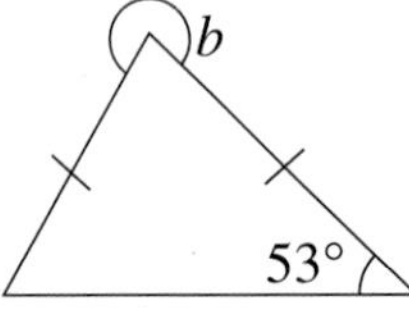

3 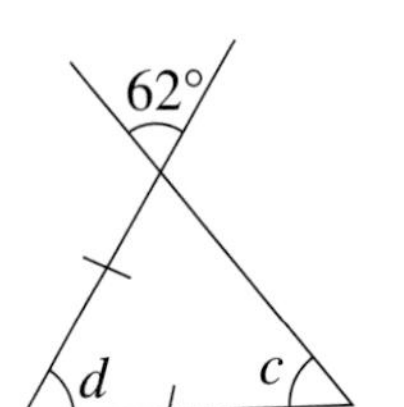

4 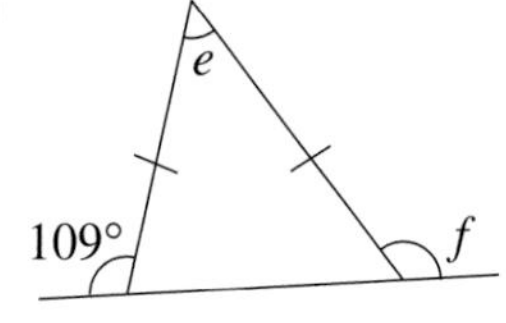

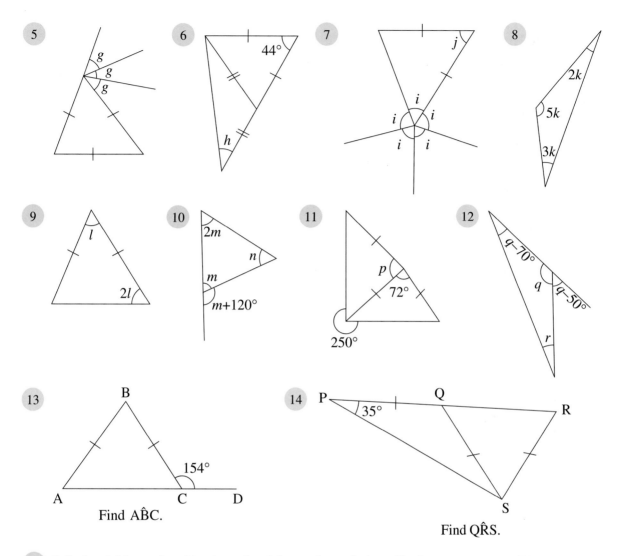

5

6

7

8

9

10

11

12

13

Find $A\hat{B}C$.

14

Find $Q\hat{R}S$.

15 Julie has laid a patio with triangular slabs as shown below. She has one space to fill (yellow below). She has 3 slabs remaining. Which slab will fit perfectly into the space? Explain why.

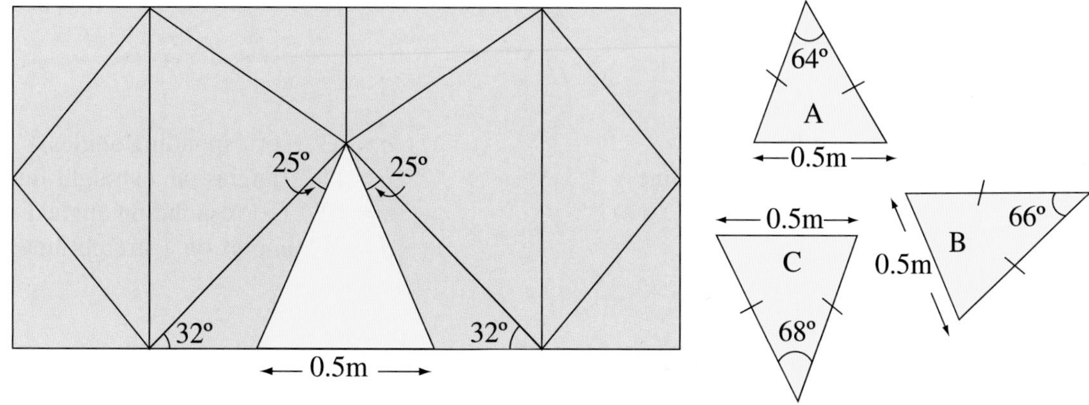

Angles and parallel lines

In this diagram all the arrow lines are parallel.

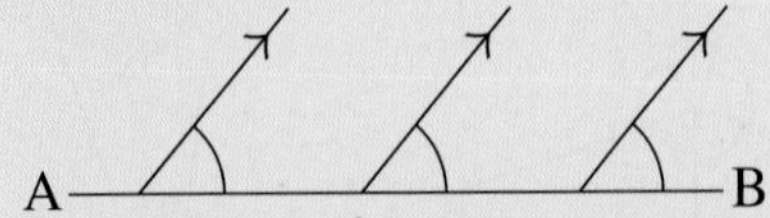

The arrows all make the same angle with the line AB. These angles are called **corresponding** angles.

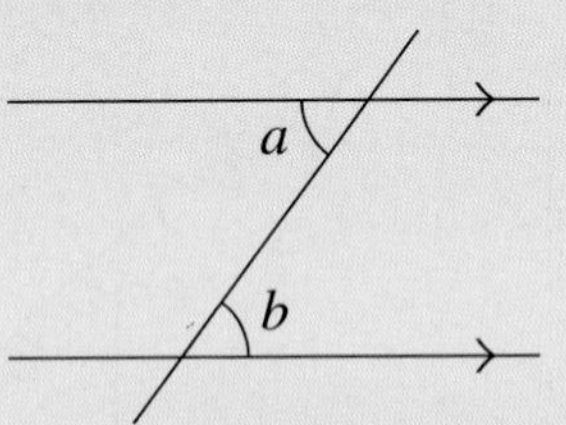

angle a = angle b
These are called *alternate* angles.

Many people think of corresponding angles as 'F' angles.

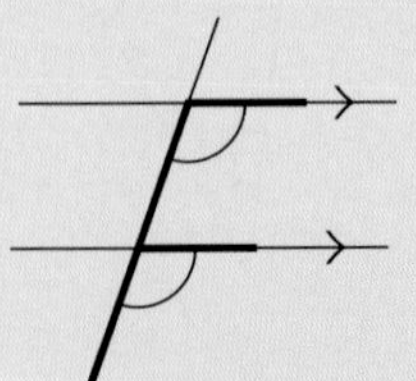

Many people think of alternate angles as 'Z' angles.

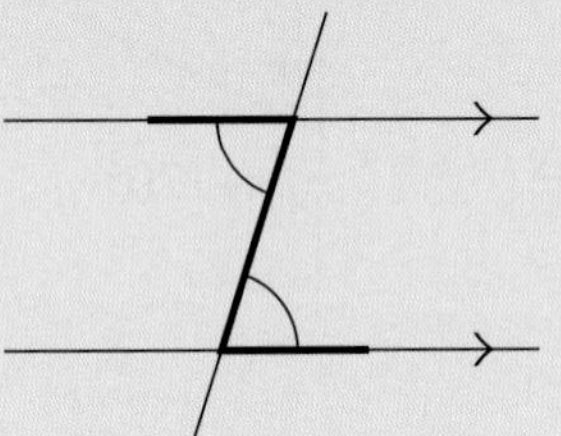

Find the angles marked with letters.

(a)

70°

q p

$p = 70°$ (corresponding angles)
$q = 110°$ (angles on a straight line)

(b)

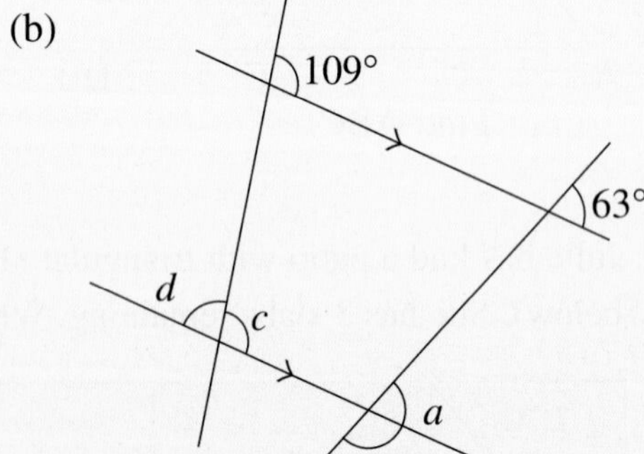

$a = 63°$ (corresponding angles)
$b = 117°$ (angles on a straight line)
$c = 109°$ (corresponding angles)
$d = 71°$ (angles on a straight line)

Exercise 5M

Find the angles marked with letters.

1
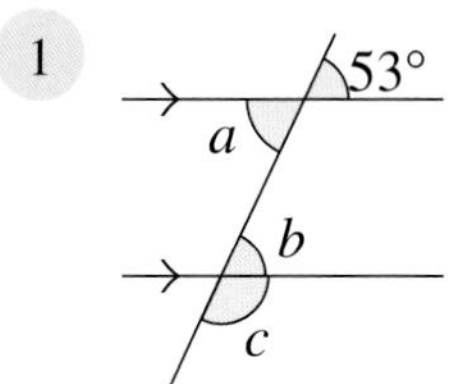

2

3

4
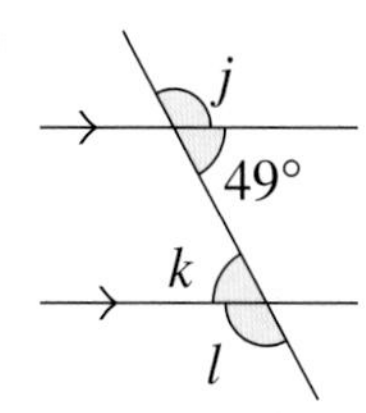

5
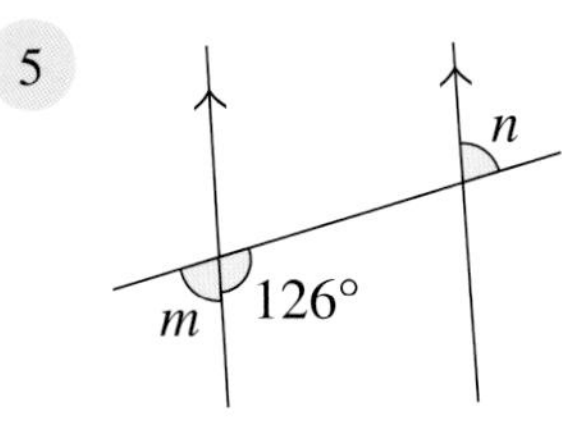

6

7

8
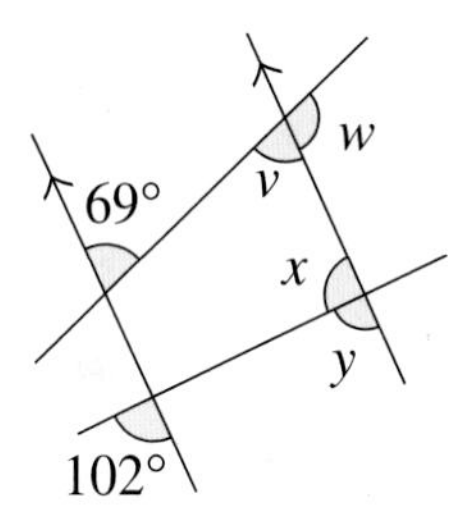

9
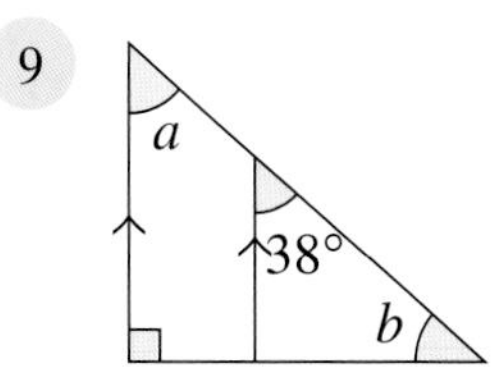

10
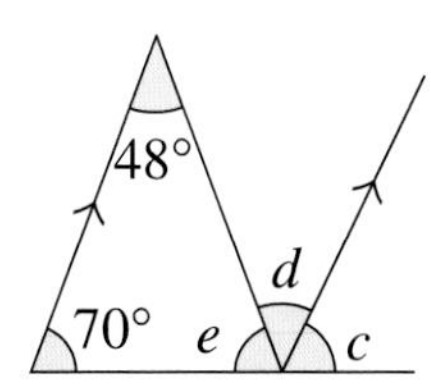

11
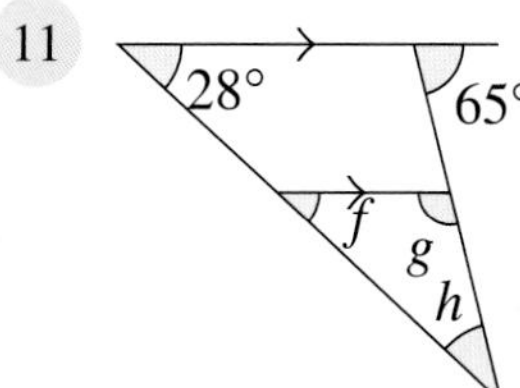

12
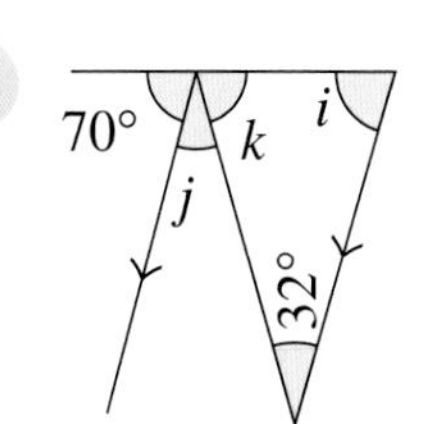

Angles in a quadrilateral

Draw a quadrilateral of any shape on a piece of paper or card and cut it out. Mark the four angles *a, b, c* and *d* and tear them off.

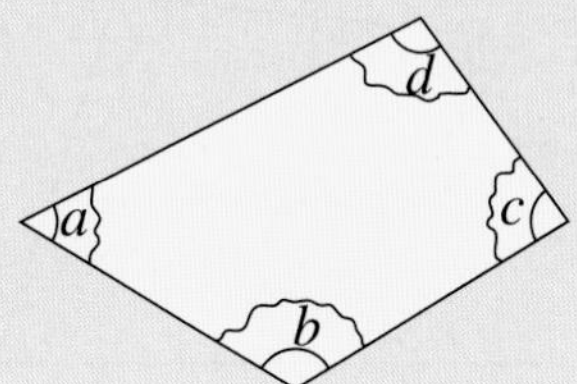

Arrange the four angles about a point.

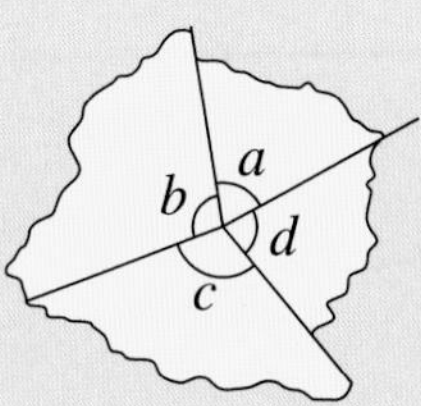

We see that:

The angles in a quadrilateral add up to 360°

Mixed questions

Exercise 5E

Find the angles marked with letters.

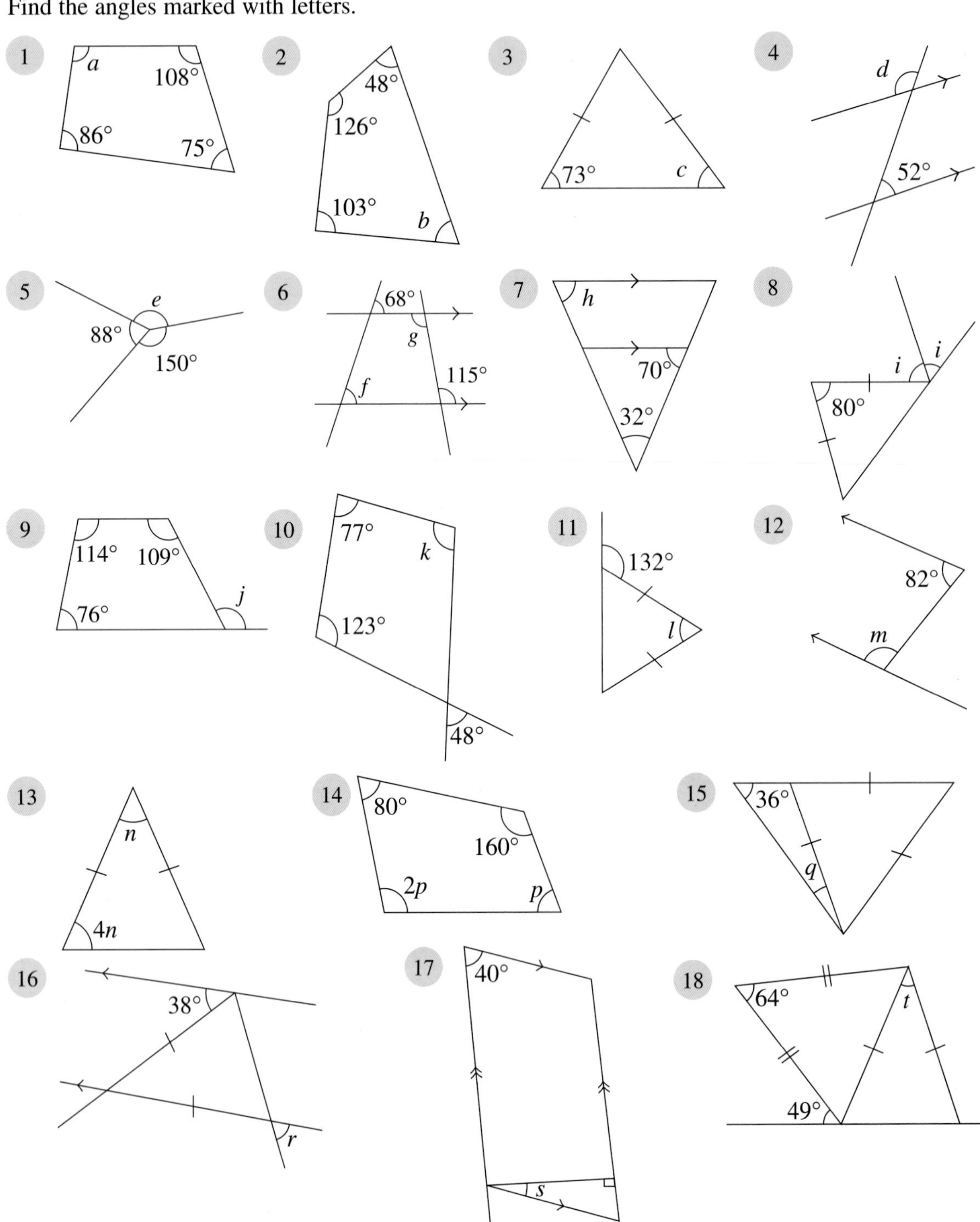

19

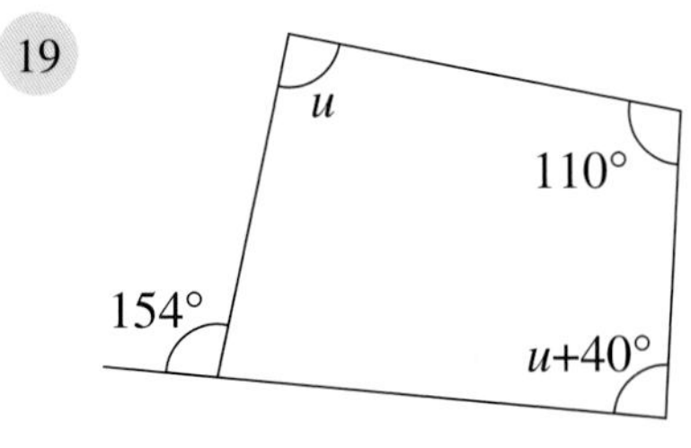

20

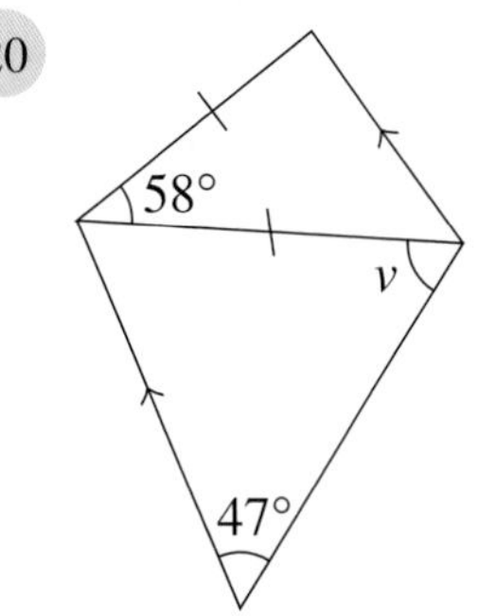

21

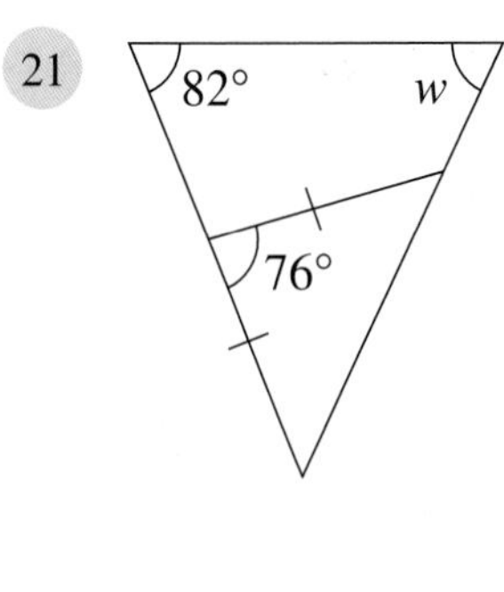

CHECK YOURSELF ON SECTION 2.4

1 Labelling angles

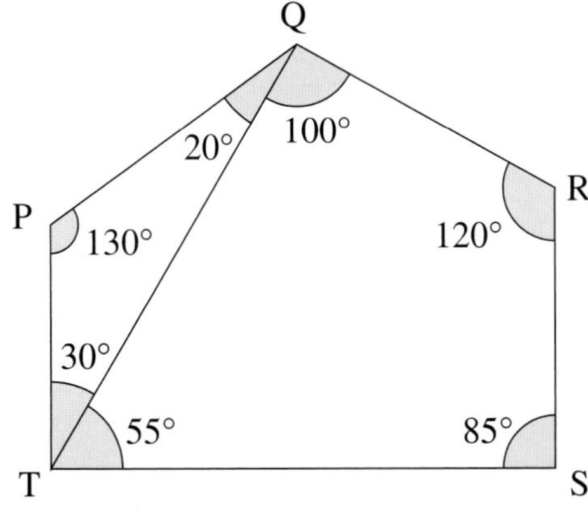

Write down the size of each angle stated below:

(a) $R\hat{S}T$

(b) $P\hat{T}Q$

(c) $R\hat{Q}T$

2 Measuring and drawing angles with a protractor

Use a protractor to measure the two angles below.

(a)

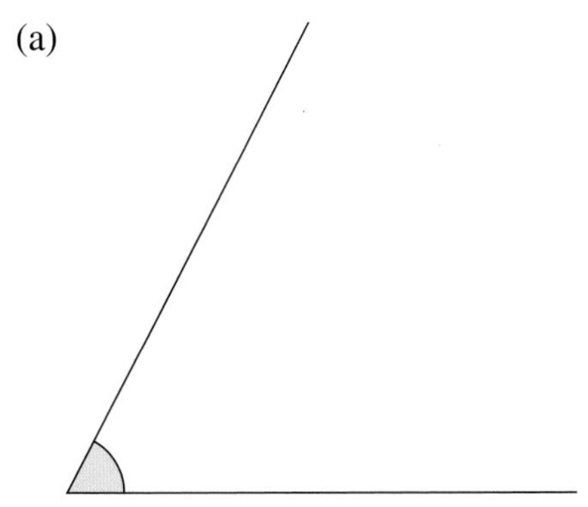

(b)

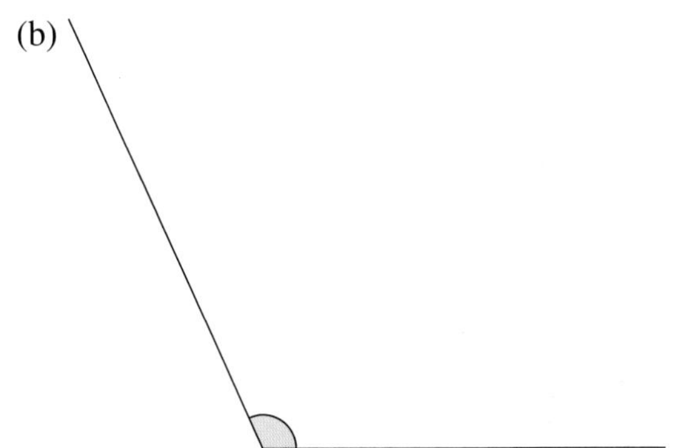

Use a protractor to draw angles of (c) 73° (d) 135°

3 Calculating angles on a straight line and at a point

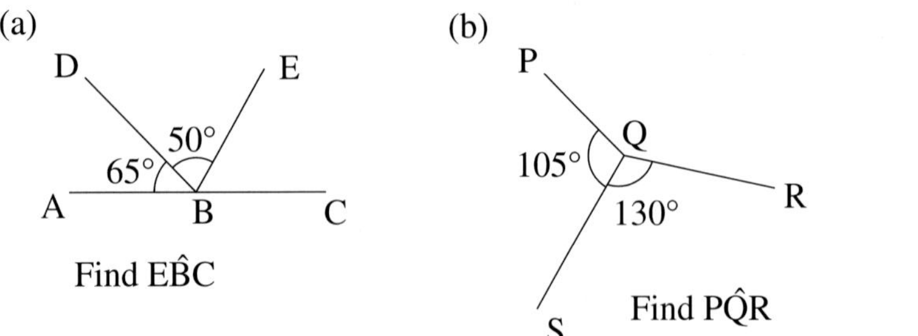

(a) Find $E\hat{B}C$

(b) Find $P\hat{Q}R$

(c) Find $X\hat{W}Y$ and $V\hat{W}X$

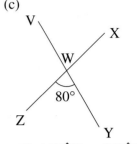

4 Calculating angles in a triangle

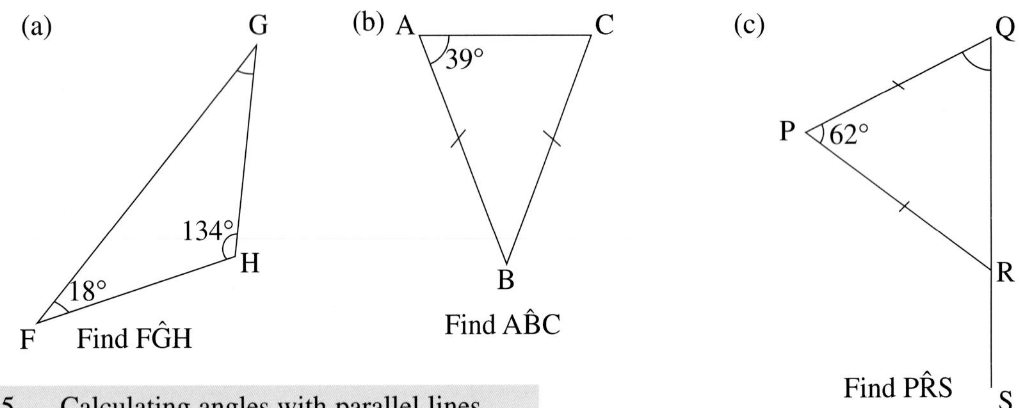

(a) Find $F\hat{G}H$

(b) Find $A\hat{B}C$

(c) Find $P\hat{R}S$

5 Calculating angles with parallel lines

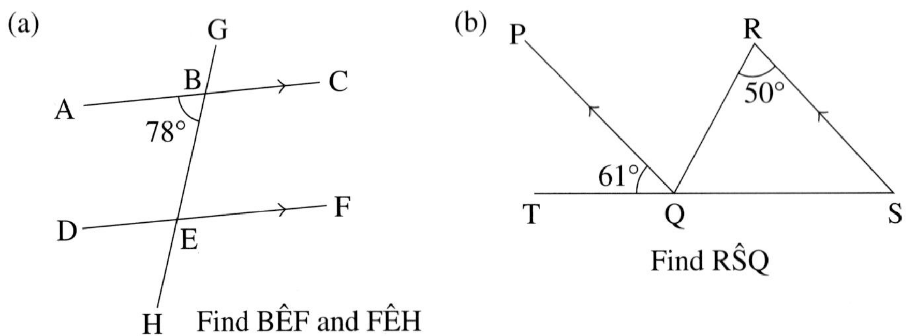

(a) Find $B\hat{E}F$ and $F\hat{E}H$

(b) Find $R\hat{S}Q$

6 Calculating angles in a quadrilateral

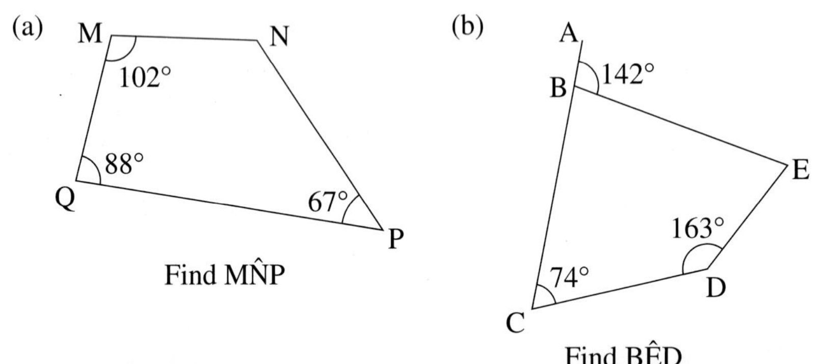

(a) Find $M\hat{N}P$

(b) Find $B\hat{E}D$

2.5 Rules of Algebra

In section 2.5 you will learn how to:

- use letters for numbers
- collect like terms
- multiply algebraic terms
- substitute numbers into a formula
- tackle balance puzzles

Using letters for numbers

Many problems can be solved by using letters instead of numbers. This is called using *algebra*.

Remember: the *letters stand for numbers*

- Suppose there are N cows in a field. If the farmer puts 3 more cows in the field, there will be $N + 3$ cows in the field.
- $N + 3$ is an expression. An expression is usually a mixture of letters, numbers and signs. An expression has no '=' sign.
- Suppose there are y people on a bus. At a bus stop n people get off the bus. There are now $y - n$ people on the bus.
- $y - n$ is an expression.
- If I start with a number N and treble it, I will have $N \times 3$. In algebra the '×' sign is left out and the number is written before the letter so I will have $3N$.
- If I start with a number x then double it and add 4, I will have $2x + 4$.
- $2x + 4$ is an expression.
- $x \div 4$ is written as $\frac{x}{4}$

Exercise 1M

1 I start with a number d then take away 9.

2 I start with a number x then double it.

3 I start with a number y then add 25.

4 I start with a number m then divide it by 6.

5 I start with a number k, double it then subtract 8.

6 I start with a number M, treble it then take away 4.

7 I start with a number p and multiply it by 25.

8 I start with a number w, double it then add 15.

9 I start with a number q, multiply it by 10 then subtract 8.

10 I start with a number n, divide it by 3 then add 5.

11 I start with a number b, multiply it by 3 then add 8.

12 I start with a number y, divide it by 8 then subtract 7.

13 I start with a number f, multiply it by 3 then divide it by 10.

14 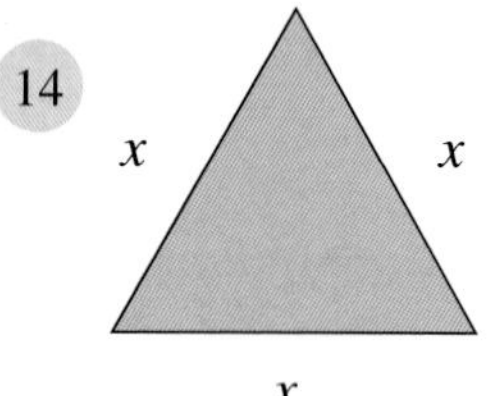

The perimeter p of the triangle is

$$p = x + x + x$$

This is written as $p = 3x$

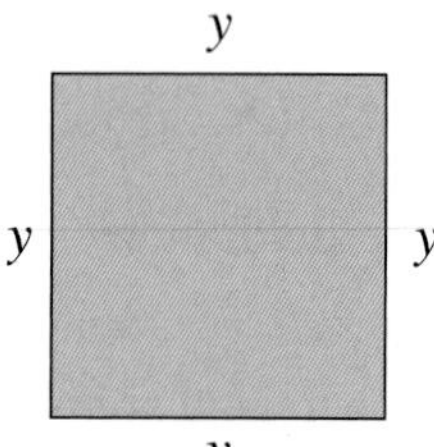

Complete the statement below for the perimeter p of this square

$p =$ . . . .

Use algebra to find the perimeter p of each shape in questions 15 to 20.

15 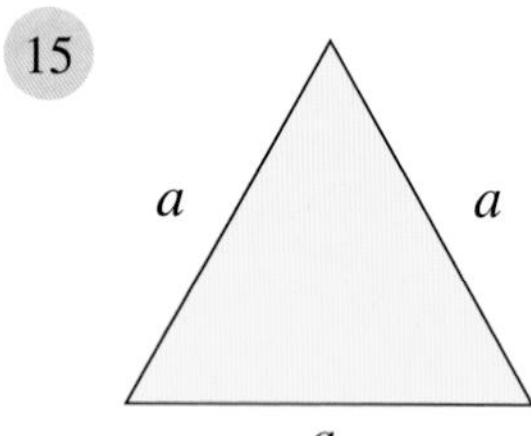

16

17 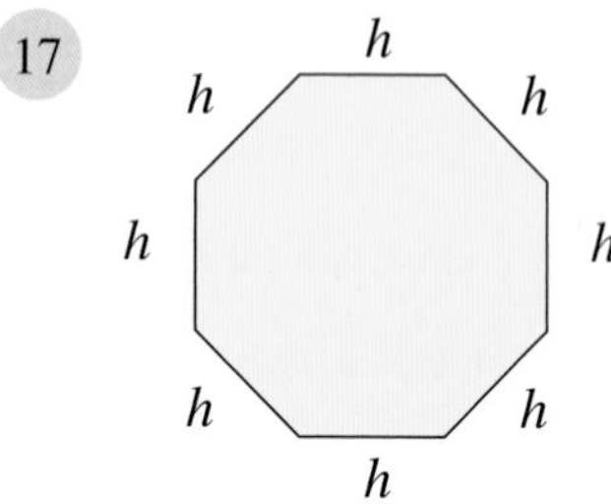

18 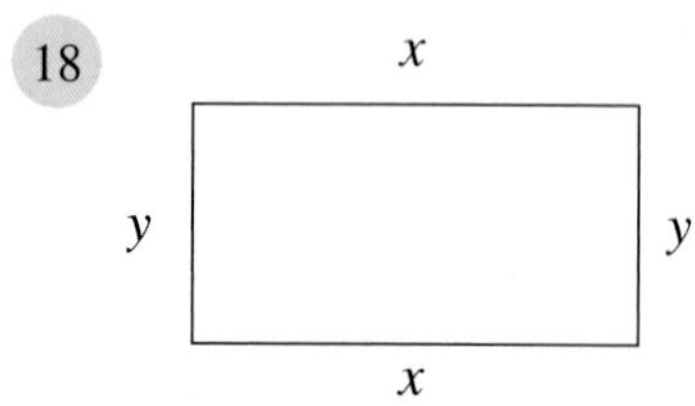

19 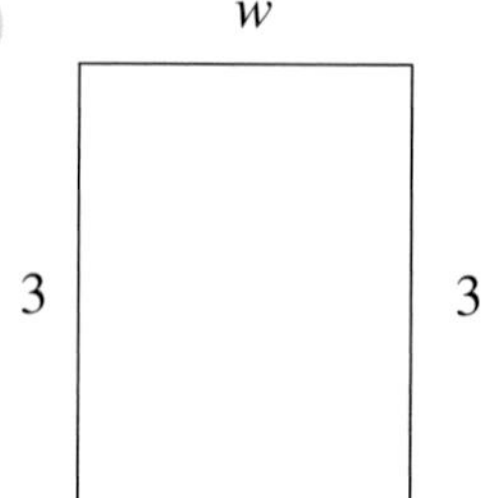

20 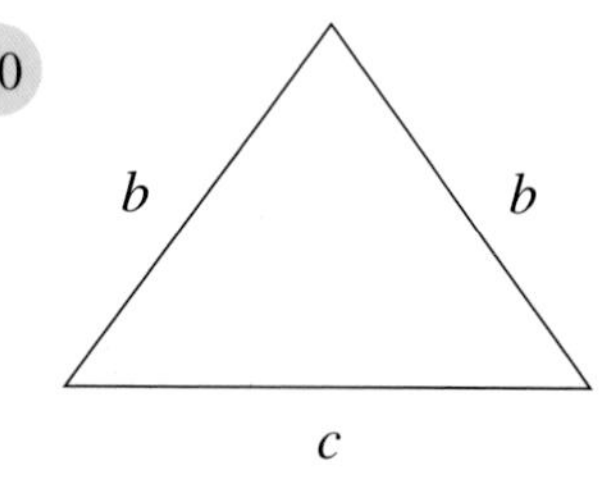

Exercise 1E

In questions 1 to 10 write down the expression.

1 I start with x, double it and then add y.

2 I start with s, treble it and then take away w.

3 I start with $4x$, take away y and then add 5.

4 I start with n, divide it by 5 and then subtract 3.

5 I subtract f from g and then add n.

6 I start with $2y$, add $3w$ and then take away x.

7 I add together p and q then multiply the total by 4.

8 I start with m then multiply by 6 and add $3n$.

9 I subtract $3p$ from $5q$ then add $4m$.

10 I start with n, double it, divide by 9 and then add 6.

11 A sweet weighs x grams. How many grams do five sweets weigh?

12 A piece of rope is 20 m long. A prisoner ties on an extra piece of rope of length y metres. How long is the entire piece of rope now?

13 Jackie shares N pounds equally between six children. How much money does each child receive?

14 A piece of wood is w cm long. I cut off a piece 9 cm long. What is the length of the remaining piece of wood?

15 Carl has m CDs. Shalina has 3 times as many CDs. How many CDs does Shalina have?

16 On Tuesday there are x people in a cinema. On Saturday there are four times as many people plus another 45. How many people were in the cinema on Saturday?

17 w toffees are shared equally between you and three others. How many toffees do you receive?

18 Tania spends £n on magazines. Chris spends £4 more than Tania. How much money does Chris spend?

19 Draw and label a triangle whose perimeter p is given by the formula $p = 2x + 5$.

20 Draw and label a rectangle whose perimeter p is given by the formula $p = 2a + 2b$.

Collecting like terms

The expression $4a + 3a$ can be *simplified* to $7a$.

This is because $4a + 3a$ means four a s plus three a s which gives seven a s.

a means $1a$ so $6a - a = 6a - 1a = 5a$

$5x$ and $3x$ are called *like* terms

$5x$ and $3y$ are called *unlike* terms

The sum or difference of two terms can only be simplified if the terms are *like* terms.

We can collect like terms.

(a) $5 + n + 2 + 4n = 5n + 7$

(b) $y + 3 + y + 4 + w = w + 2y + 7$

collect in alphabetical order, with letter terms written before any numbers on their own

(c) $4x - 4$ cannot be simplified (no like terms)

(d) $5y + x - 5y = x$

do not write $0y$
do not write $1x$

(e) Simplify $6x + 4y + 2x - 2y$

$(6x)\ (+4y)\ (+2x)\ (-2y) = 8x + 2y$

6x means +6x

(f) Simplify $6m + 3x - m + 6 - 3x$

$(6m)(+3x)(-m)(+6)(-3x) = 5m + 6$

Exercise 2M

Simplify the following expressions where possible.

1 $3a + 5a$
2 $6x - 2x$
3 $4a + 3b$
4 $6c - 4d$
5 $3d + d$
6 $3x + 2$
7 $7y + 2y$
8 $5h - 3h$
9 $8w - 5w$
10 $6y - 5y$
11 $7x + y$
12 $8m + m$
13 $16y - 9y$
14 $6m + 5n$
15 $4x + 6$
16 $5b + 8b$
17 $20t - 8t$
18 $7p - 6p$
19 $10n + 15n$
20 $6a - 5$
21 $8x + 2$
22 $14h + 16h$
23 $9 - 7x$
24 $8b - 4$
25 $7a + 6$
26 $5c + c$
27 $12y - 12$
28 $12y - y$

Exercise 2E

Simplify the following expressions as far as possible by collecting like terms.

1 $3a + 5b + 3a + 2b$

2 $2x + 4y + 7x + 3y$

3 $8x + 4y - 5x - 2y$

4 $7m + 5n - 4m + 3n$

5 $6a + 5 + a + 4$

6 $8a + 3b - 6a + 4b$

7 $5x + 9 - 2x - 7$

8 $7p + 9q + 2p - 4q$

9 $7x + 8 + x - 6$

10 $a + 14b + 5a - 4b$

11 $6m + 8 + 6m - 7$

12 $3h + 20 - h + 5$

13 $5m + 2n + 4n + 7m$

14 $8p + 6q - 3q - 2p$

15 $6x + 10 - 6 + 3x$

16 $7x + 3y + x + 6$

17 $8a + 3b - 4a + 4c$

18 $5w + 8 - 3w + w$

19 $8 + 4a + 7 - 2a$

20 $4y + 8 - 5 - 3y$

21 $5c - c + 6a + 8c$

22 $5p + 6q + 4p - 4q$

23 $7m + 9n - 7n + 4$

24 $6x + 8 - x + 9x$

25 Write down an expression for the perimeter of each shape below. Collect like terms where possible.

(a)

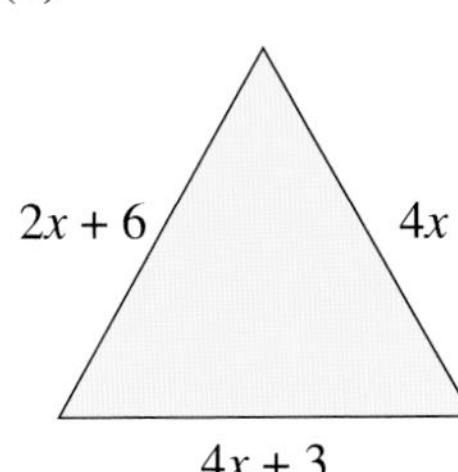

(b)

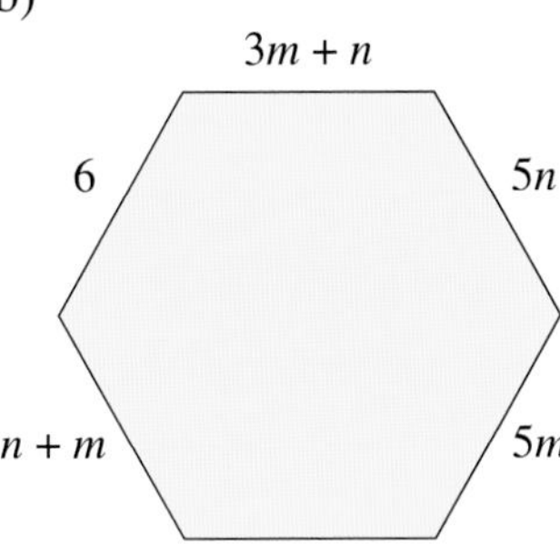

(c)

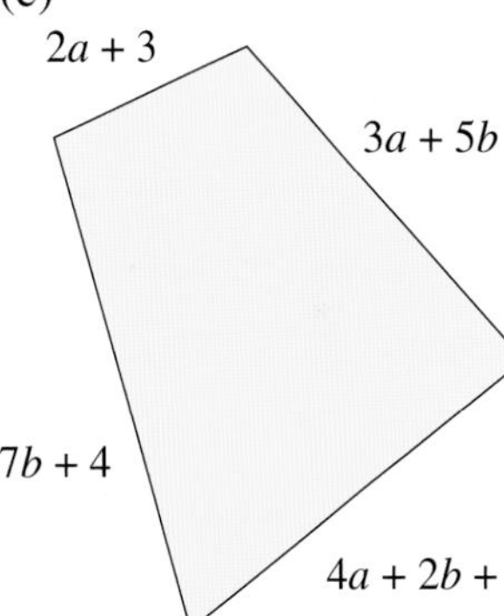

26 Which two expressions below are *equivalent* (this means they give the same answer when the like terms are collected).

(a) $5x + 3 - 2x + 6y + x$ (b) $3y + 4x + 3y + 6 - 2$ (c) $7 + 4y + 4x + 2y - 3$

More rules

$a + b = b + a$

$a \times b = b \times a$ ($a \times b$ is written as ab so $ab = ba$)

$a \times a = a^2$

$\frac{a}{b} = a \div b$

Exercise 3M

1 (a) Write down any pairs of expressions from below that are equal to each other.

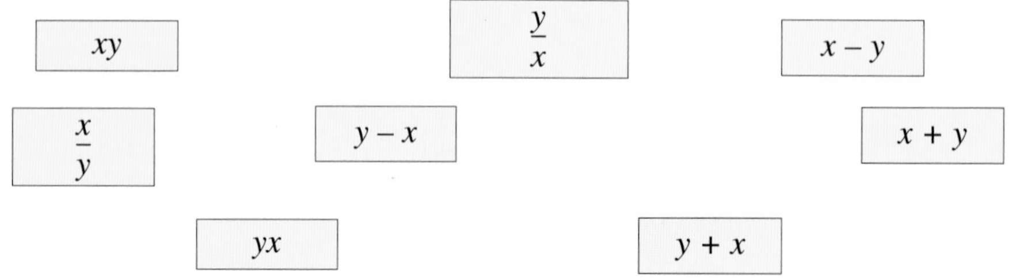

(b) For each chosen pair from part (a), write down a pair of values for x and y which show that you are correct.

2 (a) Write down any pairs of expressions from below that are equal to each other.

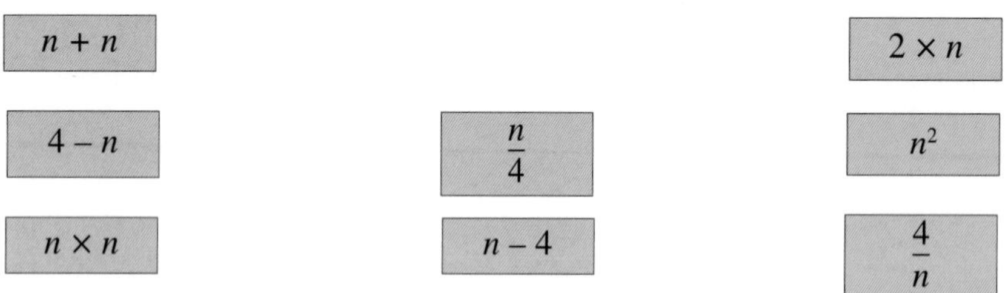

(b) For each chosen pair from part (a), write down a value for n which shows that you are correct.

In questions 3 to 14 write down each statement and say whether it is 'true' or 'false' for all values of the symbols used.

If you are not sure, try different values for the letters

3 $x + x + x = 3x$

4 $xw = wx$

5 $m \times m = 2m$

6 $m + n = n + m$

7 $5y - y = 5$

8 $a \times 5 = 5a$

9 $\frac{x}{2} = \frac{2}{x}$

10 $a \times a \times a = 3a$

11 $a^2 = 2a$

12 $a \div 3 = 3 \div a$

13 $\frac{1}{2}$ of $b = \frac{b}{2}$

14 $3n^2 = (3n)^2$

15 Simplify the following expressions.

(a) $\frac{m}{m}$ (b) $\frac{4a}{4}$ (c) $\frac{n^2}{n}$ (d) $\frac{6x}{x}$

Multiplying terms

(a) Simplify $3b \times 6a$

$3b \times 6a = 3 \times b \times 6 \times a$
$= 3 \times 6 \times b \times a$
$= 18ba$

write in alphabetical order
$= 18ab$

(b) Simplify $xy + 3x + 5yx - 2$

$5yx = 5xy$
so xy and $5yx$ are like terms
$xy + 5yx = xy + 5xy = 6xy$

Answer: $xy + 3x + 5yx - 2$
$= 6xy + 3x - 2$

Exercise 3E

Simplify

1. $4a \times 2b$
2. $5c \times 3d$
3. $6m \times 7n$
4. $3p \times 8q$
5. $9b \times 2a$
6. $2m \times n \times 5p$
7. $7a \times 3b \times 2c$
8. $4q \times 6r \times p$
9. $5a \times 3 \times 2b$
10. Use algebra to write down an expression for the area of each rectangle below.

(a) rectangle $4x$ by $3y$

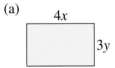

(b) rectangle $2x$ by $6w$

(c) rectangle $8m$ by n

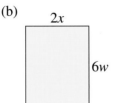

11. Simplify by collecting like terms

(a) $pq + qp$
(b) $3xy + 4mn - 2mn + 4yx$
(c) $5m + nm + 3mn - 2m$
(d) $4ab + 3a - 2ba - a + 3ab$
(e) $x + y + xy + 3yx - x + 3xy$
(f) $6cd + 4dc + ab - 2c + 3cd + ba$
(g) $2a + 3ba - a + 5ab - 2ba$
(h) $3q + 4pq - 2q + 3qp + 4$

12.

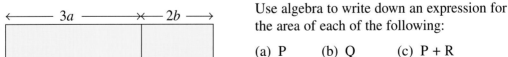

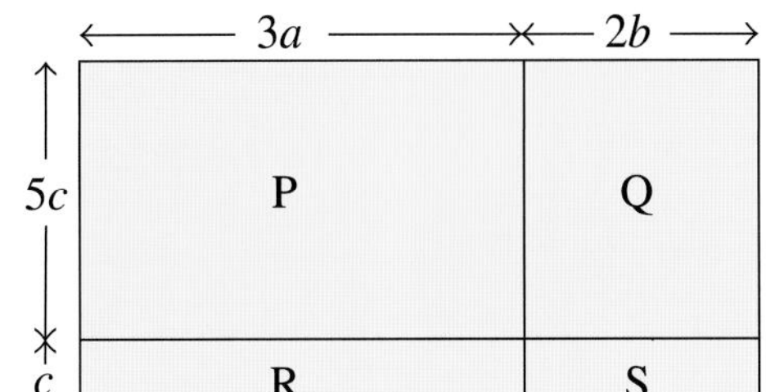

Use algebra to write down an expression for the area of each of the following:

(a) P (b) Q (c) P + R
(d) S (e) Q + S (f) P + Q + R + S

13 What must be added to $6ba$ to give $8ab$?

14 What must be added to $3x + 7yx$ to give $5x + 8xy$?

15 Neil multiplies two algebraic terms together and gets the answer $12ab$. Write down all the different pairs of terms that Neil may have used (numbers used must be whole numbers).

Investigation – Number walls

Here we have three bricks with a number written inside each one.

A wall is built by putting more bricks on top to form a sort of pyramid.

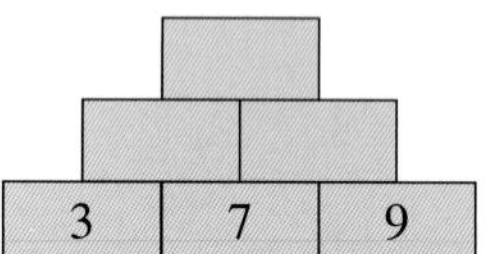

The number in each of the new bricks is found by adding together the numbers in the two bricks below like this:

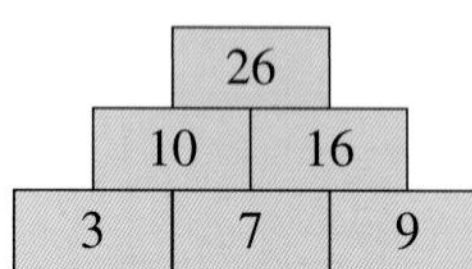

Part A

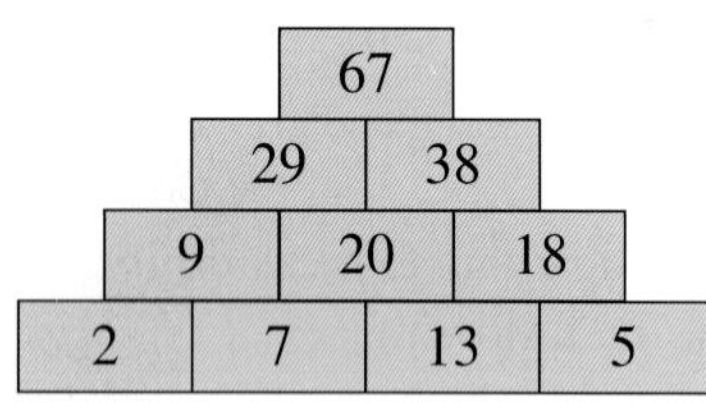

Here is another wall.

1 If you rearrange the numbers at the bottom, does it affect the total at the top?

2 What is the largest total at the top that you can get using the same numbers?

3 What is the smallest total?

4 *How* do you get the largest total?

Part B

1 What happens to the total at the top if the bottom numbers are

(a) the same? (eg. 5, 5, 5, 5)
(b) consecutive? (eg. 2, 3, 4, 5)

2 Write down any patterns or rules that you notice.

Part C

1 What happens if you use different numbers at random (eg. 7, 3, 5, 11)

2 Given 4 numbers at the bottom, can you find a way to predict the top number without finding all the bricks in between?

Part D

Can you find a rule with 3 bricks at the bottom, or 4 bricks?
Can algebra help? (Hint: see diagram)

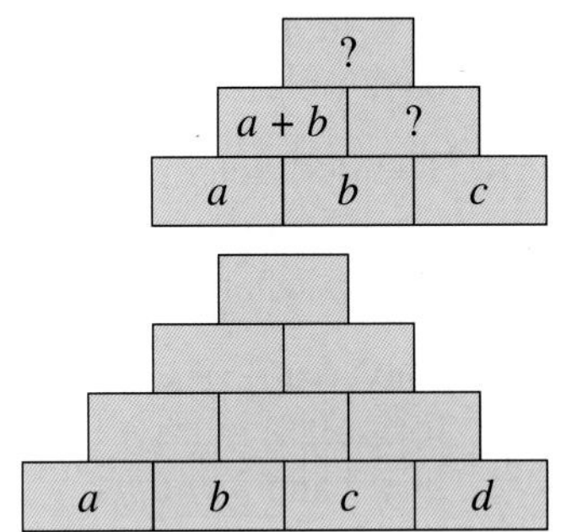

Substituting into a formula

(a) The perimeter p of this shape is given by the formula

$p = 3a + 2b$

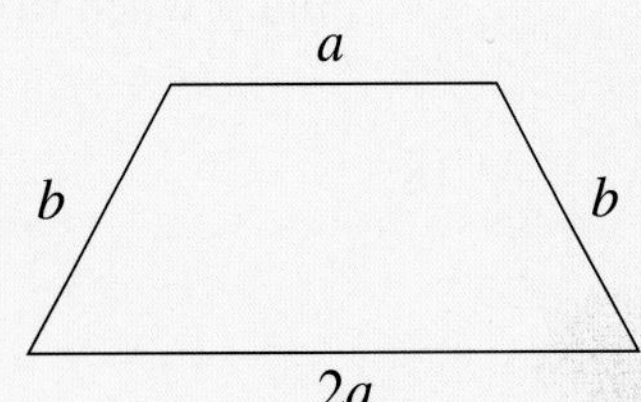

Find p when $a = 5$ and $b = 4$.

$p = 3a + 2b$

$p = (3 \times 5) + (2 \times 4)$

$p = 15 + 8$

$p = 23$

(b) $h = 4\ (x + 3)$ Find h when $x = 7$.

(Remember: always work out brackets first)

$h = 4\ (x + 3)$

$h = 4\ (7 + 3)$ do brackets first

$h = 4 \times 10$

$h = 40$

Exercise 4M

1 The perimeter p of this triangle is given by the formula $p = 3x$
Find p when $x = 6$.

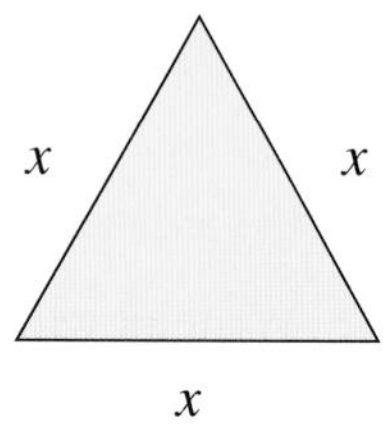

2 The perimeter p of a four-sided shape (quadrilateral) is given by the formula $p = 4w + 17$.
Find p when $w = 5$.

3 The cost in pounds, C, for hiring a car is given by the formula $C = 2n + 25$ where n is the number of miles travelled.
Find C when $n = 150$.

4 The cost in pounds, C, for hiring a video camera is given by the formula $C = 4d + 15$ where d is the number of days of hire. Find C when $d = 8$.

5 The perimeter p of a rectangle with sides x and y is given by the formula $p = 2(x + y)$.
Find p when $x = 8$ and $y = 6$.

6 The area A of a shape is given by the formula $A = bh + 16$. Find A when $b = 7$ and $h = 6$.

7 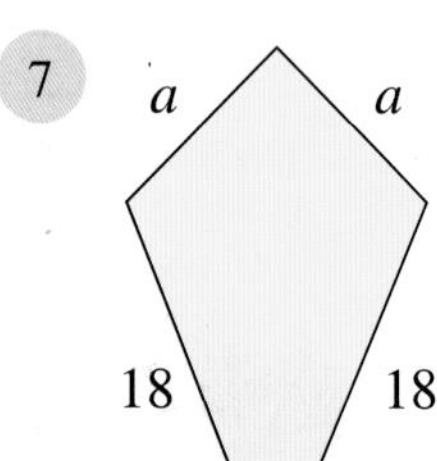

A formula for the perimeter p of this kite is given by the formula

$$p = 2a + 36$$

Find p when (a) $a = 7$ (b) $a = 43$ (c) $a = 3.5$

8 A formula to work out the speed v of an object is $v = u + at$.
Find v when $u = 5$, $a = 10$ and $t = 7$.

Exercise 4E

A formula is given in each question. Find the value of the letter required in each case.

1 $a = 3b + 5$
Find a, when $b = 4$

2 $p = 4n - 9$
Find p, when $n = 6$

3 $h = 18 - 2g$
Find h, when $g = 6$

4 $w = 4(p + 5)$
Find w, when $p = 3$

5 $p = 7(q - 4)$

Find p, when $q = 8$

6 $y = \frac{m}{4}$

Find y, when $m = 36$

7 $a = \frac{b}{3} + 16$

Find a, when $b = 21$

8 $c = \frac{d}{8} + 7$

Find c, when $d = 56$

9 $y = ab - 8$

Find y, when $a = 8$, $b = 3$

10 $x = m(9 - n)$

Find x, when $m = 10$, $n = 4$

11 $f = gh + h$

Find f, when $g = 5$, $h = 9$

12 $k = a(a + b)$

Find k, when $a = 8$, $b = 2$

13 $c = 3fg$

Find c, when $f = 2$, $g = 9$

14 $y = a^2 - b^2$

Find y, when $a = 8$, $b = 3$

15 $h = 3w + yw$

Find h, when $w = 4$, $y = 6$

16 $a = \frac{3b + 2}{4}$

Find a, when $b = 6$

17 $n = \frac{x}{y} + x$

Find n, when $x = 12$, $y = 4$

18 $r = \frac{5s}{t}$

Find r, when $s = 8$, $t = 10$

19 $w = \frac{x^2 - x}{2}$

Find w, when $x = 5$

20 $y = mn + m^2$

Find y, when $m = 9$, $n = 3$

Balance Puzzles

On the balance ○ and △ represent weights

Find ○ if △ = 5 for this balance puzzle

Clearly for these scales to balance exactly, then ○ =10

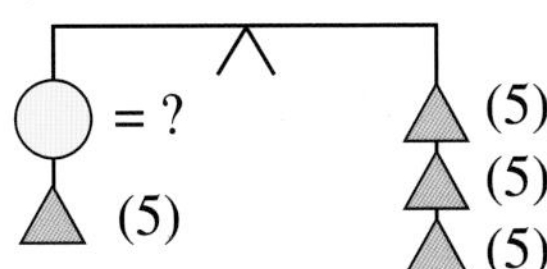

Exercise 5M

Copy each diagram and find the value of the required symbol.

1 Find □ if △ = 4.

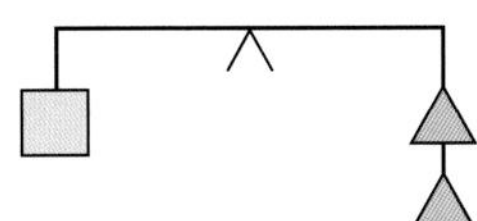

2 Find ○ if △ = 10.

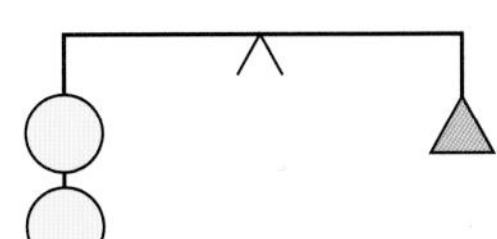

3 Find ○ if □ = 4.

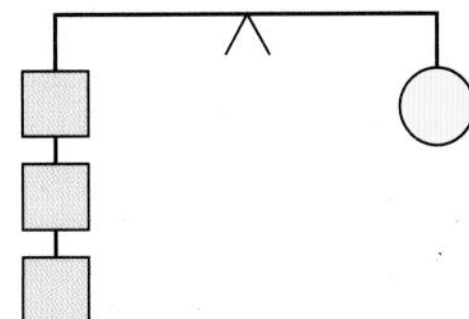

4 Find □ if △ = 12

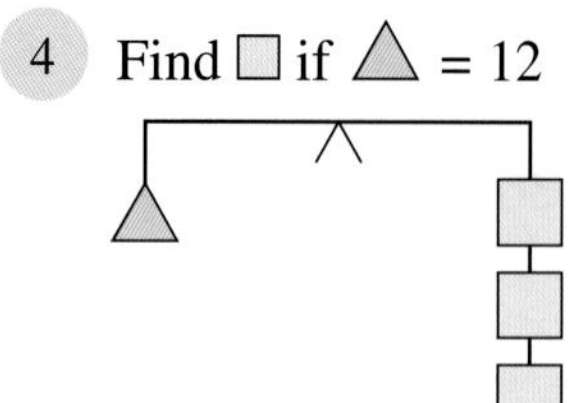

5 Find △ if □ = 2

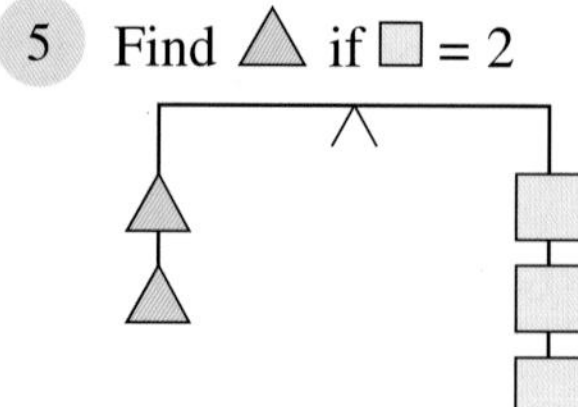

6 Find △ if ○ = 6

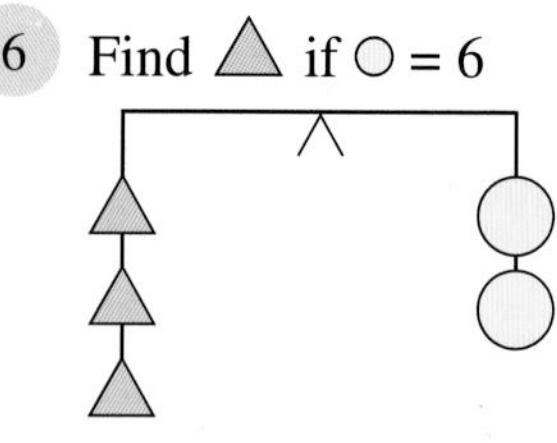

7 Find □ if ○ = 8.

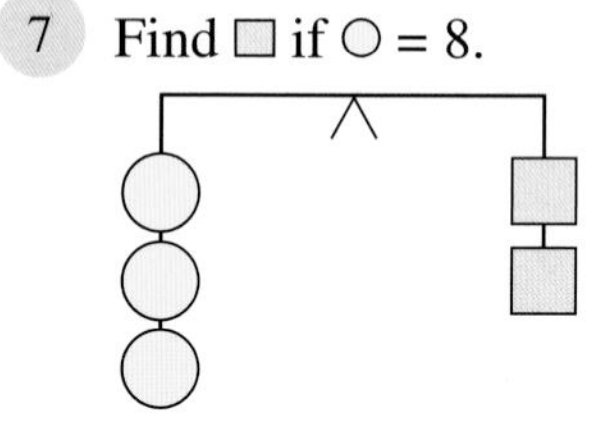

8 Find △ if □ = 15.

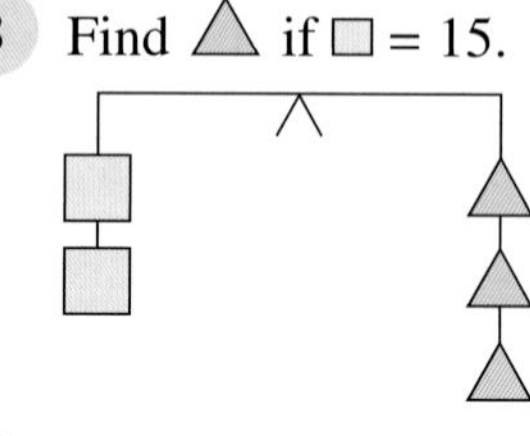

9 Find △ if ○ = 14.

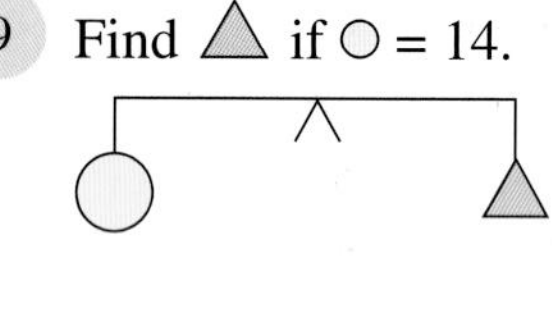

10 Find □ if ○ = 8.

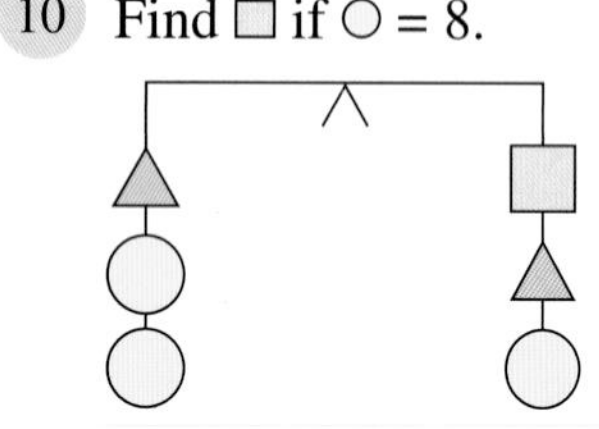

11 Find ○ if △ = 6.

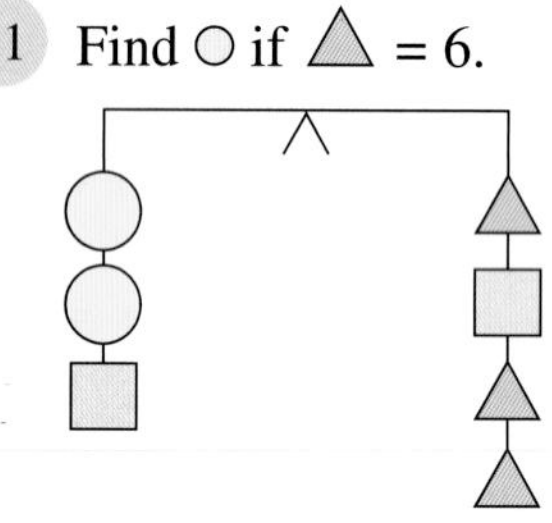

12 Find ○ if □ = 5

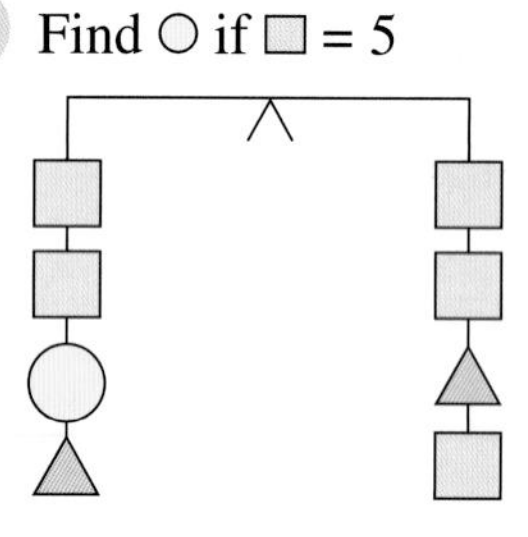

Exercise 5E

Copy each diagram and find the value of the unknown symbols.

1 ○ = 10, find △ and □.

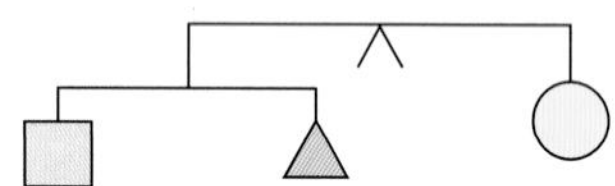

2 △ = 8, find ○ and □.

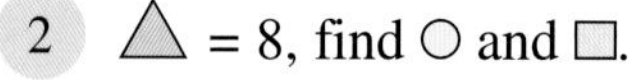

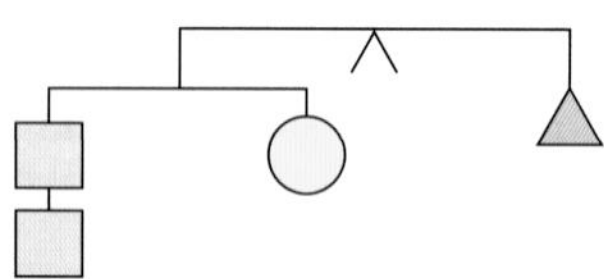

3 □ = 14, find ○ and △.

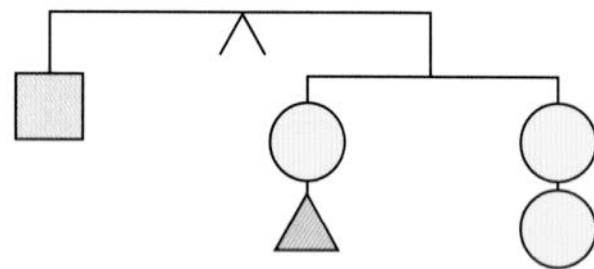

4 □ = 6, find ○ and △.

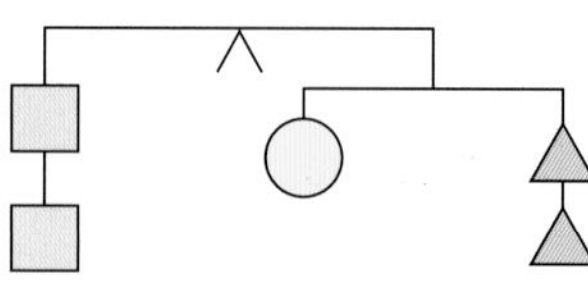

5 ○ = 8, find □ and △.

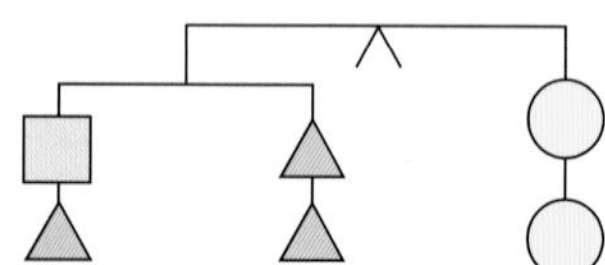

6 □ = 4, find ○ and △.

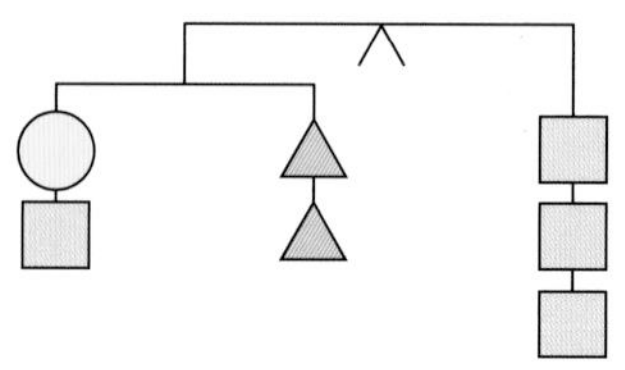

7 △ = 4, find ○ and □.

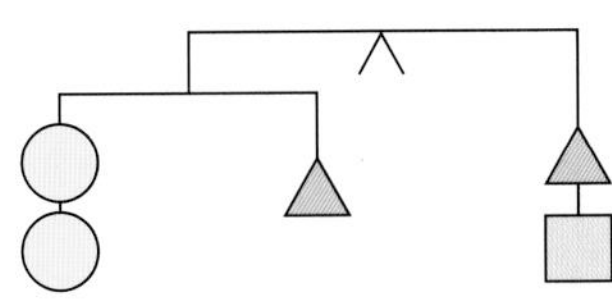

8 ○ = 10, find △ and □.

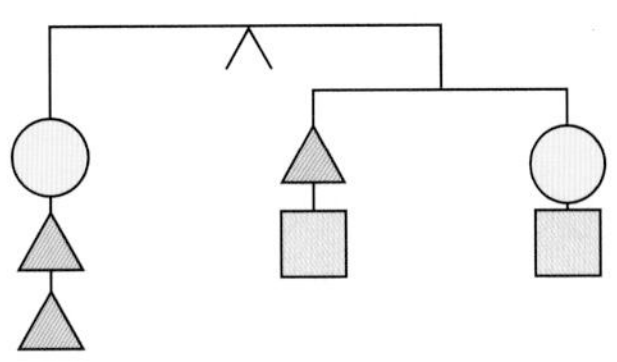

9 △ = 5, find ○ and □.

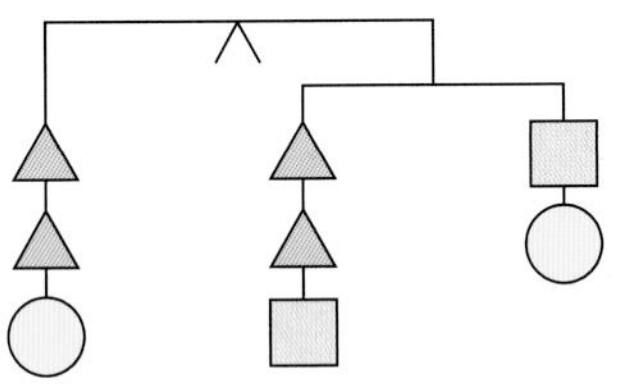

10 □ = 3, find ○ and △.

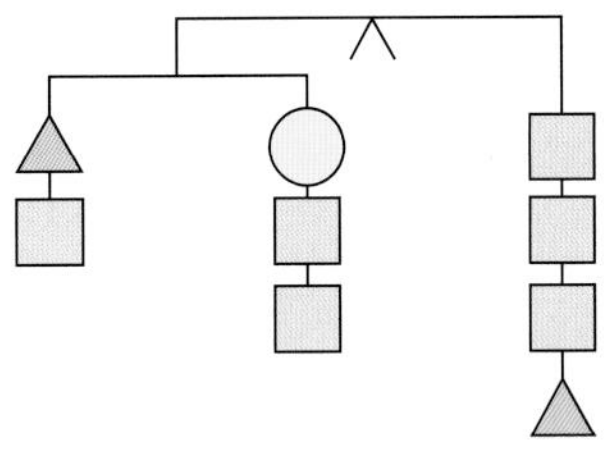

11 □ = 6, find △ and ○.

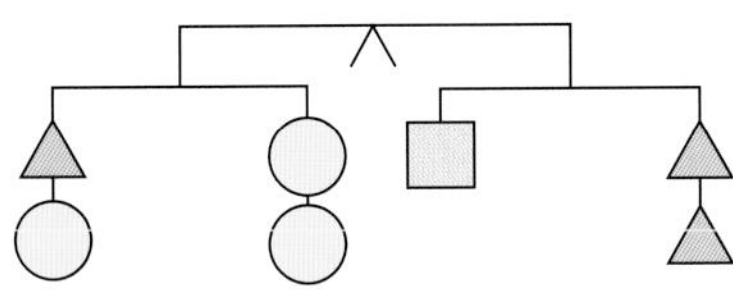

12 ○ = 5, find □ and △.

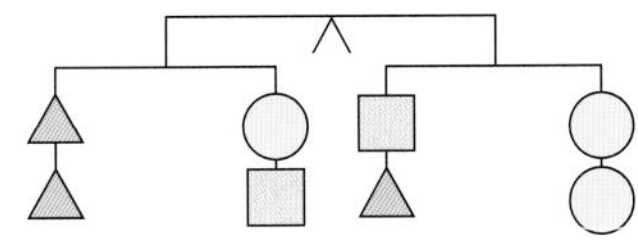

13 △ = 4, find ○ and □.

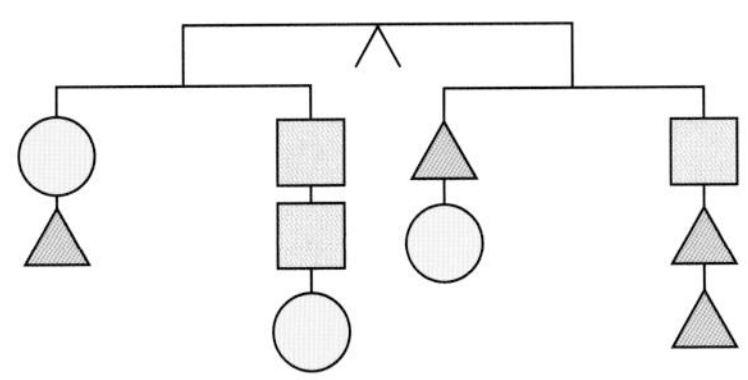

14 ○ = 8, find □ and △.

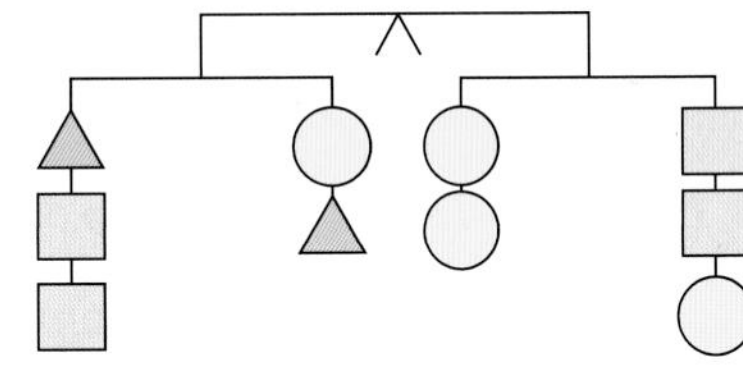

15 □ = 4, find ○ and △.

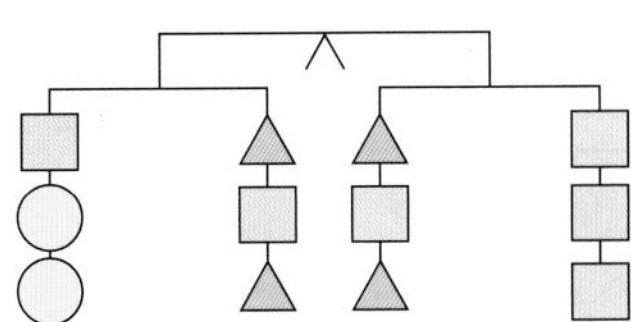

16 ○ = 3, find ⬡.

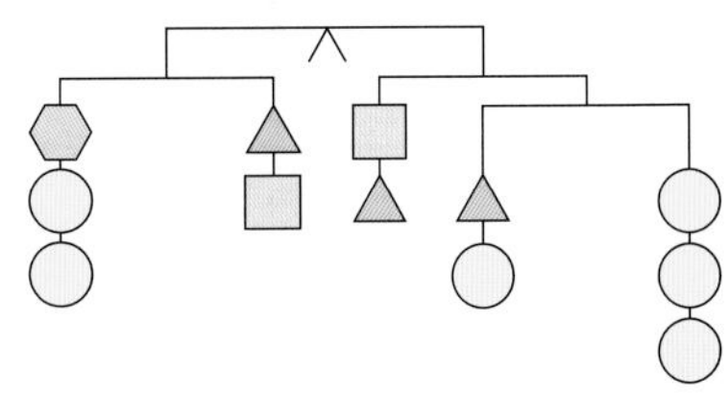

CHECK YOURSELF ON SECTION 2.5

1 Using letters for numbers

(a) Joe has n mints. He gives six mints to his sister. Write down an expression for how many mints Joe now has.

(b) I start with a number x, multiply it by 5 and then subtract 8. Write down an expression for what I now have.

(c) Write down an expression for the perimeter of this shape.

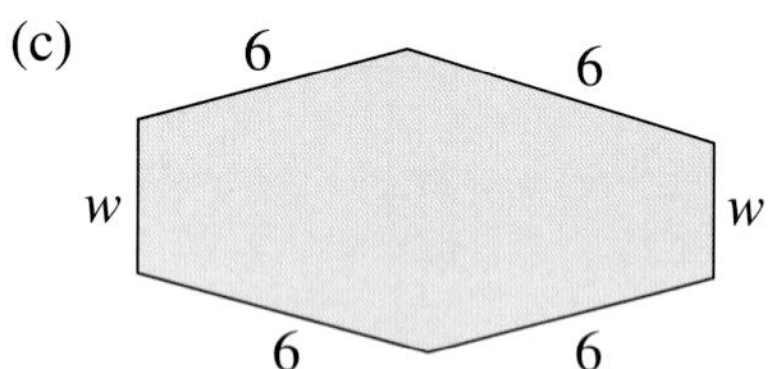

2 Collecting like terms

Simplify the following expressions as far as possible

(a) $4m + 3n - 2m + 6n$ (b) $8y - y$

(c) $8p + 6 + 3p - 7p$ (d) $6xy + 3y + y - 2yx$

3 Multiplying algebraic terms

Simplify (a) $4m \times 7n$ (b) $8p \times q \times 4r$

(c) Which two rectangles below have the same area?

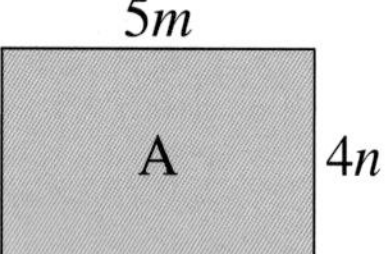

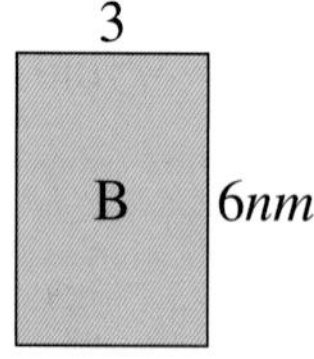

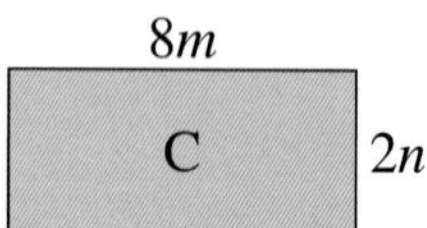

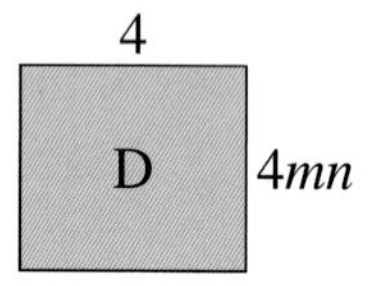

4 Substituting numbers into a formula

(a) The cost in pounds, C, for hiring a van is given by the formula $C = 3n + 45$ where n is the number of miles travelled.
Find C when $n = 200$.

(b) $y = 3(7 - x)$

Find y when $x = 5$.

(c) $m = \frac{n}{6} - 9$

Find m when $n = 72$.

5 Tackling balance puzzles

(a) Find □ if ○ = 12

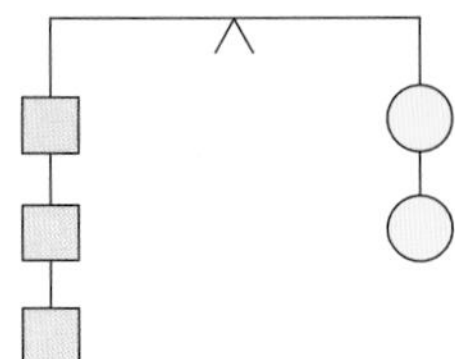

(b) Find □ and ○ if △ = 6

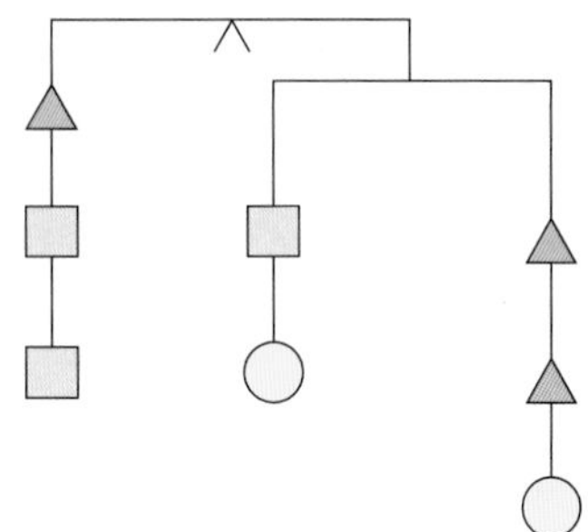

UNIT 2 MIXED REVIEW

Part one

1 Work out

(a) $\frac{3}{5} + \frac{1}{5}$ (b) $\frac{3}{8} - \frac{1}{4}$ (c) $\frac{3}{5} - \frac{1}{15}$

2 What is the name of the triangle with two equal angles?

3 Write down an expression for the perimeter of each shape.

(a)

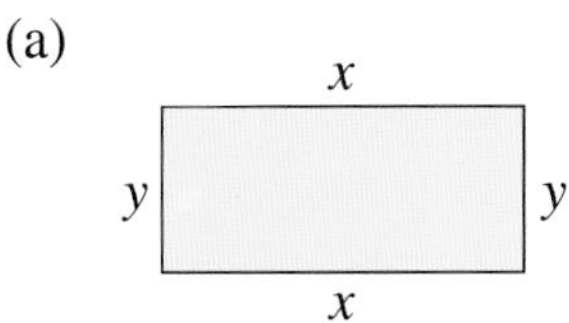

(b)

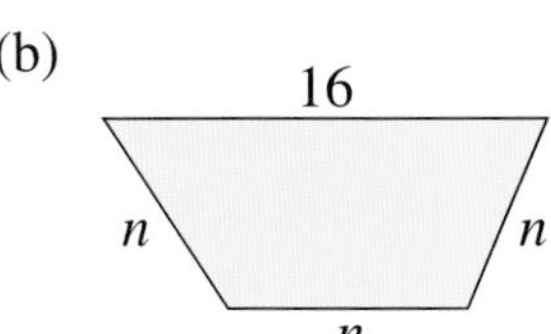

4 Draw a shape with a perimeter of $m + 2n$.

5 Simplify:

(a) $6p + 2q - p + 4q$ (b) $3m + 5 - m - 3$ (c) $3xy + 2y - yx + 6y$

6 Write down the value of the angles marked with letters.

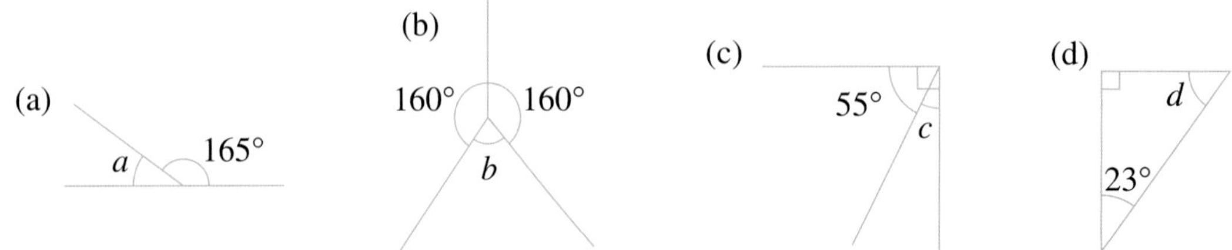

7 What is 90% as a fraction?

8 What is the smaller angle between the hands of a clock at

(a) half past two (b) twenty past six

9 What is the value of $1-0.15$ as a fraction?

10 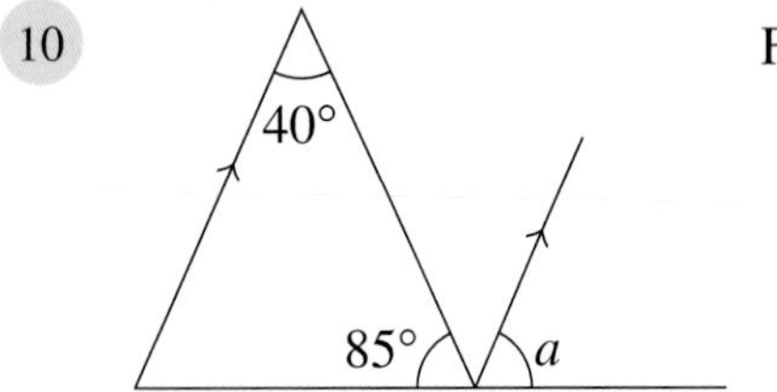

Find the size of angle a.

11 Write down five consecutive numbers whose mean value is 37.

12 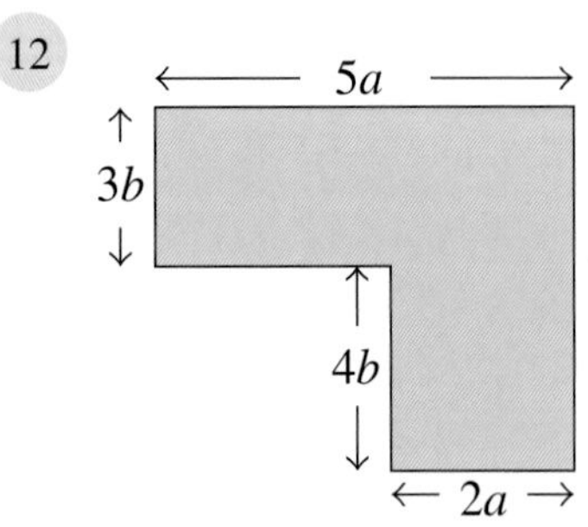

Write down an expression for the total area of this shape.

13 Kelly has 5 cards.

The mean of the five cards is 8.

The range of the five cards is 6.

What numbers are on the other two cards?

14 Find the size of $A\hat{D}B$.

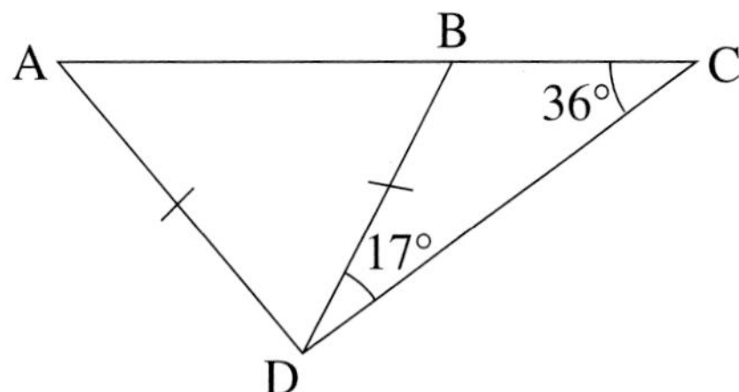

15 The test results of 100 students are shown below.

mark	5	6	7	8	9	10
frequency	10	22	12	17	10	29

Work out the mean test result for these 100 students.

16 A vet treats 36 sick mice with a new antibiotic.
After 6 hours $\frac{1}{3}$ of the mice have recovered and are running around happily.

After 12 hours $\frac{3}{4}$ of the remaining mice are cured but unfortunately the others have died.

(a) How many mice eventually recovered?
(b) How many mice died?

17

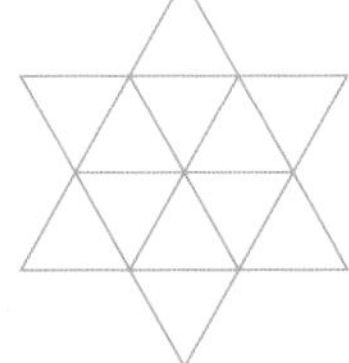

Draw a copy of the star

(a) Shade in $\frac{1}{4}$ of the triangles.
(b) Draw ticks (√) in $\frac{2}{3}$ of the unshaded triangles.
(c) How many triangles are neither shaded nor have ticks in them?

Part two

1 Copy and complete this table showing equivalent fractions, decimals and percentages.

fraction	decimal	percentage
		16%
	0.7	
$\frac{1}{4}$		

2 Use a ruler and protractor to draw this triangle accurately. Measure the length marked x.

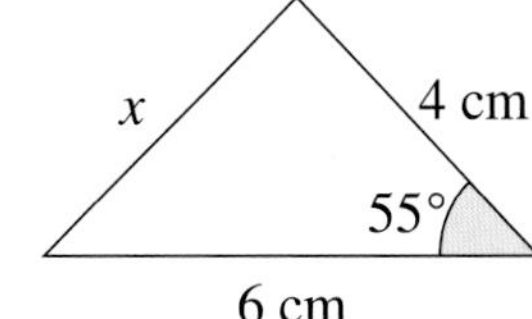

3 Here is a diagram of a designer's logo for 'speedo' training shoes:

(a) Make an accurate drawing of the logo using a ruler, pencil and protractor.

(b) Measure the length AB on your drawing.

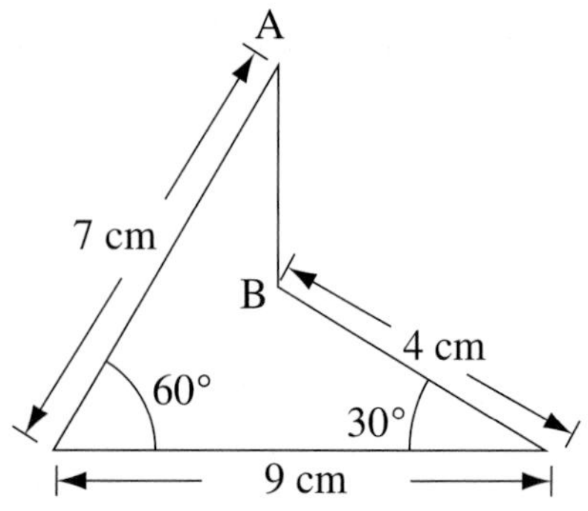

4 The distance s travelled by an object is given by the formula

$$s = \frac{1}{2} t (u + v)$$

Find s when $t = 8$, $u = 3$ and $v = 8$.

5 In number walls each brick is made by adding the two bricks underneath it.

$m + n$
m | n

Fill in the missing expressions on these walls

(a)
?
$a + c$ | $a + b$

(b)
?
? | ?
$a + b$ | $a - b$ | b

(c)
?
? | ?
$2m$ | $m + n$ | $m + 3n$

6 There are 72 houses in the village of Cowsley. There are 98 houses in the village of Sefton. Last Halloween $\frac{3}{8}$ of the houses in Cowsley put out pumpkins and $\frac{2}{7}$ of the houses in Sefton put out pumpkins. Which village had more houses with pumpkins?

7 Find the angles marked with letters.

(a)

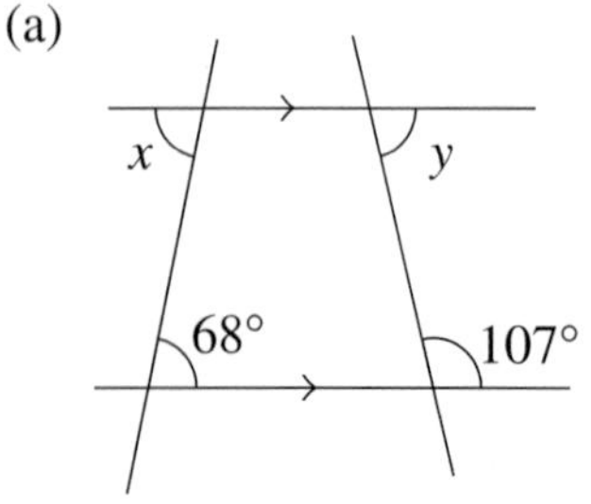

(b)

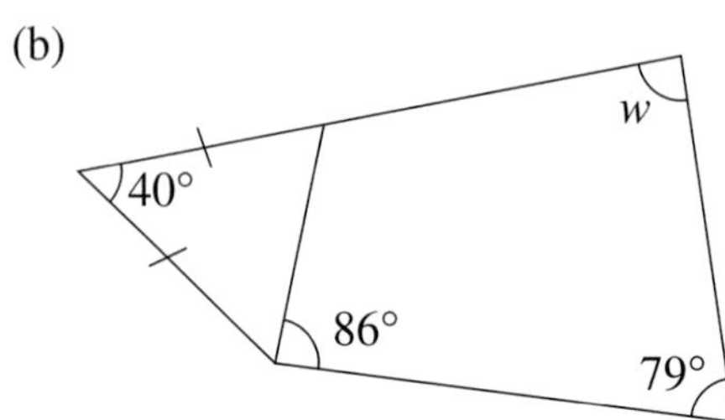

8 There were four candidates in a class election. Sheena got $\frac{1}{3}$ of the votes, George got $\frac{1}{4}$ and Dan got $\frac{1}{6}$. What fraction of the votes did Jade, the fourth candidate get?

9 Work out $\frac{8}{25} + 0.25$

10 Work out $\frac{3}{5}$ of 19

11 Solve the following balance puzzle, writing your answer $x =$…

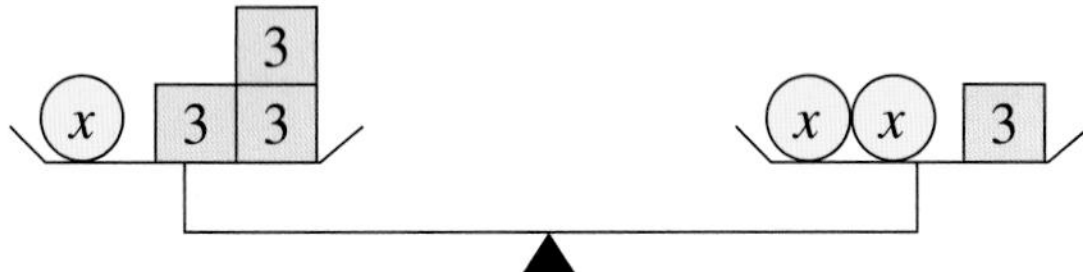

12 Find the size of the largest angle in this triangle.

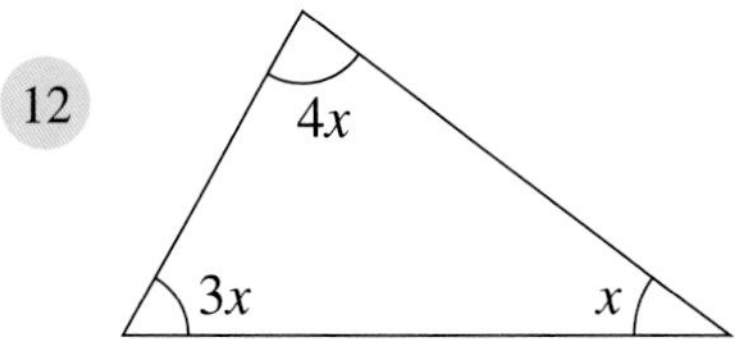

13 Which fraction is closer to 1? $\frac{7}{8}$ or $\frac{8}{7}$
Explain your answer.

14 If n is a number between 0 and 1, which of the following expressions is the larger?

$\frac{2}{n}$ or $\frac{n}{2}$

Explain your answer.

15 Here are six algebra cards.

A $2n + 1$ B $4n$ C $3n$
D $n + 2n$ E $2n + 3$
F $4 - n$

(a) Add the expressions on card B and card E.
(b) Which two cards always have the same value?
(c) Which card has the largest value when $n = 3$.
(d) Add the expressions on all six cards.

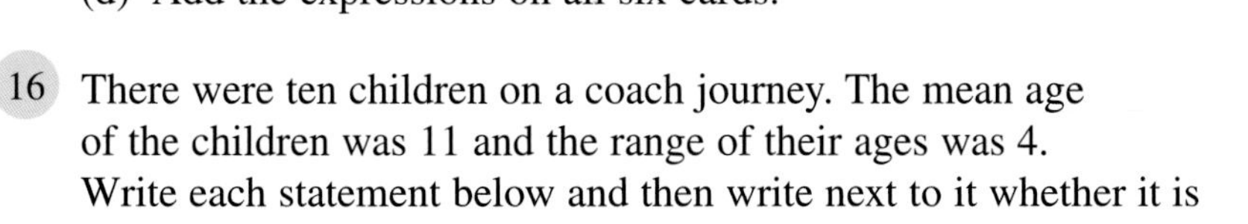

16 There were ten children on a coach journey. The mean age of the children was 11 and the range of their ages was 4.
Write each statement below and then write next to it whether it is *True*, *Possible* or *False*.

(a) The youngest child was 9 years old.
(b) Every child was 11 years old.
(c) All the children were at least 10 years old.

17 In the diagram KL is parallel to NM and LJ = LM. Calculate the size of angle JLM.

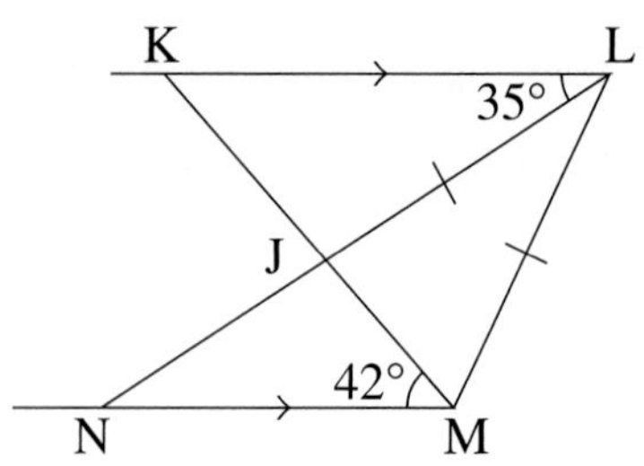

18 Javed is painting all the window frames on his parents' house. On the first day he paints $\frac{1}{3}$ of the frames and on the second day he paints $\frac{1}{3}$ of the remainder. On the third day he paints the rest.

If there are 72 window frames on the house, how many did Javed paint on

(a) the second day,
(b) the third day?

Puzzles and Problems 2

Cross numbers

Make four copies of the pattern below and complete the puzzles using the clues given. To avoid confusion it is better not to write the small reference numbers 1–18 on your patterns

1		2		3			4
				5			
	6		7			8	
9					10		
		11					12
				13	14		
15	16				17		
			18				

Part A [No calculators]

Across

1. 499 + 43

3. 216 × 7

5. 504 ÷ 9

6. 8214 – 3643

8. Half of 192

9. 20% of 365

10. Prime number between 30 and 36

11. 213 + 62 + 9

13. 406 ÷ 7

15. 316 × 23

17. 1000 – 731

18. Next prime number after 200

Down

1. 1% of 5700

2. 600 – 365

4. 6^3

7. 4488 ÷ 6

8. $30^2 + 3 \times 6$

9. 10 000 – 2003

11. 4 × 4 × 4 × 4

12. 58.93 × (67 + 33)

14. 1136 – 315

16. $11^2 - 10^2$

In parts **B, C** and **D** a calculator may be used [where absolutely necessary!] Write any decimal points on the lines between squares.

Part B

Across

1. $9 \times 10 \times 11$

3. Ninety less than ten thousand

5. $\left(7\frac{1}{2}\right)^2$ to the nearest whole number

6. $140.52 \div 0.03$

8. Last two digits of 99^2

9. $3^2 + 4^2 + 5^2 + 6^2$

10. Angle between the hands of a clock at 2.00 pm

11. Eight pounds and eight pence

13. Next prime number after 89

15. 11% of 213

17. 3.1 m plus 43 cm, in cm

18. Area of a square of side 15 cm.

Down

1. $\dfrac{5 \times 6 \times 7 \times 8}{2} - 11 \times 68$

2. 26% as a decimal

4. 0.1^2

7. Next in the sequence $102\frac{1}{2}$, 205, 410

8. $1 - 0.97$

9. 52% of £158.50

11. $0.0854 \div (7 - 6.99)$

12. $10^3 + 11^3$

14. $3 \times 5 \times 7^2$

16. Half of a third of 222

Part C

Across

1. Next square number after 144

3. 5.2 m written in mm

5. Total of the numbers on a dice

6. $0.1234 \div 0.01^2$

8. Ounces in a pound

9. Inches in a yard

10. $3^4 + 56.78 \times 0$

11. Next in the sequence 1, 2, 6, 24, 120

13. One foot four inches, in inches

15. 234 m written in km

17. $\frac{1}{25}$ as a decimal

18. [Number of letters in 'ridiculous']^2

Down

1. $1\frac{4}{5}$ as a decimal

2. $\dfrac{12^2 + 352}{1.4 + 0.2}$

4. 66% as a decimal

7. Days in a year minus 3

8. Number of minutes between 1322 and 1512

9. Seconds in an hour

11. Double 225 plus treble 101

12. A quarter to midnight on the 24 h clock

14. $2^3 \times 3 \times 5^2$

16. $\left(5\frac{1}{3}\right)^2$ to the nearest whole number

Part D

Across

1. 20% of 15% of £276
3. $81.23 \times 9.79 \times 11.2$, to the nearest thousand
5. Three dozen
6. 1.21 m in mm
8. Solve $2x - 96 = 72$
9. Inches in two feet
10. $6.6 \div 0.1$
11. $\frac{1}{4} - \frac{1}{5}$ as a decimal
13. Volume of a cube of side 4 units
15. $555 + 666 + 777$
17. A gross
18. $\left(19\frac{1}{4}\right)^2$ to the nearest whole number

Down

1. Next in the sequence 25, 36, 49, 64
2. $900 - \left(\frac{17 \times 12}{3}\right)$
4. 0.2×0.2
7. Solve $x^3 = 1$ million
8. $9 - 0.36$
9. $8^3 + 9^3 + 10^3$
11. 99% as a decimal
12. 20% of 2222
14. $0.2055 \div 0.0005$
16. 4 score plus ten

Mental Arithmetic Practice 2

There are two sets of mental arithmetic questions in this section. Ideally a teacher will read out each question twice, with pupils' books closed. Each test should take about 20 minutes.

Test 1

1. Share a cost of £72 between 8 people.
2. Write three fifths as a percentage.
3. How many angles has a pentagon?
4. I have five 20p, six 10p and three 2p coins. How much do I have?
5. Write the number seventeen thousand and twelve in figures.
6. Change two and a quarter metres into centimetres.
7. A train leaves at 7.40 and arrives at 9.30. How long is the journey in minutes?
8. Write three hundredths as a decimal.
9. Take away 18 from 300.
10. Work out ten per cent of £42.
11. A plane flies at 140 km/h for three hours. How far does it fly?
12. What five coins make 62p?
13. The product of two numbers is forty-five. What are the two numbers? Give two possible answers.
14. How many 5p coins do I need for 65p?
15. How many centimetres are there in a kilometre?
16. What is the cost of three CDs at £2.99 each?
17. An MP3 player costs £40. How much do I pay if there is a ten per cent discount?

18 A drink costs £1.65. What is the change from £5?

19 What number is half way between 5 and 5.3?

20 What is the perimeter of a square which has an area of 36 cm^2?

21 I have three mice and two snakes. What percentage of my pets are mice?

22 Oranges cost 75 pence for five. How much does one cost?

23 Greg saves 25 pence a day. How long will it take to save four pounds?

24 How many lengths of 8 cm can be cut from 60 cm?

25 Increase eighty pounds by 25 per cent.

Test 2

1 What four coins make 42p? Give two possible answers.

2 I buy two pens at 99 pence each. What change do I get from £5?

3 What is 20 per cent of sixty kilograms?

4 What number is three times as big as eighteen?

5 I have ninety-four 2 pence coins. How much is that in pounds and pence?

6 What is the smaller angle between the hands of a clock at two o'clock?

7 One pound is the same as 1.5 euros. How many euros do I get for twenty pounds?

8 A football costs £8.95. Find the change from £20.

9 A book is six millimetres thick. How tall is a pile of fifty books? Give your answer in metres.

10 Add together £2.75 and £2.50.

11 Write one twentieth as a percentage.

12 In a room sixteen out of fifty children are boys. What percentage is that?

13 How many 5p coins are needed to make £4?

14 Two angles of an isosceles triangle are each 65°. What is the third angle?

15 A lottery prize of eight million pounds is shared equally between 100 people. How much does each person receive?

16 Add together 11, 27 and 9.

17 What is two thirds of thirty-nine?

18 Find the sum of the first four prime numbers?

19 A square has sides of length one metre. Find the area of the square in square centimetres.

20 If May 11th is a Monday, what day of the week is May 20th?

21 True or false: 'There are six inches in a foot'.

22 How many minutes are there between eleven a.m. and two p.m. on the same day?

23 What is three point nought three multiplied by one thousand?

24 Write down any square number greater than seventy.

25 A coach starts at four fifty. It takes twenty-five minutes. At what time does it arrive?

A long time ago! 2

The Four Colour Theorem

If you need to colour the areas on a map (in geography, history, etc), it should be possible to use no more than 4 colours. At no boundary between the two areas must the same colour be used for both areas.

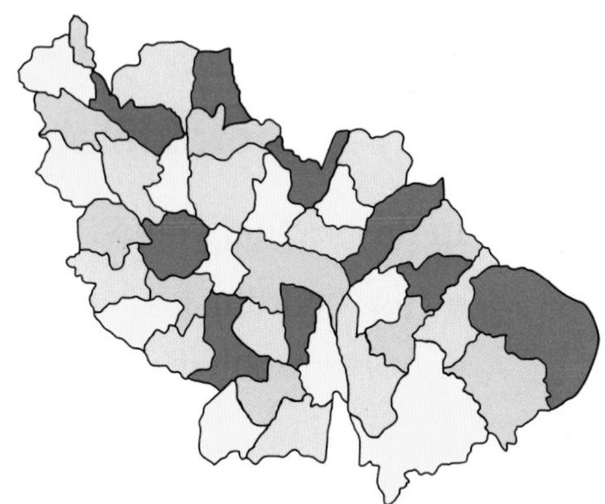

You may have two areas of the same colour meeting at a single point if necessary. A gentleman called August Ferdinand Möbius first wrote about this problem in the nineteenth century.

Exercise

Make a rough copy of each map below and try to colour each section using 4 colours only. The colour in one section must not be the same as that in any section next to it.

1

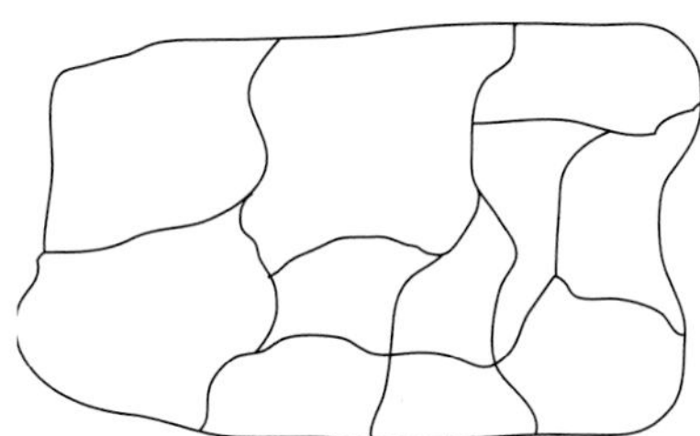

2

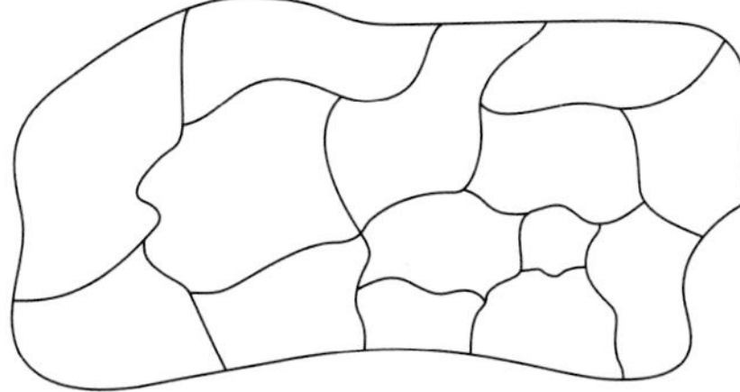

3

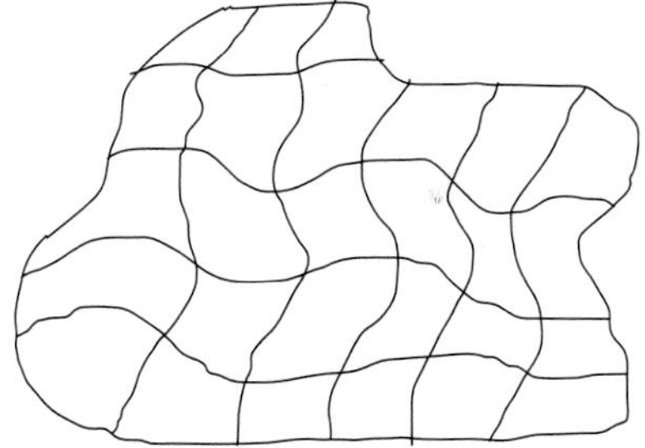

4 Have you managed with 4 colours only so far? Now draw your own map and see if no more than 4 colours are needed to fill it in.

At last! This theorem was finally proved to be correct late in the twentieth century by using a computer programme.

UNIT 3

3.1 Coordinates

In this section you will learn how to:

- use coordinates with positive and negative numbers
- solve problems involving shapes

- To get to the point P on this grid we go **across** 1 and **up** 3 from the bottom corner.

  The position of P is (1, 3).

  The numbers 1 and 3 are called the **coordinates** of P.

  The coordinates of Q are (4, 2).

  The *origin* is at (0, 0).

  We call the first coordinate the *x*-coordinate and the second coordinate the *y*-coordinate.

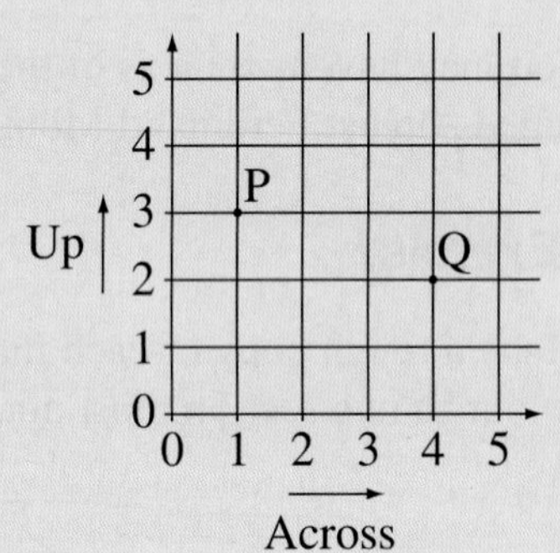

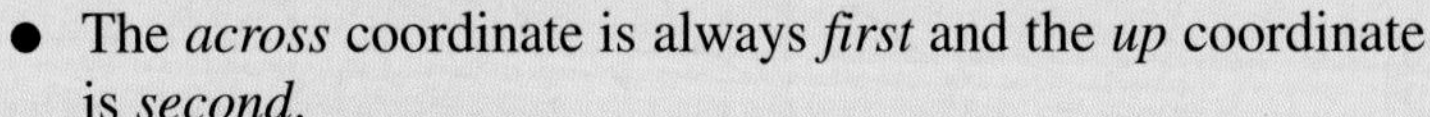

- The *across* coordinate is always *first* and the *up* coordinate is *second*.

  Remember: 'Along the corridor and up the stairs'.

- Notice also that the *lines* are numbered, *not* the squares.

Exercise 1M

1 Write down the coordinates of all the points marked like this:
A(5, 1) B(1, 4)
Don't forget the brackets.

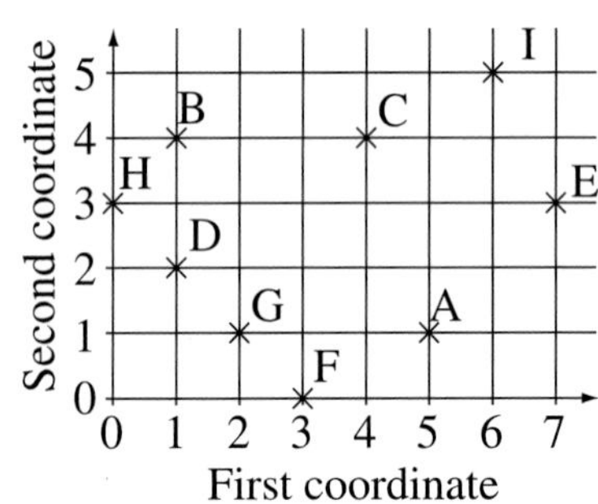

2 The map below shows a remote Scottish island used for training by the S.A.S. Write down the coordinates of the following places:

(a) Rocket launcher
(b) H.Q.
(c) Hospital A
(d) Rifle range
(e) Officers' mess
(f) Radar control

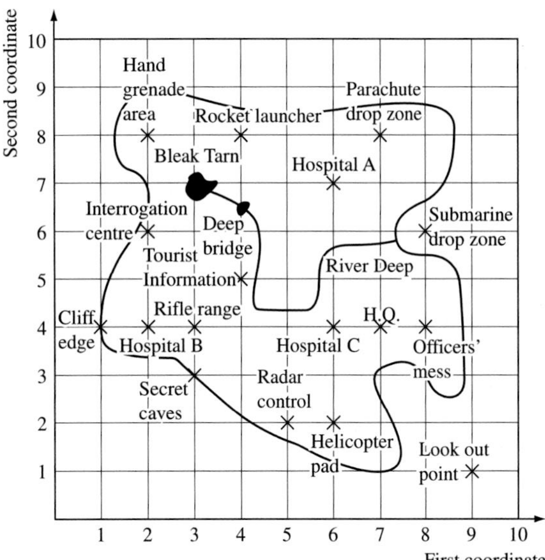

3 Make a list of the places which are at the following points:

(a) (2, 8) (b) (7, 8) (c) (3, 3)
(d) (6, 4) (e) (2, 6) (f) (6, 2)
(g) (2, 4) (h) (9, 1)

4 Make up your own map and mark points of interest.

Negative coordinates

The x axis can be extended to the left and the y axis can be extended downwards to include the negative numbers -1, -2, -3 etc.

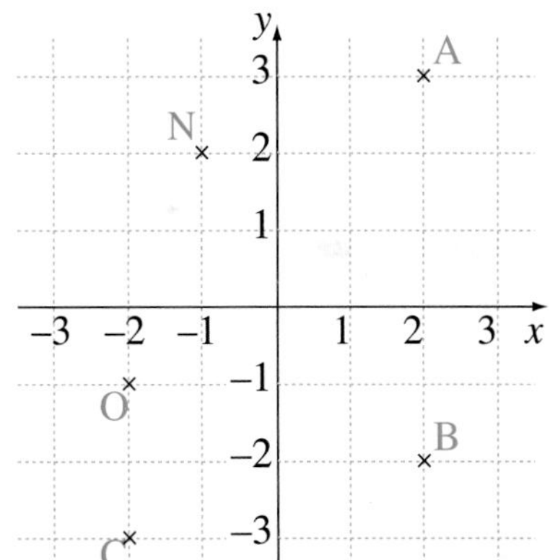

The word 'BACON' can be found using the letters in the following order:
(2, –2), (2, 3), (–2, –3), (–2, –1), (–1, 2)

Similarly the coordinates of the points which spell out the word 'CAN' are
(–2, –3), (2, 3), (–1, 2)

Exercise 1E

Copy the crossword grid and complete it using the clues on the next page.
The letters are found using coordinates on the grid on the next page.

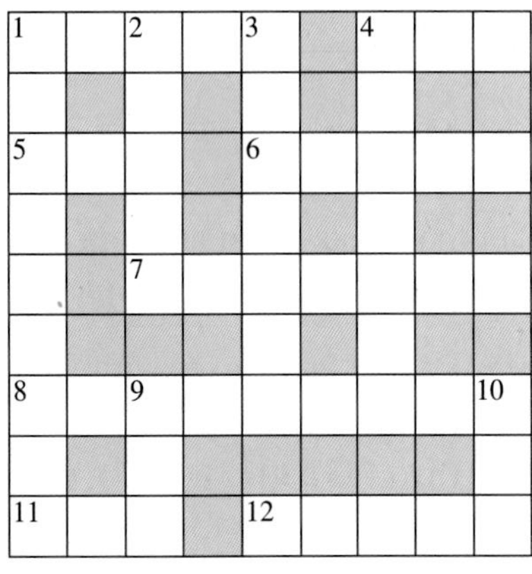

Across

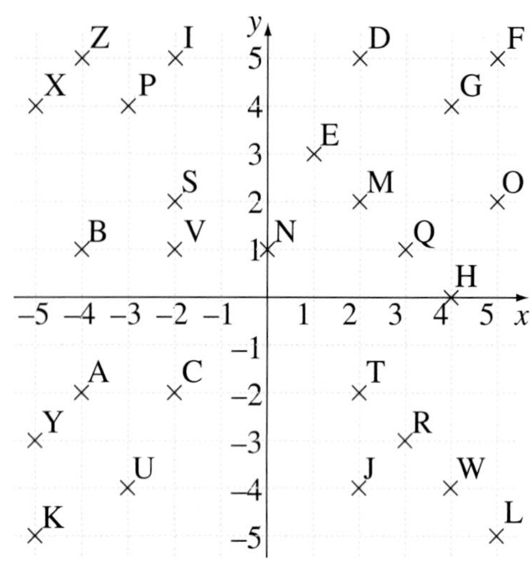

1. (−3, 4) (−4, −2) (−3, 4) (1, 3) (3, −3)
4. (5, 5) (−4, −2) (3, −3)
5. Internet provider
6. (−4, −2) (−3, −4) (3, −3) (−4, −2) (5, −5)
7. (2, −2) (3, −3) (−2, 5) (−4, 1) (−3, −4) (2, −2) (1, 3)
8. (3, −3) (1, 3) (−3, 4) (−3, −4) (4, 4) (0, 1) (−4, −2) (0, 1) (2, −2)
11. German for 'THE'.
12. (−4, 1) (−4, −2) (−2, −2) (5, 2) (0, 1)

Down

1. (−3, 4) (5, −5) (−4, −2) (−2, 2) (2, −2) (1, 3) (3, −3) (1, 3) (2, 5)
2. (−3, 4) (−2, 5) (5, −5) (5, 2) (2, −2)
3. Useful for books
4. Used in mathematics
9. (−3, 4) (−4, −2) (3, −3)
10. (2, −2) (−4, −2) (0, 1)

Coordinate pictures

Plot the points below and join them up in order

(a) (3, 3), (1, 3), (0, 4), (3, 5), (4, 6), (6, 6), (7, 4), (7, 3), (8, 2), (5, 1), (4, 2), (1, 3)

(b) (5, 5), (5, 4), (6, 2), (7, 3)

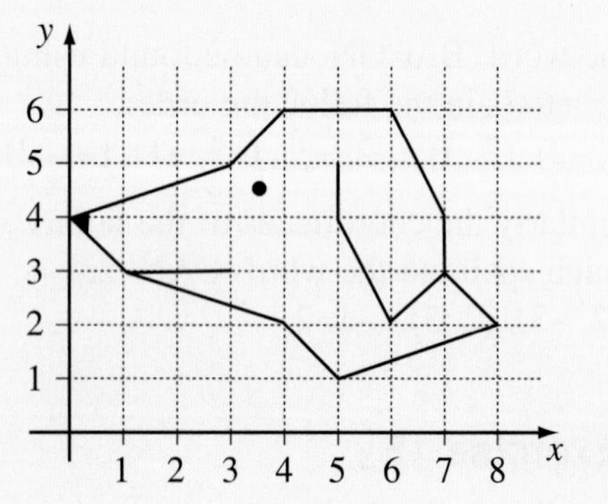

Exercise 2M

Plot the points given and join them up in order.
Write on the grid what the picture is.

1. Draw x and y axes with values from 0 to 14.
   (a) (6, 13), (1, 3), (2, 1), (12, 1), (8, 9), (6, 5), (4, 5), (8, 13), (6, 13), (8, 13), (13, 3), (12, 1).
   (b) (1, 3), (9, 3), (7, 7), (6, 5), (8, 5).
   Now colour in the shape.

2 Draw x and y axes with values from 0 to 10.

(a) (3, 2), (4, 2), (5, 3), (3, 5), (3, 6), (2, 7), (1, 6), (1, 8), (2, 9), (3, 9), (5, 7), (4, 6), (4, 5), (6, 4), (8, 4), (8, 5), (6, 7), (5, 7).
(b) (7, 4), (9, 2), (8, 1), (7, 3), (5, 3).
(c) (1, 6), (2, 8), (2, 9), (2, 7).
(d) Draw a dot at (3, 8).
Colour in the shape.

3 Draw x and y axes with values from 0 to 16

(a) (4, 7), (6, 5), (7, 5), (8, 3), (9, 5), (11, 5), (12, 7), (15, 9), (15, 10), (12, 11), (9, 11), (8, 14), (7, 11), (6, 11), (4, 9), (1, 11), (3, 8), (1, 5), (4, 7).
(b) (15, 12), (16, 12), (16, 13), (15, 13), (15, 12).
(c) (14, 14), (13, 14), (13, 15), (14, 15), (14, 14).
(d) (12, 8), (13, 8).
(e) Draw a dot at (13, 10). Colour in the shape.

4 Draw axes with both x and y from 0 to 17.

(a) (5, 1), (6, 6), (6, 3), (7, 2), (6, 2), (5, 1).
(b) (8, 11), (8, 8), (10, 10), (11, 12), (11, 15).
(c) (2, 14), (1, 14), (1, 15), (2, 15).
(d) (12, 1), (11, 2), (10, 2), (10, 4), (9, 6), (8, 7), (7, 10), (8, 11), (9, 13), (11, 15), (10, 17), (8, 17), (7, 16), (4, 16), (2, 15), (2, 14), (3, 13), (5, 13), (6, 12), (4, 7), (4, 2), (3, 2), (2, 1), (12, 1).
(e) (7, 16), (7, 15).
(f) (5, 13), (6, 13).

5 Draw axes with both x and y from 0 to 11.

(a) (7, 1), (3, 1), (1, 10), (2, 11), (3, 10), (4, 11), (5, 10), (6, 11), (7, 10), (8, 6), (8, 5), (9, $4\frac{1}{2}$), (9, 4), (8, 4), (9, 3), (5, 3), (5, 2), (7, 1).
(b) (5, 5), (4, 6), (5, 7), (6, 6), (7, 7), (8, 6), (7, 5), (6, 6), (5, 5).
(c) (5, 2), (6, 2), (6, $1\frac{1}{2}$).
(d) (7, 5), (8, 5).
(e) (7, 4), (8, 4).
(f) (3, 7), (2, $6\frac{1}{2}$), (3, 6).
(g) Put dots at (5, 6) and (7, 6).

6 Draw axes with both x and y from 0 to 18.

(a) (0, 3), (1, 4), (2, 6), (4, 8), (6, 8), (8, 9), (12, 9), (13, 11), (12, 12), (12, 14), (14, 12), (15, 12), (17, 14), (17, 12), (16, 11), (17, 10), (17, 9), (16, 9), (15, 8), (14, 9), (13, 9).
(b) (16, 9), (16, 7), (14, 5), (14, 1), (15, 1), (15, 6), (13, 4), (13, 1), (12, 1), (12, 4), (11, 5), (9, 5), (9, $6\frac{1}{2}$), (9, 4), (8, 3), (8, 1), (7, 1), (7, 4), (6, 6), (6, 4), (5, 3), (5, 1), (6, 1), (6, 3), (7, 4), (6, 6), (6, 7), (3, 2), (1, 2), (0, 3).

7 Design your own coordinates picture.

Complete the shape

Two sides of a rectangle are drawn

Find (a) the coordinates of the fourth vertex of the rectangle
(b) the coordinates of the centre of the rectangle.

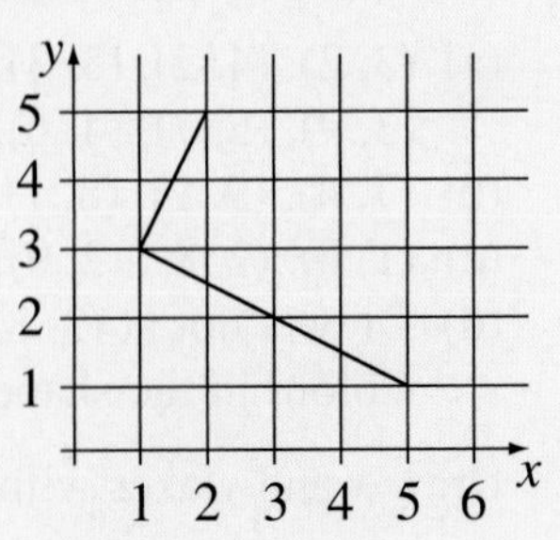

The complete rectangle is shown.

(a) Fourth vertex is at (6, 3)
(b) Centre of rectangle is at $(3\frac{1}{2}, 3)$

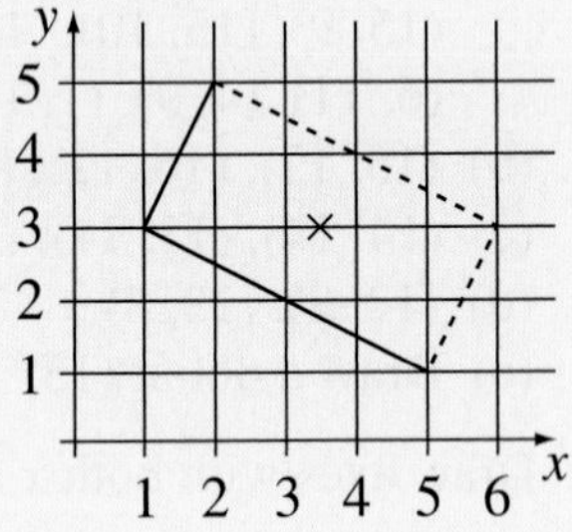

Exercise 2E

1 The graph shows several incomplete quadrilaterals.
Copy the diagram and complete the shapes.
(a) Write down the coordinates of the fourth vertex of each shape.
(b) Write down the coordinates of the centre of each shape.

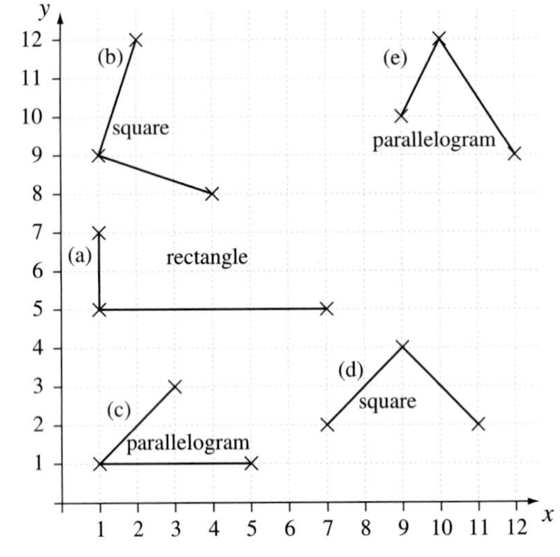

2 Copy the graph shown.
(a) A, B and F are three corners of a square. Write down the coordinates of the other corner.
(b) B, C and D are three corners of another square. Write down the coordinates of the other corner.
(c) D, E and F are three corners of a rectangle. Write down the coordinates of the other corner.

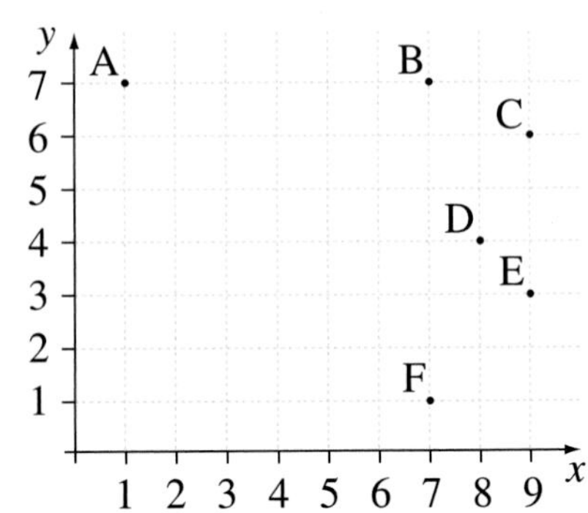

3 Draw a grid with values from 0 to 10. Plot the three points given and then find the coordinates of the point which makes a square when the points are joined up.

(a) (1, 2), (1, 5), (4, 5)
(b) (5, 6), (7, 3), (10, 5)
(c) (0, 9), (1, 6), (4, 7)

4 You are given the vertices but not the sides of two parallelograms P and Q.

For each parallelogram find *three* possible positions for the fourth vertex.

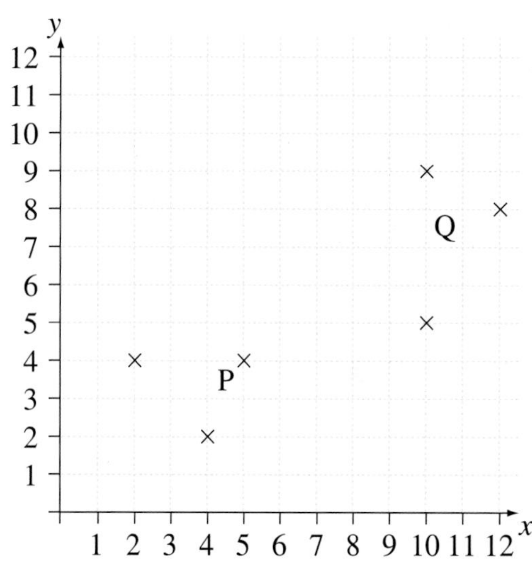

5 Copy the graph shown.

(a) A, B and C are three corners of a square. Write down the coordinates of the other corner.
(b) C, A and D are three corners of another square. Write down the coordinates of the other corner.
(c) B, D and E are three corners of a rectangle. Write down the coordinates of the other corner.
(d) C, F and G are three vertices of a parallelogram. Write down the coordinates of the other vertex.

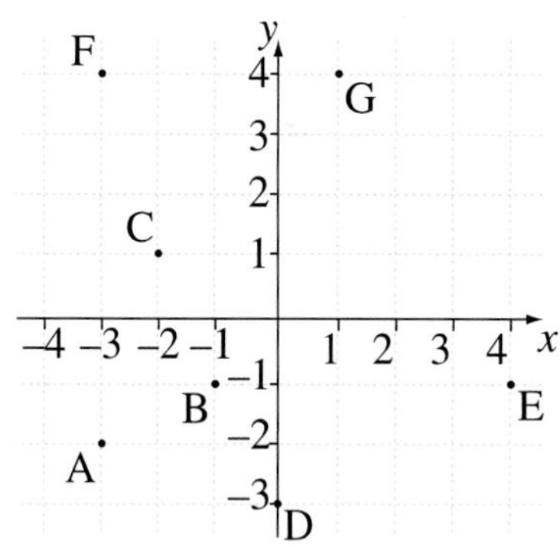

6

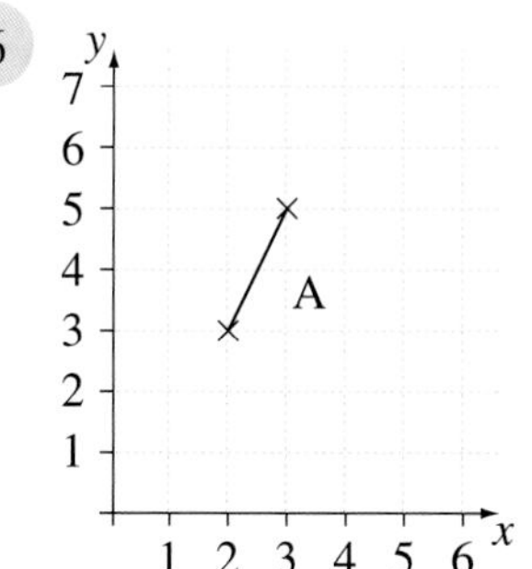

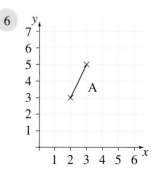

The crosses mark two vertices of an isosceles triangle A.

Find as many points as you can, with whole number coordinates, for the third vertex of the triangle.

[There are, in fact, 12 possible points for the third vertex. Find as many as you can.]

7 The diagram shows one side of an isosceles triangle B.

(a) Find *six* possible points, with whole number coordinates, for the third vertex of the triangle.

(b) Explain how you could find the coordinates of several more positions for the third vertex.

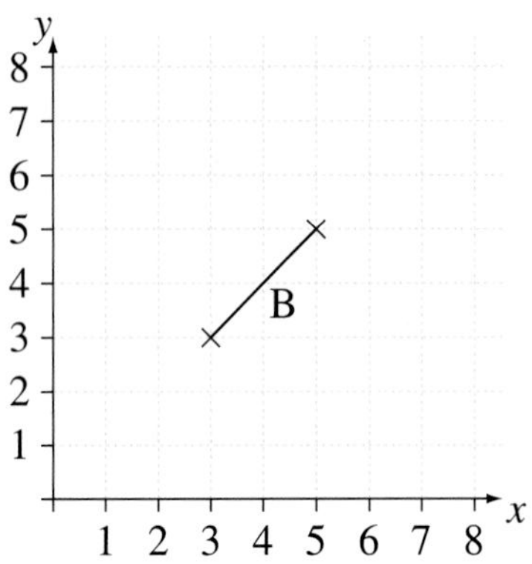

8 (a) Draw a pair of axes with values of x and y from 0 to 12.

(b) Draw a line from A(2, 0) to B(9, 7).

(c) Draw a line from C(1, 11) which is perpendicular to AB and meets AB at point D.

(d) Write down the coordinates of D.

(e) Draw a line from point E (4, 2) which is perpendicular to BC and meets BC at point F.

(f) Write down the coordinates of the point where line EF intersects line CD.

(g) Draw a line through F parallel to AB. Write down the coordinates of the point where this line meets the y axis.

3.2 Long multiplication and division 2

In section 3.2 you will:

- practise long multiplication and long division
- solve word problems

Reminder. See section 1.2

42 × 37

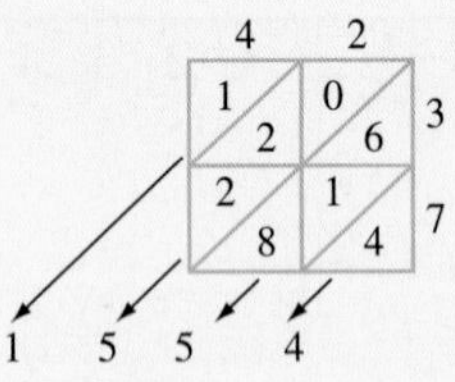

327 × 45

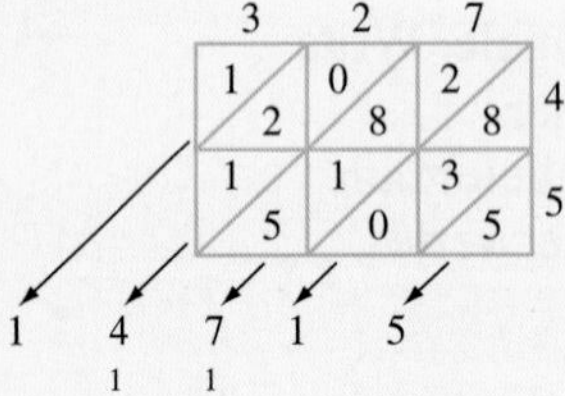

1161 ÷ 27

```
       4 3
27)1161
  - 108↓    (27 × 4)
      81
    - 81    (27 × 3)
       0
```

Exercise 1M

1 Copy and complete or use your own method.

(a)

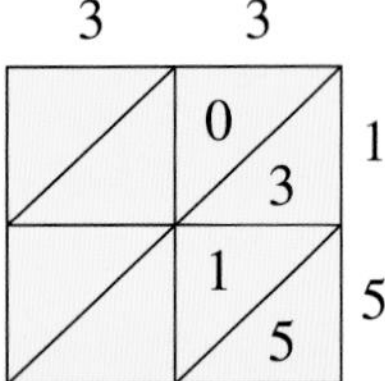

(b)

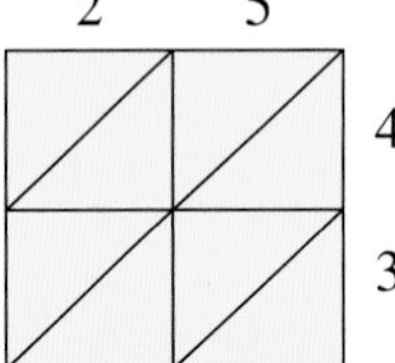

(c)

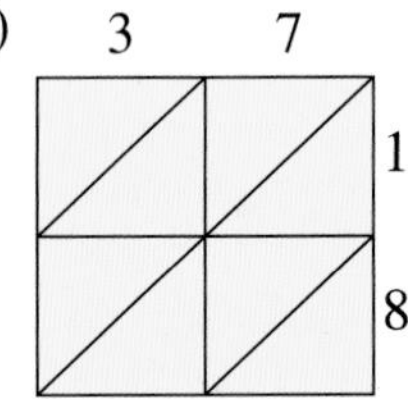

2 Work out

(a) 36×29 (b) 54×21 (c) 312×24
(d) 207×32 (e) 27×27 (f) 241×32

3 Copy and complete

(a)
```
      3 2
11) 3 5 2
  - □ □↓      (3 × 11)
    -----
      2 2
      □□      (2 × 11)
```

(b)
```
      5 3 remainder □
13) 6 9 1
  - □ □↓      (5 × 13)
    -----
      4 1
      □□      (3 × 13)
    -----
        □
```

Work out

4 $480 \div 15$

5 $714 \div 21$

6 $962 \div 26$

7 Copy and complete

(a) $32 \times 17 =$ □□□ (b) $11 \times$ □□□ $= 3575$
(c) □□ $\times 17 = 408$ (d) $22 \times 55 =$ □□□□

8 Work out the total cost of 45 pens at 22p each. Give your answer in pounds.

9 A box of 15 golf balls costs 975 pence. How much does each ball cost?

10 There are 23 rooms in a school and each room has 33 chairs. How many chairs are there altogether?

Exercise 1E

Work out and give the remainder where necessary.

1 $267 \div 12$

2 $409 \div 11$

3 $637 \div 15$

4 $714 \div 23$

5 $819 \div 25$

6 $561 \div 37$

7 A shop owner buys 52 tins of paint at 84p each. How much does he spend altogether?

8 Eggs are packed twelve to a box. How many boxes are needed for 444 eggs?

9 Bambi the cat eats one tin of cat food every day. How much will it cost to feed Bambi for 31 days if each tin costs 45p?

10 In this multiplication the missing digits are 2, 3, 4, 5. Find the missing numbers

```
    □□
  × □□
 -------
 1 2 4 2
```

11 How many 23-seater coaches will be needed for a school trip for a party of 278?

12 Joe wants to buy as many 34p stamps as possible. He has £5 to spend. How many can he buy and how much change is left?

13 It costs £972 to hire a boat for a day. A trip is organised for 36 people. How much does each person pay?

14 Tins of spaghetti are packed 24 to a box. How many boxes are needed for 868 tins?

15 On average a school needs 87 exercise books a week. How many books are needed for 38 weeks?

16 A prize of 470 chocolate bars is shared equally between 18 winners. How many bars does each winner get and how many are left over?

17 Each class of a school has 31 pupils plus one teacher and there are 15 classes in the school. The school hall can take 26 rows of chairs with 18 chairs in a row. Is that enough chairs for all the pupils and teachers?

18 When Philip was digging a hole in his garden he struck oil! The oil came out at a rate of £17 for every minute of the day and night. How much does Philip receive in a 24-hour day?

3.3 Decimals 2

In section 3.3 you will learn how to:

- add, subtract, multiply and divide with decimal numbers

(a) 7.8 – 3.64

$$\begin{array}{r} 7\,.\,{}^{7}\not{8}\,{}^{1}0 \\ -3\,.\,6\,4 \\ \hline 4\,.\,1\,6 \end{array}$$

line up the decimal points

(b) 4.2 × 0.6

$$\begin{array}{r} 4\,.\,2 \\ \times\ 0\,.\,6 \\ \hline 2\,.\,5\,2 \\ {}_{1} \end{array}$$

The answer has the same number of figures after the point as there are in the numbers being multiplied

(c) 10.56 ÷ 8

$$\begin{array}{r} 1\,.\,3\ \ 2 \\ 8\overline{)\,10\,.\,{}^{2}5\ \ {}^{1}6} \end{array}$$

Exercise 1M

1. 11.07 + 15
2. 18 – 3.7
3. 0.304 × 100
4. 8.7 ÷ 5
5. 11.63 ÷ 10
6. 5.1 + 0.51 + 7
7. 1.52 × 7
8. 11.4 – 8.26
9. 0.002 × 10 000
10. 4.1 × 300
11. 200 – 5.5
12. 1.7 × 0.4
13. 5.6 × 0.7
14. 0.79 ÷ 5
15. 0.3 × 0.02
16. 28.74 + 19.852

Copy and complete by finding the missing number.

17. 8.2 + □ = 13
18. 7.2 × □ = 0.072
19. □ ÷ 3 = 9.14
20. □ – 3.64 = 7.5
21. □ ÷ 11 = 8.2
22. □ × 7 = 24.78
23. The perimeter of the rectangle shown is 35.2 cm.

    Work out the area of the rectangle.

10.2 cm

Exercise 1E

Copy and complete by writing +, –, × or ÷ in the box.

1. 2.1 □ 2 = 4.2
2. 80 □ 3.2 = 25
3. 0.2 □ 1 = 0.2
4. 0.6 □ 0.6 = 0.36
5. 7 □ 0.4 = 2.8
6. 3.36 □ 2.1 = 1.6
7. A chocolate cake weighing 1.4 kg is cut into eight equal pieces.
   What is the mass of each piece?
8. One litre of petrol costs £0.96. Work out the cost of 52 litres of petrol.
9. An isosceles triangle has two sides of length 4.44 cm and one side on length 3.7 cm.
   What is the perimeter of the triangle?
10. | £1 = € 1.46 | Using the rate of exchange given, how many euros can you get for £95?
11. The weights of five players in a basketball team are 60.4 kg, 47.8 kg, 71.6 kg, 55 kg and 68.6 kg. Calculate the mean weight of the players.

12 Find the missing numbers

(a) $18 + (4.27 \div \square) = 18.61$ (b) $8 - (\square \times 0.2) = 7.16$

13 The perimeter of a square room is 20.8 m. Calculate the area of the room.

14 You can buy eight cans of drink for £9.60. How many cans can you buy for £15.60?

15 Two books cost £13.50 in total. One book is one-and-a-half times the price of the other. How much does each book cost?

16 The owner of a wine bar buys wine at £8.50 per litre. He sells the wine in glasses containing 20 ml at £2.40 per glass. How much profit does he make per litre?

17 Tickets for a charity event cost £1.80 for adults and 75p for children. How much in £s was paid altogether when the event attracted 432 adults and 216 children?

18 A pile of ten 10p coins is 18 mm high. When Izrie emptied her piggy bank she had enough 10p coins to make three towers of height 1.53 m. Work out the value in pounds of the coins which Izrie had saved?

19

> Sad news of the sparrow that was killed a year ago in Leeuwarden in the Netherlands, in dramatic circumstances. The sparrow flew onto a set on which an attempt at creating a world record of toppled dominoes was being made. The bird knocked over 23,000 dominoes before it was cornered and shot to prevent it causing further mayhem.

It takes an experienced domino technician 5.2 seconds to place each piece in position for the record attempt.
How long will it take to repair the damage caused by the unfortunate sparrow? Give your answer in hours, correct to one decimal place.

Exercise 2M

1 Answer true or false

(a) $0.1 \times 0.1 = 0.1$ (b) $0.1 - 0.01 = 0.09$ (c) $0.1 \div 100 = 0.01$
(d) $0.1 > 0.02$ (e) $3.3 - 0.6 = 0.6 - 3.3$ (f) $0.71 = 710 \div 1000$

2 Copy each number chain and find the numbers shown with a question mark.

(a) 0.74 → [× 2] → ? → [÷ 10] → ? → [+ 0.002] → ? → [× 1000] → ?

(b) 1.35 → [− 0.3] → ? → [+ 0.25] → ? → [× 0.2] → ? → [× 10] → ?

(c) 8.5 → [÷ 5] → ? → [+ 0.17] → ? → [+ 0.13] → ? → [÷ 50] → ?

3 Draw a copy of the crossnumber puzzle and then fill it in using the clues given.

Clues across

1. (0.352 × 10) × 100
3. 47.6 ÷ 7
5. $(0.9)^2 \times 100$
6. 2 – 0.56
7. $7^2 + 21^2$
8. 45 × 0.4
10. $1.6^2 + 4.72$
11. 4.7 × 20
12. (1 + 0.01 + 0.002) × 1000

Clues down

1. 77 ÷ 2
2. 17 × 0.3
3. $2^7 \times 5$
4. 588 ÷ 7
6. 100 × 0.19
7. 7 × 7 – (19 × 0.01)
8. 600 ÷ 5
9. 8.82 × 5
10. 8 × 9 – (4 × 0.25)

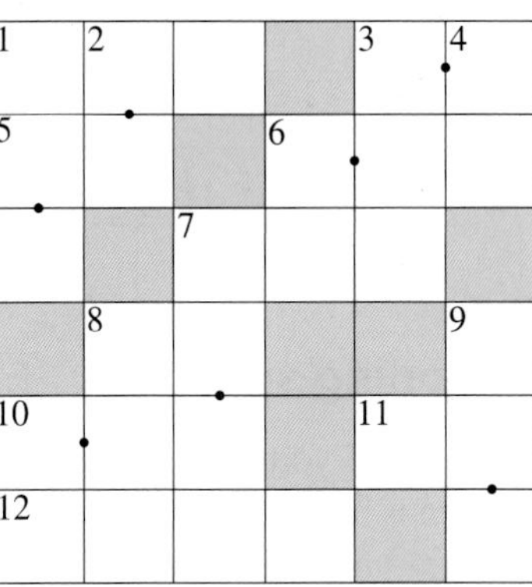

Exercise 2E

Operator squares

Each empty square contains either a number or an operation (+, –, ×, ÷,). Copy each square and fill in the missing details. The arrows are equals signs.

1

57	÷	3	→	
+		×		
		53	→	200
↓		↓		
204	–		→	

2

18	×		→	90
×		+		
0.1			→	1
↓		↓		
	+		→	16.8

3

25	×		→	10
×		+		
	×		→	
↓		↓		
150	–		→	149

4

35	×		→	3500
–		÷		
	×		→	
↓		↓		
34.8	+	0.1	→	

5

48	×	9	→	
÷		×		
	×		→	
↓		↓		
	+	117	→	120

6

5	–		→	4.8
÷		+		
	–		→	98
↓		↓		
0.05	+		→	

7

10	×		→	2
÷		×		
	÷		→	
↓		↓		
2.5	–	1.6	→	

8

19.6	÷	7	→	
×		–		
0.1	×		→	0.03
↓		↓		
	+		→	

9

8.42	–		→	8.22
×		×		
15	×		→	1200
↓		↓		
	+		→	

10

20	÷	100	→	
×		÷		
	×	200	→	
↓		↓		
440	×		→	

11

1.22	×	7	→	
+		−		
	+		→	
↓		↓		
5	÷		→	1.25

12

	+		→	90.2
÷		−		
9	×	52	→	
↓		↓		
	×	5.8	→	

Designing squares

- Make up your own operator squares starting from a blank grid like the one shown. Try to make your square difficult to solve, but give enough information so that it can be done.

			→	
			→	
↓		↓		
			→	

- The grid shown opposite is much more difficult to fill (as you will discover!)
  Try to make up one of these 'super operator' squares.

			→	
			→	
↓		↓		↓
			→	

Here is one that works.

10	×	8	→	80
÷		÷		÷
2	×	2	→	4
↓		↓		↓
5	×	4	→	20

3.4 Properties of numbers

In section 3.4 you will learn about:

- prime numbers
- factors of numbers
- multiples of numbers
- square numbers and cube numbers

Prime numbers

A *prime* number is divisible by only two different numbers: by itself and by one. The first six prime numbers are 2, 3, 5, 7, 11, 13. Note that one is *not* a prime number.

Exercise 1M

1 Find the one number in each line which is prime.

(a) 18, 19, 20, 21, 22
(b) 8, 9, 10, 11, 12
(c) 36, 37, 38, 39, 40

2 The prime numbers up to 100 or 200 can be found as follows:

- Write the numbers in 8 columns (leave space underneath to go up to 200 later).
- Cross out 1 and draw circles around 2, 3, 5 and 7.
- Draw 4 vertical lines to cross out the even numbers (apart from 2).
- Draw 6 diagonal lines to cross out the multiples of 3.
- Draw 2 diagonal lines to cross out the multiples of 7.
- Cross out any numbers ending in 5.
- Draw circles around all the numbers which have not been crossed out. These are the prime numbers. Check that you have 25 prime numbers up to 100.

3 Selmin looked at her circled prime numbers and she thought she noticed a pattern. She thought that all the prime numbers in columns A and B could be written as the sum of two square numbers.
For example $17 = 1^2 + 4^2$
$41 = 4^2 + 5^2$

Was Selmin right? Can *all* the prime numbers in columns A and B be written like this?

4 Extend the table up to 200 and draw in more lines to cross out multiples of 2, 3 and 7. You will also have to cross out any multiples of 11 and 13 which would otherwise be missed. (Can you see why?) Does the pattern which Selmin noticed still work?

Exercise 1E

Part one

1 Write down the two numbers in each line which are prime.

(a) 14, 17, 21, 27, 29, 39
(b) 41, 45, 49, 51, 63, 67
(c) 2, 57, 71, 81, 91, 93

2 How many prime numbers are there between 1 and 100?

3 Write down two prime numbers which add up to another prime number. Do this in three ways.

4 How many of the prime numbers are even?

5 How many of the prime numbers between 1 and 100 are odd?

6 Find three pairs of prime numbers with a difference of 4 between the numbers.

7 When two prime numbers are added the answer is 22.
What could the two numbers be?

8 (a) List the prime numbers ending in 1.
(b) List the prime numbers ending in 7.
(c) Apart from 5 why do no prime numbers end in 5?

9 Answer *true* or *false* for the statement below:
'For all whole numbers greater than one there is at least one prime number between that number and its double.'

10 A rectangle has an area of 23 cm^2.
Its length and width are both a whole number of centimetres.
What is the perimeter of the rectangle?

11 Find three prime numbers which add up to another prime number.

(a) Is 307 a prime number?

You might think that we need to test whether 307 is divisible by 2, 3, 4, 5, 6, 7, 8,... 306. This would be both tedious and unnecessary.
In fact, if 307 is divisible by any number at all it will certainly be divisible by a prime number less than $\sqrt{307}$.
Since $\sqrt{307}$ is about 17.5, we only need to test whether 307 is divisible by 2, 3, 5, 7, 11, 13, 17.

Using a calculator, we find that 307 is not divisible by any of these, so we know that 307 *is* a prime number.

(b) Is 689 a prime number?

Since $\sqrt{689} \approx 26.2$, we only need to test whether 689 is divisible by 2, 3, 5, 7, 11, 13, 17, 19, 23.
Using a calculator we find that 689 is divisible by 13. We do not need to go any further than this.
We now know that 689 is *not* a prime number.

Part two

1 Use your calculator to find which of the following are prime numbers.

(a) 293	(b) 407	(c) 799	(d) 335
(e) 709	(f) 1261	(g) 923	(h) 1009

2 One very large prime number is $2^{86243} - 1$. The number has 25962 digits.

(a) How long would it take to write out this number, assuming that you could maintain a rate of 1 digit every second? Give your answer in hours, minutes and seconds.

(b) How many pages would you need to write out this number if you could write 50 digits on a line and 30 lines on a page?

3 (a) Multiply the first two prime numbers together and then add 1. Is the answer a prime number?

(b) Work out $(2 \times 3 \times 5) + 1$. Is the answer prime?

(c) Work out $(2 \times 3 \times 5 \times 7) + 1$. Is the answer prime?

(d) Work out $(2 \times 3 \times 5 \times 7 \times 11) + 1$. Is the answer prime?

(e) Do we always get a prime number using this method?

Factors

- The number 12 can be written as two numbers multiplied together in three different ways

  1×12 2×6 3×4

  The numbers 1, 12, 2, 6, 3, 4 are all the *factors* of 12.

- $1 \times 8 = 8$ $2 \times 4 = 8$

  The factors of 8 are 1, 2, 4, 8.

Exercise 2M

Write down all the factors of the following numbers

1 6	2 4	3 10	4 7	5 15
6 18	7 24	8 21	9 36	10 40
11 32	12 31	13 60	14 63	15 85

16 Find two 1-digit numbers that have 4 factors.

17 Find two numbers less than 20 that have 6 factors.

18 The number in each circle is the product of the numbers in the squares on either side. Find the missing numbers.

(a)

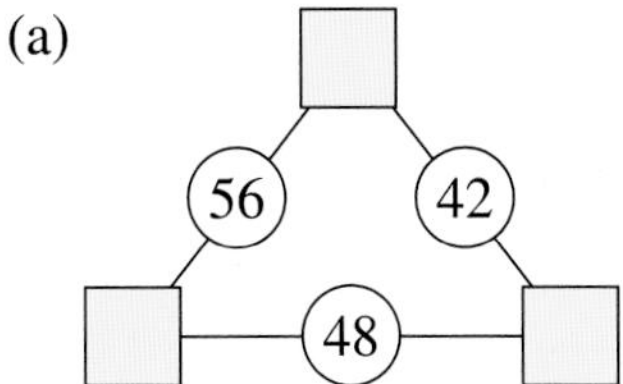

(b)

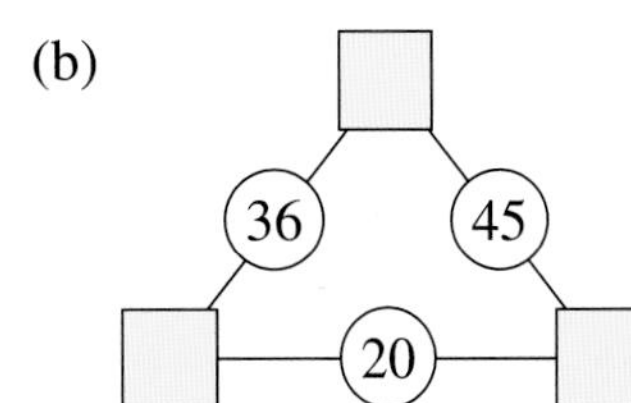

(c)

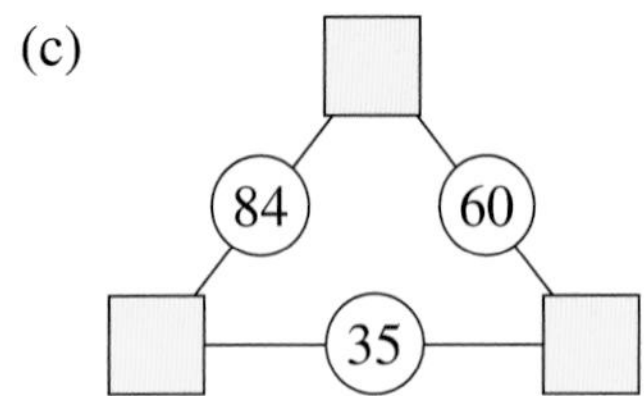

(d)

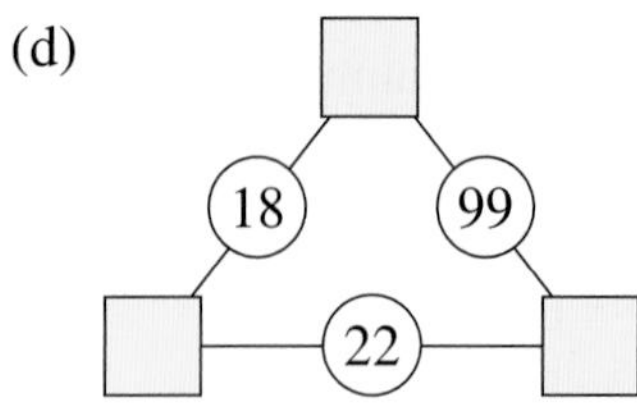

19 What is the smallest number with exactly 3 factors?

20 What is the smallest number with exactly.

(a) 4 factors (b) 5 factors?

Exercise 2E

1 Write down all the factors of the following numbers

(a) 50 (b) 44 (c) 100 (d) 29

2 Factors of a number which are also prime numbers are called *prime factors*. We can find these prime factors using a 'factor tree'

(a) Here is a factor tree for 60

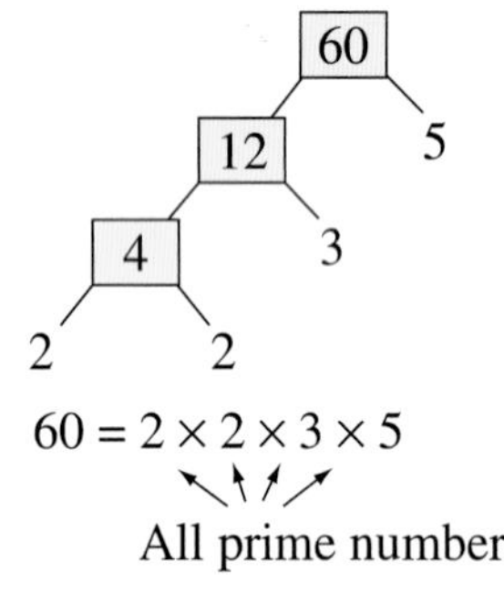

(b) Here is a factor tree for 24

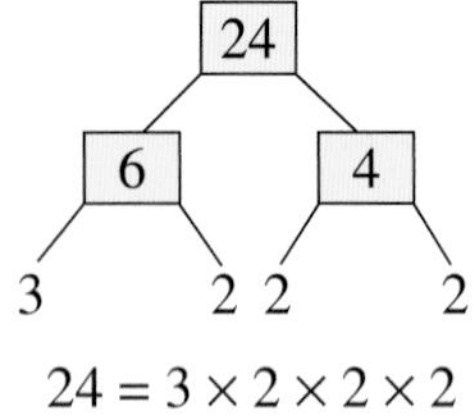

(c) You can turn the diagram upside down and then draw a trunk around the number and branches to give a real 'tree shape'. Some people like to draw the prime factors inside apples, pears, bananas and so on.

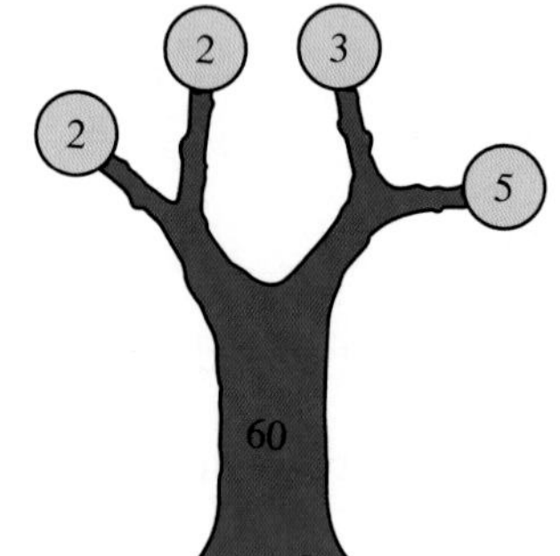

(d) Draw a factor tree for 36.

In questions 3 to 14 draw a factor tree for each number.

3 28 4 32 5 34 6 81

7 84 8 216 9 294 10 200

11 1500 12 2464 13 4620 14 98175

15 The digit sum of 16 is 7 [1 + 6]. How many factors has 16?

16 (a) Find the digit sum and the number of factors of
(i) 24 (ii) 84
(b) Can you find any other 2-digit numbers whose digit sum is equal to the number of its factors?

17 The number 345 has 3 and 5 as factors.
Write another three-digit number which has 3 and 5 as factors.

18 The number 432 has 2 and 9 as factors.
Write another three-digit number which has 2 and 9 as factors.

19 Which number less than 100 has the most prime factors?

20 Which number less than 1000 has the most *different* prime factors? (You cannot repeat a factor.)

21 What is the smallest whole number which is exactly divisible by all the numbers from 1 to 10 inclusive?

Multiples

The *multiples* of 5 divide by 5 with no remainder.

The first four multiples of 5 are 5, 10, 15, 20.

The first four multiples of 6 are 6, 12, 18, 24.

'The multiples of 5 are the numbers in the 5 times table'

Exercise 3M

Write down the first four multiples of:

1 3 2 4 3 2 4 7 5 10

Write down the first six multiples of:

6 5 7 8 8 9 9 11 10 20

11 Copy and complete
(a) 25, 30, 35 and 60 are all multiples of □
(b) 14, 21, 35 and 70 are all multiples of □
(c) 8, 12, 20 and 28 are all multiples of □ and □

In questions 12 to 16 find the 'odd one out'. (The number which is not a multiple of the number given.)

12 Multiples of 6: 18, 24, 32, 48, 54.

13 Multiples of 11: 33, 77, 101, 132.

14 Multiples of 10: 5, 10, 20, 30, 60.

15 Multiples of 9: 18, 27, 45, 56, 72.

16 Multiples of 7: 49, 77, 91, 105, 18.

17 Write down the numbers in the hoop which are:
(a) multiples of 12
(b) factors of 12

4
24
80
60
6
120

18 Write each line with either 'multiple' or 'factor' in the space.

(a) 15 is a ☐ of 5
(b) 8 is a ☐ of 32
(c) 9 is a ☐ of 90
(d) 6 is a ☐ of both 18 and 30

19 Find three numbers that are multiples of both 3 and 4.

20 Find three numbers that are multiples of both 2 and 5.

21 Find three numbers that are multiples of 2, 3 and 5.

22 Find two numbers that are multiples of 2, 4 and 6.

L.C.M. and H.C.F.

The first few multiples of 4 are 4, 8, 12, 16, (20), 24, 28 …

The first few multiples of 5 are 5, 10, 15, (20), 25, 30, 35 …

The *Least Common Multiple* (L.C.M) of 4 and 5 is 20.

It is the lowest number which is in both lists.

Exercise 3E

1 (a) Write down the first six multiples of 2
(b) Write down the first six multiples of 5
(c) Write down the L.C.M. of 2 and 5

2 (a) Write down the first four multiples of 4
(b) Write down the first four multiples of 12
(c) Write down the L.C.M. of 4 and 12

3 (a) Write down the first six multiples of 3
(b) Write down the first six multiples of 5
(c) Write down the L.C.M. of 3 and 5

4 Find the L.C.M. of

(a) 6 and 9 (b) 8 and 12 (c) 14 and 35
(d) 2, 4 and 6 (e) 3, 5 and 10 (f) 4, 7 and 9

The factors of 12 are 1, 2, 3, (4), 6, 12

The factors of 20 are 1, 2, (4), 5, 10, 20

The *Highest Common Factor* (H.C.F.) of 12 and 20 is 4

It is the highest number which is in both lists.

5 The table shows the factors and common factors of 24 and 36

number	factors	common factors
24	1, 2, 3, 4, 6, 8, 12, 24	} 1, 2, 3, 4, 6, 12
36	1, 2, 3, 4, 6, 9, 12, 18, 36	

Write down the H.C.F. of 24 and 36.

6 The table shows the factors and common factors of 18 and 24

number	factors	common factors
18	1, 2, 3, 6, 9, 18	} 1, 2, 3, 6
24	1, 2, 3, 4, 6, 8, 12, 24	

Write down the H.C.F. of 18 and 24.

7 Find the H.C.F. of

(a) 12 and 18 (b) 22 and 55 (c) 45 and 72
(d) 12, 18 and 30 (e) 36, 60 and 72 (f) 20, 40 and 50

8 Don't confuse your L.C.M. s with your H.C.F. s!

(a) Find the H.C.F. of 12 and 30.
(b) Find the L.C.M. of 8 and 20.
(c) Write down two numbers whose H.C.F. is 11
(d) Write down two numbers whose L.C.M. is 10

9 Given that $30 = 2 \times 3 \times 5$ and $165 = 3 \times 5 \times 11$, find the highest common factor of 30 and 165 [i.e. The highest number that goes into 30 and 165]

10 If $315 = 3 \times 3 \times 5 \times 7$ and $273 = 3 \times 7 \times 13$, find the highest common factor of 315 and 273.

11 Given that $1386 = 2 \times 3 \times 3 \times 7 \times 11$ and $858 = 2 \times 3 \times 11 \times 13$, find the highest common factor of 1386 and 858.

12 If $1170 = 2 \times 3 \times 3 \times 5 \times 13$ and $10\,725 = 3 \times 5 \times 5 \times 11 \times 13$, find the highest common factor of 1170 and 10 725.

Square numbers and cube numbers

Exercise 4M

1

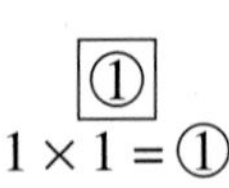

1 × 1 = ①

④

2 × 2 = ④

⑨

3 × 3 = ⑨

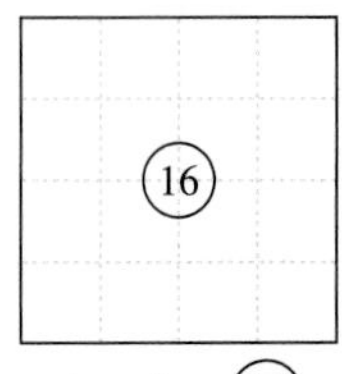

4 × 4 = ⑯

(a) The first four *square* numbers are 1, 4, 9, 16
(b) Draw diagrams with labels to show the next three square numbers.

2 A square number is obtained by multiplying a number by itself.
3×3 is written 3^2 (We say '3 squared . . .')
4×4 is written 4^2

Work out

(a) 5^2 (b) 8^2 (c) 10^2 (d) 1^2

3 Work out

(a) $3^2 + 4^2$ (b) $1^2 + 2^2 + 3^2$ (c) $9^2 + 10^2$

4 The sum of the square numbers 9 and 81 is 90. Find a pair of square numbers with a sum of

(a) 13 (b) 73 (c) 40 (d) 181
(e) 125 (f) 97 (g) 74 (h) 113

5 Here is a 6×6 square divided into 9 smaller squares.
Draw a 5×5 square and design a pattern which divides it into nine smaller squares.

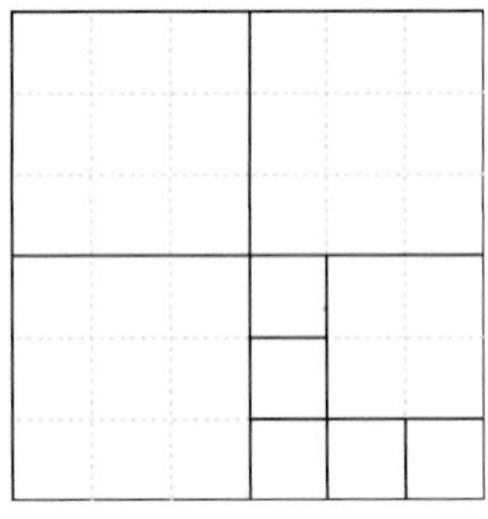

6 Which square number is between

(a) 50 and 70 (b) 70 and 100 (c) 150 and 180?

7 (a) Write down this sequence and fill in the missing numbers

1 = 1 = 1^2
1 + 3 = 4 = 2^2
1 + 3 + 5 = □ = $□^2$
1 + 3 + 5 + 7 = □ = $□^2$

(b) Write down the next five lines of the sequence.

Exercise 4E

1 Which numbers below are not square numbers?

1 4 8 25 49 84

2 What number when multiplied by itself gives

(a) 49 (b) 121 (c) 169

3 Look at the numbers in the pentagon.
Write down the numbers which are:

(a) factors of 16 (b) prime numbers
(c) multiples of 3 (d) square numbers

16 7 2
1000 15
9
3 8
21 64
4

4 Find a pair of square numbers with a difference of:

(a) 7 (b) 80 (c) 84 (d) 300
(e) 45 (f) 32 (g) 39 (h) 105

5 The *square root* of a number is the number which is multiplied by itself to give that number. The symbol for square root is √.

So $\sqrt{9} = 3$, $\sqrt{16} = 4$, $\sqrt{100} = 10$

Work out

(a) $\sqrt{25}$ (b) $\sqrt{81}$ (c) $\sqrt{49}$ (d) $\sqrt{1}$

6 Copy the following and fill in the spaces

(a) $7^2 = 49$, $\sqrt{49} = \square$ (b) $14^2 = 196$, $\sqrt{196} = \square$
(c) $21^2 = 441$, $\sqrt{\square} = 21$ (d) $3.3^2 = 10.89$, $\sqrt{\square} = 3.3$

7 *Lagrange's theorem.* A famous mathematician called Lagrange proved that every whole number could be written as the sum of four or fewer square numbers.

For example: $21 = 16 + 4 + 1$
$19 = 16 + 1 + 1 + 1$
$35 = 25 + 9 + 1$

Check that the theorem applies to the following numbers.

(a) 10 (b) 24 (c) 47 (d) 66 (e) 98
(f) 63 (g) 120 (h) 141 (i) 423

If you can find a number which needs more than four squares you will have disproved Lagrange's theorem and a new theorem will be named after you.

8 The numbers 1, 8, 27 are the first three *cube* numbers.

$1 \times 1 \times 1 = 1^3 = 1$ (we say '1 cubed')
$2 \times 2 \times 2 = 2^3 = 8$ (we say '2 cubed')
$3 \times 3 \times 3 = 3^3 = 27$ (we say '3 cubed')

Work out the next three cube numbers.

9 Look at the diagram in question 3.
Write down the numbers which are cube numbers.

10 The odd numbers can be added in groups to give an interesting sequence:

1	= 1	$= 1^3$
3 + 5	= 8	$= 2^3$
7 + 9 + 11	= 27	$= 3^3$

Write down the next three rows of the sequence to see if the sum of each row always gives a cube number.

11 In its prime factors, $588 = 2 \times 2 \times 3 \times 7 \times 7$.
What is the smallest number by which you can multiply 588 so that the answer is a square number?

12 Write 8820 in its prime factors. What is the smallest number by which you can multiply 8820 so that the answer is a square number?

Satisfied numbers

The number 4 is an even number *and* a square number. It *satisfies* both categories.

1 Copy the grid below and use a pencil for your answers (so that you can rub out mistakes.)
Write the numbers from 1 to 9, one in each box, so that all the numbers satisfy the conditions for both the row and the column.

	Number between 5 and 9	Square number	Prime number
Factor of 6	6	?	?
Even number	?	?	?
Odd number	?	?	?

2 Copy the grid and write the numbers from 1 to 9, one in each box.

	Prime number	Multiple of 3	Factor of 16
Number greater than 5			
Odd number			
Even number			

3 This one is more difficult. Write the numbers from 1 to 16, one in each box. There are several correct solutions. Ask a friend to check yours.

	Prime number	Odd number	Factor of 16	Even number
Numbers less than 7				
Factor of 36				
Numbers less than 12				
Numbers between 11–17				

4 Design a grid with categories of your own and ask a friend to solve it.

Happy numbers

- (a) Take any number, say 23.
  (b) Square the digits and add: $2^2 + 3^2 = 4 + 9 = 13$
  (c) Repeat (b) for the answer: $1^2 + 3^2 = 1 + 9 = 10$
  (d) Repeat (b) for the answer: $1^2 + 0^2 = 1$
  23 is a so-called 'happy' number because it ends in one.
- Take another number, say 7.
  Write 7 as 07 to maintain the pattern of squaring and adding the digits.
  Here is the sequence:

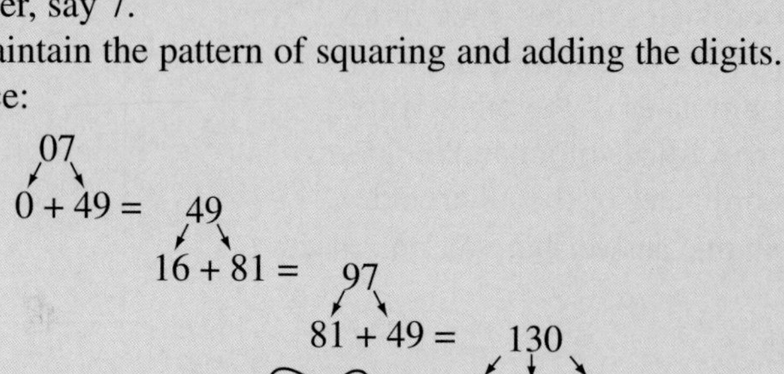

So 7 is a happy number also.

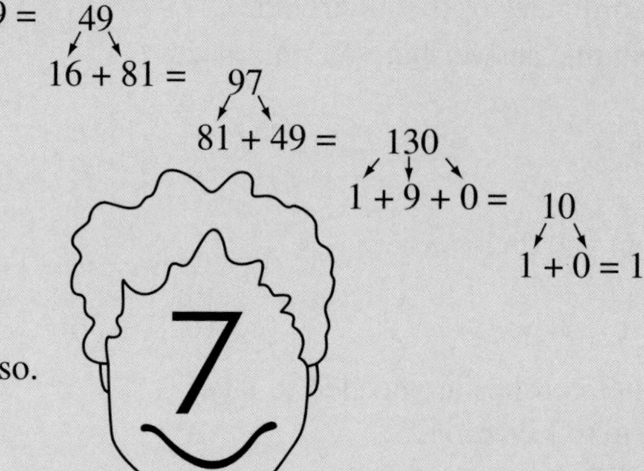

With practice you may be able to do the arithmetic in your head and write:

$07 \rightarrow 49 \rightarrow 97 \rightarrow 130 \rightarrow 10 \rightarrow 1$.

You may find it helpful to make a list of the square numbers $1^2, 2^2, 3^2, \ldots 9^2$.

- Your task is to find all the happy numbers from 1 to 100 and to circle them on a grid like the one shown. This may appear to be a very time-consuming and rather tedious task! But remember: Good mathematicians always look for short cuts and for ways of reducing the working.

So think about what you are doing and good luck!

As a final check you should find that there are 20 happy numbers from 1 to 100.

1	2	3	4	5	6	7	8	9	10
11	12	13	14	15	16	17	18	19	20
21	22	23	24	25	26	27	28	29	30
31	32	33	34	35	36	37	38	39	40
41	42	43	44	45	46	47	48	49	50
51	52	53	54	55	56	57	58	59	60
61	62	63	64	65	66	67	68	69	70
71	72	73	74	75	76	77	78	79	80
81	82	83	84	85	86	87	88	89	90
91	92	93	94	95	96	97	98	99	100

CHECK YOURSELF ON UNITS 3.1, 3.2, 3.3 and 3.4

1 Using coordinates to solve problems involving shapes

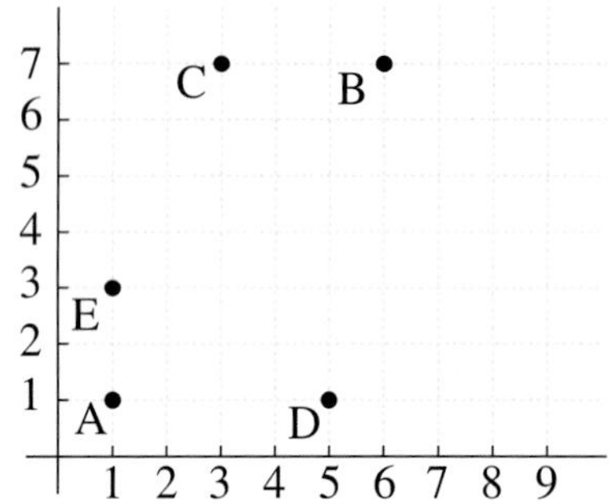

(a) Points A, D and E are three vertices of a rectangle. Write down the coordinates of the other vertex.

(b) C, E and D are three vertices of a square. Write down the coordinates of the other vertex.

(c) B, C and E are three vertices of a parallelogram. Write down the coordinates of the other vertex. (There is more than one answer but you only need to give one.)

2 Long multiplication and division

(a) 27×35 (b) 54×327 (c) $1620 \div 36$

(d) How many 49-seater coaches are needed to take 530 people on a trip to Liverpool?

3 Solving problems involving decimals

(a) Find the missing numbers

5.1 → [× 2.4] → ? → [+ 0.76] → ? → [÷ 5] → ?

(b) If 7 jars of mustard cost £16.45, find the cost of 5 jars.

(c) The perimeter of the rectangle shown is 22.6 cm. Work out the area of the rectangle.

4 Prime numbers and factors

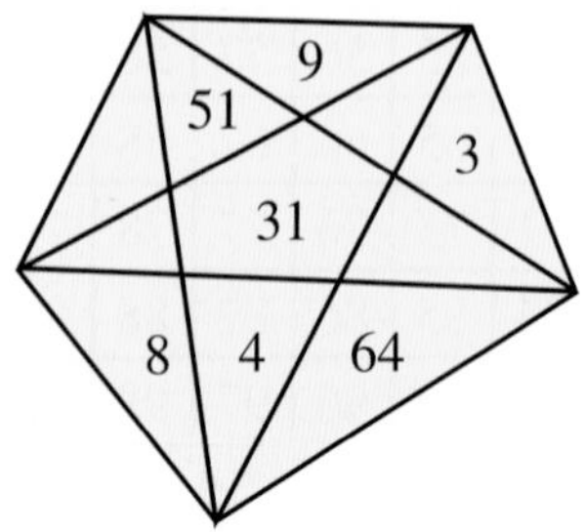

(a) Look at the numbers in the diagram.

(i) Which numbers are prime numbers?
(ii) Which numbers are factors of 51?
(iii) Which numbers are factors of 32?

(b) Write 100 as the sum of two prime numbers in two different ways

5 Multiples, square numbers and cube numbers

(a) Find the L.C.M. of 8 and 12
(b) Find the H.C.F. of 60 and 75
(c) Work out $1^1 \times 2^2 \times 3^3$
(d) Work out (i) $\sqrt{81}$ (ii) $4^3 + 5^3$ (iii) $\sqrt{6^2 + 8^2}$
(e) x, y and z are whole numbers such that $x^2 + y^2 = z^2$.
Find the values of x, y and z.

3.5 Straight line graphs

In section 3.5 you will learn about:

- lines which are parallel to the axes
- sloping lines
- finding the equation of a line
- drawing straight line graphs

Lines parallel to the axes

- The points P, Q, R and S have coordinates (4, 4), (4, 3), (4, 2) and (4, 1) and they all lie on a straight line. Since the x-coordinate of all the points is 4, we say the *equation* of the line is $x = 4$.

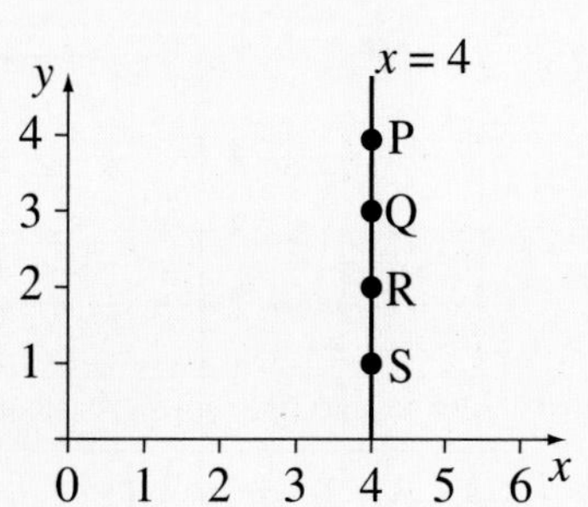

- The points A, B, C and D have coordinates (1, 3), (2, 3), (3, 3) and (4, 3) and they all lie on a straight line. Since the y-coordinate of all the points is 3, we say the *equation* of the line is $y = 3$.

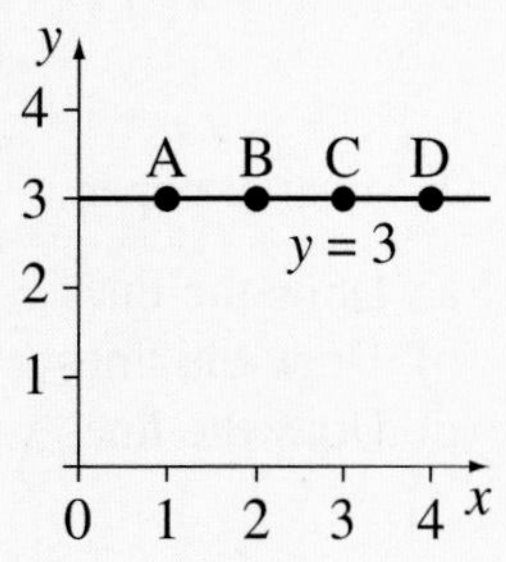

Exercise 1M

1 Write down the equations for the lines marked A, B and C.

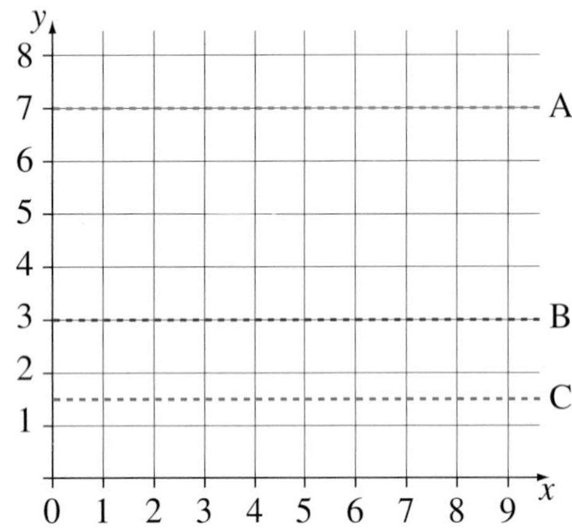

2 Write down the equations for the lines marked P, Q and R.

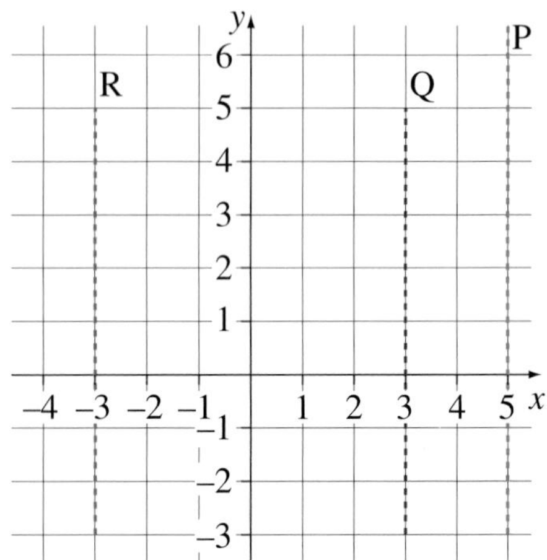

In questions 3 and 4 below there is a red line A, a blue line B and a green line C.
Write down the equations of the lines in each question.

3

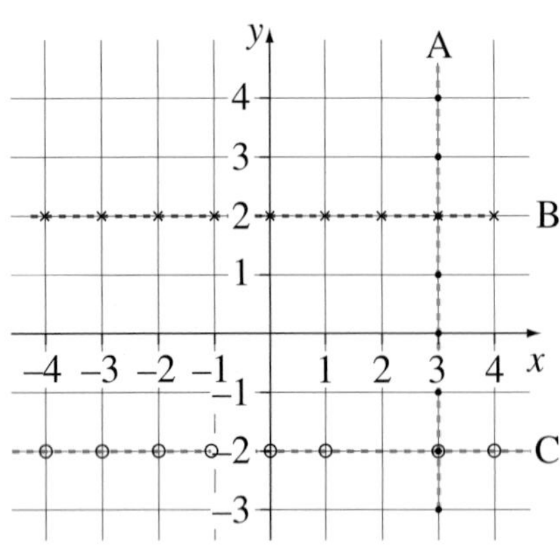

4

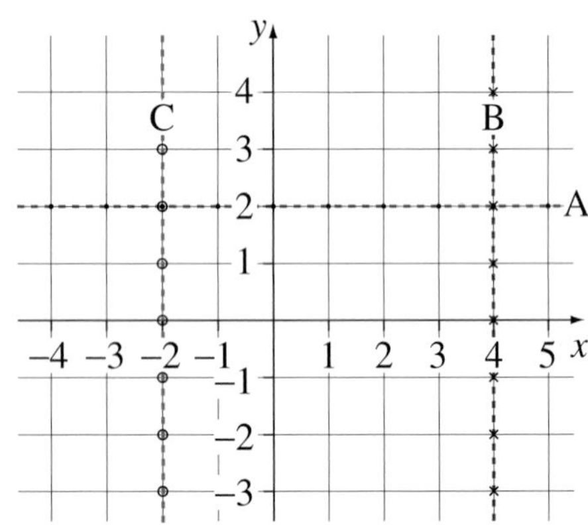

5 On squared paper

(a) Draw the lines $y = 2$ and $x = 3$. At what point do they meet?
(b) Draw the lines $y = 5$ and $x = 1$. At what point do they meet?
(c) Draw the lines $x = 7$ and $y = 3$. At what point do they meet?

6 In the diagram, E and N lie on the line with equation $y = 1$. B and K lie on the line $x = 5$. In parts (a) to (h) find the equation of the line passing through the points given:

(a) A and D
(b) A, B and I
(c) M and P
(d) I and H
(e) L and E
(f) D, K and G
(g) C, M, L and H
(h) P and F

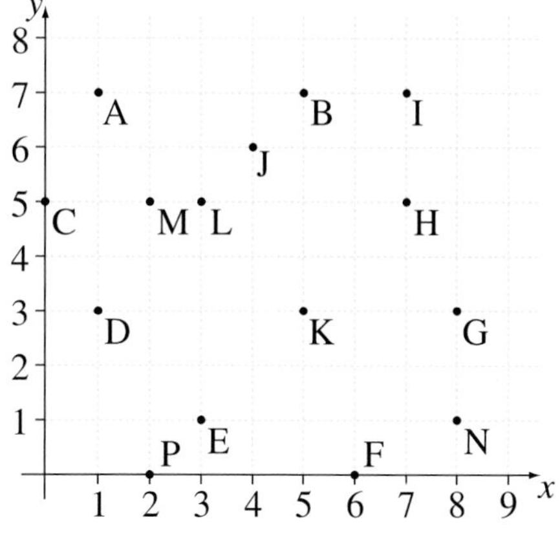

Relating *x* and *y*

- The sloping line passes through the following points: (1, 1), (2, 2), (3, 3), (4, 4), (5, 5).

  For each point, the y coordinate is equal to the x coordinate.

  The equation of the line is $y = x$ (or $x = y$).

  This is the rule for any point on the line.

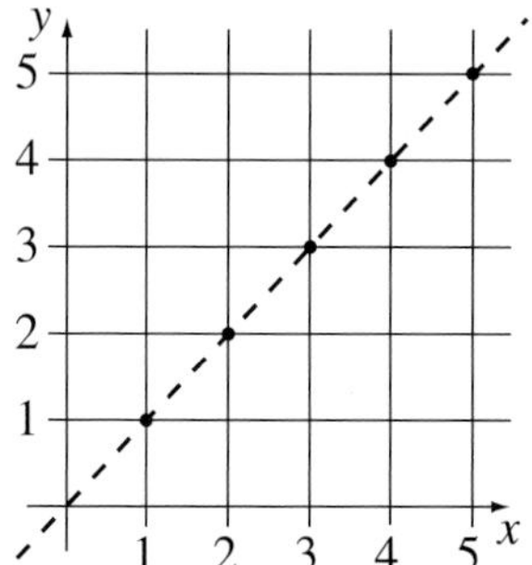

- This line passes through: (0, 1), (1, 2), (2, 3), (3, 4), (4, 5).

  For each point the y coordinate is one more than the x-coordinate.

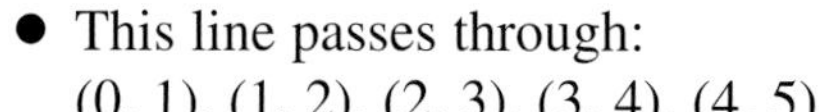

The equation of the line is $y = x + 1$.

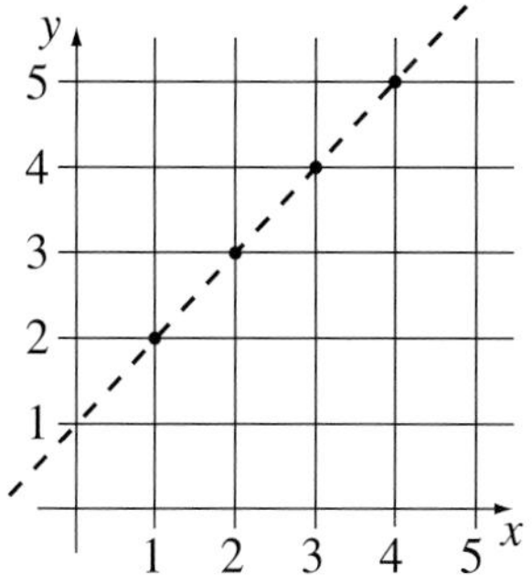

We could also say that the x coordinate is always one less than the y coordinate. The equation of the line could then be written as $x = y - 1$.
[Most mathematicians use the equation beginning '$y =$ '].

- This line slopes the other way and passes through: (0, 5), (1, 4), (2, 3), (3, 2), (4, 1), (5, 0).

  The sum of the x coordinate and the y coordinate is always 5.

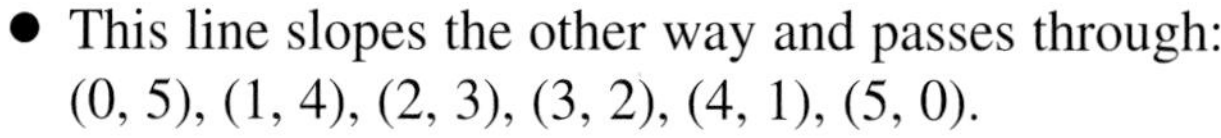

The equation of the line is $x + y = 5$ (or $y = 5 - x$)

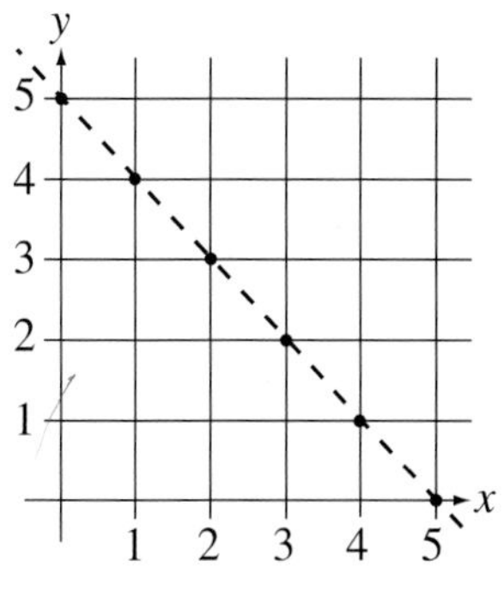

Exercise 1E

For each question write down the coordinates of the points marked. Find the equation of the line through the points.

1

2 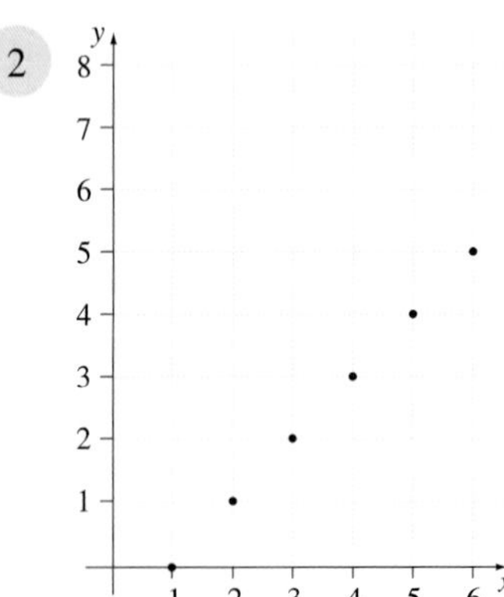

3 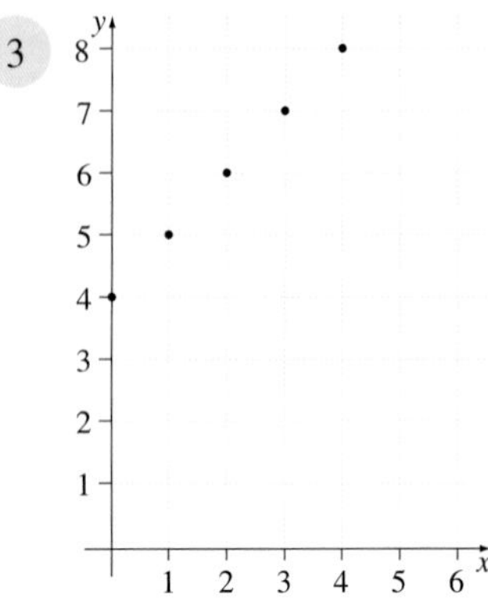

4

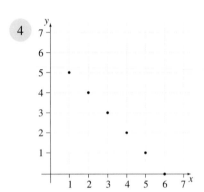

5 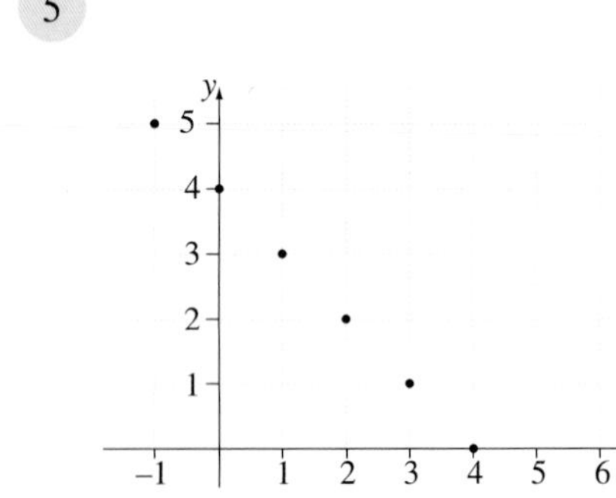

6 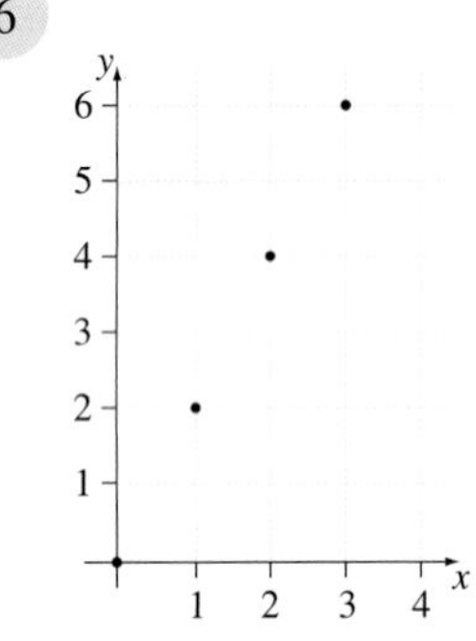

7 Look at the graph. Find the equation for
(a) line A
(b) line B
(c) line C
(d) line D

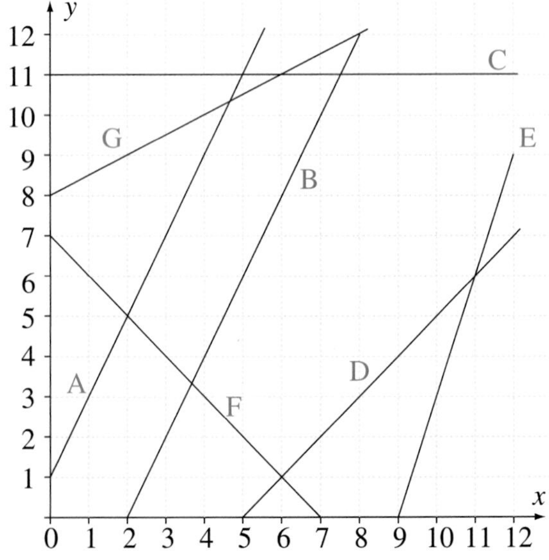

8 This is the table of the points on line G

x	0	2	4	6
y	8	9	10	11

Find the equation for line G.
[Hint: It starts $y = \frac{1}{2}x + \ldots$]

9 This is the table for the points on line E.

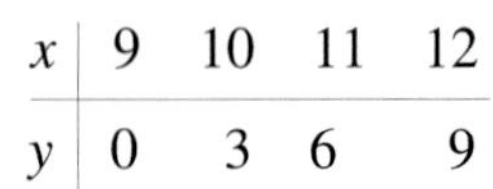

x	9	10	11	12
y	0	3	6	9

Find the equation of line E.

10 Make a table for the points on line F.

x	0	1	2	3
y	7			

Find the equation of line F.

Finding points on a line

The rule (or equation) for a line is $y = x + 1$.

Points which lie on the line satisfy the equation $y = x + 1$.

So when $x = 3$, $y = 3 + 1 = 4$. The point $(\underset{x}{3}, \underset{y}{4})$ is on the line.

and when $x = 5$, $y = 5 + 1 = 6$. The point (5, 6) is on the line.

Exercise 2M

1 For the line $y = x + 4$, find the y values for

(a) $x = 3$ (b) $x = 5$ (c) $x = 0$

2 For the line $y = x - 3$, find the y values for

(a) $x = 6$ (b) $x = 8$ (c) $x = 10$

3 For the line $y = 3x$, find the y values for

(a) $x = 2$ (b) $x = 5$ (c) $x = 0$

4 Which of the points below lie on the line $y = x + 7$?

A(3, 10) B(6, 1) C(5, 12)

5 Which of the points below lie on the line $y = 2x - 1$?

A(0, 1) B(2, 3) C(5, 9)

6 Look at the graph. Decide which of the equations below matches each line.

$y = x - 2$, $y = 4$,
$y = 8 - x$, $y = 2x$,
$x = 4$.

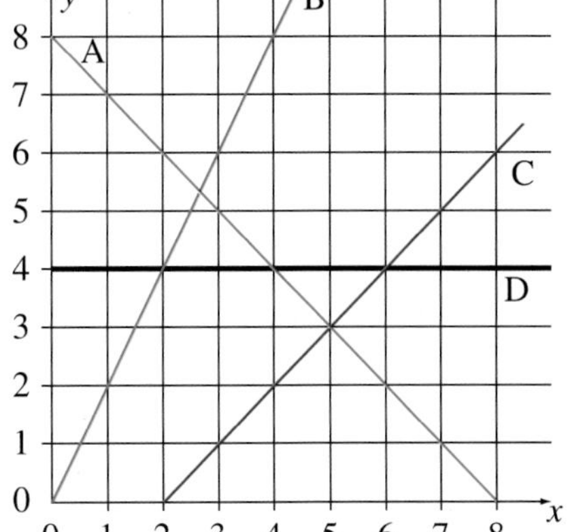

7 Consider the two lines: $y = x + 2$ and $y = 2x$.
State which of the points below lie on each line.

A(5, 7) B(4, 8) C (0, 0)
D(1, 2) E(10, 12) F(0, 2)

8 Consider the two lines: $y = x - 3$ and $y = 3x - 2$.
State which of the points below lie on each line.

P(2, 4) Q(3, 0) R(5, 2)
S(0, –2) T(3, 7) U(7, 4)

Drawing graphs

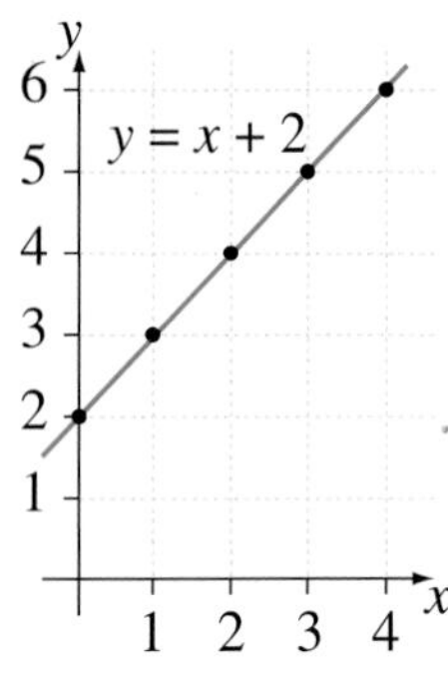

- The equation of a line is $y = x + 2$. Here is a list of five points on the line: (0, 2), (1, 3), (2, 4), (3, 5), (4, 6)

  The points are plotted on a graph and the line $y = x + 2$ is drawn. Notice that the line extends beyond (0, 2) and (4, 6).

Exercise 2E

1 The equation of a line is $y = x + 3$. Copy and complete a list of points on the line:
(0, 3) (1, 4) (2, □) (3, □) (4, □)
Draw the graph of $y = x + 3$

2 The equation of a line is $y = x + 5$. Copy and complete a list of points on the line:
(0, 5) (1, 6) (2, □) (3, □) (4, □)

In questions 3 to 10 you are given the equation of a line and a list of points on the line. Fill in the missing numbers and then draw the graph.

3 $y = x - 2$; (0, –2), (1, –1), (2, □), (3, □), (4, □)

4 $y = x - 4$; (0, – 4), (1, –3), (2, □), (3, □), (4, □)

5 $y = 2x$; (0, 0), (1, 2), (2, □), (3, □), (4, □)

6 $y = 2x + 1$; (0, □), (2, □), (4, □)

7 $y = 2x - 2$; (0, □), (2, □), (4, □)

8 $y = 6 - x$; (1, □), (3, □), (5, □), (6, □)

9 $y = 4 - x$; (0, □), (2, □), (4, □)

10 $y = 3x + 2$; (0, □), (1, □), (2, □)

11 (a) Draw axes with values of x from 0 to 5 and with values of y from –1 to 7.
(b) Draw the lines $y = 5 - x$ and $y = 2x - 1$ on the same graph.
(c) Write down the coordinates of the point where the lines meet.

12 (a) Draw axes with values of x from 0 to 10 and values of y from 0 to 12.
(b) On the same graph draw the lines

$$y = x + 3$$
$$y = \frac{1}{2}x + 3$$
$$y = 15 - x$$

(c) Write down the coordinates of the vertices of the triangle formed by the three lines.

3.6 Handling data

In section 3.6 you will learn about:

- bar charts and bar-line graphs
- data in groups and line graphs
- pie charts
- problems answered using statistics

Bar charts and bar-line graphs

When you do a survey the information you collect is called *data*. This data is usually easier for someone else to understand if you display it in some sort of chart or graph.

(a) The scores of 35 golfers competing in a tournament were

68 74 71 72 71 68 70
74 69 71 70 67 73 71
70 74 69 72 73 74 71
72 74 71 72 72 70 73
67 68 72 73 72 71 71

(b) A tally chart/frequency table is made for the scores.

score	tally	frequency
67	‖	2
68	‖|	3
69	‖	2
70	||||	4
71	~~||||~~ |||	8
72	~~||||~~ ||	7
73	||||	4
74	~~||||~~	5

(c) This data can be displayed on either a bar chart or on a bar-line graph. The '⌇' shows that a section on the horizontal axis has been cut out.

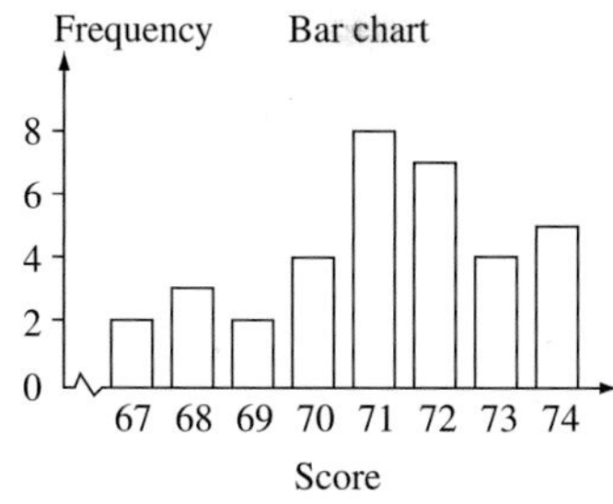

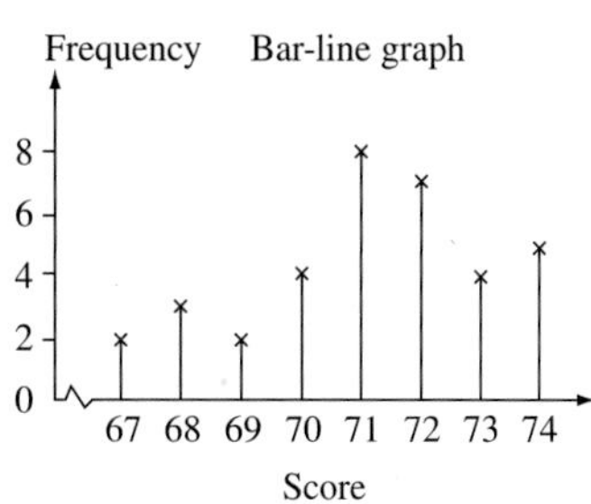

Exercise 1M

1 In a survey children were asked to name their favourite sport.

(a) What was the most popular sport?
(b) How many children chose Athletics?
(c) How many children took part in the survey?

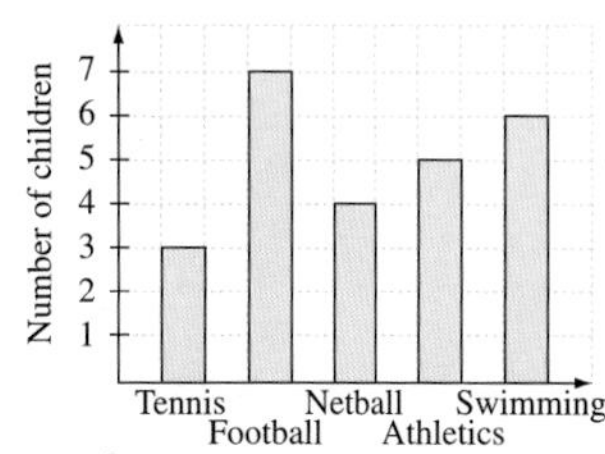

2 Here is a *bar-line graph* showing the number of children in the families of children in a school.

(a) How many families had three children?
(b) How many families were there altogether?

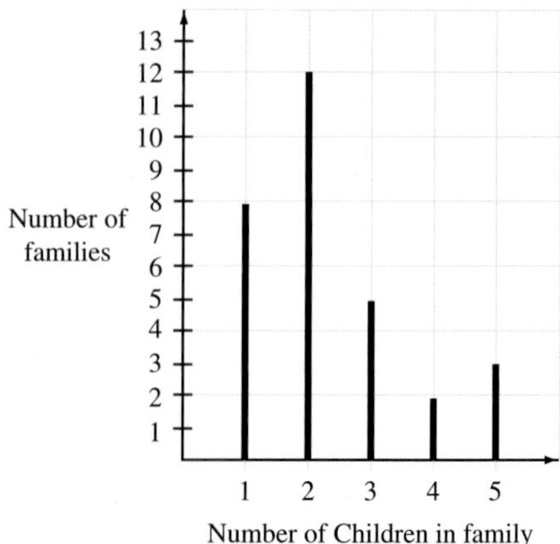

3 Collect your own data for a bar line graph like the one in question 2. Ask lots of people to state the number of children in their families.
Draw a graph of the results and use colour to make it more attractive.

4 This table shows the number of different sorts of snacks sold by a shop.

(a) How many snacks were sold on Thursday?
(b) Each Aero costs 45p. How much was spent on Aeros in the whole week?
(c) Draw a bar chart to show the number of each kind of snack sold in a week.

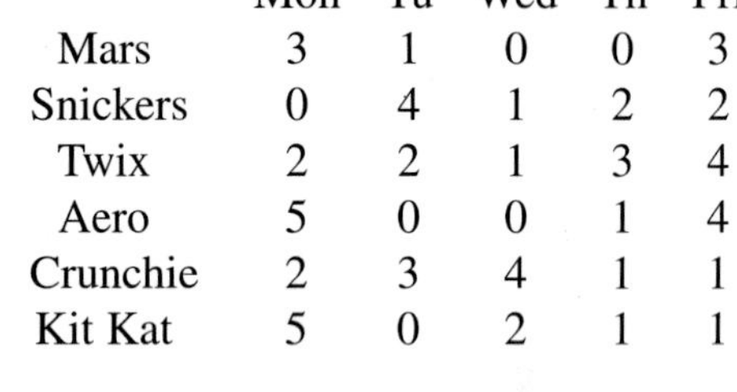

	Mon	Tu	Wed	Th	Fri
Mars	3	1	0	0	3
Snickers	0	4	1	2	2
Twix	2	2	1	3	4
Aero	5	0	0	1	4
Crunchie	2	3	4	1	1
Kit Kat	5	0	2	1	1

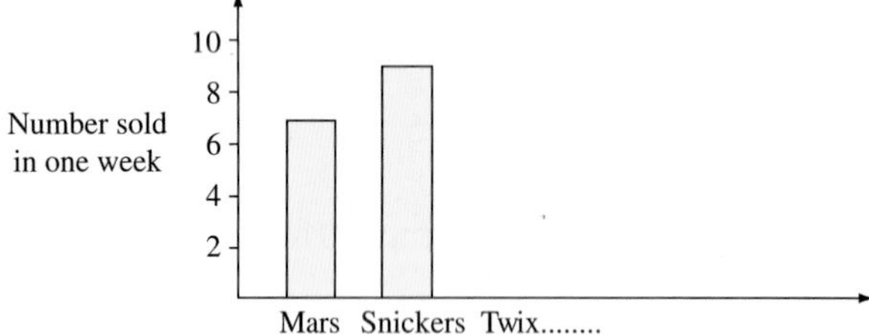

5 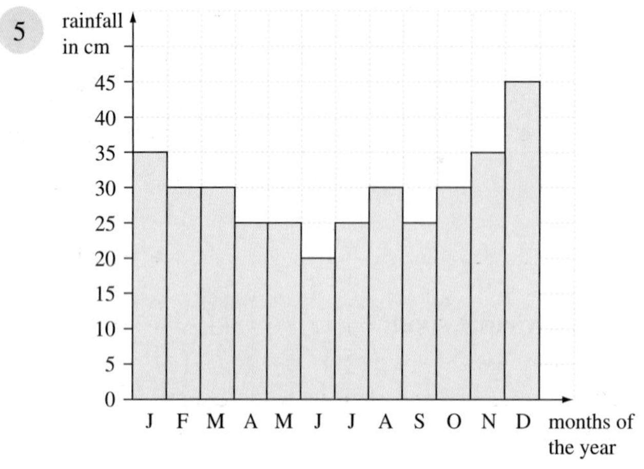

The monthly rainfall in the Lake District is shown left.

(a) How much rain fell in August?
(b) Which was the driest month in the year?
(c) Which was the wettest month in the year?
(d) In which months did 25 cm of rain fall?
(e) In which months did 30 cm of rain fall?

Exercise 1E

1 The bar charts show the sale of different things over a year but the labels on the charts have been lost. Decide which of the charts A, B, C or D shows sales of:

(a) Christmas trees
(b) Crisps
(c) Flower seeds
(d) Greetings cards [including Christmas, Valentine's Day, etc.]

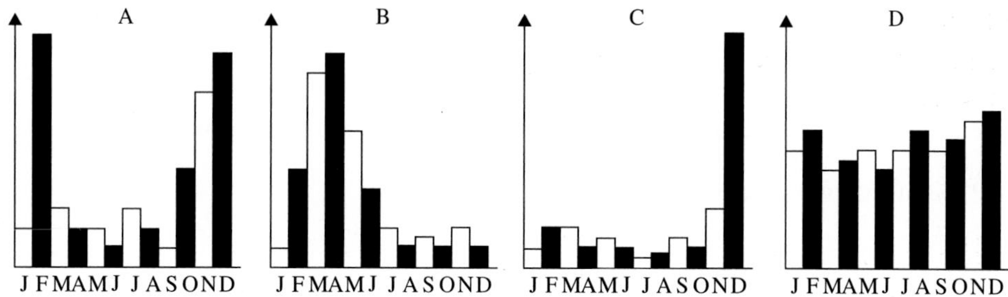

2 The number of people staying in two different hotels in each month of the year is shown below.

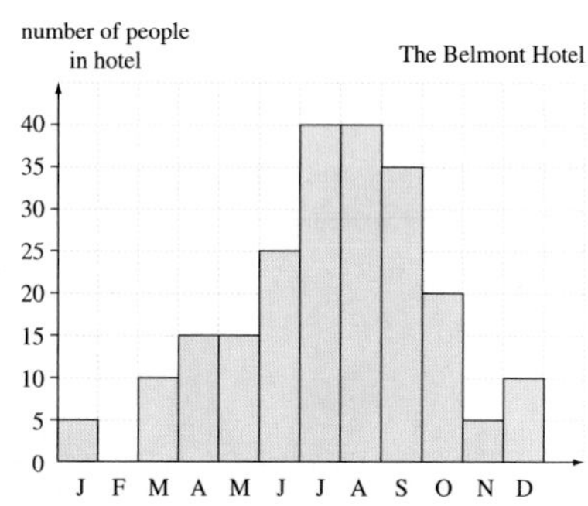

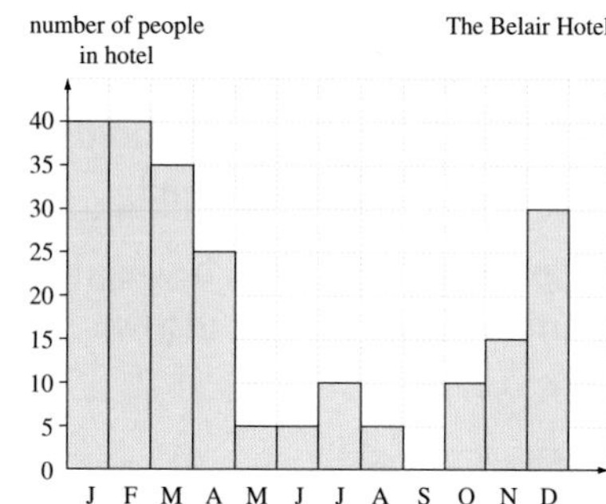

(a) How many people stayed in the 'Belmont' in July?
(b) How many people stayed in the 'Belair' in July?
(c) What was the total number of people staying in the two hotels in April?
(d) One hotel is in a ski resort and the other is by the seaside. Which is in the ski resort?

3

Percentage loss/gain
Residential
Transport, utilities
Outdoor recreation
Industry, commerce
Health, education, etc.
+60
+40
+20
0
−20
−40
−60
Woodland
Vacant
Farming
[SOURCE: Council for the Protection of Rural England From DOE figures]

This chart shows changes of land use in rural areas in England between 1960 and 2000.

(a) What was the change in the area of land used for farming?
(b) Write down three activities that would go in the 'outdoor recreation' category.
(c) Describe the main features of the chart.

4 The chart shows the agricultural production figures for four crops in Pakistan. Pakistan has low rainfall but in recent years major irrigation schemes have been introduced. About 50% of the population is employed in agriculture.

Describe how the production of the four crops has changed over the years from 1960 to 2000.

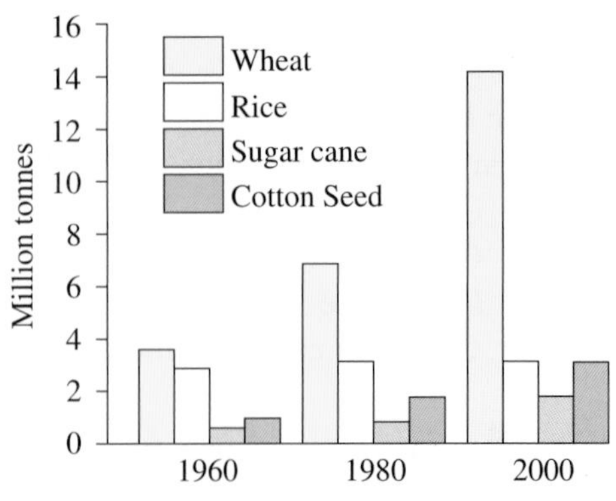

5 Here are details of the official languages spoken in countries around the world.

English	27% of the world population	French	4%
Chinese	19%	Arabic	3%
Hindi	14%	Portuguese	3%
Spanish	6%	Malay	3%
Russian	5%	Bengali	3%
		Japanese	2%

(a) Draw a bar chart to illustrate this data.
(b) England is a fairly small country compared to China. How can you explain the figures given?

6 Some children were asked to state which was their favourite T.V. programme from the list below.

East Enders	E
MTV	M
Football Highlights	F
Neighbours	N
The Simpsons	S

The replies were:

S N S M N E M F N M E M M E N
F S N M M E S E N S E N N E N
N M E N N E M F N S E M N F N

Make a tally chart and then draw a bar chart to show the results

		Tally	Total
East Enders	E		
MTV	M		
Football Highlights	F		
Neighbours	N		
The Simpsons	S		

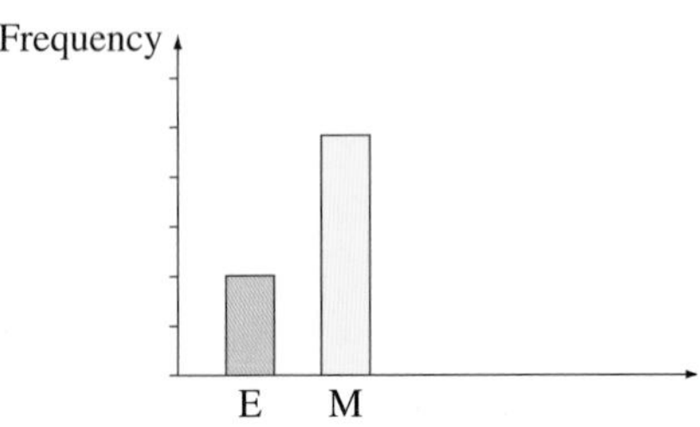

7 Here are two paragraphs: one in English and one in French.
There is the same number of letters in each paragraph.

Luciano Gaucci Perugia's "Chairman Gau" signed Al Saadi Gaddafi, the son of the Libyan dictator, who was described by an Italian paper as "twice as slow as slow itself". He then attempted to sign a Sweden international – Hanna Ljungberg, a star of women's football. He also tried to dismiss Ahn Jung Hwan because the South Korea forward scored against Italy in the 2002 World Cup finals.

Eurogoals Magazine Les plus beaux buts des championnats européens de football. Ce magazine hebdomadaire de cinquante-deux minutes présente une sélection des meilleures rencontres du Championnat espagnol, portugais, belge, néerlandais ou français. L'accent est mis sur les buts, et les matchs se soldant par un 0–0 sont systématiquement écartés. Les grandes équipes telles que l'Ajax d'Amsterdam ou le Real.

(a) For each paragraph make a tally chart to record how many letters there are in each word.
(b) Draw a bar chart for each language and write a sentence about the main differences in the two charts.

Word length	Tally
1 2 3	

Data in groups and line graphs

- Here are the ages of the people at a wedding.
  33 11 45 22 50 38 23 54 18 72 5 58
  37 3 61 51 7 62 24 57 31 27 66 29
  25 39 48 15 52 25 35 18 49 63 13 74
  With so many different numbers over a wide range it is helpful to put the ages into *groups*.

- Here is the start of a tally chart

Ages	Tally	Total (Frequency)
0–9	III	3
10–19	~~IIII~~	5
20–29	~~IIII~~ II	7
30–39		
40–49		
50–59		
60–69		
70–79		

- Here is the start of a frequency chart

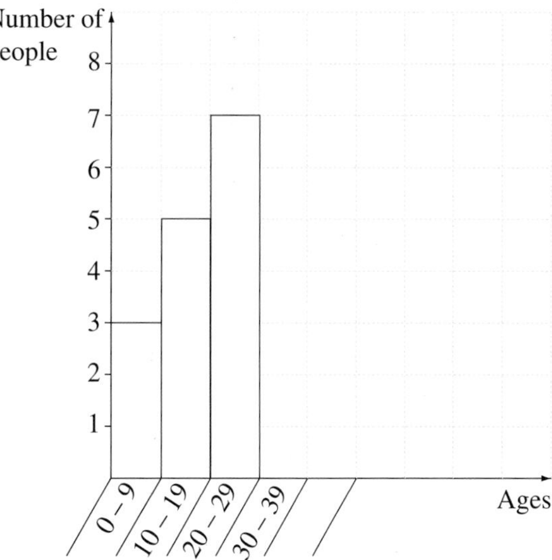

- Finish the tally chart and the frequency diagram.
  Notice that when the data is in groups the bars are touching.

Exercise 2M

1 Shruti started with one frog but it laid eggs and now she has lots!
One day she measures all her little pets. Here are the lengths in mm.

82 63 91 78 27 93 87 48 22 15
42 28 84 65 87 55 79 66 85 38

(a) Make a tally chart and then draw the frequency diagram.

Length (mm)	Tally	Frequency
0–20		
21–40		
41–60		
61–80		
81–100		

(b) How many frogs were more than 60 mm long?

2 The heights, in cm, of 30 children are shown below

134 146 141 147 151 141 137 159 142 146
151 157 143 154 146 143 149 151 141 148
136 144 147 152 147 137 133 140 139 155

(a) Put the heights into groups

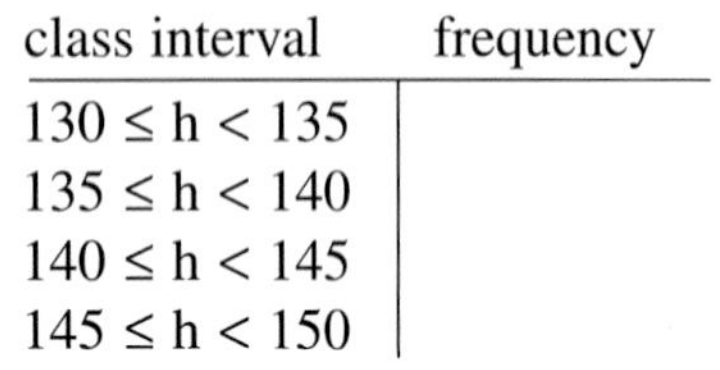

class interval	frequency
$130 \le h < 135$	
$135 \le h < 140$	
$140 \le h < 145$	
$145 \le h < 150$	

(b) Draw a frequency diagram

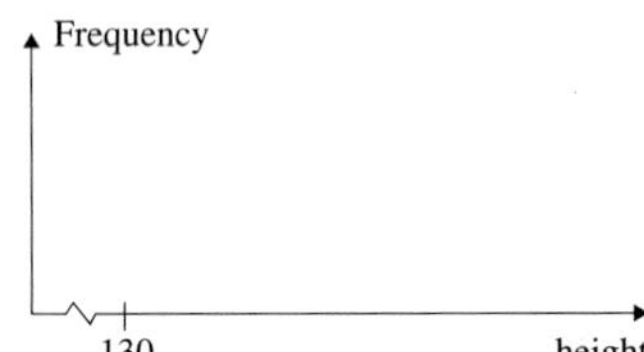

3 A group of 7 year-olds were each accompanied by one of their parents on a coach trip to a zoo. Each person on the coach was weighed in kg. Here are the weights.

21.1, 45.7, 22.3, 26.3, 50.1, 24.3, 44.2,
54.3, 53.2, 46.0, 51.0, 24.2, 56.4, 20.6,
25.5, 22.8, 52.0, 26.5, 41.8, 27.5, 29.7,
55.1, 30.7, 47.4, 23.5, 59.8, 49.3, 23.4,
21.7, 57.6, 22.6, 58.7, 28.6, 54.1.

(a) Put the weights into groups.

class interval	frequency
$20 \le w < 25$	
$25 \le w < 30$	
$30 \le w < 35$	
⋮	

(b) Draw a frequency diagram.

(c) Why is the shape of the frequency diagram different to the diagram you drew in question 2?

(d) What shape of frequency diagram would you expect to obtain if you drew a diagram to show the heights of pupils in your class?

4 Tom has lots of snakes and he likes to weigh them every week. The weights are shown.

(a) How many snakes weigh between 61 and 80 grams?

(b) How many snakes weigh less than 41 grams?

(c) How many snakes does he have altogether?

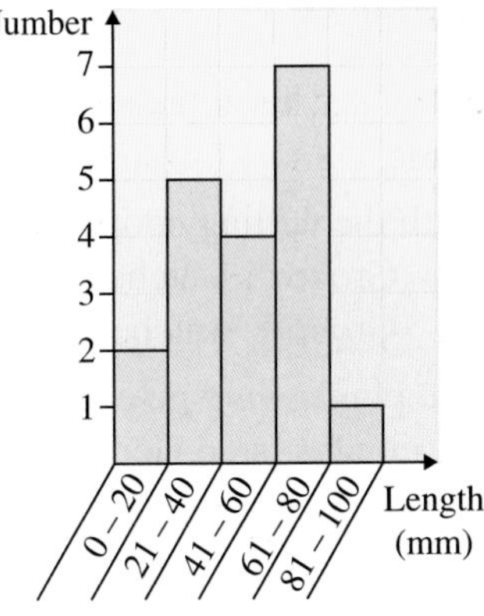

5 Farmer Gray rears pigs. As an experiment, he decided to feed half of his pigs with their normal diet and the other half on a new high fibre diet. The diagrams show the weight of the pigs in the two groups.

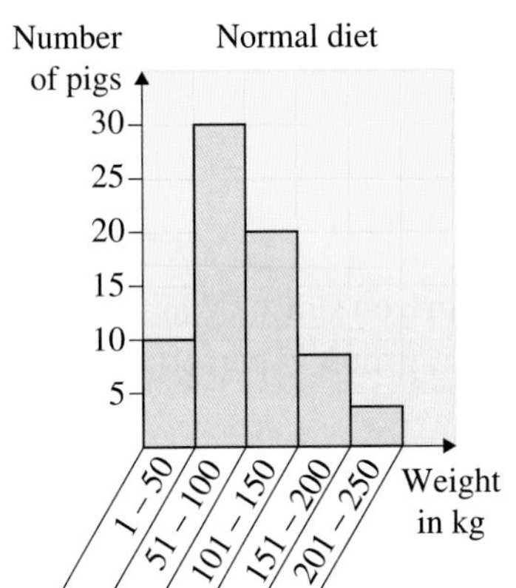

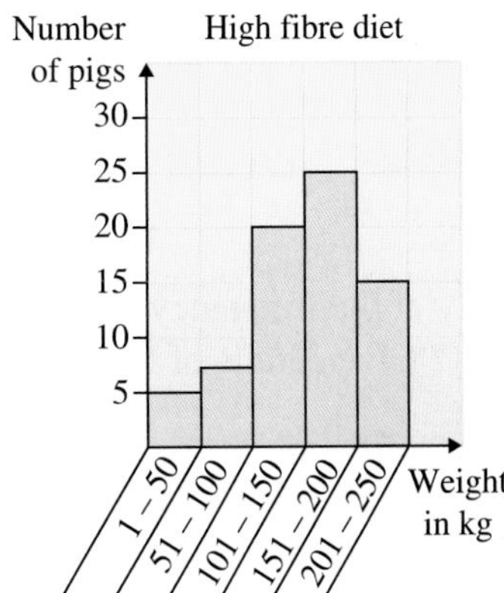

In one sentence describe what effect the new diet had.

6 A drug company claims that its new nutrient pill helps people to improve their memory. As an experiment two randomly selected groups of people were given the same memory test. Group A took the new pills for a month while group B took no pills. Here are the results of the tests: (A high score indicates a good memory).

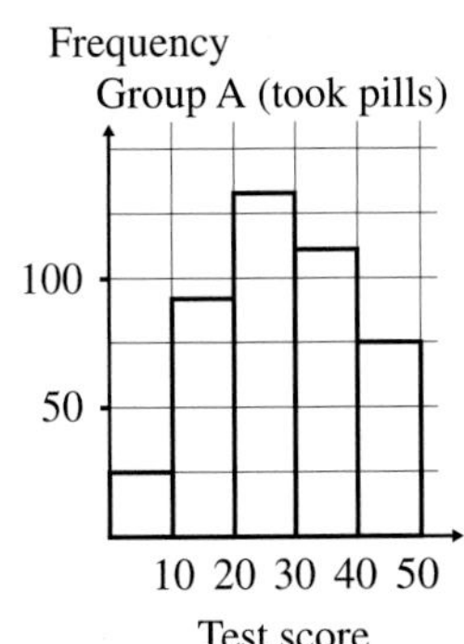

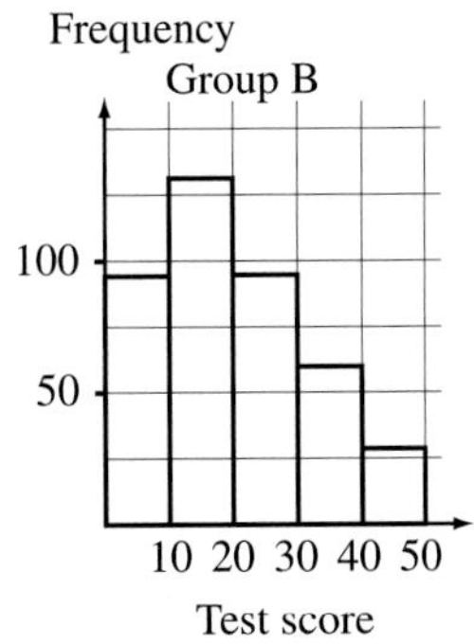

Does it appear that the new pills did in fact help to improve memory?

Exercise 2E

1 A teacher has a theory that pupils' test results are affected by the amount of T.V. watched at home.

With the willing cooperation of the children's parents, the pupils were split into two groups:

Group X watched at least two hours of T.V. per day.

Group Y watched a maximum of half an hour per day.

The pupils were given two tests: one at the start of the experiment and another test six months later. Here are the results:

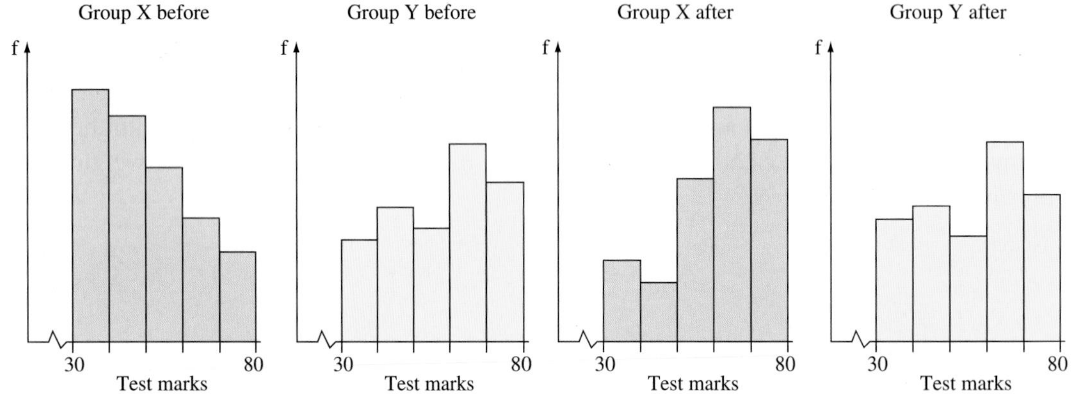

Look carefully at the frequency diagrams. What conclusions can you draw? Was the teacher's theory correct? Give details of how the pupils in group X and in group Y performed in the two tests.

2 A car went on a five hour journey starting at 12 00 with a full tank of petrol. The volume of petrol in the tank was measured after every hour; the results are shown below.

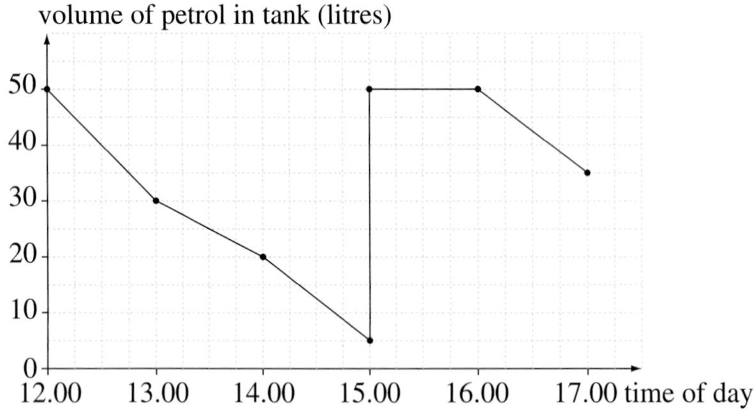

(a) How much petrol was in the tank at 13.00?
(b) At what time was there 5 litres in the tank?
(c) How much petrol was used in the first hour of the journey?
(d) What happened at 15.00?
(e) What do you think happened between 15.00 and 16.00?
(f) How much petrol was used between 12.00 and 17.00?

3 This diagram shows the temperature and rainfall readings in one week.
The rainfall is shown as the bar chart.
The temperature is shown as the line graph.

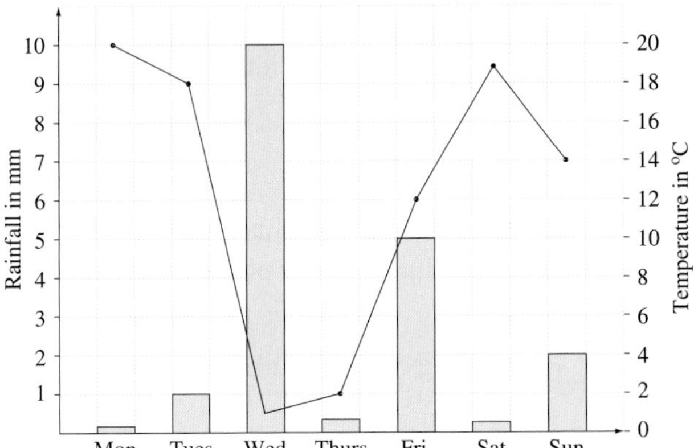

(a) Use both graphs to describe the weather on Monday.
(b) On which day was the weather cold and wet?
(c) Compare the weather on Thursday and Saturday.

4 Here is an age distribution pyramid for the children at a Center Parcs resort.
(a) How many girls were there aged 5–9?
(b) How many children were there altogether in the 0–4 age range?
(c) How many girls were at the resort?

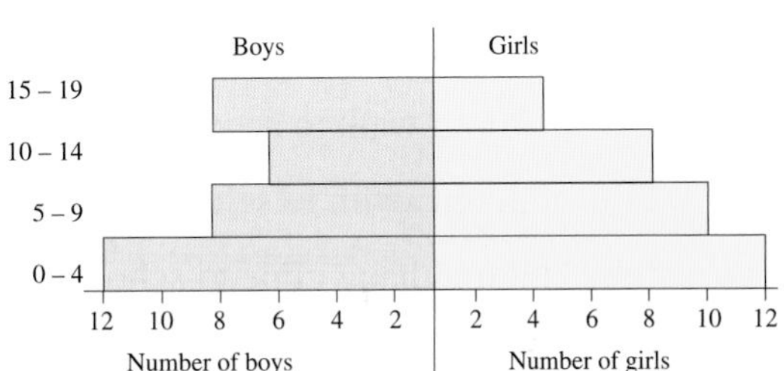

5 Here are age distribution pyramids for the U.K., Kenya and Saudi Arabia. The bars represent the percentage of the population in the age group shown.

U.K.

Kenya

Saudi Arabia

(a) For the U.K. about what percentage of the population are *male aged 20–24*?
(b) For Kenya about what percentage are *female aged 0–4*?
(c) What percentage of the population are *female aged 75+*
  (i) for the U.K?
  (ii) for Kenya?

[P.T.O for (d), (e)]

(d) Look carefully at the charts for the U.K. and Kenya. Write a sentence to describe the main differences in the age distribution for the two countries. Write a possible explanation for the differences you observed.

(e) Look carefully at the charts for Kenya and Saudi Arabia. Do both countries have about half male and half female populations? Explain your answer using information in the charts.

Pie charts

In a pie chart a circle is divided into sectors to display information. Pie charts are often used to show the results of a survey. The sectors of the circle show what *fraction* of the total is in each group. Here are two pie charts.

- How children go to a school in the Alps.

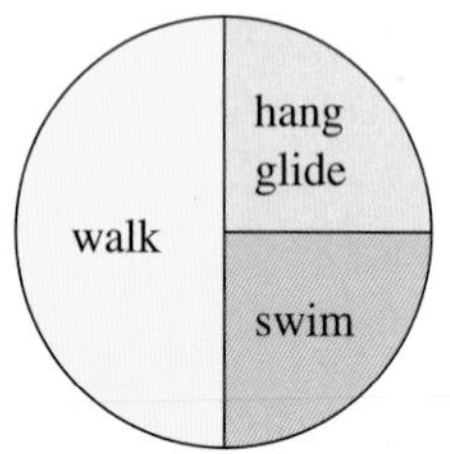

$\frac{1}{2}$ of the children walk to school

$\frac{1}{4}$ of the children swim to school

$\frac{1}{4}$ of the children hang glide to school

- People in a Spanish jail.

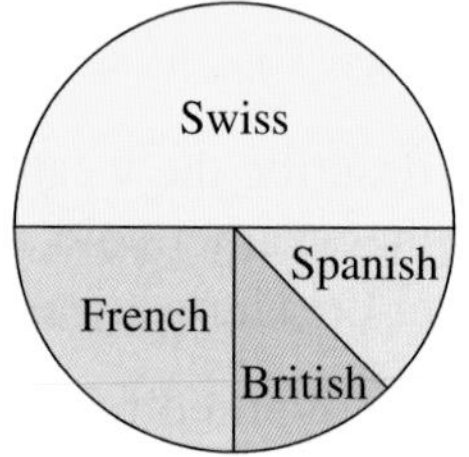

$\frac{1}{8}$ of the people were Spanish

$\frac{1}{8}$ of the people were British

$\frac{1}{4}$ of the people were French

$\frac{1}{2}$ of the people were Swiss

Exercise 3M

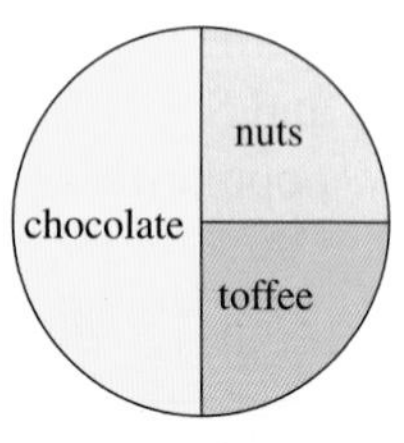

1 The pie chart shows the contents of a bar of chocolate.

(a) What fraction of the contents is chocolate?

(b) What fraction of the contents is toffee?

(c) If the total weight of the packet is 400 g, what is the weight of nuts?

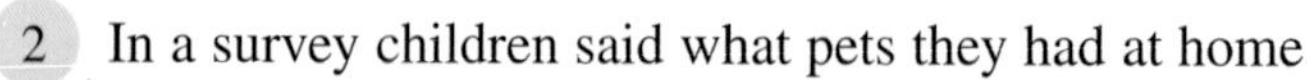

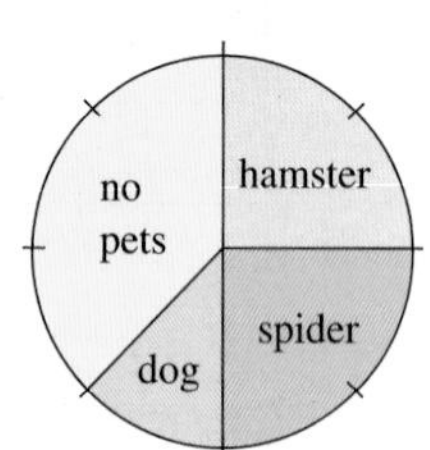

2 In a survey children said what pets they had at home.

(a) What fraction of the children had a hamster?

(b) What fraction of the children had a dog?

(c) 40 children took part in the survey. How many of these children had a pet spider?

3 In another survey children were asked what *pests* they had at home. One third of the children said, 'my sister'. What angle would you draw for the 'my sister' sector on a pie chart?

4 The pie chart shows the results of a survey in which 80 people were asked how they travelled to work. Copy this table and fill it in.

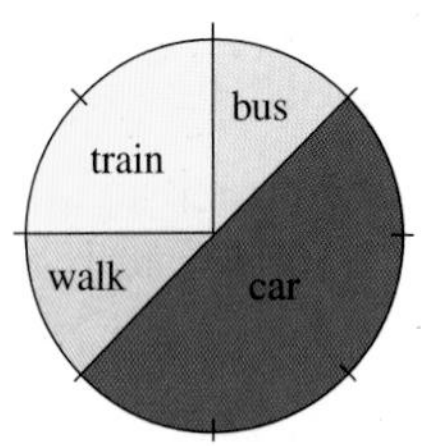

Method	car	walk	train	bus
Number of people				

5 In 2007 and 2008 children were asked in a survey to say which country they would most like to go to for a holiday. The pie charts show the results.

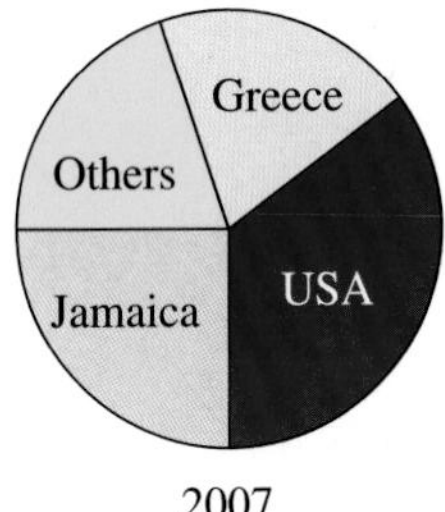

2007

100 children answered in each year

Countries in the 'others' section had only one or two votes each.

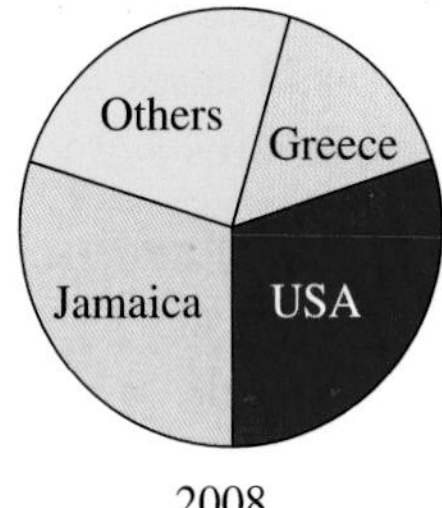

2008

(a) Which was the most popular country in the 2007 survey?
(b) Which country was less popular in 2008 than in 2007?
(c) *Roughly* how many children said 'Jamaica' in the 2007 survey?

6

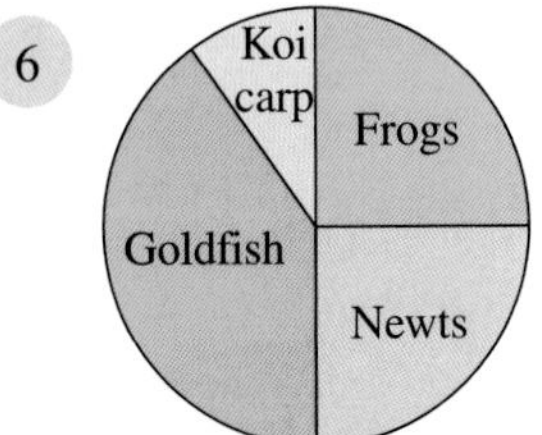

Jodie counted the different animals in her pond. Altogether there were 200 animals or fish.
(a) *About* how many frogs were there?
(b) *About* how many goldfish were there?

7 The children at a school were asked to state their favourite colour. Here are the results.

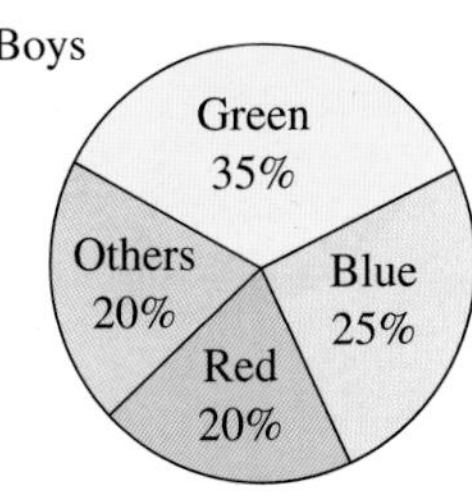

There were 40 boys

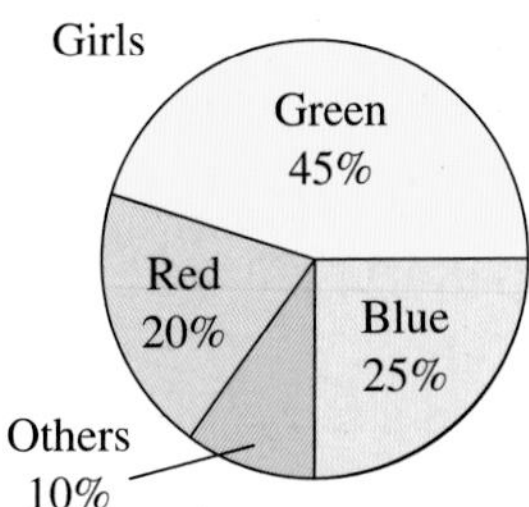

There were 25 girls

John says 'The same number of boys and girls chose red.'
Tara says 'More boys than girls chose blue.'
(a) Use both charts to explain whether or not John is right.
(b) Use both charts to explain whether or not Tara is right.

Calculating angles in pie charts

A farmer divides his land into three parts. He uses 5 acres for corn, 3 acres for carrots and 2 acres for pigs.

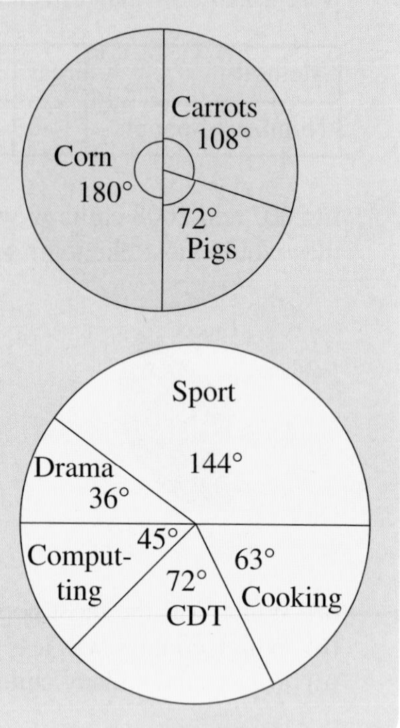

(a) Add the three parts: $5 + 3 + 2 = 10$ acres

(b) 10 acres = 360°

$$1 \text{ acre} = \frac{360}{10}$$
$$= 36^\circ$$

(c) For corn, 5 acres = $5 \times 36^\circ = 180^\circ$
For carrots, 3 acres = $3 \times 36^\circ = 108^\circ$
For pigs, 2 acres = $2 \times 36^\circ = 72^\circ$

This pie chart shows the after-school activities of 200 pupils.

(a) The number of pupils doing drama $= \frac{36}{360} \times 200 = 20$

(b) The number of pupils doing sport $= \frac{144}{360} \times 200 = 80$

(c) The number of pupils doing computing $= \frac{45}{360} \times 200 = 25$

Exercise 3E

1 Lara had £24 to spend on presents. The pie chart shows how much she spent on each person.
How much did she spend on:
(a) her mum (b) her dad
(c) her brother (d) her grandma
(e) her friend (f) her auntie?
[Make sure that your answers add up to £24.]

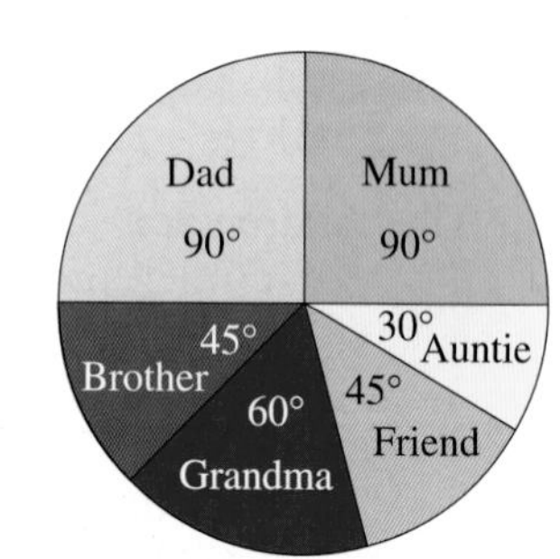

2 Six hundred families travelling home on a ferry were asked to name the country in which they had spent most of their holiday. The pie chart represents their answers.
(a) How many stayed longest (i) in Portugal?
(ii) in Spain?
(b) What angle represents holidays in Switzerland?
(c) How many families stayed longest in Switzerland?

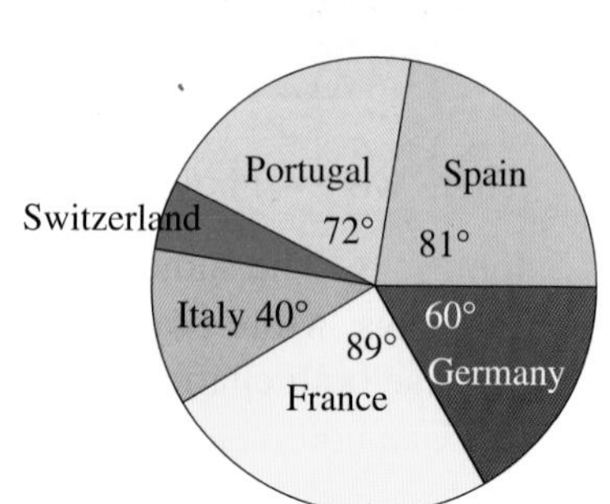

3 A 'Chewit' bar contains these four ingredients:

Oats	6 g
Barley	9 g
Sugar	3 g
Rye	18 g

(a) Work out the total weight of the ingredients.
(b) Work out the angle on a pie chart for 1 g of the ingredients [i.e. $360° \div$ (total weight)].
(c) Work out the angle for each ingredient and draw a pie chart.

In questions 4, 5, 6 work out the angle for each sector and draw a pie chart.

4 Number of programmes per night.

Programme	Frequency
News	2
Soap	5
Comedy	4
Drama	5
Film	2

5 Pupils' favourite sports.

Sport	Frequency
Rugby	5
Football	7
Tennis	4
Squash	2
Athletics	3
Swimming	3

6 Periods per subject.

Subject	Frequency
Maths	5
English	5
Science	6
Humanities	4
Arts	4
Others	16

7 At the 'Crooked Corkscrew' last Friday, 120 customers ordered meals.

40 ordered beefburger
20 ordered ham salad
16 ordered curry
25 ordered cod
19 ordered chicken.

Draw a pie chart to show this information.

8 In a survey the children at a school were asked to state their favourite sport in the Olympics.

(a) Estimate what fraction of the children chose gymnastics.
(b) There are 120 children in the school. Estimate the number of children who chose athletics.
(c) 15% of the children chose swimming. How many children was that?

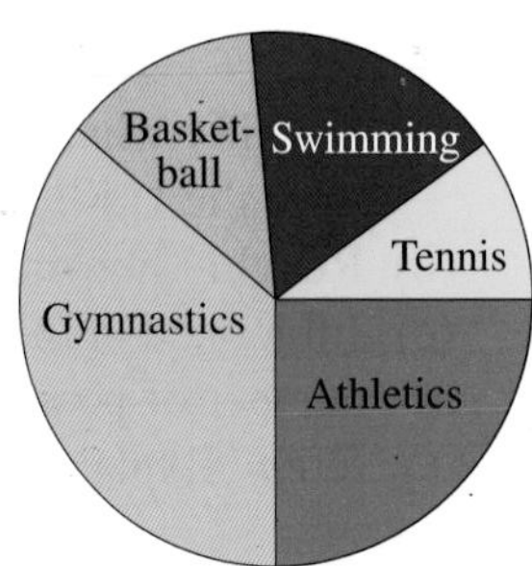

9 A hidden observer watched Stephen in a 60 minute maths lesson. This is how he spent his time:

Looking for a calculator	8 minutes
Sharpening a pencil	7 minutes
Talking	32 minutes
Checking the clock	2 minutes
Working	4 minutes
Packing up	7 minutes

Draw an accurate pie chart to illustrate Stephen's lesson.

10 The pie chart illustrates the sales of four brands of petrol.

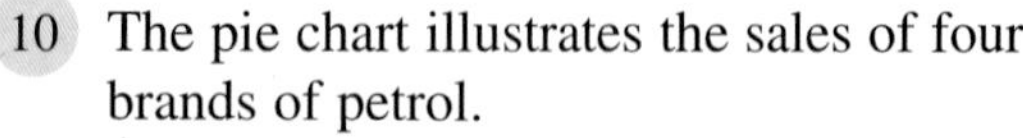

(a) What percentage of total sales does BP have?

(b) If Shell accounts for 35% of total sales, calculate the angles x and y.

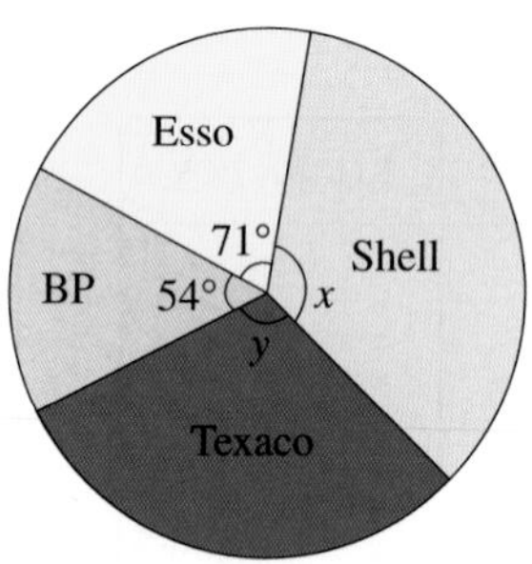

11 In a survey 320 people on an aircraft and 800 people on a ferry were asked to state their nationality.

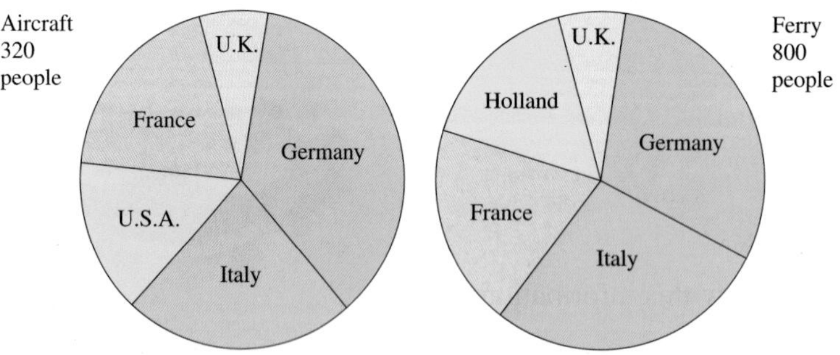

(a) Roughly what percentage of the people on the aircraft were from the U.K?

(b) Roughly how many people from France were on the ferry?

(c) Jill looked at the charts and said 'There were about the same number of people from Italy on the aircraft and on the ferry'. Explain why Jill is wrong.

Problems answered using statistics

Many problems in mathematics and other subjects, like science or geography can be solved by statistical methods.

The data relevant to such problems might be obtained from:

- a survey of a sample of people;
- an experiment;
- published material, such as tables or charts, from reference books.

Here are two examples of problems which can be answered using statistical methods.

1 Do different newspapers use words of different length or sentences of different length? Why would they do this?
In this case you could conduct an experiment by choosing a similar page from different newspapers.
Record your results in a table.

Number of words in a sentence	1–5	6–10	11–15	16–20	21 or more
Times					
Sun					
Mail					

2 What factors are most important to the customers of supermarkets?
In this case you could conduct a survey asking about price of food, quality of food, speed of checkouts, ease of car parking and so on.
You would need questions designed so that shoppers could state the importance, or otherwise, of the factors you include.

Reporting on results

Most work of this nature is easier to understand if data is presented in the form of graphs and charts. You should *justify* the choice of the data you present. You might find it helpful to include calculations of mean or range depending on the context.

Your report should highlight the main findings of your work and you should write a clear *summary* which relates back to the original problem.

3.7 Probability 1

In this section you will learn about:

- the probability scale
- experimental probability
- equally likely outcomes
- expected probability

In probability we ask questions like…

'How likely is it?'

'What are the chances of…?'

Here are some questions where we do not know the answer…

'Will it rain tomorrow?'

'With global warming will my grandchildren go to school on a camel?'

'Will the school be struck by lightning?'

Some events are certain. Some events are impossible.

Some events are in between certain and impossible.

> The probability of an event is a measure of the chance of it happening.
>
> The probability (or chance) of an event occurring is measured on a scale like this…
>
> impossible — unlikely — evens — likely — certain

Exercise 1M

Draw a probability scale like this…

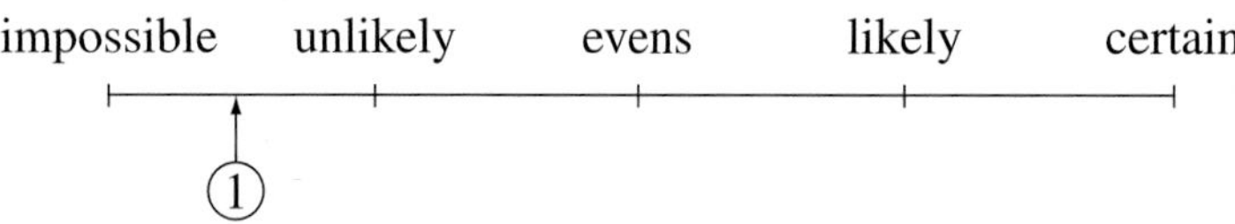

Draw an arrow to show the chance of the events below happening.

[The arrow for question 1 has been done for you.]

1. When a card is selected from a pack it will be an 'ace'.
2. When a coin is tossed it will show a 'head'.
3. You will discover a tarantula in your bed tonight.
4. When a drawing pin is dropped it will land 'point up'.
5. It will rain in Manchester on at least one day in April next year.
6. You get a total of one when two dice are thrown together.

7 The day after Monday will be Tuesday.

8 There will be a burst pipe in the school heating system next week and the school will have to close for 3 days.

9 You will blink your eyes in the next minute.

10 You will be asked to tidy your room this week.

11 When a slice of toast is dropped, it will land on the floor buttered side down.

12 The letter 'a' appears somewhere on the next page of this book.

Probability as a number

Different countries have different words for saying how likely or unlikely any particular event is. All over the world people use probability as a way of doing this, using numbers on a scale instead of words.
The scale looks like this…

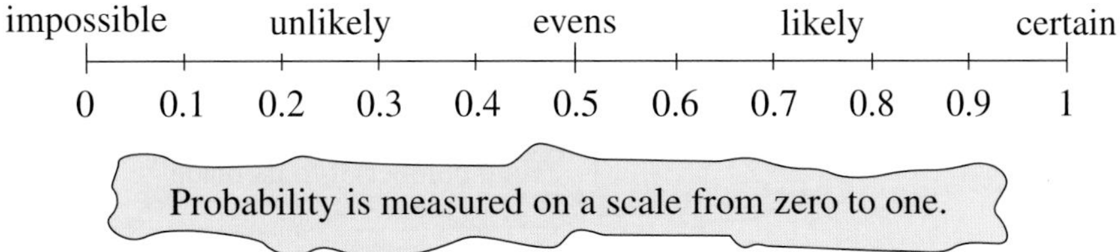

Probability is measured on a scale from zero to one.

Exercise 1E

Look at the events in the last exercise and for each one estimate the probability of it occurring using a probability from 0 to 1.

As an example in question 1 you might write 'about 0.1'. Copy each question and write your estimate of its probability at the end.

Experimental probability

The chance of certain events occurring can easily be predicted. For example the chance of tossing a head with an ordinary coin. Many events, however, cannot be so easily predicted.

Experiment: To find the experimental probability that the third word in the third line on any page in this book contains the letter 'a' (You could use a non-mathematical book if you prefer)

Step 1. We will do 50 *trials*. Write down at random 50 page numbers between 1 and 180 (say 3, 15, 16, 21, 27, etc.).

Step 2. For each page look at the third word in the third line. This is a *trial*. If there is not a third word on the third line it still counts as a trial. (The third line might be all numbers.)

> **37**
>
> **Angles in triangles**
> Draw a triangle of any shape on a piece of card and cut it out accurately. Now tear off the three corners as shown.

third line, third word

Step 3. If the word contains the letter 'a' this is a *success*.

Step 4. Make a tally chart like this…

Number of trials	Number of successes
𝍸 𝍸 II	𝍸 II

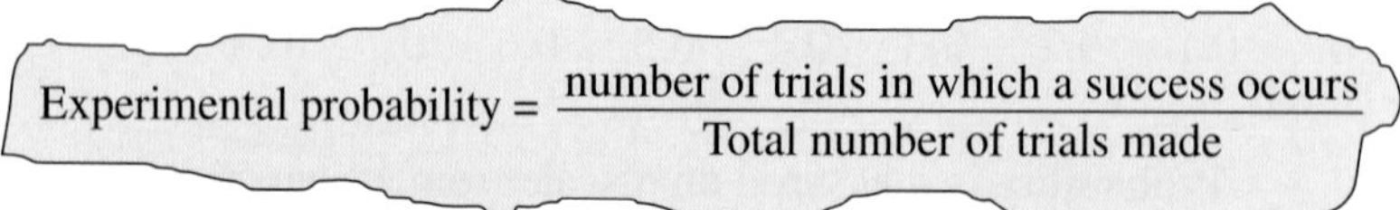

Experimental probability = number of trials in which a success occurs / Total number of trials made

Exercise 2M

Carry out experiments to work out the experimental probability of some of the following events. Use a tally chart to record your results. Don't forget to record how many times you do the experiment (the number of 'trials').

1 Roll a dice. What is the chance of rolling a six? Perform 100 trials.

2 Toss two coins. What is the chance of tossing two tails? Perform 100 trials.

3 Pick a counter from a bag containing counters of different colours. What is the chance of picking a red counter? Perform 100 trials.

4 Roll a pair of dice. What is the chance of rolling a double? Perform 100 trials.

5 Butter a piece of toast and drop it on the floor. What is the chance of it landing buttered side down? Would you expect to get the same result with margarine? How about butter and jam? Suppose you don't toast the bread?

Equally likely outcomes

When you roll a fair dice there are six *equally likely outcomes*.
You are equally likely to roll a 1, 2, 3, 4, 5 or 6.
So, for example, the probability of rolling a 3 is $\frac{1}{6}$.
You also have equally likely outcomes when you use a spinner with equal sectors.
In this spinner there are four equal sectors.
The probability of spinning yellow is $\frac{1}{4}$.

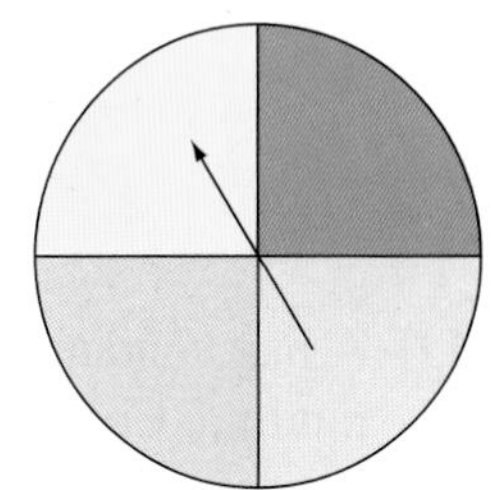

Exercise 3M

For each spinner what is the probability of getting red?

1 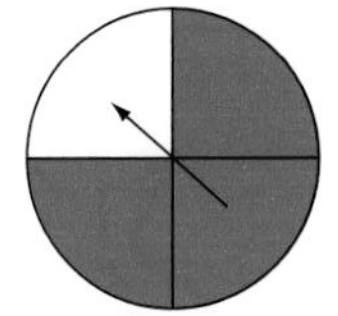

2 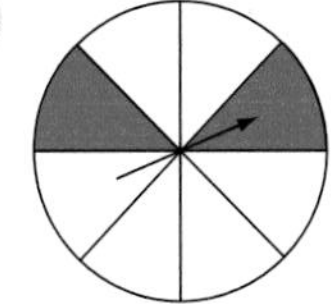

3 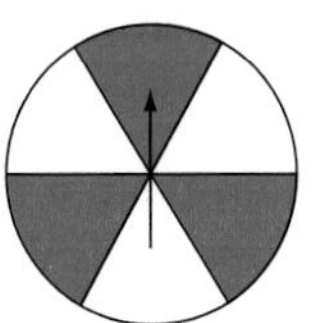

4 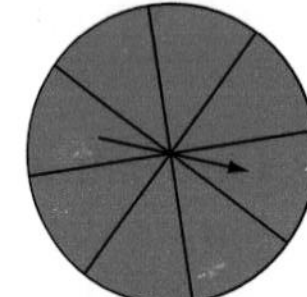

5 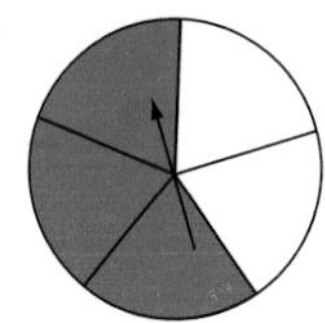

6 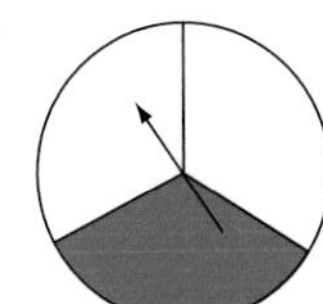

7 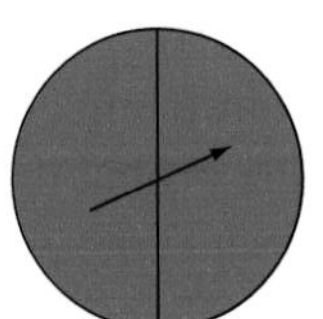

8 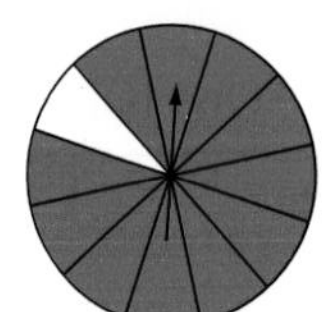

9 What is the probability of getting blue on each spinner?

(a) 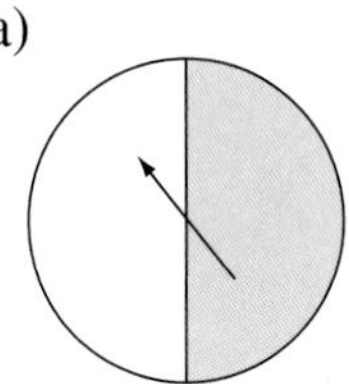

(b) 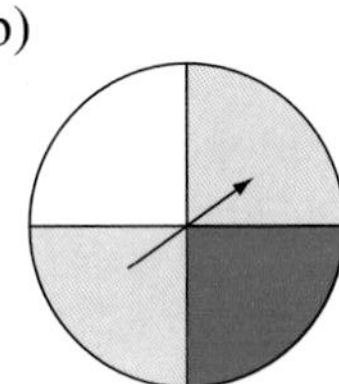

(c) 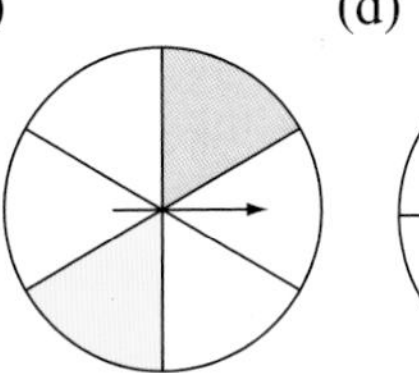

(d) 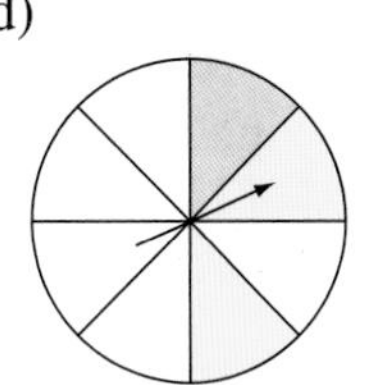

10 For this question you need a dice.

(a) Copy the table below and fill in the second row.

Number of rolls of dice	12	24	36	48	60
Number of 4s expected					
Actual number of 4s					

(b) Now roll the dice 60 times, filling in the third row every 12 rolls.

11

One peg is selected at random from those shown. What is the probability of selecting a red peg?

12 A bag contains a red ball, a blue ball and a yellow ball. One ball is chosen at random. Copy and complete these sentences.

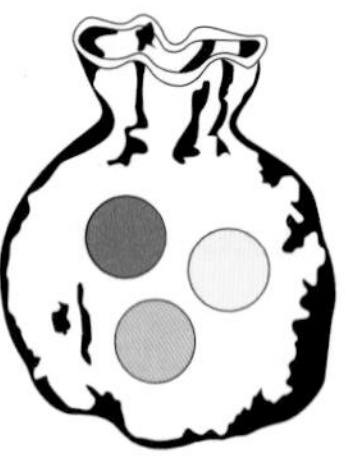

(a) The probability that the red ball is chosen is . . . $\frac{\square}{3}$

(b) The probability that the blue ball is chosen is . . . $\frac{\square}{\square}$

(c) The probability that the yellow ball is chosen is . . . $\frac{\square}{\square}$

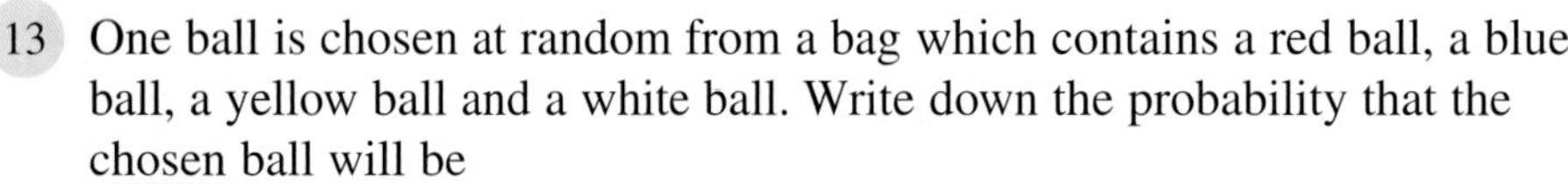

13 One ball is chosen at random from a bag which contains a red ball, a blue ball, a yellow ball and a white ball. Write down the probability that the chosen ball will be

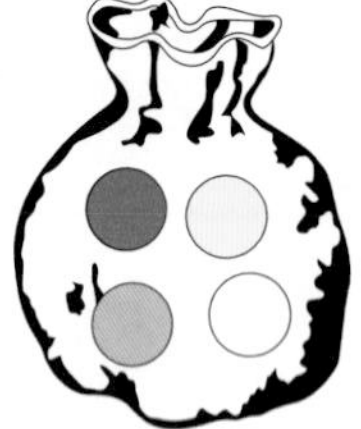

(a) red (b) blue (c) yellow

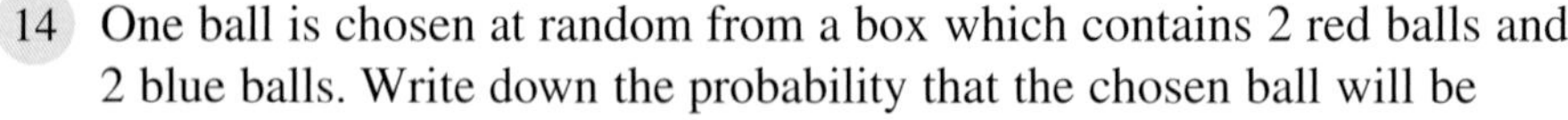

14 One ball is chosen at random from a box which contains 2 red balls and 2 blue balls. Write down the probability that the chosen ball will be
(a) red
(b) blue
(c) yellow

Expected probability

For simple events, like throwing a dice or tossing a coin, we can work out the expected probability of an event occurring.

For a fair dice the *expected probability* of throwing a '3' is $\frac{1}{6}$,

For a normal coin the expected probability of tossing a 'head' is $\frac{1}{2}$

$$\text{Expected probability} = \frac{\text{the number of ways the event can happen}}{\text{the number of possible outcomes}}$$

Random choice: If a card is chosen at random from a pack it means that every card has an equal chance of being chosen.

Nine identical discs numbered 1, 2, 3, 4, 5, 6, 7, 8, 9 are put into a bag.
One disc is selected at random.
In this example there are 9 possible equally likely outcomes of a trial.

(a) The probability of selecting a '4' = $\frac{1}{9}$

This may be written p (selecting a '4') = $\frac{1}{9}$

(b) p (selecting an odd number) = $\frac{5}{9}$

(c) p (selecting a number greater than 5) = $\frac{4}{9}$

Exercise 3E

1 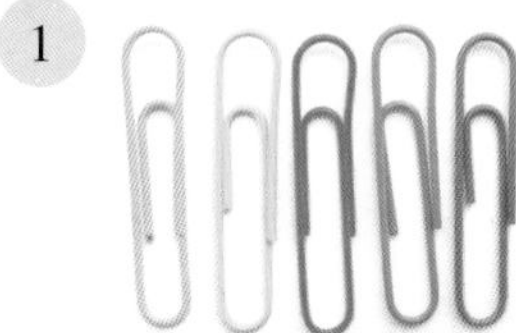

One paper clip is chosen at random from these.
Find the probability that it is
(a) green (b) blue (c) silver

2 A hat contains 2 white balls and 1 black ball. One ball is chosen at random. Find the probability that it is.
(a) white
(b) black

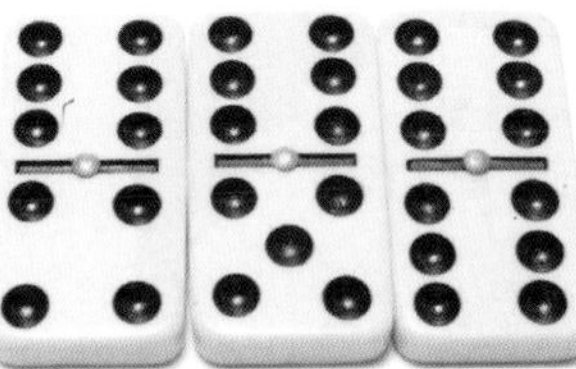

3 One domino is selected from those shown.
Find the probability that the total number of spots on the domino is
(a) 11 (b) more than 10

4 A pencil case contains pencils of the following colours:- 6 red, 3 black, 1 green and 1 blue.
One pencil is selected without looking. Find the probability that the pencil is
(a) red (b) black (c) green (d) not blue

5 One number is selected at random from these.
Find the probability that it is
(a) an '8' (b) yellow or green (c) a prime number

6 I roll an ordinary dice. Find the probability that I score
(a) 3
(b) 1
(c) less than 5

7 Eight identical discs numbered 1, 2, 3, 4, 5, 6, 7, 8 are put into a bag. One disc is selected at random. Find the probability of selecting
(a) a '5' (b) an odd number (c) a number less than 6

8 Nine identical discs numbered 1, 3, 4, 5, 7, 8, 10, 11, 15 are put into a bag. One disc is selected at random. Find the probability of selecting.
(a) a'10' (b) an even number (c) a number more than 6

9 I buy a fish at random from a pond containing 3 piranhas, 2 baby sharks and 7 goldfish. Find the probability that the fish I chose is
(a) a goldfish (b) a baby shark
(c) dangerous (d) glad I rescued it!
(e) able to play the piano

10 A bag contains 4 red balls and 7 white balls. One ball is selected at random. Find the probability that it is
(a) red (b) white

11 A bag contains 2 red balls, 4 white balls and 5 blue balls. One ball is selected at random. Find the probability of selecting.
(a) a red ball (b) a white ball (c) not a white ball

12 One card is selected at random from the cards shown. Find the probability of selecting
(a) the king of hearts (b) a Joker
(c) a 2 (d) an Ace

13 A bag contains fifty balls numbered from 1 to 50. One ball is selected at random. Find the probability that it is
(a) a multiple of 10 (b) a square number
(c) a prime number (d) divisible by 9
(e) a cube number (f) a factor of both 7 and 15

14 What is the probability of spinning?
(a) yellow (b) green
(c) pink or yellow (d) blue
(e) not blue?

15

The alphabet bricks are put in a bag and one brick is selected at random.
Find the probability that the letter chosen is

(a) a vowel (b) the 'z'
(c) a letter in the word 'HAT'
(d) a letter in the word 'MUSIC'

CHECK YOURSELF ON UNITS 3.5, 3.6 and 3.7

1 Lines parallel to the axes

ABCD is a rectangle.

(a) Write down the coordinates of A.
(b) Write down the equation of line AD.
(c) Write down the equation of line DC.
(d) N is in the middle of the rectangle. What are the coordinates of N?

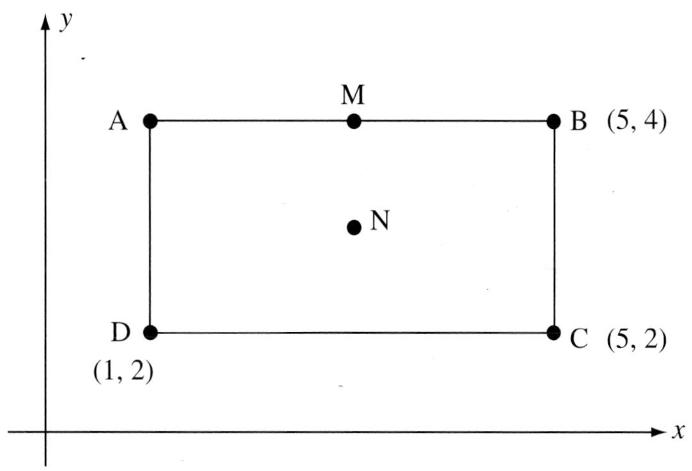

2 Finding the equation of a line and drawing graphs

(a) Which is the equation of line C?
$y = 2x$, $y = x$, $y = x - 2$

(b) Write down the equation of (i) line A (ii) line B

(c) Which of the points below lie on the line $y = x + 1$?
P (4, 5) Q (6, 5) R (0, 1)

(d) Fill in the missing numbers for the line $y = 2x - 1$
(0, –1), (1, □), (2, □), (3, □)

(e) Draw the graph of $y = 2x - 1$

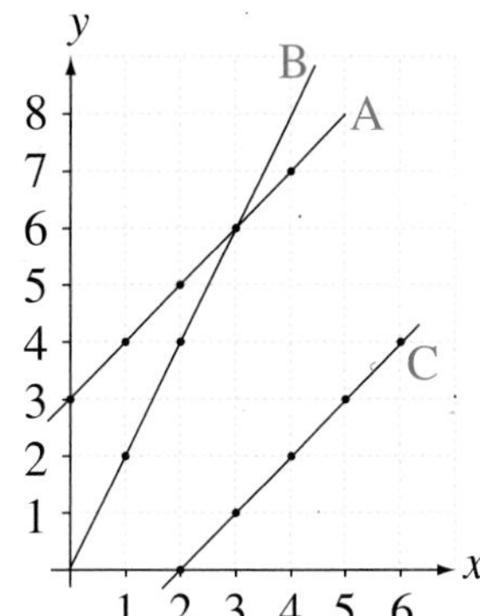

3 Data in groups and line graphs

(a) At a medical inspection the 11/12 year-olds in a school have their heights measured. The results are shown.

136.8, 146.2, 141.2, 147.2, 151.3, 145.0, 155.0,
149.9, 138.0, 146.8, 157.4, 143.1, 143.5, 147.2,
147.5, 158.6, 154.7, 144.6, 152.4, 144.0, 151.0.

(i) Put the heights into groups

class interval	frequency
$135 \le h < 140$	
$140 \le h < 145$	
$145 \le h < 150$	

(ii) Draw a frequency diagram

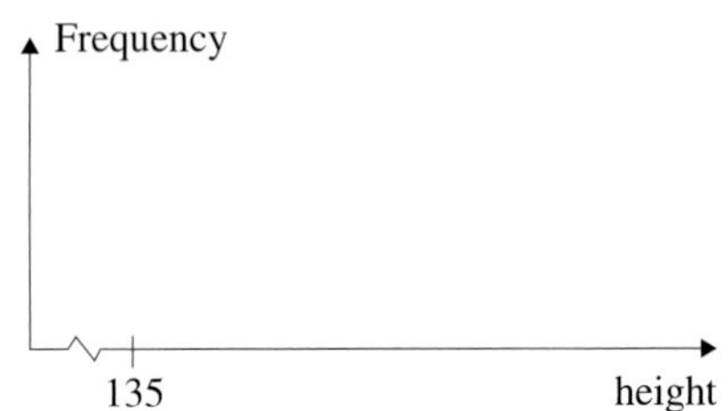

(b) Some keen gardeners collect rain water from the roofs of their homes into rain barrels. They use the water from the barrel when the ground is dry to save using tap water.

Look at this graph and write down what you think is happening. Use the labels A, B, C...

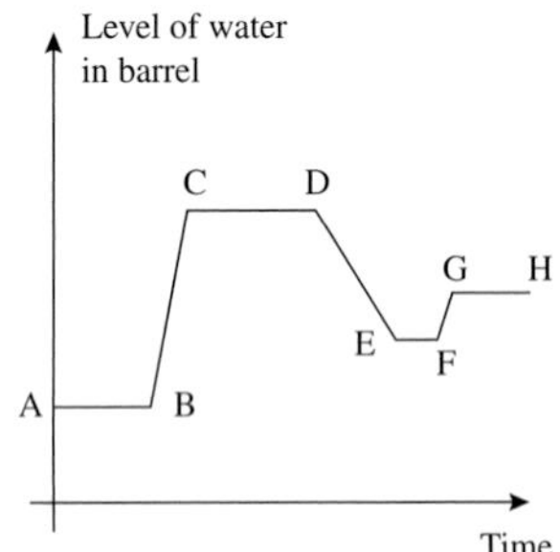

4 Pie charts

In a survey 900 children at a school were asked to state their favourite sport in the Olympics.

(a) How many chose swimming?
(b) How many chose gymnastics?
(c) How many chose either tennis or basket ball?

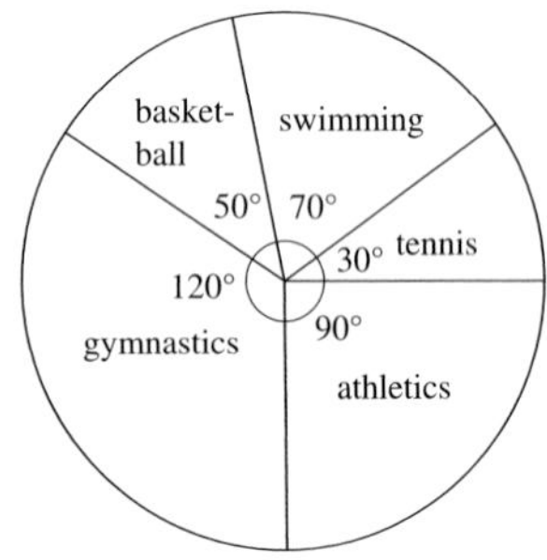

5 Probability involving equally likely outcomes

(a) For each spinner state the probability of getting blue.

(i)

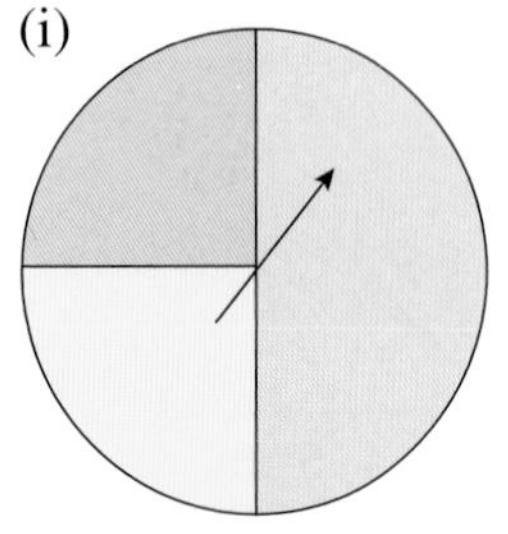

(ii)

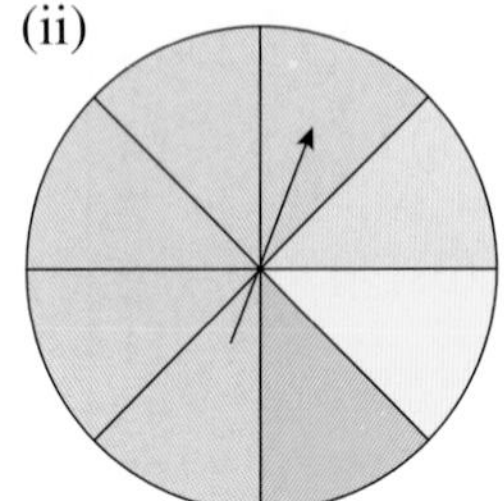

(iii)

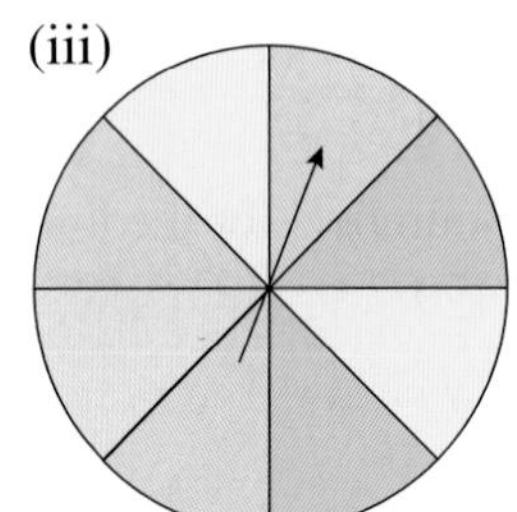

(iv)

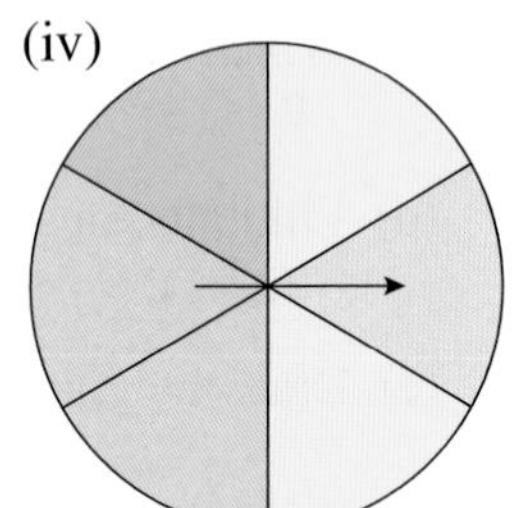

(b) One card is selected at random from a normal pack of 52 playing cards. Find the probability of selecting:

(i) the king of diamonds (ii) an ace (iii) a red card

6 Expected probability

A bag contains 1 blue ball, 3 red balls and 7 white balls.

(a) If I select a ball at random from the bag without looking, what colour ball am I most likely to select?

(b) What is the probability I select:

(i) a white ball?
(ii) a red ball?
(iii) a green ball?
(iv) a blue ball?

3.8 Applying mathematics in a range of contexts

In section 3.8 you will try to:

- solve problems in a variety of real life situations
- solve a range of puzzles
- investigate problems with more than one solution

Exercise 1M

1 A school play was attended by 226 adults, each paying £1.50, and 188 children, each paying 80p. How much in £s was paid altogether by the people attending the play?

2 An Airbus 360 leaves Paris at 07:00 and arrives in New York at 10:20.
A cargo plane leaves Paris at 07:10 and flies at half the speed of the Airbus. When should it arrive in New York?

3 In a new office building there are 82 doors, and each door is fastened by 3 hinges. If each hinge requires 6 screws, what is the total number of screws required to fit all the doors?

4 Use the table to write the calculation $2 \times 4 = 8$ using Chinese symbols.

(Use $\times$ for the multiplication unless you know the Chinese symbol. If you know the Chinese symbol please inform the authors of this book.)

絵 Picture	水 Water	月 Moon	楽 Fun	朝 Morning	考 Think	雪 Snow	鳥 Bird
夢 Dream	人 Person	火 Fire	友 Friend	心 Heart	七 Seven	雨 Rain	宝 Treasure
金 Gold	花 Flower	夜 Night	八 Eight	空 Sky	風 Wind	強 Strength	土 Earth
猫 Cat	星 Star	二 Two	九 Nine	一 One	二 Two	三 Three	四 Four

5 A shopkeeper buys coffee beans at £4.20 per kg and sells them at 95p per 100 g. How much profit does he make per kg?

6 An Audi A6 uses 8 litres of petrol for every 50 km travelled. Petrol costs 97p per litre. Calculate the cost in £ s of travelling 600 km.

7 Write the number 'six million twelve thousand and eleven' in figures.

8 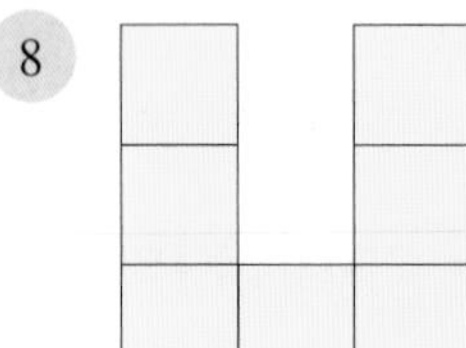

The area of the 'U' shape is 175 cm^2.

(a) Find the area of each small square.

(b) Work out the length of the perimeter of the shape.

9 There are 208 pupils in Year 7 of a school.
How many teams of six can be formed?
How many pupils will be left over?

10 (a) What is the length of this line in millimetres?
(b) What is this length in centimetres?

Exercise 2M

1 Write the next number in each sequence

(a) 1 5 9 13 ☐

(b) 32 31 29 26 ☐

(c) 24 12 6 3 ☐

(d) 0.2 2 20 ☐

2 In a 'magic square' all rows (↔) columns (↕) and main diagonals (⤡) add up to the same 'magic number'. Copy and complete this magic square.

11			10
2	13	16	
		4	
7	12		6

3 A book has pages numbered 1 to 300 and the thickness of the book, without the covers, is 12 mm. How thick is each page?

4 Write 30 billion pence in pounds and pence.

5 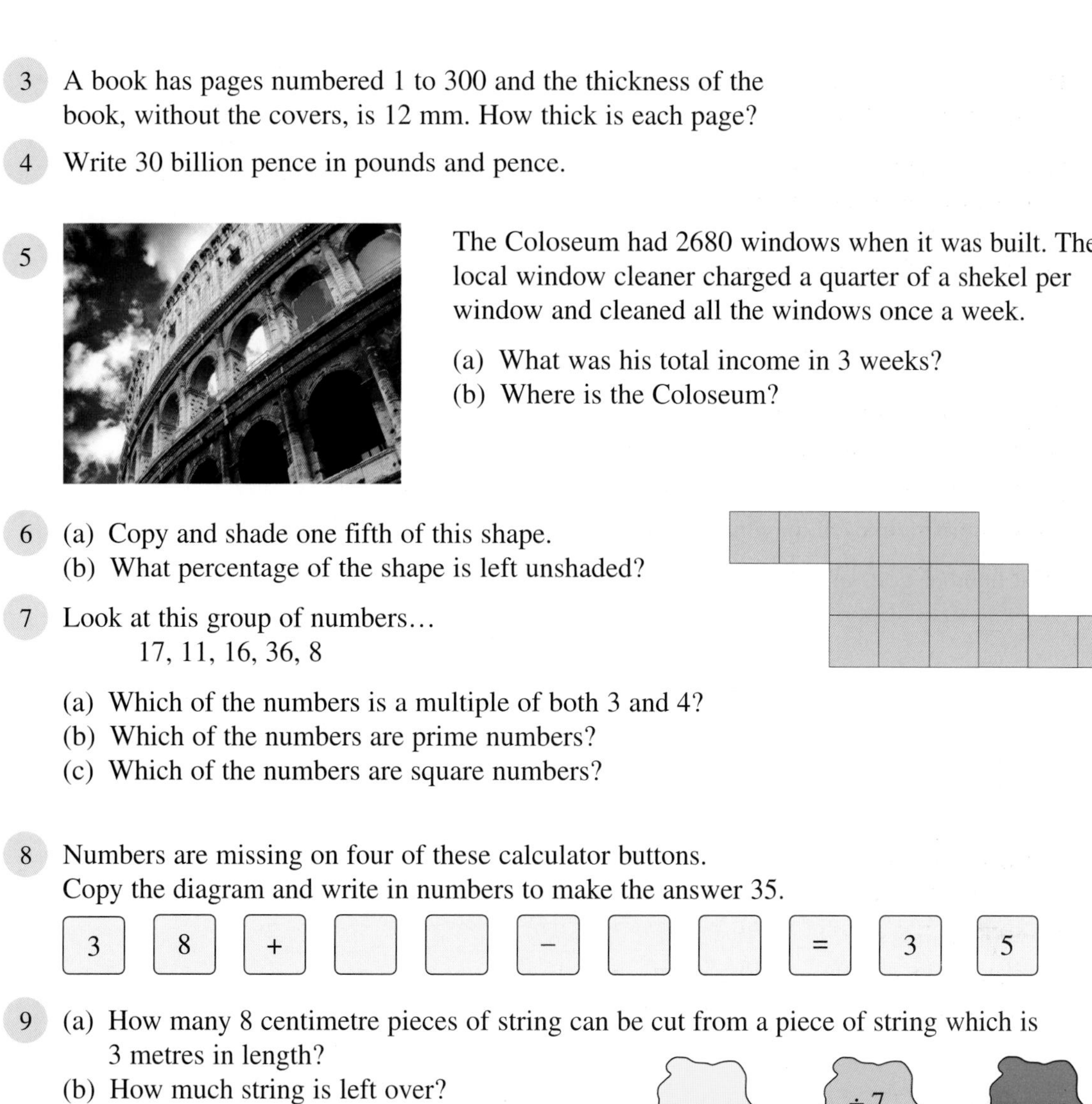

The Coloseum had 2680 windows when it was built. The local window cleaner charged a quarter of a shekel per window and cleaned all the windows once a week.

(a) What was his total income in 3 weeks?
(b) Where is the Coloseum?

6 (a) Copy and shade one fifth of this shape.
(b) What percentage of the shape is left unshaded?

7 Look at this group of numbers…
17, 11, 16, 36, 8

(a) Which of the numbers is a multiple of both 3 and 4?
(b) Which of the numbers are prime numbers?
(c) Which of the numbers are square numbers?

8 Numbers are missing on four of these calculator buttons.
Copy the diagram and write in numbers to make the answer 35.

3	8	+	□	□	−	□	□	=	3	5

9 (a) How many 8 centimetre pieces of string can be cut from a piece of string which is 3 metres in length?
(b) How much string is left over?

10 What number, when divided by 7 and then multiplied by 11, gives an answer of 132?

?
÷ 7
× 11
= 132

Exercise 3M

1 Write down these calculations and find the missing digits.

(a)
```
  5 □ 5
+ 3 2 □
  9 0 1
```

(b)
```
  3 □ 9
+ 5 8 □
  □ 5 3
```

(c)
```
  □ 1 □
+ 5 □ 4
  7 5 0
```

2 Find the remainder when 370 is divided by 20.

3 The rule for the number sequences below is '*double and add 1*'
Write down each sequence and fill in the missing numbers.
(a) 2 → 5 → 11 → □
(b) □ → 7 → 15 → □
(c) □ → 13 → □ → □

4 A mixed school has a total of 852 pupils.
There are 24 more girls than boys.
How many girls are there?
[Hint: check your answer.]

5 Draw a copy of the grid shown. The sum of the numbers in each column ↕ is the same as the sum of the numbers in each diagonal ↙ or ↘ .

What number goes in the centre?

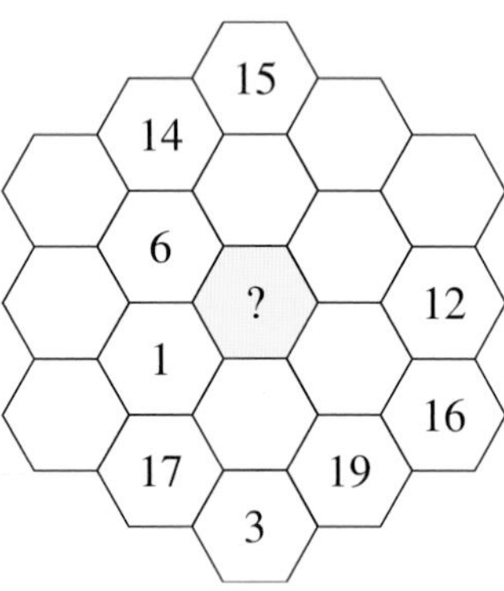

6 In an election 7144 votes were cast for the two candidates. Mr Putin won by 424 votes. How many people voted for Putin?

7 A shopkeeper has a till containing a large number of the following coins:
£1, 50p, 20p, 10p, 5p, 2p, 1p.
He needs to give a customer 57p in change. List all the different ways in which he can do this using no more than six coins.

8 

A book has 648 pages. Gina has read 42 pages in 3 days. At that rate how long will it take her to read the whole book?

9 Work out the missing numbers
(a) 204 + 360 = □ (b) 273 + □ = 800 (c) 25 × □ = 1700
(d) □ + 305 = 5000 (e) □ − 4.1 = 27.95 (f) □ ÷ 12 = 536

10 Ronnie has the same number of 10p and 20p coins. The total value of the coins is £6.
How many of each coin does he have?

Exercise 4M

1. The ingredients for a chocolate cake cost £1.25 and the chef charges £1.10 to make each cake. A shop sells the cakes at £11.99. Calculate the total profit made if 200 cakes are sold.

2. Find two numbers which multiply together to give 65 and which add up to 18

   ☐ × ☐ = 65 ☐ + ☐ = 18

3. Jesse is paid a basic weekly wage of £65 and then a further 30p for each item completed. How many items must be completed in a week when she earns a total of £171.50?

4. Place the numbers in order of size, smallest first.
   0.32 0.201 0.2 0.03 0.4

5. An artist won the Turner art prize by 'carefully' walking across his canvas with bare feet. Unfortunately his prize winning piece was thrown in the bin by the cleaner at his studio. The painting was on sale for £620 000. The cleaner offered to make up for her mistake by paying the artist £20 per week. How many years would it take to pay the full amount?

6. As an incentive to tidy her bedroom, a girl is given 1p on the first day, 2p on the second day, 4p on the third day and so on, doubling the amount each day.
   How much has she been given after 10 days?

7. The tenth number in the sequence 1, 3, 9, 27, …. is 19683. What is the ninth number?

8. Copy each calculation and find the missing numbers?

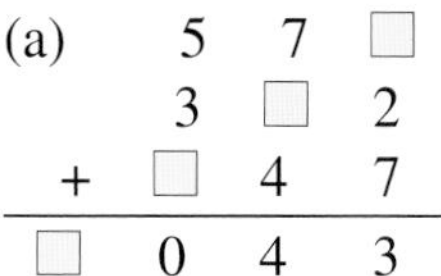

(a)

	5	7	☐
	3	☐	2
+	☐	4	7
☐	0	4	3

(b)

☐	3	2	4
3	☐	0	2
+ 2	3	☐	5
8	1	4	☐

9. Seven oak trees were planted in Windsor when Queen Victoria was born. She died in 1901 aged 82. How old were the trees in 2008?

10. I am a 2 digit prime number.
    I am a factor of 184.
    What number am I?

Exercise 5M

1 Four 4s can be used to make 12: $\dfrac{44 + 4}{4}$

(a) Use three 6 s to make 2
(b) Use three 7 s to make 7
(c) Use three 9 s to make 11
(d) Use four 4 s to make 9
(e) Use four 4 s to make 3

2 Look at the photo of the pile of matches.

(a) Each match is 3 mm thick. How many matches are there in a tower of height 3 cm?
(b) How high a tower can you build with 14 boxes of matches if each box contains 48 matches?

3

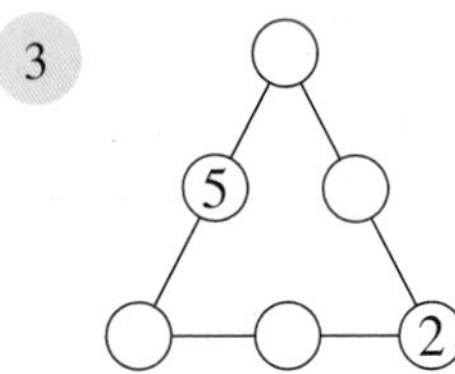

This is a number triangle.
The numbers along each edge add up to 9.

Copy and complete the triangle.

The six numbers are 1, 2, 3, 4, 5, 6.

4 A box has a mass of 230 g when empty.
When it is full of sugar the total mass is 650 g.
What is its mass when it is half full?

5 Write the number 'five and a quarter million' in figures.

6 A piece of A4 size paper measures 297 mm by 210 mm.

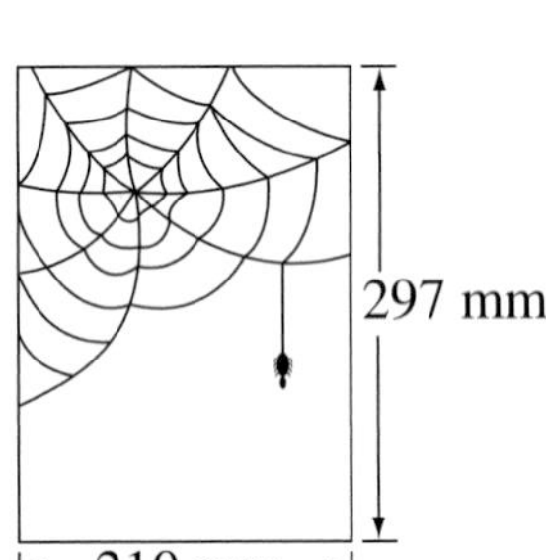

(a) A money spider starts at a corner and decides to walk around all sides of the paper. How far will the spider walk in millimetres?
(b) Change your answer in part (a) into centimetres.
(c) Has the spider travelled more or less than one metre?

7 In this calculation use each of the digits 1, 2, 3, 4, 5, 6.
Put one digit in each box to make the statement true.

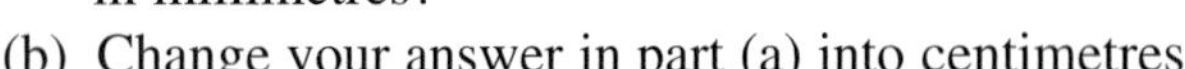

8 The test results of 50 students are shown below.

Mark	5	6	7	8	9	10
Frequency	0	2	12	17	10	9

What percentage of the students scored 8 marks or more?

9 A jar with 8 chocolates in it weighs 160 g. The same jar with 20 chocolates in it weighs 304 g. How much does the jar weigh on its own?

10 The rule for the number sequences is '*treble* and *subtract 1*'. Write down each sequence and fill in the missing numbers.

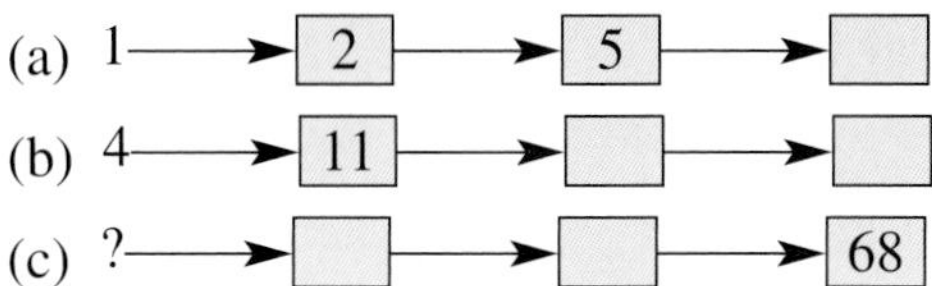

Exercise 6M

1 **Still coining it**

Elvis Presley $49 million
John Lennon $44 million
Charles M. Schulz $35 million
George Harrison $22 million
Albert Einstein $18 million
Andy Warhol $15 million
Theodor Geisel $13 million
Tupac Shakur $9 million
Marilyn Monroe $7 million
Steve McQueen $6 million

£1 = $2.06
£1 = €1.43

This newspaper cutting shows the earnings in 2008 of some famous people who died some time ago.

(a) What were the earnings of Elvis Presley in pounds?
(b) How much in euros was earned on behalf of Albert Einstein?
[Give your answers to the nearest million]

2 A map has a scale of 1 to 100 000. Calculate the actual length of a lake which is 8 cm long on the map.

3 This table shows the approximate weights of coins

1p	2p	5p	10p	20p
3.6 g	7.2 g	3.2 g	6.5 g	5.0 g

(a) What is the lightest weight with a value of 12p made from these coins?
(b) A group of mixed coins weighs 228 g, of which 48 g is the silver coins.
What is the value of the bronze coins?

4 A floor measuring 5 m by 3.6 m is to be covered with square tiles of side 10 cm. A packet of 20 tiles costs £6.95. How much will it cost to tile the floor?

5 A small boat travels 350 km on 125 litres of fuel. How much fuel is needed for a journey of 630 km?

6 Work out (a) $1^1 + 2^2 + 3^3 + 4^4$

(b) $\frac{1}{3} \times \frac{2}{4} \times \frac{3}{5} \times ...... \times \frac{9}{11} \times \frac{10}{12}$.

7 A shop keeper bought 30 books at £3.40 each and a number of C.D.s costing £8.40 each. In all he spent £312. How many C.D.s did he buy?

8 It costs 18p per minute to hire a tool. How much will it cost to hire the tool from 08:50 to 11:15?

9 The numbers '7' and '3' multiply to give 21 and add up to 10. Find two numbers which:

(a) multiply to give 48 and add up to 19.
(b) multiply to give 180 and add up to 27.

10 The words for the numbers from one to ten are written in a list in alphabetical order. What number will be third in the list?

11 The diagram shows a corner torn from a sheet of graph paper measuring 18 cm by 28 cm. Calculate the total length of all the lines drawn on the whole sheet of graph paper.

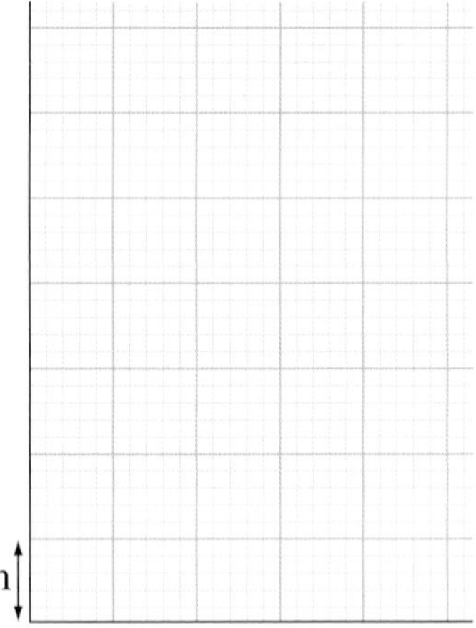

12 Sima has the same number of 10p and 50p coins. The total value is £9. How many of each coin does she have?

Number Rings, an investigation

- This is a number ring
  Start with any number and multiply the units digit by 4 and then add the tens digit.

  For example (14) ⟶ 4 × 4 + 1 ⟶ (17)

  The rule is then repeated on 17.

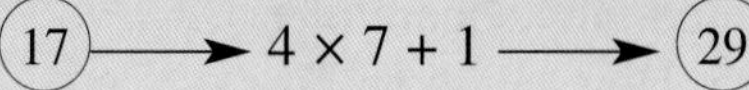

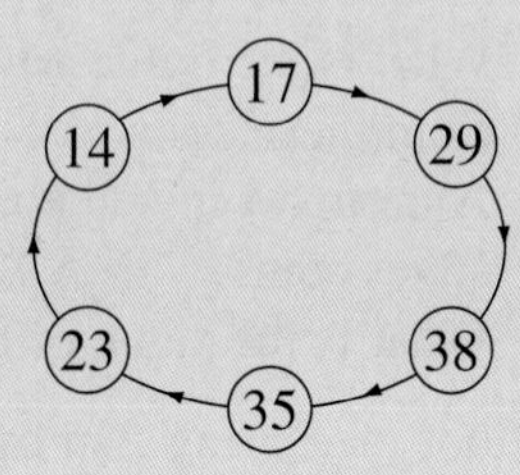

- Use the same rule to complete this number ring.
- Does it matter where you start in the ring?
  In the ring on the previous page could you start at 35? …. or 23?
- Do you get a closed ring when you start with any 1 or 2 digit number? Hint: Write 1 digit numbers with a zero. (Eg 02)
- Do any numbers get 'stuck'?

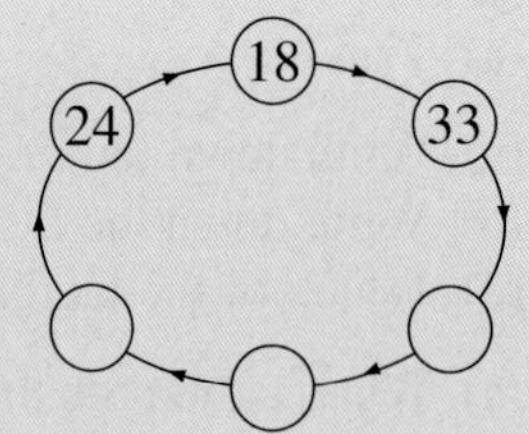

Find out as much as you can and then write a few sentences to show what you discovered.

UNIT 3 MIXED REVIEW

Part one

1 Copy and complete

(a) 0.71 × 10 = □ (b) 1.52 × □ = 152 (c) 86.2 ÷ □ = 8.62

(d) 406 ÷ □ = 0.406 (e) 0.014 × □ = 1.4 (f) 0.1 × 1000 = □

2 The letters from A to Z are shown on the grid.
Decipher the following messages

(a) (5, 5) (4, 0) (1, 3) (2, 5) □ (4, 2) (–4, 2) □ (–5, –3) (–4, 2) (–2, 5) □ (–2, –2) (1, 3) (–5, –5) (–5, –5) □ (1, 3) □ (4, –4) (1, 3) (0, 1) □ (5, 5) (–2, 1) (2, 5) (4, 0) □ (1, 3) □ (5, –2) (–5, 4) (1, 3) (4, 2) (–2, 2) □ (–2, 1) (0, 1) □ (4, 0) (–2, 1) (5, –2) □ (4, 0) (–2, 2) (1, 3) (4, 2) ? □ (4, 2) (–4, 2) (–2, 5) (4, 4) !

(b) Change the seventh word to: (5, 5) (–2, 1) (2, 5) (4, 0) (–4, 2) (–2, 5) (2, 5).
Change the last word to: (4, 2) (–4, 2) (–2, 5) (4, 4) (–5, –5) (1, 3) (5, –2).

(c) (5, 5) (4, 0) (1, 3) (2, 5) □ (4, 2) (–4, 2) □ (–5, –3) (–4, 2) (–2, 5) □ (–2, –2) (1, 3) (–5, –5) (–5, –5) □ (1, 3) □ (4, 2) (–2, 2) (1, 3) (4, 2) □ (–5, 4) (1, 3) (–3, –4) (–3, –4) (–4, 2) (2, 5) ? □ (–5, 4) (–4, 2) (–5, –5) (–5, –3) (4, 4) (–4, 2) (0, 1) !

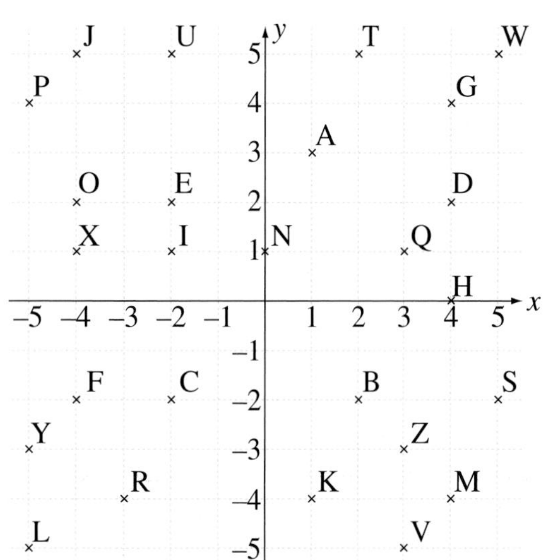

3 Look at the graph in question 2. Write down the equation of the line through

(a) T and B (b) P and G (c) G and C

4 (a) Write down the first five multiples of 4.
(b) Write down the factors of 12.
(c) Which of the factors of 12 are prime numbers?

5 (a) What is the probability of rolling a dice and getting a six?
(b) What is the probability of not getting a six?

6 Different batteries were tested to see how long a set of 'chattering teeth' keep working. The winning battery worked for 8 minutes. Each battery costs 90p. How much would it cost to keep the teeth chattering for four hours?

7 Find the missing digits.

(a)
$$\begin{array}{r} 3\cdot 2\ \square \\ +\ 1\cdot \square\ 4 \\ \hline \square\cdot 0\ 1 \end{array}$$

(b)
$$\begin{array}{r} \square\cdot 5\ 5 \\ +\ 0\cdot \square\ 3 \\ \hline 5\cdot 1\ \square \end{array}$$

(c)
$$\begin{array}{r} 3\cdot 6\ \square \\ -\ \square\cdot \square\ 7 \\ \hline 2\cdot 0\ 7 \end{array}$$

8 A corn field is a rectangle measuring 300 m by 600 m. One hectare is 10 000 m^2 and each hectare produces 3.2 tonnes of corn. How much corn is produced in this field?

9 Find the number

(a)

a 2-digit number a multiple of both 3 and 4 the sum of its digits is 15

(b)

a 3-digit number a square number the product of its digits is 2

10 Write the numbers in order of size, smallest first.
(a) 0.71, 0.605, 0.65, 0.7, 0.702
(b) 0.99, 0.08, 0.079, 0.1
(c) 2^3, 3^2, 1^3, (2×3), 0.007×10^2

11 The equation of a line is $y = x - 2$. Some points on the line are:

(0, –2) (1, –1) (2, $\square$) (3, $\square$) (4, $\square$)

Fill in the missing numbers and then draw the line.

12 36 small cubes are stuck together to make the block shown and the block is then painted on the outside. How many of the small cubes are painted on:

(a) 1 face (b) 2 faces

(b) 3 faces (d) 0 faces?

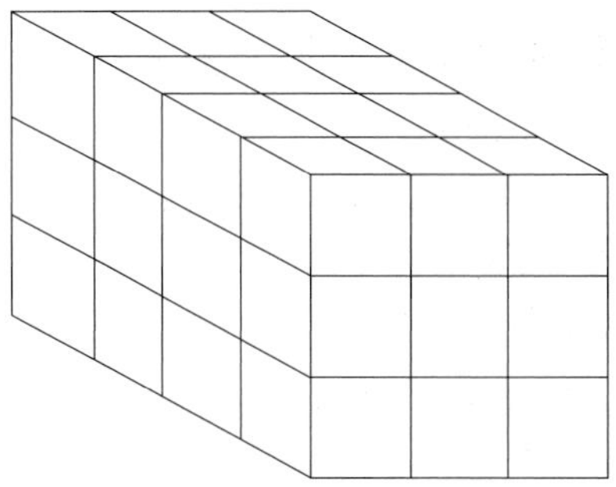

13 An ice cream and a can of drink together cost 85p. Two ice creams and a can of drink together cost £1.40.

(a) How much does one ice cream cost?

(b) How much would you pay for three ice creams and two cans of drink?

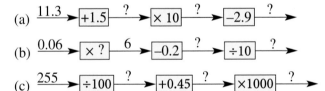

14 The smiley face with banana and berries won a competition to promote healthy eating. The prize was £95. How many euros was that? [£1 = €1.5]

15 Copy and complete each chain.

(a) 11.3 → [+1.5] → ? → [× 10] → ? → [−2.9] → ? →

(b) 0.06 → [× ?] → 6 → [−0.2] → ? → [÷10] → ? →

(c) 255 → [÷100] → ? → [+0.45] → ? → [×1000] → ? →

Part two

1 This bar chart shows the marks achieved by children in a test.

(a) How many children scored between 41 and 60 marks?

(b) How many children scored over 60 marks?

(c) How many children took the test?

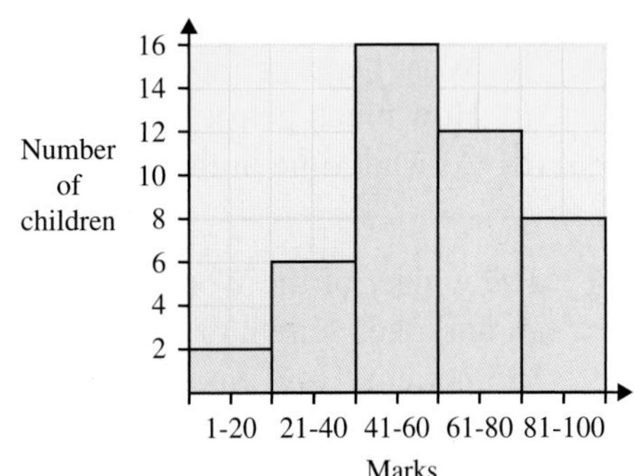

2 Find the number.

(a)
a multiple of 11
a multiple of 7
the product of its digits is 6

(b)
a square number
a 3-digit number
the product of its digits is 20

3 

It is not easy to burn a match completely.
In fact it takes thirteen seconds.
A box contains 47 matches.
How long would it take to completely burn the matches, one after another, in 10 boxes?

4 A car travels 7.4 miles on a litre of petrol and petrol costs 104p per litre. In six months the car is driven a total of 4750 miles. Find the cost of the petrol to the nearest pound.

5 (a) Write down the first seven multiples of four.
(b) Write down the first six multiples of seven.
(c) Write down the lowest common multiple of four and seven.

6 The line graph below shows the fuel gauge reading of a car at different times throughout a day…

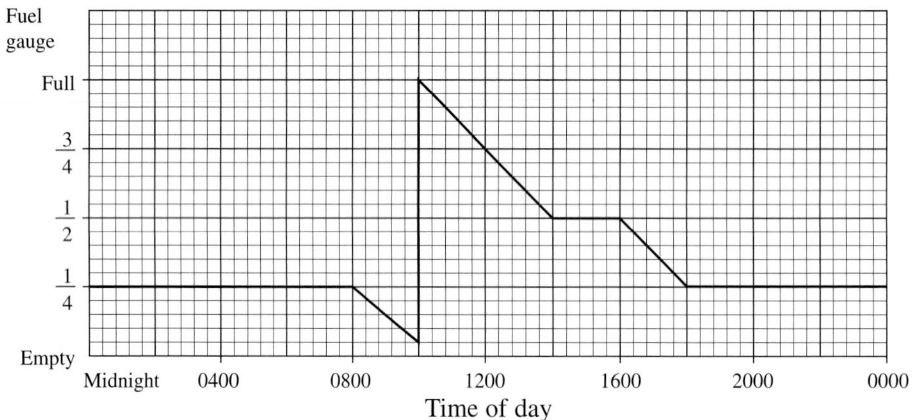

(a) Was the car moving or stationary between midnight and 8.00 am?
(b) What happened to the car at 10.00 am?
(c) How much petrol was used between 10.00 am and 2.00 pm?
(d) At what time in the evening was the car put in the garage?

7 The winner of the World Apple Peeling Championship peeled an unbroken length of 231 cm from a Bramley apple. His prize was \$35 per cm. How much did he win?

8 A book has pages numbered 1 to 300 and the thickness of the book, without the covers is 10 mm. How thick is each page?

9 This pie chart shows the number of hours in one evening spent watching television by 40 children. Copy and complete the table

20% 1
30% 2 hours
10% 0
3+ 3 hours
10%
30%

HOURS	CHILDREN
0	
1	
2	
3	
3+	

10 A bag contains 4 balls. The probability of selecting a white ball from the bag is 0.5. A white ball is taken from the bag and left on one side. What is the probability of selecting a white ball from the bag now?

11 Copy and complete

(a) $3.25 + \square = 5$ (b) $100 \times \square = 3.7$

(c) $\square - 0.23 = 2.5$ (d) $(\square + 1.2) \times 10 = 25$

12 A 10p coin is 2 mm thick. Alex has a pile of 10p coins which is 16.6 cm tall. What is the value of the money in Alex's pile of coins?

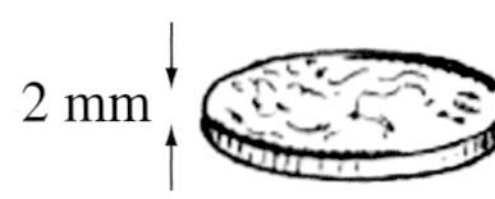

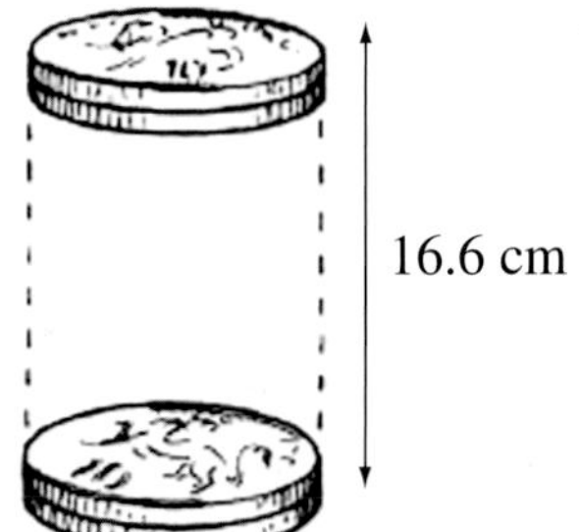

13 How many spots are there on twenty-four ordinary dice?

14 In a 'magic' square the sum of the numbers in any row, column or main diagonal is the same. Find x in each square.

(a)

3		
8		4
7	x	

(b)

14		7	2
x		12	
	5	9	16
15			3

15 Answer true or false:

(a) $4^2 = 2^4$ (b) $1 \div 100 = (0.1)^2$ (c) 20% of 20 = 5

(d) $0.001 \times 100 = 0.01$ (e) 3^3 is greater than 4^2

Puzzles and Problems 3

1 In these triangle puzzles the numbers a, b, c, d are connected as follows:

$a \times b = c$

$c \times b = d$

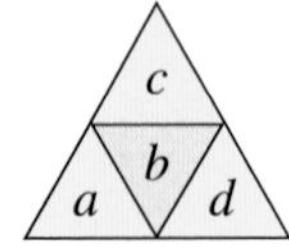

For example:

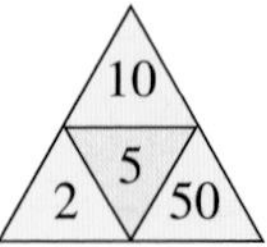

Copy and complete the following triangles:

(a)

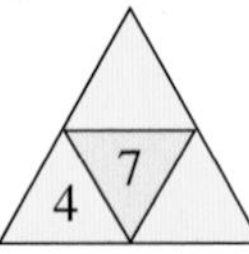

(b)

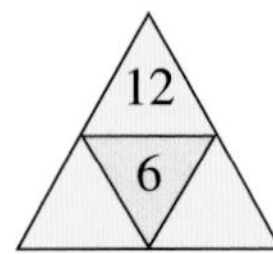

(c)

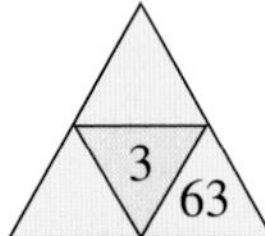

(d)

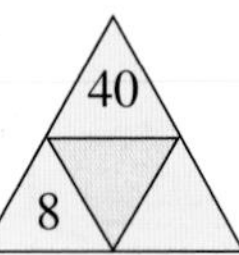

(e)

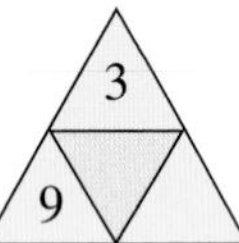

(f)

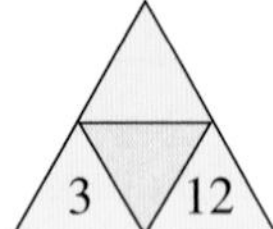

2 Write the digits 1 to 9 so that all the answers are correct.

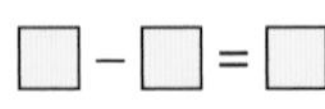

□ − □ = □
×
□ ÷ □ = □
=
□ + □ = □

3 Each of these calculations has the same number missing from all three boxes. Find the missing number in each calculation.

(a) □ × □ − □ = 12

(b) □ ÷ □ + □ = 9

(c) □ × □ + □ = 72

4 In the circle write +, −, × or ÷ to make the calculation correct.

(a) 9 × 5 ◯ 3 = 48 (b) 8 × 5 ◯ 2 = 20

(c) 8 ◯ 9 − 5 = 67 (d) 12 ◯ 2 + 4 = 10

(e) 60 ÷ 3 ◯ 5 = 15

5 Write the following with the correct signs.

(a) $5 \times 4 \times 3 \quad\bigcirc\quad 3 = 63$

(b) $5 + 4 \quad\bigcirc\quad 3 \quad\bigcirc\quad 2 = 4$

(c) $5 \times 2 \times 3 \quad\bigcirc\quad 1 = 31$

6 Draw four straight lines which pass through all 9 points, without taking your pen from the paper and without going over any line twice. [Hint: Lines can extend beyond the square].

$$\begin{array}{ccc} \bullet & \bullet & \bullet \\ \bullet & \bullet & \bullet \\ \bullet & \bullet & \bullet \end{array}$$

7 Draw six straight lines to pass through all 16 points, subject to the same conditions as in question 6.

$$\begin{array}{cccc} \bullet & \bullet & \bullet & \bullet \\ \bullet & \bullet & \bullet & \bullet \\ \bullet & \bullet & \bullet & \bullet \\ \bullet & \bullet & \bullet & \bullet \end{array}$$

In questions 8 and 9 each letter stands for a different single digit from 0 to 9. The first digit of a number is never zero. Find the value of each letter.

8 (a)
$$\begin{array}{r} M\ E \\ M\ E + \\ \hline A\ M \end{array}$$
[Find two solutions]

(b)
$$\begin{array}{r} K\ L\ M \\ L\ M \\ M\ L\ M + \\ \hline L\ M\ M \end{array}$$

(c)
$$\begin{array}{r} N\ A\ V\ E \\ W\ A\ V\ E \\ R\ A\ V\ E + \\ \hline S\ E\ V\ E \end{array}$$
Work out E, V, A and S, You will find that N, W and R can each have three different values.

Some of these questions have more than one solution.

9 (a)
$$\begin{array}{r} O\ N\ E \\ O\ N\ E + \\ \hline T\ W\ O \end{array}$$

(b)
$$\begin{array}{r} C\ U\ T \\ C\ O\ T \\ I\ F + \\ \hline O\ A\ T \end{array}$$

(c)
$$\begin{array}{r} S\ O\ N \\ S\ U\ N \\ I\ S + \\ \hline O\ W\ N \end{array}$$

(d)
$$\begin{array}{r} T\ O\ U\ R \\ S\ O\ U\ R \\ R\ O\ A\ R + \\ \hline P\ E\ R\ R \end{array}$$

(e)
$$\begin{array}{r} F\ O\ U\ R \\ F\ I\ V\ E + \\ \hline N\ I\ N\ E \end{array}$$

Mental Arithmetic Practice 3

There are two sets of mental arithmetic questions in this section. Ideally a teacher will read out each question twice, with pupils' books closed. Each test of 25 questions should take about 15–20 minutes.

Test 1

1. How many 20p coins do I need to make £300?
2. How much more than £128 is £400?
3. Work out 10% of £6000.
4. Two angles in a triangle are thirty-five and seventy-five degrees. What is the third angle?
5. A 50p coin is 2 mm thick. What is the value of a pile of 50p coins 2 cm high?
6. How many minutes are there in three and a half hours?
7. What is the perimeter of a square whose area is four centimetres squared?
8. A man died in 2003 aged 58. In what year was he born?
9. By how much is half a metre longer than 5 millimetres? (answer in mm)
10. A string of length 590 cm is cut in half. How long is each piece?
11. My watch reads twenty past seven. It is 25 minutes fast. What is the correct time?
12. By how much is four kilograms more than 700 grams?
13. What is a quarter of four hundred and ten?
14. A train travels at an average speed of 45 mph. How far does it travel in 3 hours?
15. A half is a third of a certain number. What is the number?
16. From eight times seven take away nine.
17. Find two ways of making 66p using five coins.
18. *Roughly* how many litres are there in 10 gallons?
19. A plane was due to arrive at noon on Tuesday but arrived at 7 a.m. on Wednesday. How many hours late was the plane?
20. How many square centimetres are there in one square metre?
21. Add together 18, 20 and 42.
22. Next in the sequence 10, 7, 4, 1.
23. One per cent of a billion pounds.
24. Eleven squared plus ten squared.
25. What is one twentieth as a percentage?

Test 2

1. I want to buy 4 CDs, each costing £6.49. To the nearest pound, how much will the 4 CDs cost in total?
2. What is the total of 67 and 953?
3. A triangle has a base of 6 cm and a height of 8 cm. What is its area?
4. Work out three squared plus four squared.
5. What number is exactly mid-way between 2.8 and 2.9?
6. How many magazines costing 85p can I buy with £10?
7. Sam is 28 cm taller than Holly who is 1.37 metres tall. How tall is Sam?

8 Write 9 divided by 100 as a decimal.

9 What number is next in the pattern 8, 4, 2, 1, 0.5, ..?

10 What is a tenth of 3.6?

11 How many lines of symmetry do all rectangles have?

12 I think of a number and subtract 7. The result is equal to 8 times 6. What is the number?

13 What number is 10 less than eight thousand?

14 The pupils in Shane's class are given lockers numbered from 42 to 64. How many pupils are there in Shane's class?

15 What is a quarter of a half?

16 A toy train travels 5 metres in two seconds. How far will it go in one minute?

17 Write the number '$3\frac{1}{2}$ million' in figures.

18 Work out 400 times 300.

19 How much longer is 8.5 metres than 835 centimetres?

20 Write down the next prime number after 32.

21 Ten cubed plus nine squared.

22 What is the perimeter of a rectangle with sides 7 cm and 35 cm?

23 How many 2p coins do you need to make £5?

24 Increase a price of £500 by 5 per cent.

25 A quadrilateral has three angles of 80°. What is the fourth angle?

A long time ago ! 3

Pounds, shillings and pence

In horse racing, the length of a race is often measured in furlongs. Do you know how many furlongs make one mile?

A person throwing a party might buy a firkin of beer. How many gallons would this be?
These are imperial units which are covered later in this book.
Actually 8 furlongs make one mile and 9 gallons make one firkin.

Your grandparents (and maybe parents!) used to buy things with shillings, tanners and two bob coins.
One penny was written as 1d. 12 pennies made 1 shilling (written as 1s.)
20 shillings made 1 pound.
21 shillings made 1 guinea.
(A 'tanner' was a 6d. coin and 2s. was sometimes called a 'two bob' coin)

1s. = 12d.
£1 = 20s.

Mary wants to buy a car for £27 16s. 4d, and a bike for 5s. 10d. How much does she spend in total?

£	s.	d.
27	16	4
	5	10
28	2	2
1	1	

Add the pennies first. Every 12 pennies are carried over as 1 shilling. Next add the shillings. Every 20 shillings are carried over as 1 pound.

Mary spends a total of £28 2s. 2d.

Exercise

Try these questions from a 1927 arithmetic test.

1

	£	s.	d.
	5	3	7
+	2	5	9

2

	£	s.	d.
	3	14	8
+	6	12	3

3

	£	s.	d.
	8	13	4
+	4	17	10

4

	£	s.	d.
from	8	19	3
take	4	13	9

5

	£	s.	d.
from	16	4	8
take	7	10	4

6

	£	s.	d.
from	17	3	2
take	10	14	8

7 How many $\frac{1}{2}$d. stamps could I buy with a ‘two bob’ coin?

8 How many oranges can I get for 3s. at the cost of seven oranges for 6d.?

9 How much must be added to 15s. 6d. to make a guinea?

10 I have bought a cake for 1s. 3d. and some jam for 5d. How much change should I have out of 2 shillings?

11 I have been for a week’s holiday and spent 6d. a day while I was away. How much should I have left out of 4s.?

12 **RESEARCH:** There were many units used in the nineteenth century for length, weight and capacity. Examples are ‘barleycorns’and ‘kilderkins’.

(a) How many different units can you find?
(b) Can you discover where any of the names come from?

UNIT 4

4.1 Constructing triangles

In section 4.1 you will learn how to:

- construct triangles with a protractor and ruler
- construct triangles with three sides given

A triangle is an extremely rigid structure. It is used extensively in the real world to support many objects such as the roof on your house or the brackets holding up your bookshelf.

Draw the triangle ABC full size and measure the length x.

(a) Draw a base line *longer than* 8.5 *cm*

(b) Put the centre of the protractor on A and measure an angle 64°. Draw line AP.

(c) Similarly draw line BQ at an angle 40° to AB.

(d) The triangle is formed.
Measure $x = 5.6$ cm.

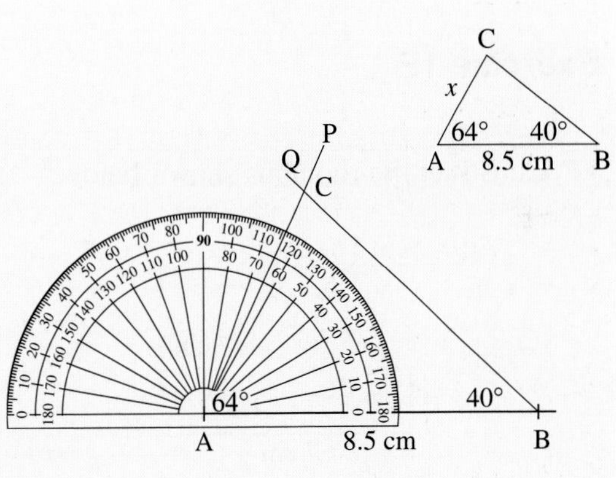

Exercise 1M

1 Construct each triangle below. Measure the third angle in each triangle. Is it what you would expect?

(a)

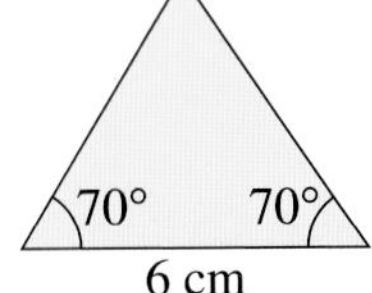

(b)

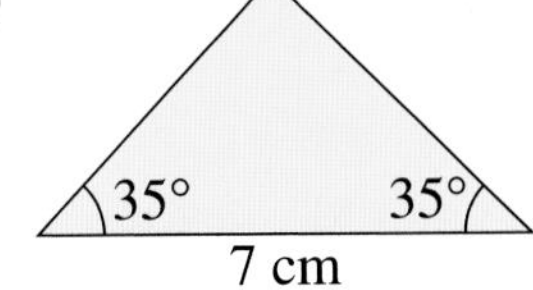

(c)

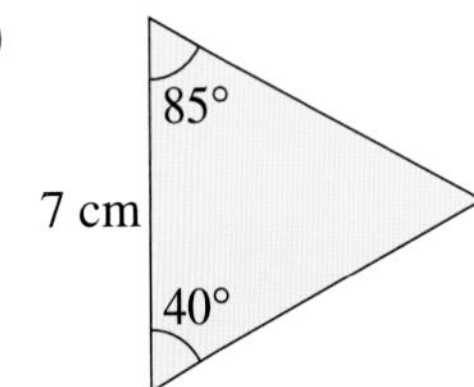

In questions 2 to 7, construct the triangles and measure the lengths of the sides marked x.

2

x

40°

60°

8 cm

3

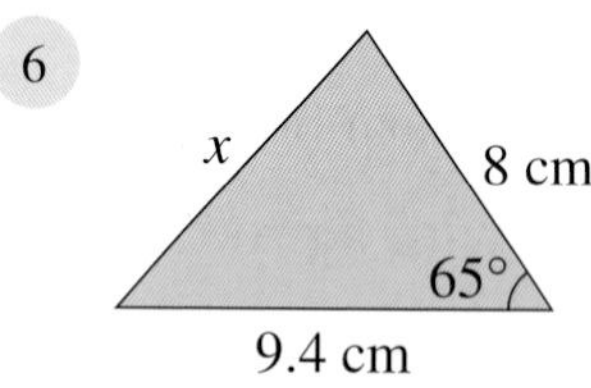

4

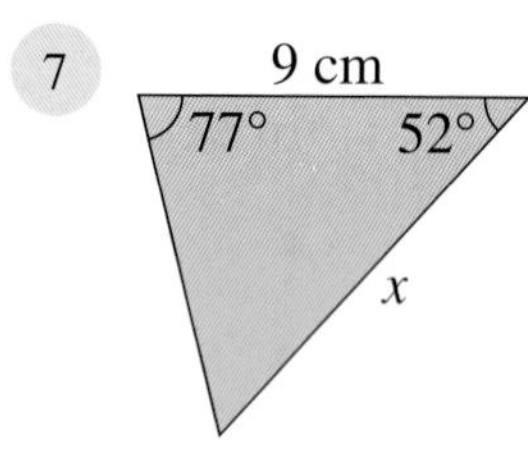

5

x

110°

40°

8 cm

6

x

8 cm

65°

9.4 cm

7

9 cm

77°

52°

x

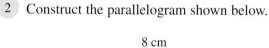

8 Construct triangle PQR where PR = 6.8 cm, $R\hat{P}Q = 72°$ and $P\hat{R}Q = 60°$.
Measure the length of QR.

9 Construct triangle ABC where AC = 7.2 cm, $B\hat{A}C = 34°$ and $A\hat{C}B = 103°$.
Measure the length of AB.

Exercise 1E

1 Construct the rhombus shown below.

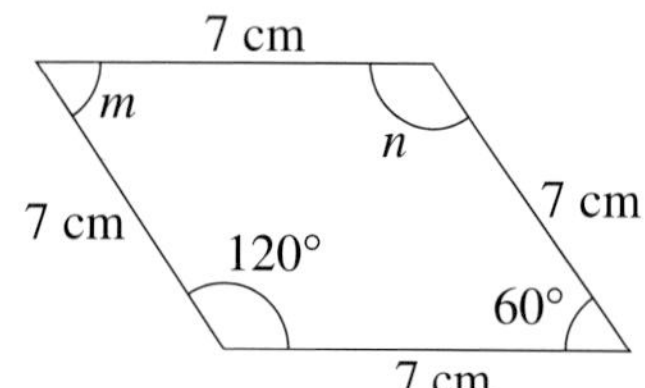

Measure the size of m and n.

2 Construct the parallelogram shown below.

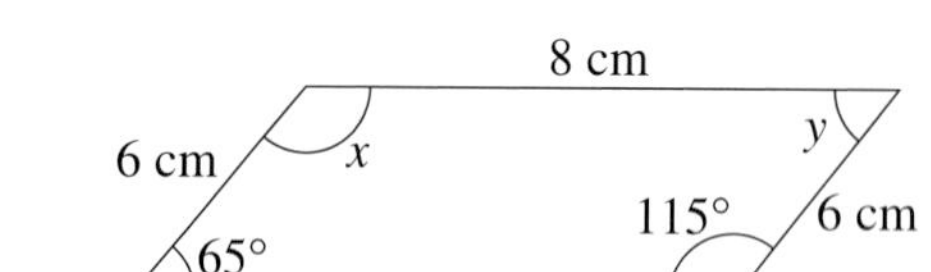

Measure the size of x and y.

In questions 3 to 5, construct the shapes below and measure the lengths of the sides marked x.

3

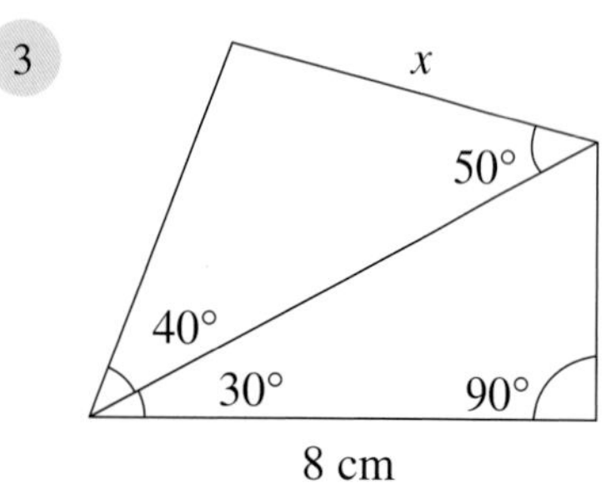

4

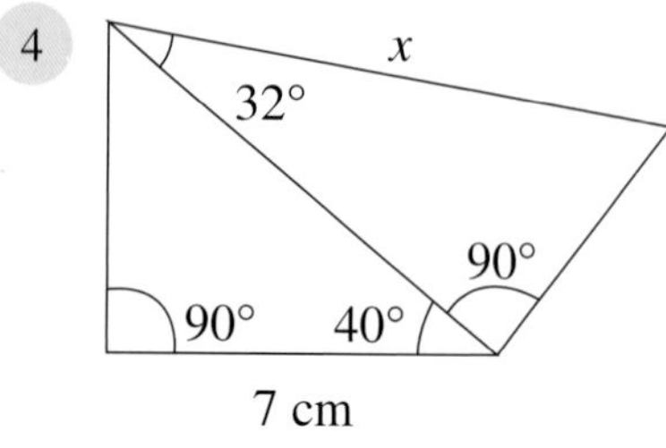

5

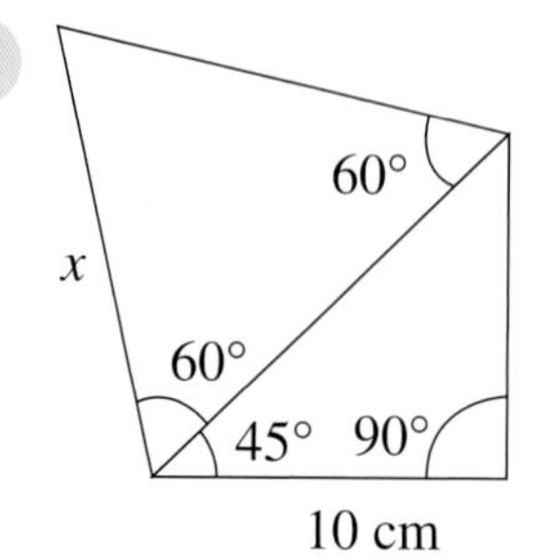

6 A rhombus has four equal sides as shown in question 1. Construct a rhombus WXYZ where WZ = 8 cm, $X\hat{W}Z = 50°$ and $Y\hat{Z}W = 130°$. Measure $X\hat{Y}Z$.

Triangles with three sides given

Draw triangle XYZ and measure $X\hat{Z}Y$.

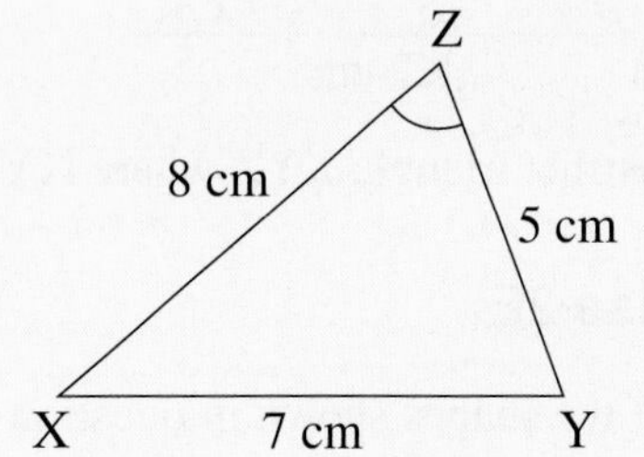

(a) Draw a base line longer than 7 cm and mark X and Y exactly 7 cm apart.

(b) Put the point of a pair of compasses on X and draw an arc of radius 8 cm.

(c) Put the point of the pair of compasses on Y and draw an arc of radius 5 cm.

(d) The arcs cross at the point Z so the triangle is formed.

Measure $X\hat{Z}Y = 60°$

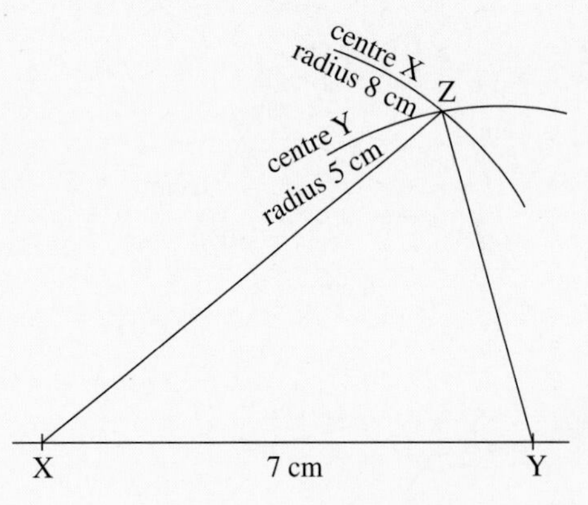

Exercise 2M

Use a ruler and a pair of compasses to construct the triangles in questions 1 to 6. For each triangle, measure the angle x.

1

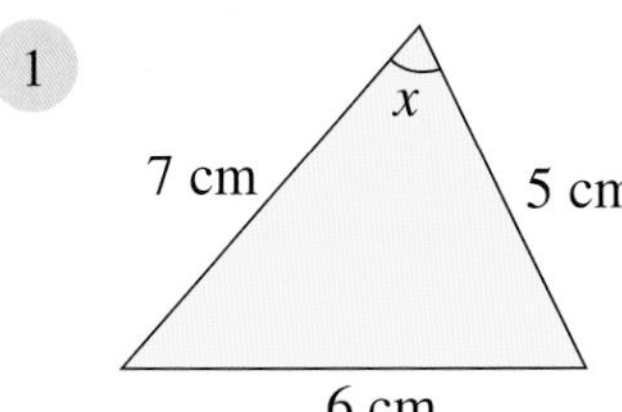

2

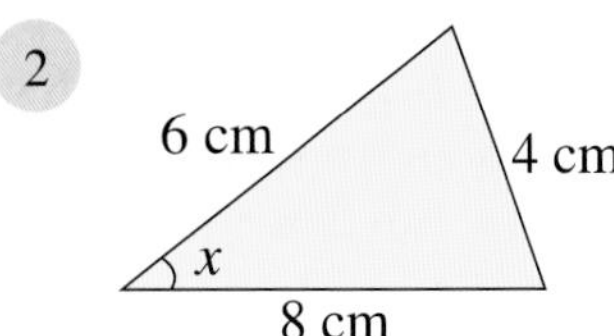

3

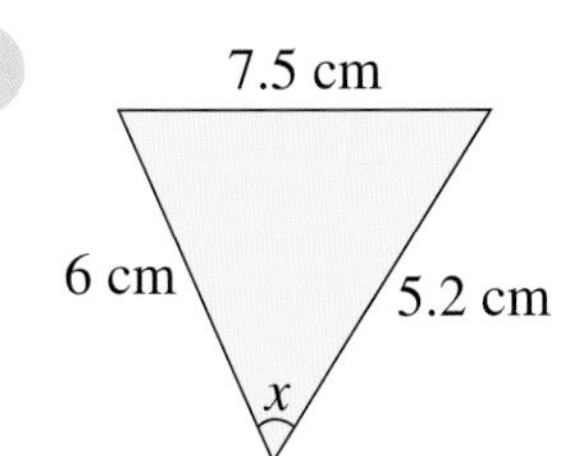

4

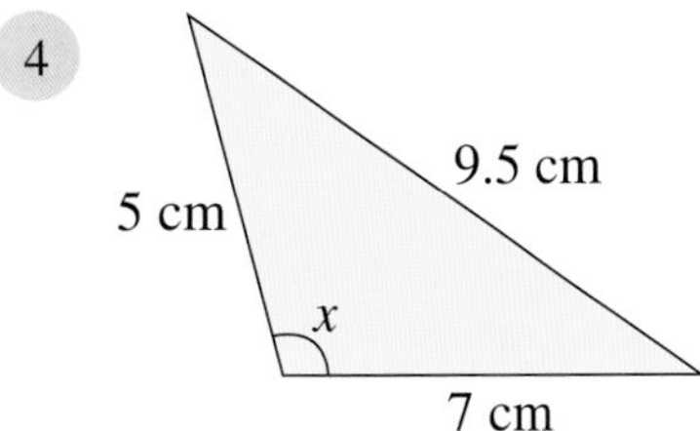

5

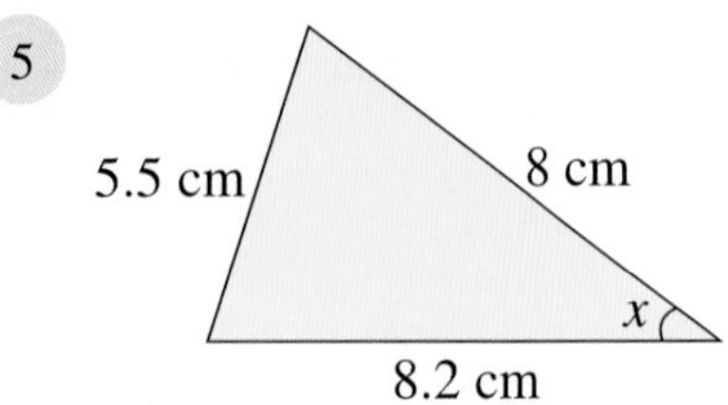

6

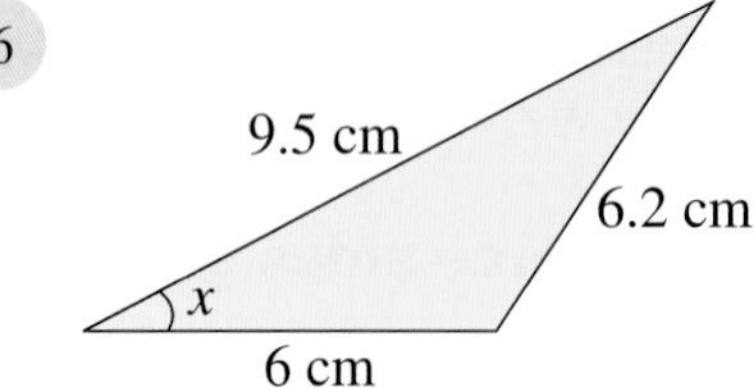

7 Construct triangle XYZ where XY = 6.7 cm, YZ = 8.2 cm and ZX = 7.9 cm. Measure $X\hat{Z}Y$.

Exercise 2E

Construct the shapes shown in questions 1 to 3. For each shape, measure the angle x.

1

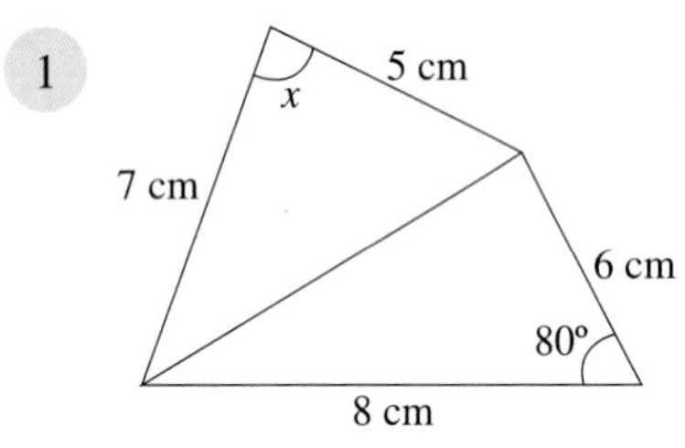

2

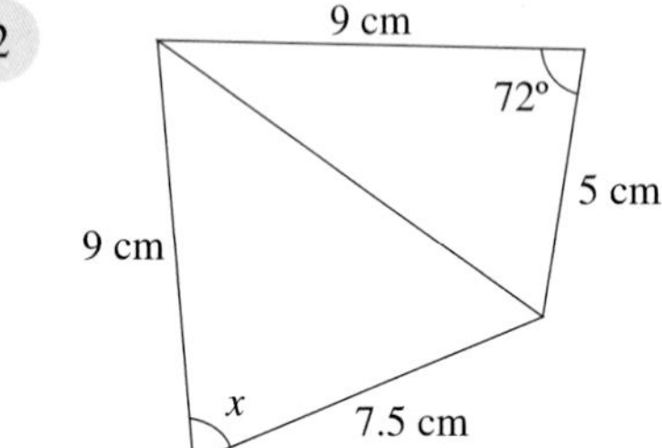

3

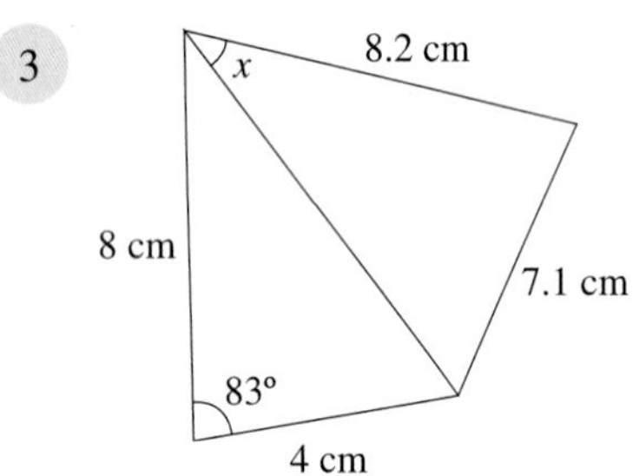

4 Construct a quadrilateral ABCD where AB = 6.1 cm, BC = 5.3 cm, CD = 6.2 cm, AD = 6.8 cm and AC = 8 cm (you may find it useful to sketch the shape first). Measure and then write down the sum of angles $A\hat{B}C$ and $A\hat{D}C$.

5 A disused airfield is to be sold at a price of £5500 per hectare. (1 hectare = 10 000 m²). The outline of the airfield is a quadrilateral but it is not a rectangle. The area can be found by splitting it into two triangles and then finding the area of each part. Find the selling price of the airfield.

[Use a scale of 1 cm to 100 m]

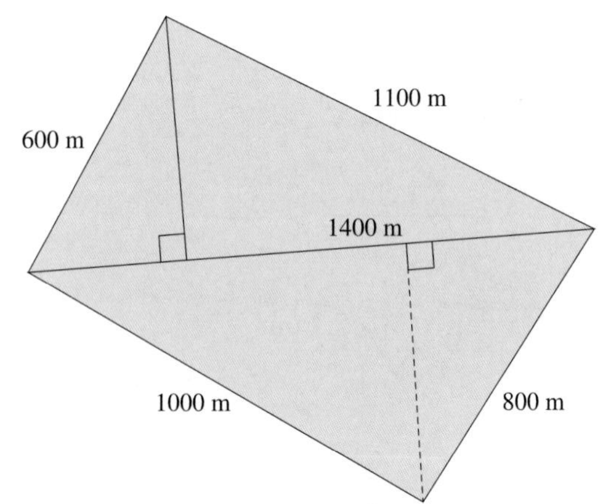

4.2 Two dimensional shapes

In section 4.2 you will learn how to:

- recognise different types of quadrilateral
- recognise different polygons
- identify symmetry properties of quadrilaterals

Quadrilaterals

A quadrilateral has four sides and four angles.
Special types of quadrilateral are shown below.

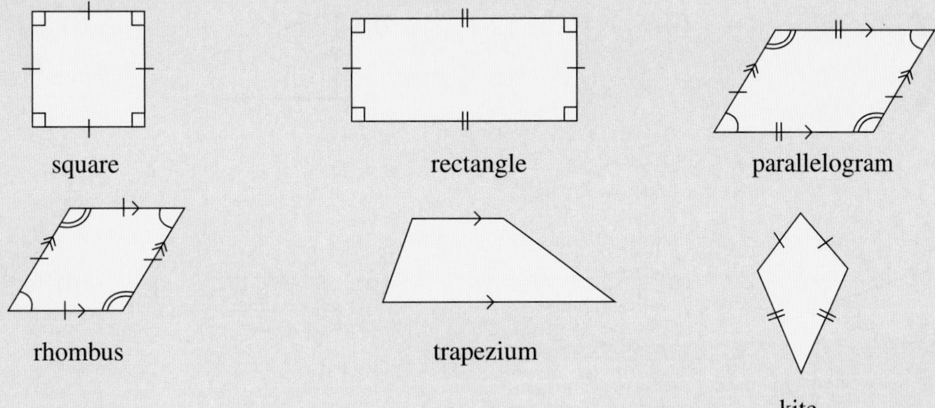

Polygons

A polygon is a shape with straight sides.

This is a five-sided polygon or pentagon.

A *regular* polygon has all its sides and angles equal.
This is a *regular* pentagon.

Names of common polygons:

hexagon (6 sides), heptagon (7 sides), octagon (8 sides), nonagon (9 sides), decagon (10 sides).

Exercise 1M

1 Write down the name for each shape below. If the shape has a special name like 'parallelogram' or 'kite' write that name. If not, write 'quadrilateral', 'hexagon', 'regular pentagon' and so on.

(a) 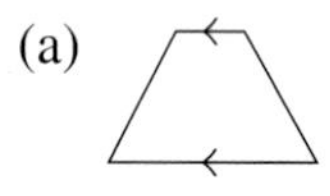

(b) 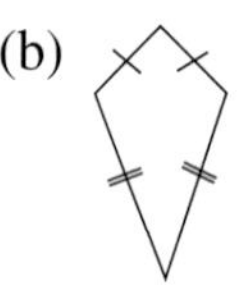

(c) 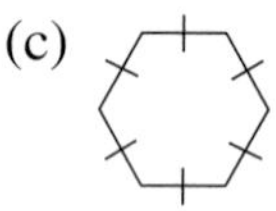

(d) 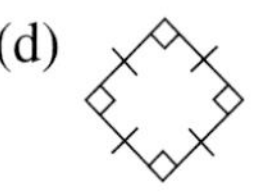

(e) 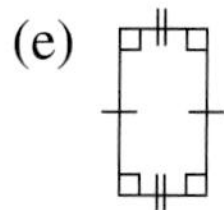

(f) 

(g) 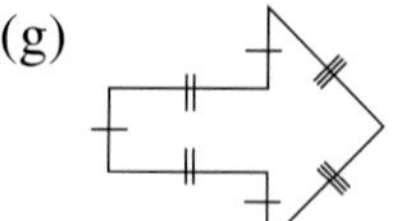

(h) 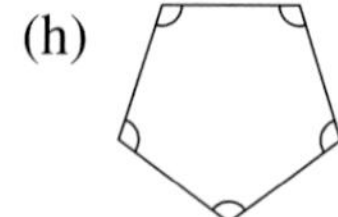

(i) 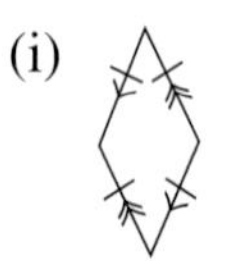

(j) 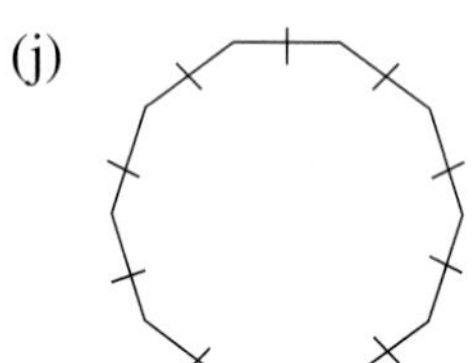

(k) 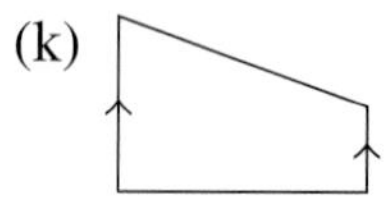

(l) 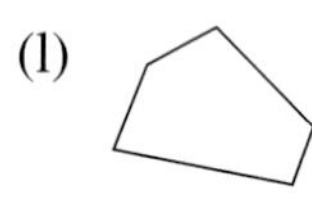

(m) 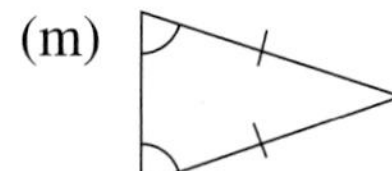

(n) 

(o) 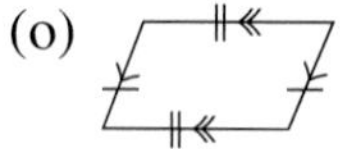

(p) 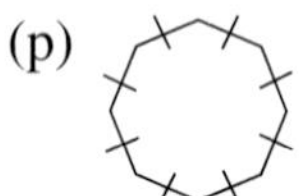

(q) 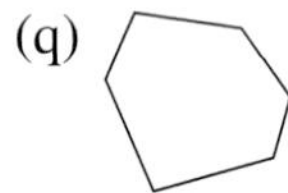

(r) 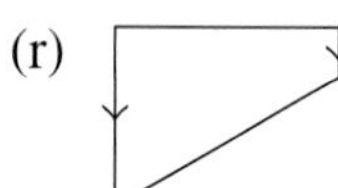

(s) 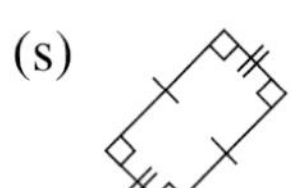

(t) 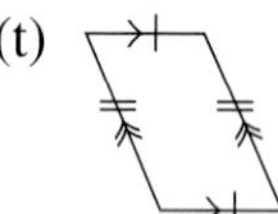

2 Which shape below is not a regular polygon?

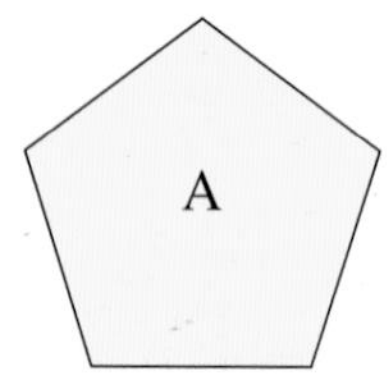

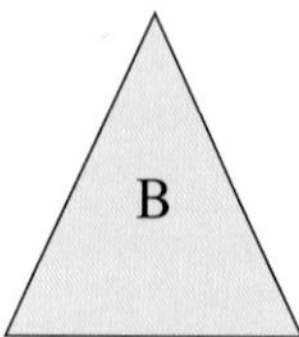

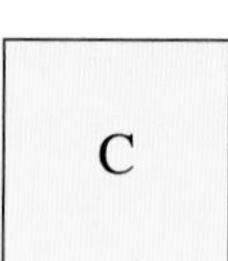

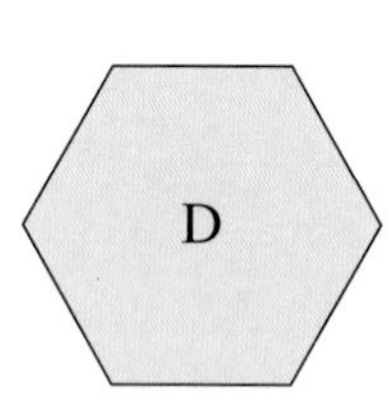

3 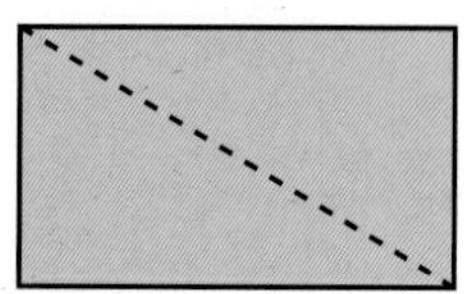

A diagonal joins one corner (vertex) of a polygon to another corner.

Draw any rhombus. Write as many facts as possible about the diagonals of a rhombus.

4 Write down the letter for which bucket each of the 6 quadrilaterals will drop into when they pass through the sorting machine.

parallelogram | square | rectangle | trapezium | kite | rhombus

Are all 4 sides equal?

- yes → Are all the angles equal to 90°?
  - yes → A
  - no → B
- no → Does it have any parallel sides?
  - no → C
  - yes → Are all the angles equal to 90°?
    - no → Are its opposite sides equal in length and parallel?
      - yes → D
      - no → E
    - yes → F

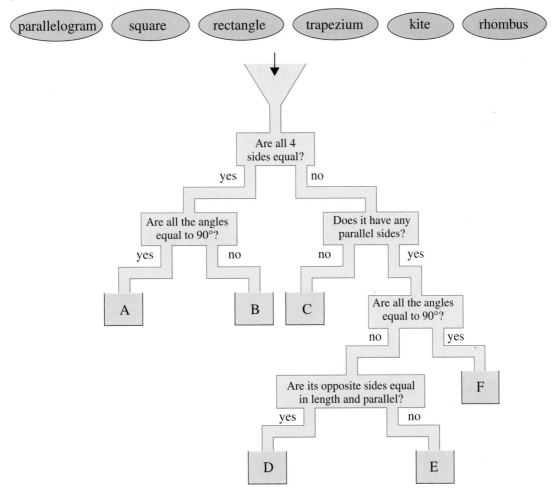

5 Draw a square, rectangle, parallelogram, rhombus, trapezium and kite.
For each of these quadrilaterals, write its name and describe the rules that make it that particular shape.
Discuss these rules with a partner and then as a class.

Quadrilaterals and symmetry

Symmetry – a reminder

A shape has line symmetry if half of its shape matches the other half exactly.

A shape has *rotational symmetry* if it fits onto itself when rotated (turned) before it gets back to its starting position.

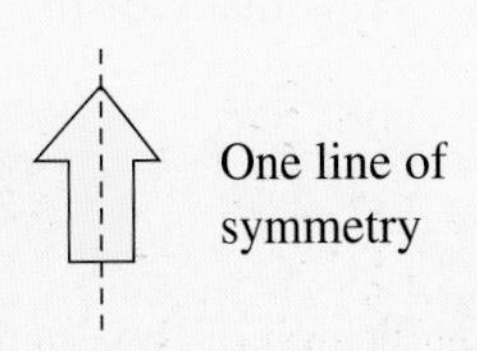

Shape A fits onto itself three times when rotated through a complete turn. We say it has rotational symmetry of *order 3*.

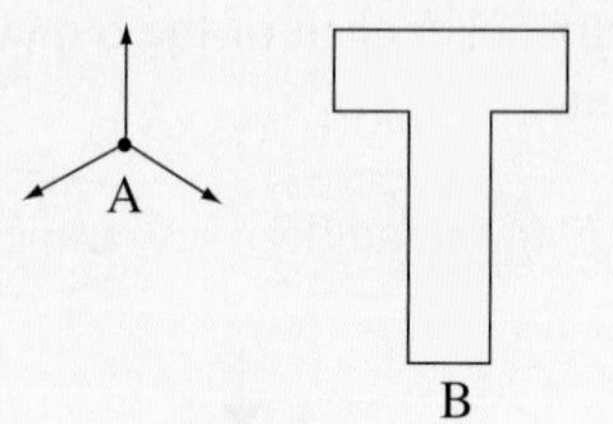

Shape B can only fit onto itself in its starting position. We say it has rotational symmetry of *order 1*.

Exercise 1E

1 The diagram shows one line of symmetry for a kite. How many more lines of symmetry does a kite have?

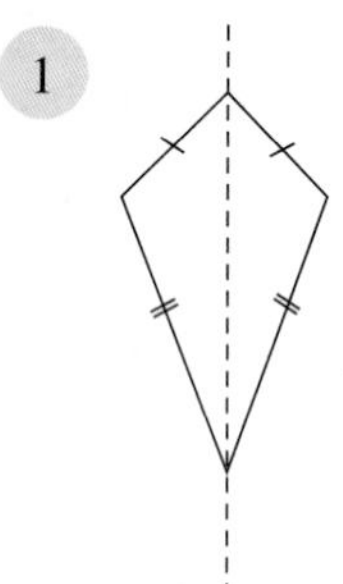

2 Draw a rectangle and show all its lines of symmetry.

3 Which common quadrilaterals have two lines of symmetry only?

4 What is the order of rotational symmetry of this rhombus?

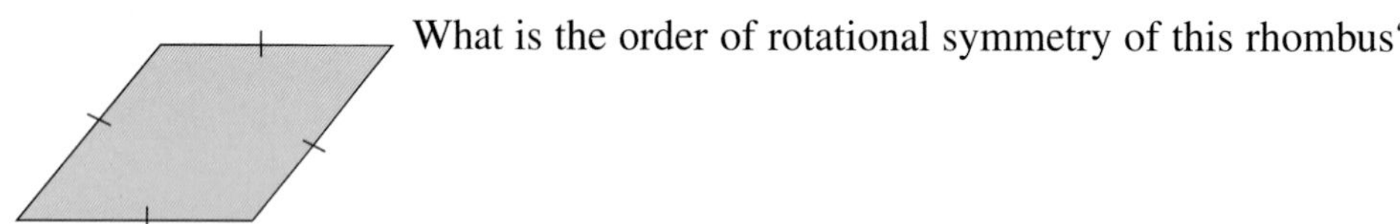

5 Which quadrilateral has rotational symmetry of order 4.

6 Draw a quadrilateral which has one line of symmetry only and one pair of parallel sides only.

7 What is the order of rotational symmetry of an equilateral triangle?

8 What is the order of rotational symmetry of this hexagon?

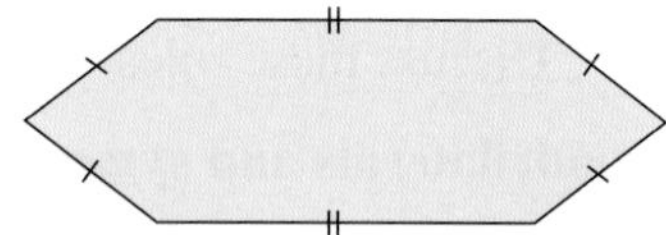

9 How many of the quadrilaterals below have rotational symmetry of order 2?

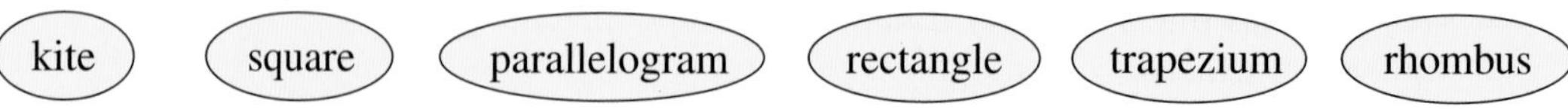

10 Which of the quadrilaterals in question 9 have rotational symmetry of order 1 (i.e: no rotational symmetry)

Investigation – triangles and quadrilaterals

On a square grid of 9 dots it is possible to draw several different triangles with vertices on dots. A vertex (plural vertices) is where two lines meet. Look at the three examples below:

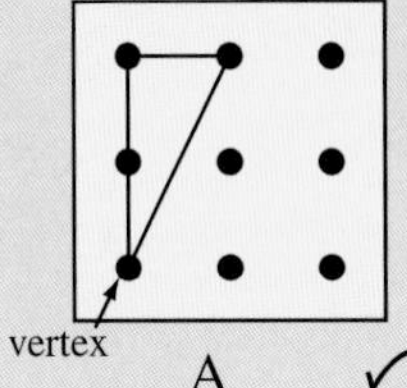

A ✓

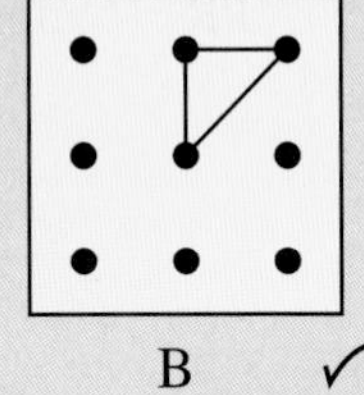
B ✓

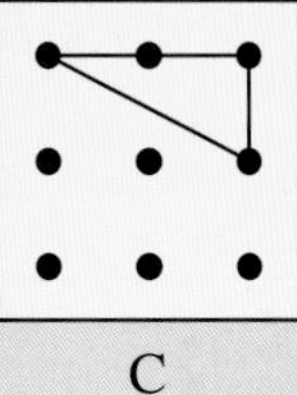
C

A and B are different triangles but C is the same as A. If a triangle could be cut out and placed exactly over another triangle then the two triangles are the same. The two triangles are called *congruent*.

Part A

Copy A and B above and then draw as many different triangles as you can.
Check carefully that you have not repeated the same triangle.

Part B

On a grid of 9 dots it is also possible to draw several different *quadrilaterals*.

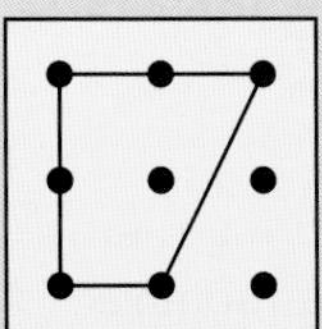

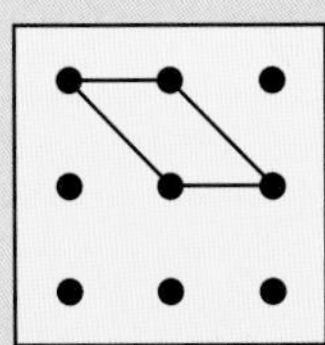

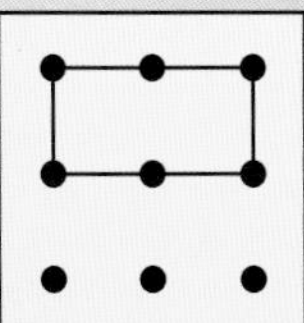

Copy the three shapes above and then draw as many other different quadrilaterals as possible. You are doing well if you can find 12 shapes but there are a few more!

Check carefully that you have not repeated the same quadrilateral. (Congruent shapes are not allowed.)

CHECK YOURSELF ON SECTIONS 4.1 and 4.2

1 Constructing triangles with a protractor and ruler

Construct each triangle below:

(a)

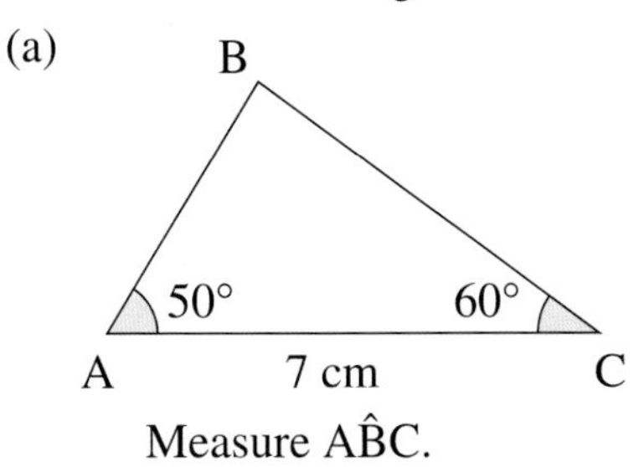

Measure $A\hat{B}C$.

(b)

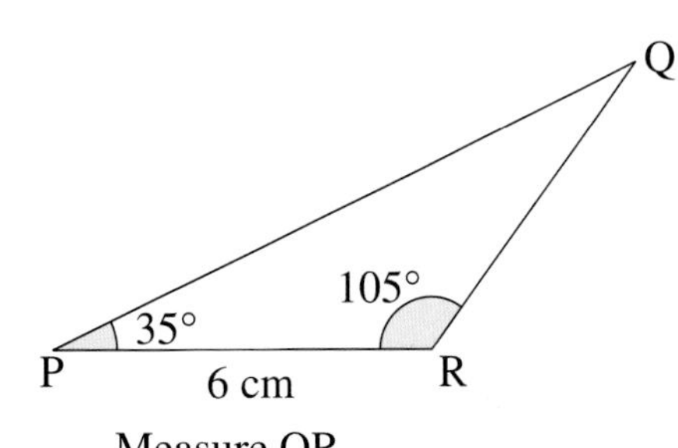

Measure QR.

2 Constructing triangles with three sides given

(a) Construct the triangle below:

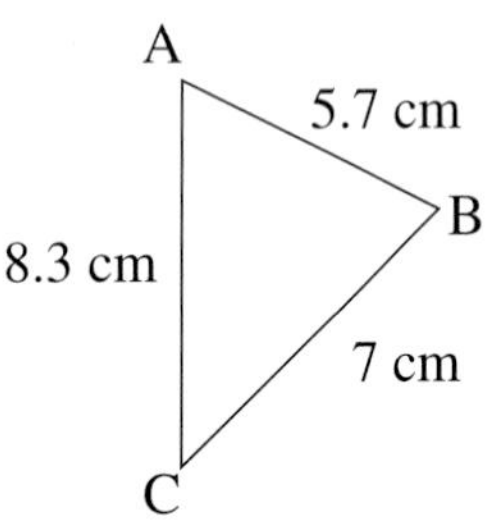

Measure $A\hat{C}B$.

(b) Construct triangle PQR where PQ = 4.9 cm, QR = 6.4 cm and PR = 5 cm. Measure $P\hat{R}Q$.

3 Recognising different types of quadrilateral

Match each quadrilateral to the correct name below:

(a)

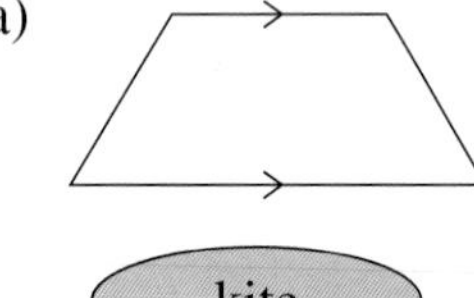

kite

(b)

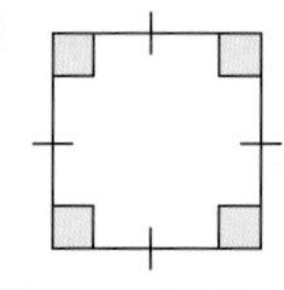

parallelogram

(c)

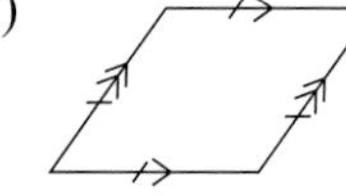

trapezium

(d)

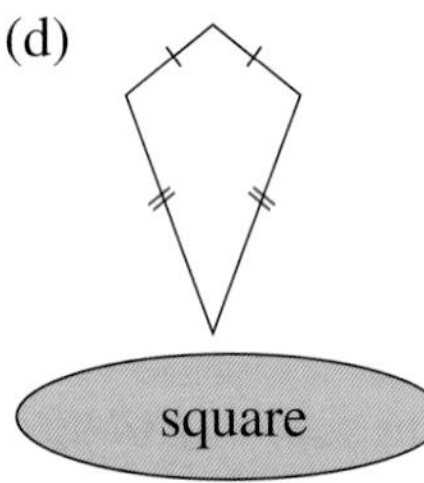

square

(e)

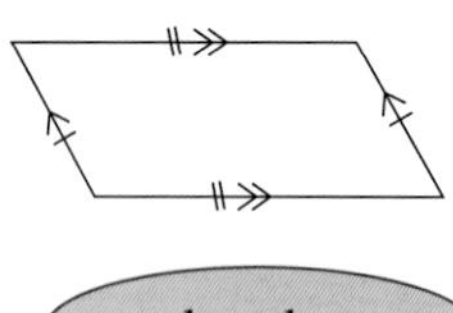

rhombus

(f) Write down the rules that make a rhombus.

4 Recognising different polygons

(a) Write down which shapes below are polygons.

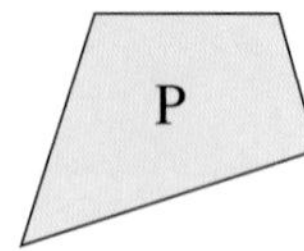

Q

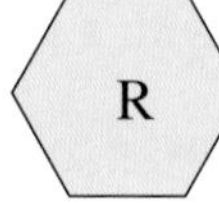

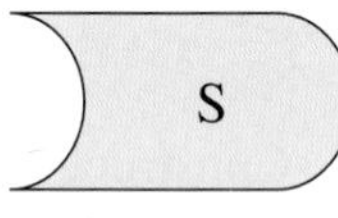

(b) How many sides has a decagon?

(c) Copy and complete the sentence below:

'This shape is a r– – – – – –   o – – – – – – –.'

5 Identifying symmetry properties of quadrilaterals

(a) What is the order of rotational symmetry of a parallelogram?

(b) What is the order of rotational symmetry of the trapezium below?

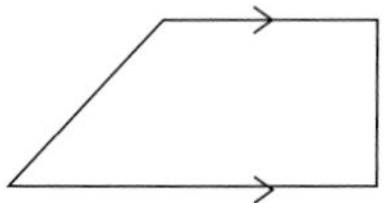

(c) *Explain* why the lines of symmetry for the rectangle below are *not* correct?

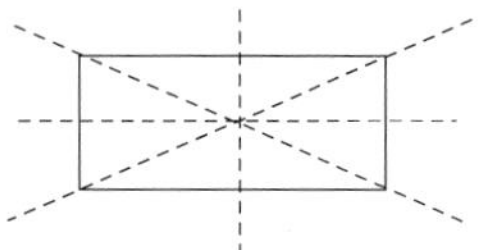

4.3 Percentages

In section 4.3 you will:

- review the conversion of fractions, decimals and percentages
- express one number as a percentage of another number
- find a percentage of a number

Fractions, decimals and percentages review

Reminder (from Section 2 work)

$\frac{3}{10} = 0.3$ $\frac{7}{100} = 0.07$ $\frac{9}{25} = \frac{36}{100} = 0.36$

convert denominator to 10, 100, etc

$0.35 = \frac{35}{100} = \frac{7}{20}$

cancel down fractions

$28\% = \frac{28}{100} = \frac{7}{25}$

'per cent' means 'out of 100'

$\frac{19}{50} = \frac{38}{100} = 38\%$ $64\% = \frac{64}{100} = 0.64$

Exercise 1M

1 Copy and complete the following statements.

(a) $\frac{3}{5} = \frac{\square}{10} = 0 \cdot \square$

(b) $\frac{11}{20} = \frac{\square}{100} = 0 \cdot \square\square$

(c) $0.9 = \frac{\square}{10} = \frac{\square\square}{100} = \square\square\%$

(d) $0.17 = \frac{\square\square}{100} = \square\square\%$

2 5% of people who go to the beach get sunburnt. What fraction of people who go to the beach get sunburnt?

3 Change these percentages into decimals.

(a) 37% (b) 60% (c) 6% (d) 19%
(e) 45%

4 Write True or False for each of the following statements.

(a) $0.09 = \frac{1}{9}$ (b) $0.25 = \frac{1}{4}$ (c) $0.2 = \frac{1}{5}$

(d) $0.4 = 4\%$ (e) $65\% = 0.65$ (f) $\frac{3}{5} = 35\%$

5 Change these decimals into fractions. Give the fractions in their most simple form.

(a) 0.8 (b) 0.47 (c) 0.16 (d) 0.85 (e) 0.75

6 Copy and complete this table.

	fraction	decimal	percentage
(a)	$\frac{7}{10}$		
(b)			24%
(c)		0.46	
(d)			95%
(e)	$\frac{3}{20}$		

Exercise 1E

1 Convert these fractions into decimals.

(a) $\frac{17}{50}$ (b) $\frac{19}{25}$ (c) $\frac{13}{20}$ (d) $\frac{90}{200}$

2 Write the numbers below in order of size, smallest first.

(a) $\frac{3}{4}$, 0.8, $\frac{7}{10}$ (b) 0.57, $\frac{11}{20}$, 60% (c) 24%, $\frac{1}{4}$, $\frac{1}{5}$ (d) $\frac{21}{25}$, 0.8, 82%

3 Mary uses 39 out of 52 cards to build a tower of cards.

(a) What fraction of all the cards did she use?
(b) What percentage of all the cards did she use?

4 Write down which fractions are equivalent to the given percentage.

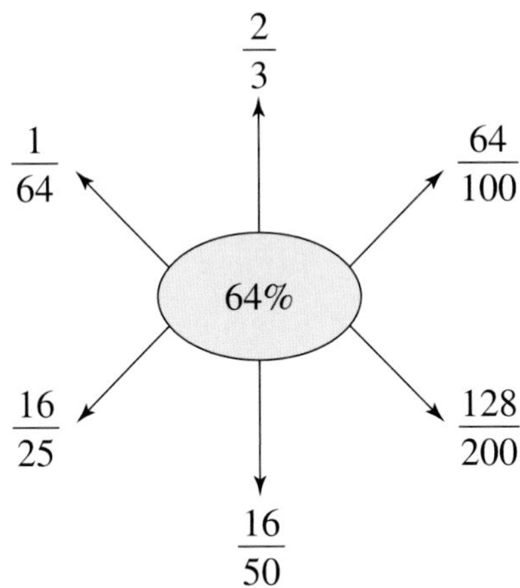

5 Convert these percentages into fractions.

(a) 49% (b) 8% (c) 56% (d) 15%

6 There are five groups of *equivalent* fractions, decimals and percentages below. Write down each group. (beware: there are two odd ones out).

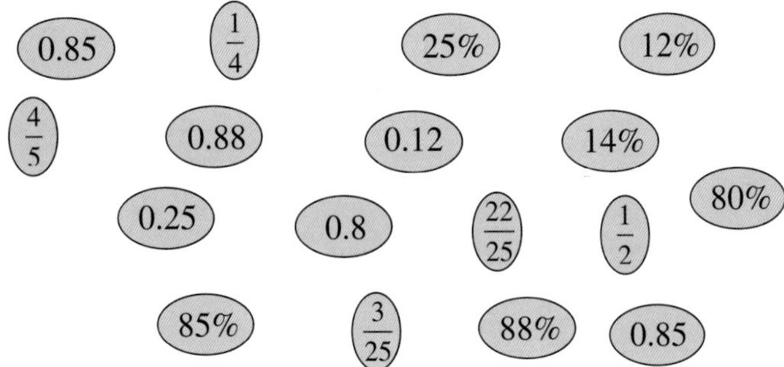

Expressing one number as a percentage of another number

25 children are playing rounders. 8 are boys.

What percentage of the children playing rounders are boys?

8 out of 25 = $\frac{8}{25} = \frac{32}{100}$ = 32%

Exercise 2M

1 50 children watch a school football match. 22 are girls. What percentage of the children are girls?

2 Tom has 20 pieces of fruit. 7 pieces of fruit are apples. What percentage of the fruit are the apples?

3 500 people were asked what their favourite film was. 85 of them said 'Lord of the Rings'. What percentage of the people chose 'Lord of the Rings'?

4 Danny plays 25 games of pool and wins 16 of them.
What percentage of the games did he *not* win?

5 Three tenths of Lorna's books were Science Fiction.
What percentage of her books were *not* Science Fiction?

6 Tania scored 60 out of 150 in a test. What percentage did she score?

7 Change each of the following into a percentage then put them in order of size, starting with the smallest.

A. 7 out of 25	B. 13 out of 20	C. 18 out of 60	D. 50 out of 200

8 Mark spent $\frac{3}{5}$ of his money on a computer game and $\frac{3}{20}$ of his money on food.
What percentage of his money has he got left?

9 At an international rugby match 37% of the crowd were from the U.K., 51% were from France and the remaining spectators came from the rest of the world. There were 31 080 people from the U.K. How many spectators came from the rest of the world?

Reminder: $\frac{1}{3} = 33\frac{1}{3}\%$ $\frac{2}{3} = 66\frac{2}{3}\%$

To change more 'tricky' numbers into a percentage of each other, write the two numbers as a fraction of each other then multiply by 100.

19 people are asked if they can drive a car. 13 of them replied with a 'yes'. What percentage of the people can drive?

13 out of 19 $= \frac{13}{19} \times 100 = 68.42$ (using a calculator)

$= 68\%$ (to the nearest %)

Exercise 2E

You may use a calculator. Give all answers to the nearest percentage.

1 There are 31 children in a class. 17 of them are girls. What percentage of the class are girls?

2 A football team scores 91 goals during one season. Crespo scores 28 of the goals. What percentage of his team's goals did he score?

3 Boris drank one third of his drink. What percentage of his drink did he have left?

4

D	O	W	E	N
E	E	D	S	O
M	A	N	Y	T
E	S	T	S	?

What percentage of the letters in this grid are
(a) the letter N
(b) the letter E

5 16 children were playing in the park. 9 of them were wearing sandals. What percentage of the children were *not* wearing sandals?

6 Some children were asked what their favourite pet was.
The results are shown in this table.
What percentage of all the children chose:
(a) dog
(b) gerbil
(c) rabbit

type of pet	number of children
cat	87
dog	136
hamster	49
rabbit	63
gerbil	24
total	359

7 A 925 g cake contains 200 g of self-raising flour. What percentage of the cake is self-raising flour?

8

```
          1
        1   1
      1   2   1
    1   3   3   1
  1   4   6   4   1
1   5  10  10   5   1
```

This triangle is known as Pascal's triangle.
What percentage of the numbers are prime numbers?
(remember: 1 is *not* prime)

Percentage of a number

Use common Percentages

$66\frac{2}{3}\%$ of 30 = $\frac{2}{3}$ of 30 = $(30 \div 3) \times 2 = 20$

Use multiples of 10% $10\% = \frac{1}{10}$

To work out 20%, find 10% then multiply by 2
To work out 30%, find 10% then multiply by 3 and so on

In a sale the price of a shirt is reduced by 20%. Find the 'sale price' if the normal price is £30.

10% of £30 = $\frac{1}{10}$ of 30 = £3

20% of £30 = 2 × £3 = £6

sale price = 30 – 6 = £24

Exercise 3M

Do not use a calculator.

1 Work out

(a) 25% of £60 (b) 75% of £24 (c) 10% of £70

(d) 20% of £70 (e) 30% of £90 (f) $33\frac{1}{3}$ % of £60

2 There are 48 dolphins in a pod. Seventy-five per cent of the dolphins are adults. How many adult dolphins are there?

3 There are 220 children in a school. 60% of the children have school meals. How many children have school meals?

4 Work out

(a) 80% of £200 (b) $66\frac{2}{3}$ % of £33 (c) 70% of £400

(d) 20% of £60 (e) 5% of £80 (f) 15% of £80

5 Which is larger? 30% of £40 or 25% of £60

6 Which is larger? 50% of £70 or 5% of £700

7 Find the odd one out

(a) 75% of £200 (b) 70% of £210 (c) 30% of £500

8 A train company increases its prices by 15%. If a ticket costs £40 now, how much will it cost after the price increase?

9 Find the sale price of each item below. The normal prices are shown in boxes.

(a) £60 30% off marked price

(b)

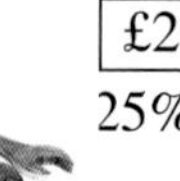

£20 25% off!

(c) £700 20% off normal price

(d)  £16 75% off

(e)  £36 $33\frac{1}{3}$% discount off the shown price

(f) £62000 5% off normal price 

10 A marathon runner weighs 60 kg at the start of a race. During the race his weight is reduced by 5%. How much does he weigh at the end of the race?

11 One Saturday 320 people go to the cinema. 40% more people go on the following Saturday. How many people go to the cinema on the following Saturday?

12 People often have to pay Value Added Tax (VAT) when they buy things. The rate of VAT is $17\frac{1}{2}$%. Here is a method for finding $17\frac{1}{2}$% of £6000 without a calculator.

$17\frac{1}{2}$% of £6000:

10%	=	£600
5%	=	£300
$2\frac{1}{2}$%	=	£150
$17\frac{1}{2}$%	=	£1050

Use this method to work out:

(a) $17\frac{1}{2}$% of £8000 (b) $17\frac{1}{2}$% of £220 (c) $17\frac{1}{2}$% of £76

13 A TV costs £720 plus $17\frac{1}{2}$% VAT. What is the total price of the TV?

14 A lizard weighs 500g. While escaping from a predator it loses its tail and its weight is reduced by 5%. How much does it weigh now?

Harder percentages of a number

$1\% = \frac{1}{100}$. To find 1% of a number, divide the number by 100.

Find 16% of a number.

Divide the number by 100 to find 1% then multiply by 16 to find 16% of the number.

Work out 29% of £18.

1% of 18 = $18 \div 100$

29% of 18 = $(18 \div 100) \times 29$

= 5.22 = £5.22

Exercise 3E

Use a calculator when needed.

1 Find 1% of:

(a) £375 (b) £370 (c) £49 (d) £180

2 Work out

(a) 8% of £460 (b) 3% of £690 (c) 32% of £240
(d) 73% of £3800 (e) 19% of £510 (f) 94% of £1200

3 Which is larger? 8% of £23 or 9% of £21

4 Work out the following, giving the correct units in your answers.

(a) 73% of 3000 kg (b) 14% of 530 km
(c) 3% of \$235 (d) 86% of 17 km
(e) 47% of 600 m (f) 98% of 7100 g

5 Find 3.2% of £7000.

6 Using a calculator we find that 13.2% of £12.65 = £1.6698.
This answer has to be rounded off to the nearest penny, since the penny is the smallest unit of currency. So 13.2% of £12.65 = £1.67, to the nearest penny.

Work out, to the nearest penny:

(a) 7% of £16.34 (b) 38% of £7.83
(c) 16% of £39.18 (d) 4.5% of £12.60
(e) 135% of £310.19 (f) $6\frac{1}{2}$% of £14.37

7 A mail order firm reduces its prices by 7%. What will be the reduced price of each of the following items.

(a) fridge £230 (b) TV £750
(c) dishwasher £470 (d) cooker £860

8 A ticket to New York City costs £230.
The price of the ticket is increased by 4%.
What is the new price of the ticket?

9 John weighs 80 kg. Over the next year his weight increases by 6%. What is his new weight?

10 (a) Increase £70 by 16%.
(b) Decrease £190 by 2%.
(c) Decrease £280 by 28%.
(d) Increase £4100 by 9%.

11 A plane ticket is advertised as being £160. It is then increased by 14%. What is the new plane ticket price?

12 A hen weighs 3kg. After laying an egg, her weight is reduced by 2%. How much does she weigh now?

13 During the day a person might shrink in height by 0.5% to 1%. Donald is 1.8 m when he wakes up. If he shrinks by 0.7% during the day, how tall is he at the end of the day?

14 Marie earns £340 each week. She is given a 6.5% pay rise. How much does she earn each week after the pay rise?

15 In 2008 the entrance fee to an exhibition of famous jewelry was £5 and 37840 visitors came. In 2009 the entrance fee was reduced by 5% and the number of visitors increased by 12.5%. How much was paid in entrance fees in 2009?

16 There are 860 children in a school. 15% cycle to school, 65% walk to school and the rest go by bus.

(a) How many walk to school?
(b) How many go by bus?

4.4 Proportion and ratio

In section 4.4 you will learn how to:

- tackle problems involving proportion
- deal with ratios

Proportion

Proportion is used to compare part of something to the whole.
A proportion is expressed as a fraction, decimal or percentage.

(a) There are 8 boys and 11 girls in a class of 19 children.
The proportion of girls in the class is $\frac{11}{19}$.

(b) If 4 bottles of lemonade contain 10 litres, how much lemonade is there in 7 bottles?

Find the amount in 1 bottle first.

4 bottles contain 10 litres

1 bottle contains $10 \div 4 = 2.5$ litres

7 bottles contain $2.5 \times 7 = 17.5$ litres

Exercise 1M

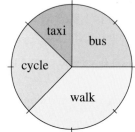

1 The chart shows how children travel to Maxwell High School.

(a) What proportion travel by bus?

(b) What proportion walk?

2 A soup contains 150 g of water and 50 g of vegetables. What proportion of the soup is vegetables?

3 Count the children in your class. What proportion of the class went to the same junior school as you?

4 The diagram shows how the government spends money on transport. Estimate, as a percentage, what proportion is spent on roads.

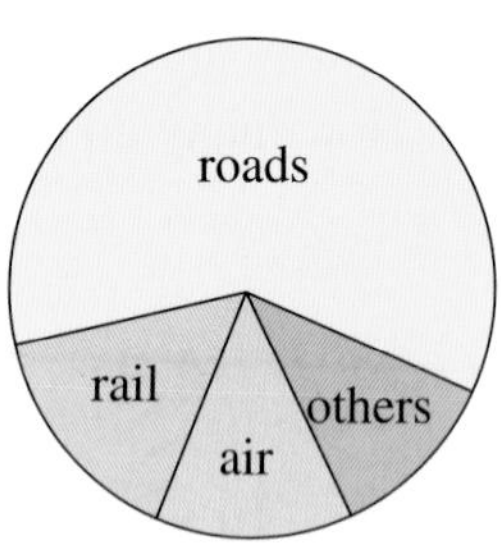

5 The total weight of 7 CDs is 84 grams. How much do 10 CDs weigh?

6 5 oranges cost 95p. How much will 9 oranges cost?

7 8 coats cost £560. Find the cost of 11 coats.

8 5 tea pots cost £7.50. Find the cost of 50 tea pots.

9 Find the cost of 7 skateboards if 4 skateboards cost £168.

10 A machine fills 1000 bottles in 5 minutes. How many bottles will it fill in 2 minutes?

Exercise 1E

1 The total cost of 8 magazines is £12. What is the total cost of 12 magazines?

2 Fishing line costs £1.80 for 50 m. Find the cost of 3000 m.

3 A train travels 30 km in 90 minutes. How long will it take to travel 55 km at the same speed?

4 If 6 cauliflowers can be bought for £5.22, how many can be bought for £13.92?

5 Jack uses 32 litres of petrol to travel 270 km. How much petrol does Jack use to travel 351 km?

6 Usually it takes 12 hours for 5 men to build a wall. How many men are needed to build a wall twice as big in 6 hours?

7 10 bags of corn will feed 60 hens for 3 days. Copy and complete the following:

(a) 30 bags of corn will feed ☐ hens for 3 days.

(b) 10 bags of corn will feed 20 hens for ☐ days.

(c) 10 bags of corn will feed ☐ hens for 18 days.

(d) 30 bags of corn will feed 90 hens for ☐ days.

8 4 machines produce 5000 batteries in 10 hours. How many batteries would 6 machines produce in 8 hours?

9 In the army all holes are dug 4 feet deep. It takes 8 soldiers 36 minutes to dig a hole 18 feet long by 10 feet wide. How long will it take 5 soldiers to dig a hole 20 feet by 15 feet?

10 It takes b beavers n hours to build a dam. How long will it take $b + 5$ beavers to build the same size dam?

Ratio

Ratio is used to compare parts of a whole.

There are 30 children in a class. 16 are boys and 14 are girls.

The ratio of boys to girls is written as 16:14.

This can be simplified by dividing both numbers by 2 so the ratio of boys to girls is 8:7.

Exercise 2M

1 For each diagram write down the ratio of blue squares to yellow squares (make ratios as simple as possible):

(a)

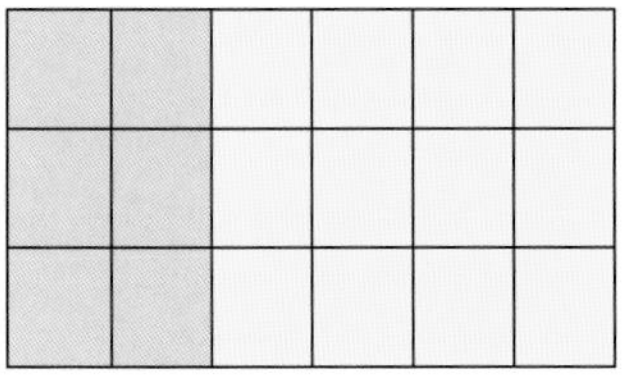

(b)

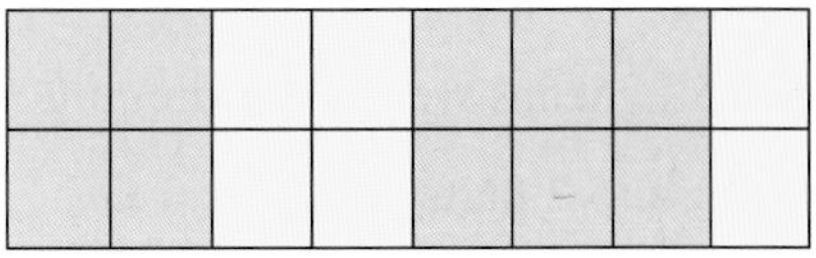

2 There are 27 children in a class. 11 are boys and 16 are girls. Write down the ratio of boys to girls.

3 One evening a vet sees 10 dogs and 6 cats. Find the ratio of dogs to cats.

4 Copy this diagram. Colour in so that the ratio of blue squares to green squares is 2:3.

5 There are 33 people on a bus. Nineteen are men. Write down the ratio of men to women.

6 Write these ratios in simplified form.

(a) 5:20 (b) 8:10
(c) 4:44 (d) 16:12
(e) 10:8:6 (f) 21:35
(g) 65:25 (h) 16:24:80

7 For each pair of ratios below, write down the value of n which makes the ratios *equivalent* to each other.

(a) $8:2 = n:1$ (b) $4:12 = 1:n$
(c) $70:40 = n:4$ (d) $24:30 = 12:n$
(e) $22:33 = 2:n$ (f) $48:32 = 6:n$

8 Pablo mixes paint for his latest masterpiece with 12 tubes of blue, 16 tubes of red and 24 tubes of green. Find the ratio of blue to red to green in the paint.

Share £35 in the ratio 5:2

The ratio 5:2 means we are dividing into '5 + 2' = 7 parts

£35 is split into 7 parts so 1 part = £5

5 parts = 5 × £5 = £25 and 2 parts = 2 × £5 = £10

Exercise 2E

1 Share £36 in the ratio: (a) 3:1 (b) 1:5 (c) 2:1

2 Share £75 in the ratio: (a) 2:3 (b) 11:14 (c) 8:7

3 There are 28 children in a class. The ratio of boys to girls is 4:3.
(a) How many boys are in the class?
(b) How many girls are in the class?

4 The ratio of dark chocolates to milk chocolates in a box is 2:3. If there are 18 dark chocolates, how many milk chocolates are in the box?

5 In a hall, the ratio of chairs to tables is 9:2. If there is a total of 99 chairs and tables, how many chairs are there?

6 Natasha and Andy are given some money in the ratio 5:3. If Andy receives £24, how much does Natasha get?

7 Mark and Ning share some sweets in the ratio 4:5. If Mark gets 28 sweets, how many sweets do they share out in total?

8 Neil, Pippa and Mel have newspaper rounds. Each week they earn a total of £28 in the ratio 3:5:6. How much money does Pippa earn?

9 In a kitchen drawer, there is a total of 36 knives, forks and spoons in the ratio 4:3:5. How many knives are there?

10 Chun Kit mixes some blue paint and some yellow paint in the ratio 7:4 to make up 33 litres of paint.
(a) How much yellow paint did she use?
(b) What is the ratio of blue paint to yellow paint if 3 more litres of yellow paint are added to the total mixture?

11 Baldeep, Millie and Mike work for a number of hours in the ratio 7:3:2. Baldeep worked for 42 hours which was the most. How many hours did Millie and Mike work for in total?

12 On a bus, the ratio of children to adults is 4:1. What proportion of the people are adults?

13 Rob, Louise, Steve and Gemma win £40 000 and divide it in the ratio 23:34:13:10. How much does each person get?

14 Three people are standing in a lift. Their combined weight is 232 kg split in the ratio 8:11:10. The lightest person gets out of the lift and a heavier person gets in so that the ratio of the weights of the people now in the lift is 11:10:12. What is the combined weight of the three people in the lift now?

CHECK YOURSELF ON SECTIONS 4.3 and 4.4

1 Conversion of fractions, decimals and percentages

Copy and complete this table.

	fraction	decimal	percentage
(a)		0.08	
(b)	$\frac{4}{5}$		
(c)		0.9	
(d)			32%
(e)	$\frac{18}{25}$		

2 Expressing one number as a percentage of another number

(a) H A P P Y What percentage of these letters is the letter 'P'?

(b) Andrew scored 12 out of 17 in a maths test, 33 out of 48 in an english test and 20 out of 32 in a science test. In which test did Andrew score his highest percentage?

3 Finding a percentage of a number

(a) Find 30% of £60.
(b) A camera costs £300. It is reduced in price by 5%. What is the new price?
(c) Find 12% of £800.
(d) Work out 4% of £18.09, giving your answer to the nearest penny.

4 Tackling problems involving proportion

(a) 22 children are playing football. Nine of the children are in Year 7, the rest are in Year 8. What proportion of the children are in Year 8?
(b) Find the cost of 7 toys if 9 toys cost £78.84.

5 Dealing with ratios

(a) Write the ratio 12:32 in simplified form.
(b) During one week Urma and Terry eat 15 ice-creams in the ratio 3:2. How many ice-creams does Urma eat?
(c) Janet buys gifts for her husband and son. She spends money in the ratio 3:7. If she spends £56 on her son, how much does she spend in total on the gifts?

4.5 Negative Numbers

In section 4.5 you will learn how to:

- add and subtract negative numbers
- multiply and divide negative numbers

Adding and subtracting negative numbers

For adding and subtracting with negative numbers a number line is very useful.

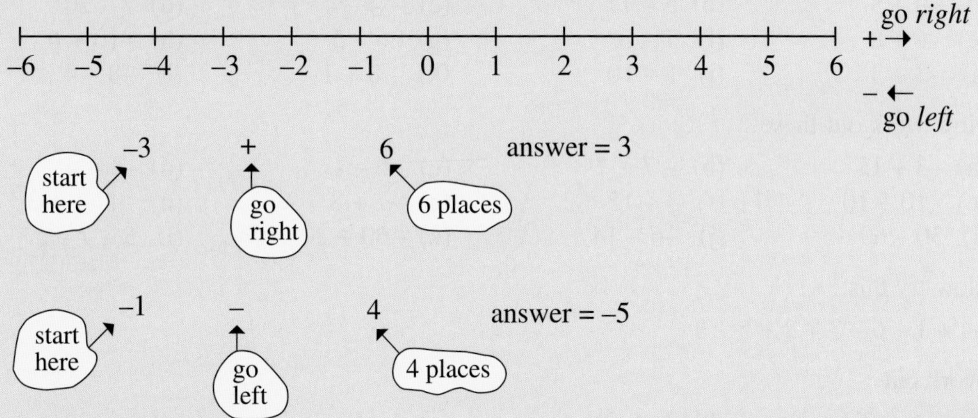

In the sequence of subtractions on the right the numbers in column A go down by one each time. The numbers in column B increase by one each time.

Continuing the sequence downwards:

We see that 8 – (–3) becomes 8 + 3.

A	B
8 – (+3) =	5
8 – (+2) =	6
8 – (+1) =	7
8 – (0) =	8
8 – (–1) =	9
8 – (–2) =	10
8 – (–3) =	11

This always applies when subtracting negative numbers. It is possible to replace *two* signs next to each other by *one* sign as follows:

+	+	=	+
–	–	=	+
–	+	=	–
+	–	=	–

Remember: 'same signs: +'
'different signs: –'

When two signs next to each other have been replaced by one sign in this way, the calculation is completed using the number line as before.

(a) $-3 + (-5)$
$= -3 - 5$
$= -8$

(b) $6 + (-12)$
$= 6 - 12$
$= -6$

(c) $4 - (-3)$
$= 4 + 3$
$= 7$

(d) $5 - (-2) + (-6)$
$= 5 + 2 - 6$
$= 1$

Exercise 1M

1 Work out

(a) $-9 + 3$ (b) $5 - 11$ (c) $-4 - 4$ (d) $7 - 20$
(e) $-6 + 8$ (f) $7 - 3$ (g) $-6 - 5$ (h) $-10 + 6$
(i) $-3 + 3$ (j) $1 - 10$ (k) $-8 + 1$ (l) $-8 - 4$

2 Now work out these

(a) $-3 + 12$ (b) $-7 + 7$ (c) $-6 - 1$ (d) $-5 - 4$
(e) $-10 + 10$ (f) $3 - 15$ (g) $-7 + 8$ (h) $-4 - 1 + 3$
(i) $30 - 60$ (j) $-6 - 14$ (k) $-60 + 20$ (l) $5 - 7 - 2$

3 Now try this:

$-4 + 1 - 6 - 3 + 2 + 5 - 3$

4 Work out

(a) $7 + (-3)$ (b) $9 - (-2)$ (c) $4 - 9$ (d) $-5 + 2$
(e) $-4 + (-5)$ (f) $-8 + (-3)$ (g) $10 - 12$ (h) $6 - (-4)$
(i) $12 - (-4)$ (j) $-6 + (-6)$ (k) $-4 - (-4)$ (l) $-5 + (-6)$

5 Copy and complete each number wall below. The number in each box is found by adding the two numbers below it.

(a)

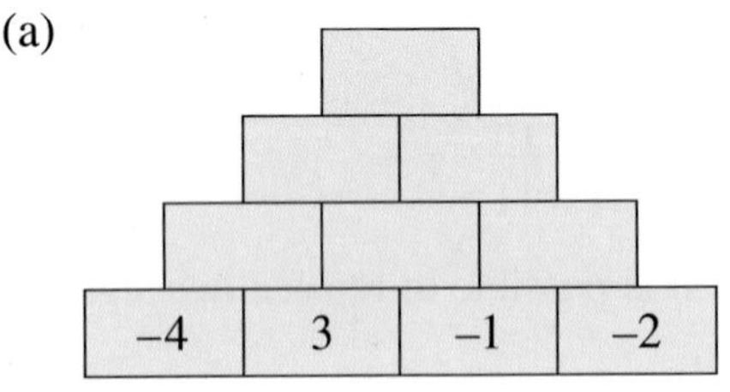

(b)

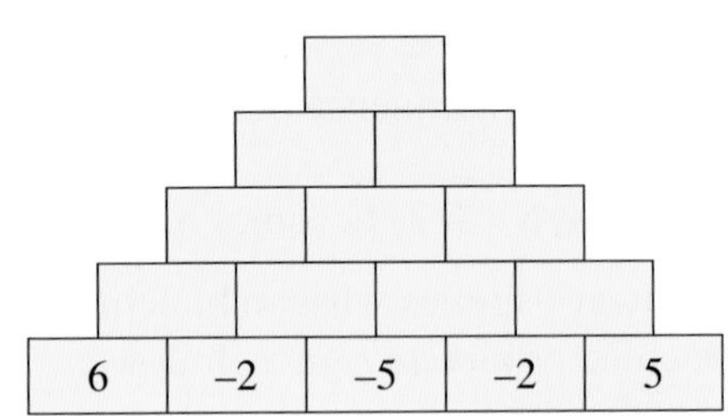

(c)

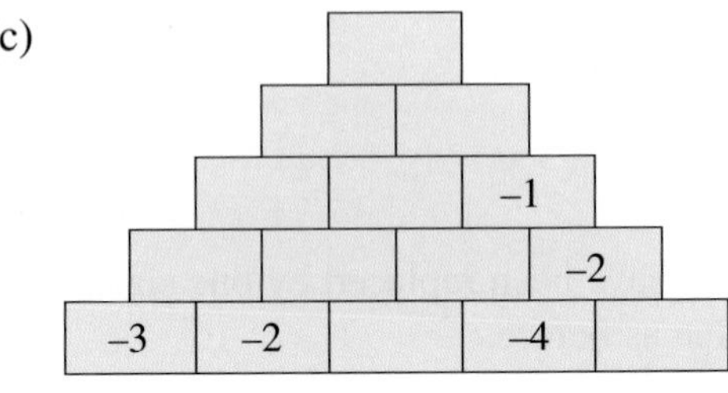

6 Work out

(a) $8 + (-7)$ (b) $-5 + (-1)$ (c) $-2 - (-3)$ (d) $-9 - (-9)$
(e) $8 - 12$ (f) $6 + (-9)$ (g) $-4 - (-3)$ (h) $3 + (-3)$
(i) $-7 - 5$ (j) $6 + (-13)$ (k) $-5 - (-6)$ (l) $3 + (-10)$

7 What is the missing number for each box below?

(a) $\square - (-3) = 7$ (b) $\square + (-4) = 6$ (c) $3 + \square = 1$
(d) $4 - \square = 8$ (e) $\square - 6 = -8$ (f) $8 + \square = -1$

8 Copy and complete the magic squares

(a)

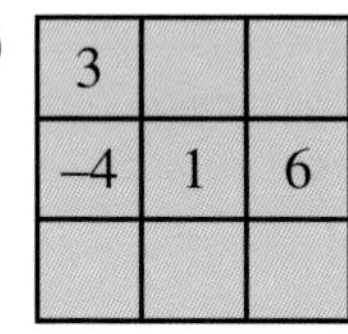

3		
–4	1	6

(b)

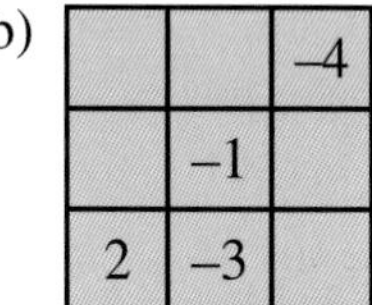

		–4
	–1	
2	–3	

9 Write down whether each statement below is true or false

(a) $4 + (-6) = -2$ (b) $8 - (-2) = 6$ (c) $-7 - 2 = -9$
(d) $8 - (-4) = 12$ (e) $5 + (-5) = -10$ (f) $2 - (-2) = 0$
(g) $16 + (-3) = 13$ (h) $10 + (-3) = 13$ (i) $-6 - (-8) = -14$

Multiplying and dividing negative numbers

A		B
↓		↓
5 × 3	=	15
5 × 2	=	10
5 × 1	=	5
5 × 0	=	0

In the sequence of multiplications shown, the numbers in column A go down by one each time. The numbers in column B go down by five each time.

$5 \times -1 = -5$
$5 \times -2 = -10$
$5 \times -3 = -15$

We see that:

When a positive number is multiplied by a negative number the answer is negative.

C		D
↓		↓
–3 × 3	=	–9
–3 × 2	=	–6
–3 × 1	=	–3
–3 × 0	=	0

In this sequence the numbers in column C go down by one each time.

$-3 \times -1 = 3$
$-3 \times -2 = 6$
$-3 \times -3 = 9$

The numbers in column D *increase* by 3 each time.

We see that:

When two negative numbers are multiplied together the answer is positive.

For division, the rules are the same as for multiplication.

$-4 \times (-6) = 24$ $\quad 7 \times (-3) = -21$ $\quad -15 \div 3 = -5$

$40 \div (-4) = -10$ $\quad -60 \div (-20) = 3$ $\quad (-2) \times (-3) \times (-2) = -12$

Exercise 1E

Work out

1 (a) $4 \times (-2)$ (b) $5 \times (-4)$ (c) -3×4 (d) $-2 \times (-3)$
(e) -6×3 (f) $8 \times (-2)$ (g) $-5 \times (-6)$ (h) -1×7

2 (a) $12 \div (-3)$ (b) $20 \div (-4)$ (c) $-8 \div 2$ (d) $-12 \div (-4)$
(e) $-18 \div (-6)$ (f) $25 \div (-5)$ (g) $-15 \div 3$ (h) $-30 \div (-10)$

3 (a) $-40 \div 20$ (b) $8 \times (-6)$ (c) $-4 \times (-7)$ (d) $4 \times (-8)$
(e) $-50 \div (-25)$ (f) $24 \div (-8)$ (g) $10 \times (-9)$ (h) $-63 \div (-7)$

4 Write down two negative numbers which multiply together to make 8. Are there any other pairs of negative numbers which will multiply together to make 8? Write them down.

5 Copy and complete the squares below:

(a)

×	–4	–7	2	0	–8	5
3	–12					
–9						
6						
–4						
–6						
–1						

(b)

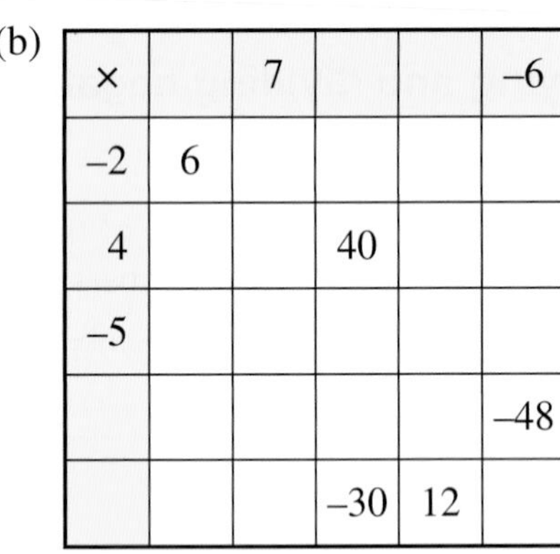

×		7			–6
–2	6				
4			40		
–5					
					–48
			–30	12	

6 Work out

(a) $(-2) \times (-4) \times (-1)$ (b) $3 \times (-5) \times (-2)$ (c) $(-3)^2$ (d) $(-6)^2$
(e) $4 \times (-2) \times 4$ (f) $(-5) \times (-2) \times (-4)$ (g) $(-1)^2$ (h) $(-2)^3$

7 What is the missing number for each box below?

(a) $-4 \times \square = -28$ (b) $-6 \times \square = 42$ (c) $32 \div \square = -16$
(d) $-45 \div \square = 5$ (e) $\square \div (-10) = 5$ (f) $\square \div (-9) = -8$
(g) $\square \times (-9) = 108$ (h) $6 \times \square = -90$ (i) $\square \div 7 = -3$

4.6 More algebra

In section 4.6 you will:

- review section 2 algebra
- solve equations
- multiply out single brackets

Review of section 2 algebra

Exercise 1M

1 I start with a number w, double it then subtract 18. Write down an expression for what I now have.

2 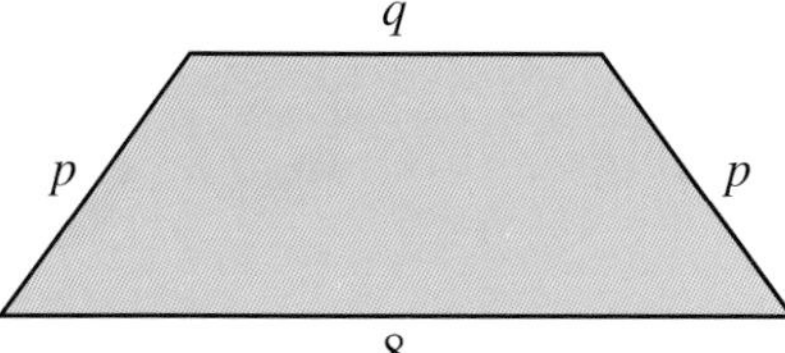

Write down an expression for the perimeter of this trapezium.

3 Simplify the following expressions where possible.

(a) $5y - 2y$ (b) $8m + 2$ (c) $7x - x$ (d) $5w - 3$

4 Which pair of expressions below are equal to each other?

$2n + 1$ $2n + n$ $n \times n \times n$ $3n$ $n + 3$

5 Simplify (a) $\frac{2w}{w}$ (b) $\frac{w^2}{w}$

6 $V = IR$ is an electrical formula. Find the value of V when $I = 0.5$ and $R = 68$.

7 $w = 25 - 4n$
Find w, when $n = 5$.

8 $a = 2(b - 6)$
Find a, when $b = 10$.

9 $p = 2q + 5r$
Find p, when $q = 6$ and $r = 7$.

10 $a = b\,(c - 7)$
Find a, when $b = 10$ and $c = 15$.

11 $y = \frac{x}{6} - 9$
Find y, when $x = 72$.

12 $m = n^2 + p^2$
Find m, when $n = 8$ and $p = 11$.

Negative numbers can be substituted into formulas

$m = 6 - n$
Find m, when $n = -2$

$m = 6 - (-2)$
$m = 6 + 2$
$m = 8$

$y = 3x + w$
Find y, when $x = 4$ and $w = -8$

$y = (3 \times 4) + (-8)$
$y = 12 - 8$
$y = 4$

Exercise 1E

1 I start with x, divide it by 9 and then subtract 14.
Write down an expression for what I now have.

2 Marie has n sweets. She gives y sweets to her brother Barney. She eats 3 sweets. Write down an expression for how many sweets she now has.

3 Simplify the following expressions by collecting like terms.
(a) $5m + 7n + 2n - 3m$
(b) $8y + 3w + 5y - w$
(c) $3x + 6 - 2x + 1$
(d) $6a + 3 - 2a + 5a + 3b$

4 Simplify
(a) $4m \times 2n$
(b) $3y \times 5w \times z$
(c) $6p \times 4q \times 3r$

5

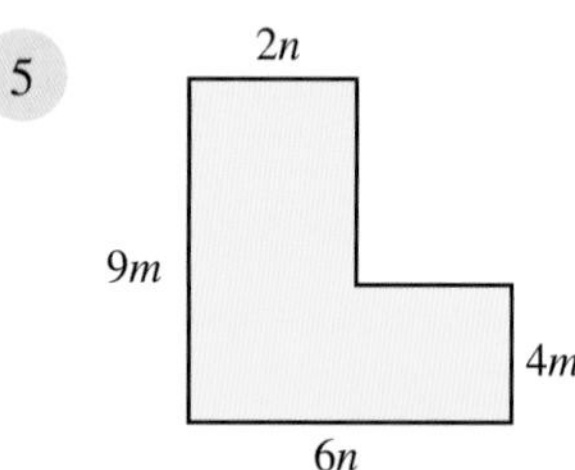

Use algebra to find the area of this shape.
Simplify your answer as far as possible.

6 Simplify the following expressions by collecting like terms.
(a) $mn + nm + mn$
(b) $3xy + 6x - 2xy + x$
(c) $p + pq + 6pq - p$
(d) $4a + 9 - 3a + ab + 6ba$

7 $w = 16 - p$
Find w, when $p = -3$.

8 $h = 3g - 6$
Find h, when $g = -6$.

9 $n = 5x - y$
Find n, when $x = -10$ and $y = -40$.

10 $p = m^2$
Find p, when $m = -6$.

11 $y = 3(8 - x)$
Find y, when $x = -2$.

12 $p = -2(8 + q)$
Find p, when $q = -3$.

13 $a = 2b + 2c$
Find a, when $b = -4$ and $c = -5$.

14 $y = mx + c$
Find y, when $m = 4$, $x = -6$ and $c = 3$.

15 $p = q^2 + r^2$
Find p, when $q = -5$ and $r = -3$.

16 $m = n^2 + p$
Find m, when $n = -9$ and $p = -20$.

Solving equations

- Tom is thinking of a mystery number. He knows that if he doubles the number and then adds nine, the answer is twenty-three.

  He could write [?] for the mystery number.

  So 2 × [?] + 9 = 23

  This is an *equation*. It contains an '=' sign.

  There is one unknown number shown by the question mark.

- People prefer to use *letters* to stand for unknowns when they write equations.

  Tom's equation would be

  $2 \times n + 9 = 23$ where n is the mystery number.
  or $2n + 9 = 23$ (any letter could be used)

  What is Tom's mystery number?

- Equations are like weighing scales which are balanced. The scales remain balanced if the same weight is added or taken away from both sides.

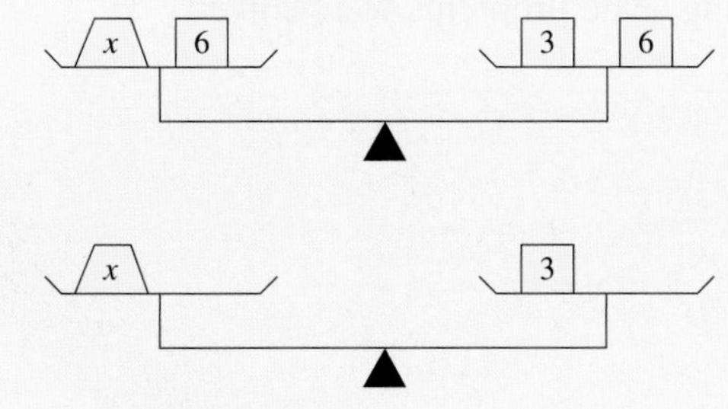

On the left pan is an unknown weight x plus a 6 kg weight. On the right pan there is a 6 kg weight and a 3 kg weight.

If the two 6 kg weights are taken from each pan, the scales are still balanced so the weight x is 3 kg.

Exercise 2M

Find the weight x by removing weights from both pans. Weights are in kg.

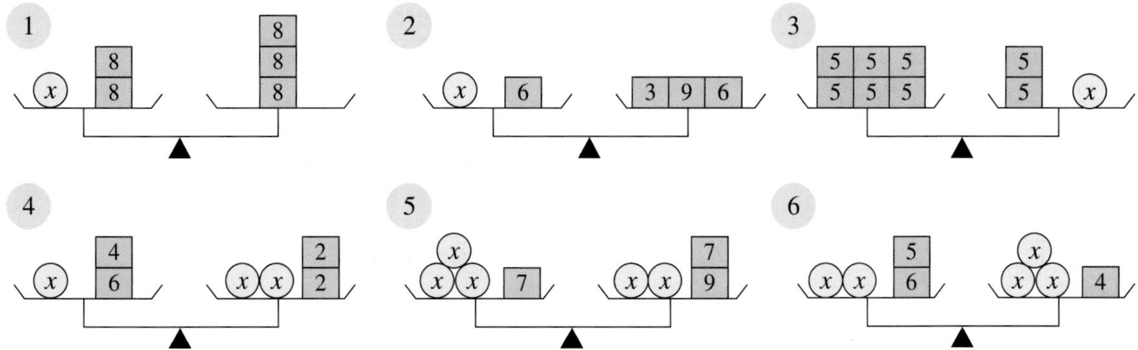

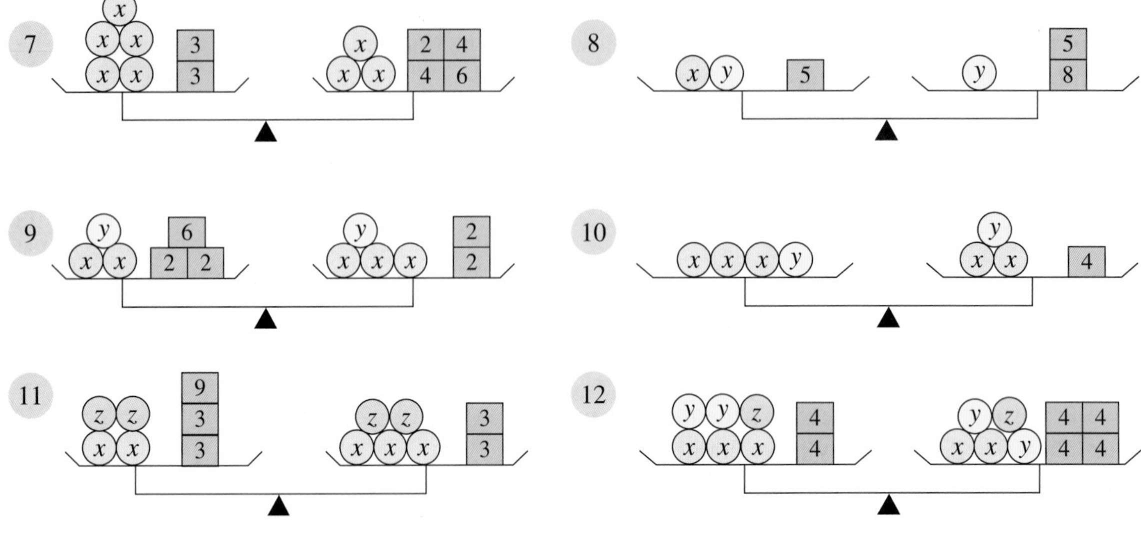

Rules for solving equations

Equations can be solved in the same way as the weighing scale problems were solved.

The main rule is

Do the same thing to both sides

If you need to, you may:

add the same thing to both sides

subtract the same thing from both sides

multiply both sides by the same thing

divide both sides by the same thing

Solve the equations. The circles show what is done to both sides of the equation.

(a) $x + 4 = 16$

(−4) (−4)

$x = 12$

(b) $x - 5 = 14$

(+5) (+5)

$x = 19$

(c) $3x = 18$

(÷3) (÷3)

$x = 6$

(d) $\frac{x}{2} = 6$

(×2) (×2)

$x = 12$

Exercise 3M

Solve the equations below.

1. $x + 6 = 19$
2. $x - 9 = 8$
3. $6 = x - 2$
4. $3 + x = 3$
5. $x - 14 = 10$
6. $17 = 5 + x$

Questions 7 to 21 involve multiplication and division.

7. $7x = 21$
8. $4x = 12$
9. $5x = 45$
10. $10 = 2x$
11. $8 = 8x$
12. $2x = 1$
13. $4x = 100$
14. $6x = 0$
15. $\frac{x}{3} = 2$
16. $\frac{x}{5} = 4$
17. $70 = 7x$
18. $3x = 2$
19. $\frac{x}{8} = 3$
20. $\frac{x}{4} = 1$
21. $10 = \frac{x}{12}$

Exercise 3E

Solve the equations below to find n.

1. $n - 17 = 21$
2. $5 = n + 5$
3. $15n = 45$
4. $\frac{n}{5} = 20$
5. $2 = \frac{n}{8}$
6. $3n = 1$
7. $n - \frac{1}{3} = \frac{2}{3}$
8. $120 = n + 36$
9. $3n = \frac{1}{3}$
10. $\frac{1}{2} = \frac{n}{10}$
11. $4n = 412$
12. $140 = n - 20$

Solve the equations below to find x.

13. $109 = x - 206$
14. $\frac{x}{3} = 9$
15. $0 = 15x$
16. $\frac{1}{5}x = 100$
17. $16\frac{1}{2} = x - 2\frac{1}{2}$
18. $\frac{x}{10} = 6$
19. $\frac{1}{2}x = 35$
20. $x + 14 = 14$
21. $x + \frac{1}{8} = \frac{1}{4}$
22. $11 = x + 1.4$
23. $0.02 = \frac{x}{10}$
24. $150 = 210 + x$
25. $\frac{1}{3} + x = \frac{1}{2}$
26. $x + 123 = 1000$
27. $x - 0.24 = 0.03$
28. $\frac{x}{11} = 145$
29. $\frac{x}{4} = \frac{1}{12}$
30. $0.2 = x + \frac{1}{8}$

Equations with two operations

(a) $6n - 5 = 19$

$(+5)\quad(+5)$

$6n = 24$

$(\div 6)\quad(\div 6)$

$n = 4$

(b) $8x + 4 = 9$

$(-4)\quad(-4)$

$8x = 5$

$(\div 8)\quad(\div 8)$

$x = \frac{5}{8}$

Exercise 4M

Solve the equations below to find x.

1 $4x - 1 = 11$

2 $2x + 3 = 17$

3 $6x - 9 = 15$

4 $9x + 4 = 13$

5 $7x - 6 = 15$

6 $2x - 10 = 8$

7 $7x - 10 = 25$

8 $9x = 7$

9 $5x = 2$

10 $5 + 2x = 6$

11 $8 + 3x = 26$

12 $4x - 7 = 73$

In questions 13 to 24 solve the equations to find n.

13 $5n - 9 = 31$

14 $7n + 3 = 5$

15 $8n + 3 = 59$

16 $2 + 3n = 3$

17 $2n - 38 = 62$

18 $9n + 4 = 8$

19 $7n - 40 = 100$

20 $3n - 10 = 3$

21 $6 + 10n = 6$

22 $5n - 3 = 1$

23 $7 + 2n = 19$

24 $8 + 3n = 10$

Solve the equations where the 'x' terms are on the right hand side.

(a) $7 = 5x - 8$

$(+8)\quad(+8)$

$15 = 5x$

$(\div 5)\quad(\div 5)$

$3 = x$

(b) $9 = 6 + 5x$

$(-6)\quad(-6)$

$3 = 5x$

$(\div 5)\quad(\div 5)$

$\frac{3}{5} = x$

Exercise 4E

Solve the equations below to find x.

1 $37 = 4x + 1$

2 $7 = 2x - 5$

3 $7 = 20x - 13$

4 $33 = 2x + 9$

5 $16 = 16 + 3x$

6 $0 = 7x - 4$

7 $59 = 4x + 3$

8 $10 = 7 + 5x$

9 $9 = 8 + 4x$

10 $13x + 15 = 16$

11 $65 = 55 + 40x$

12 $31 = 3x + 29$

In questions 13 to 24 find the value of the letter in each question.

13 $5t - 4 = 8$

14 $7 = 7 + 9y$

15 $30 = 4c + 20$

16 $6x - 9 = 45$

17 $540 = 3m - 63$

18 $0 = 9p - 7$

19 $47 = 8n - 25$

20 $106 = 16 + 2w$

21 $20 = 50a + 19$

22 $2y + \frac{1}{2} = 1$

23 $2q + \frac{1}{4} = \frac{1}{2}$

24 $3x - 1\frac{1}{2} = \frac{1}{2}$

Using equations to solve problems

Tina is thinking of a number. She tells us that when she trebles it and adds 8, the answer is 24. What number is Tina thinking of?

Let x be the number Tina is thinking of.

She tells us that $3x + 8 = 24$

Subtract 8 from both sides: $3x = 16$

Divide both sides by 3: $x = \frac{16}{3} = 5\frac{1}{3}$

So Tina is thinking of the number $5\frac{1}{3}$.

Exercise 5M

In each question I am thinking of a number. Write down an equation then solve it to find the number.

1 I double the number and then add 17.
The answer is 37.

2 I multiply the number by 5 and then subtract 11.
The answer is 24.

3 I treble the number and then subtract 13.
The answer is 2.

4 I multiply the number by 4 and then add 15.
The answer is 135.

5 I multiply the number by 3 and then add 5. The answer is 16.

6 I multiply the number by 5 and then subtract 8. The answer is 4.

7 I multiply the number by 11 and then subtract 15. The answer is 7.

8 I multiply the number by 6 and then add 23. The answer is 28.

9 I multiply the number by 5 and then subtract $\frac{1}{3}$. The answer is $11\frac{2}{3}$.

10 I multiply the number by 40 and then subtract 3. The answer is 7.

The sum of the ages of Annie, Ben and Cath is 60 years.
Ben is five times as old as Annie and Cath is 4 years older than Annie. How old is Annie?

Let the age of Annie be x years (a *general rule is to let x be the quantity you are asked to find*).

Write down the ages of each person using x.

Annie	Ben	Cath
x	$5x$	$x + 4$

Ben is five times as old as Annie so Ben's age is $5x$ years.
Cath is 4 years older than Annie so Cath's age is $x + 4$ years.

The sum of the ages is 60 years.

$$x + 5x + x + 4 = 60$$
$$7x + 4 = 60$$
$$7x = 56$$
$$x = 8$$

Annie is 8 years old.

Exercise 5E

1 For each shape, write down an equation then solve it to find x.

(a)

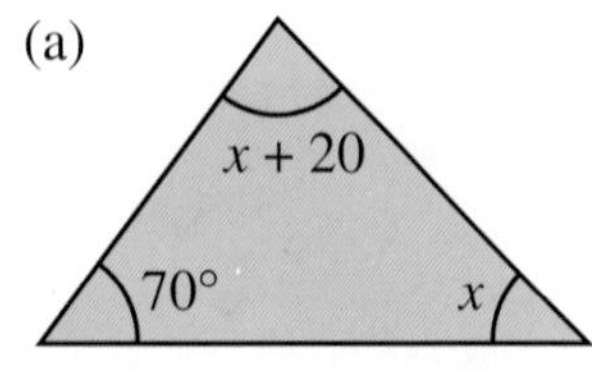

(b)

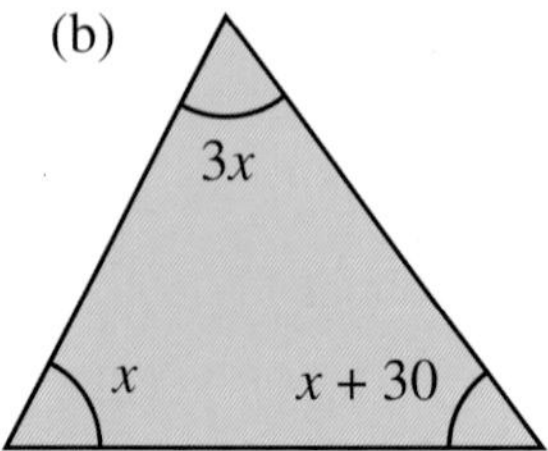

(c)

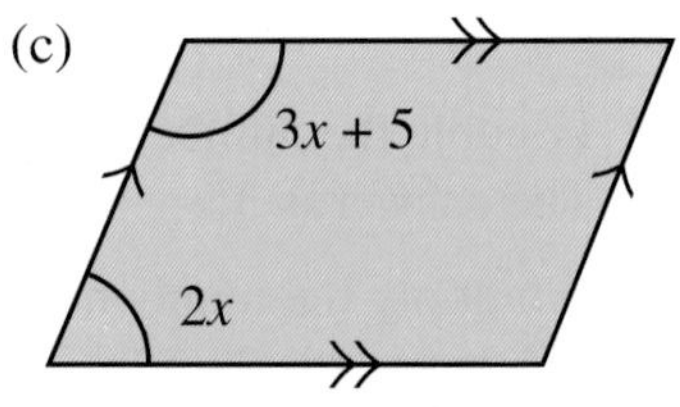

2 The angles of a triangle are A, B and C. Angle B is three times as big as angle A. Angle C is 45° bigger than angle A. Find the size of angle A. (Hint: let the size of angle A be $x°$)

3 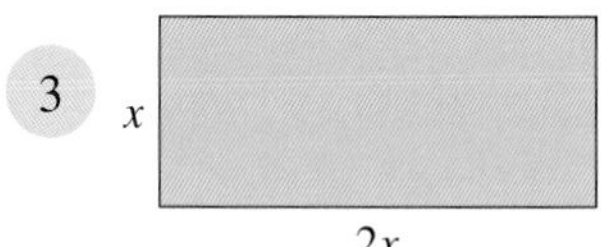

The length of a rectangle is twice its width. If the perimeter is 48 cm, find its width.

4 The length of a rectangle is four times its width. If the perimeter of the rectangle is 50 cm, find its width.

5 The length of a rectangle is 5 cm more than its width. If the perimeter of the rectangle is 38 cm, find its width.

6 The total mass of three coins A, B and C is 33 grams. Coin B is twice as heavy as coin A and coin C is 3 grams heavier than coin B. Find the mass of coin A.

7 Number walls are formed by adding adjacent numbers to get the number above. Find n in these walls.

(a)

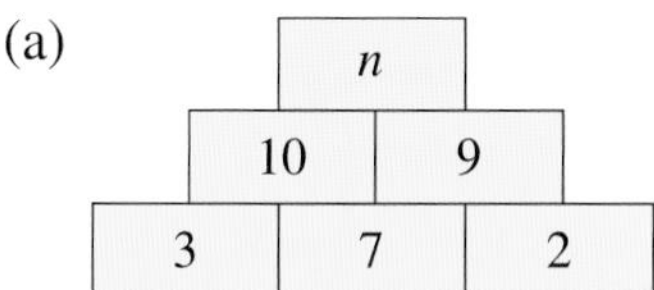

(b)

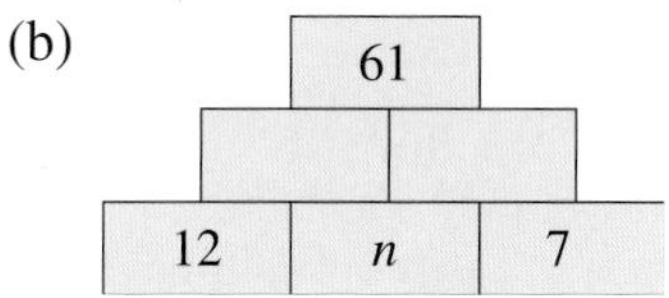

8 The total mass of four boxes A, B, C and D is 133 kg. Box C is three times as heavy as box B and box A is 20 kg heavier than box C. Box D is 7 kg lighter than box B. Find the mass of each box (Let x be the mass of box B to begin with).

9 In a quadrilateral ABCD, BC is twice as long as AB and AD is three times as long as AB. Side DC is 10 cm long. The perimeter of ABCD is 31 cm. Write an equation and solve it to find the length of AB.

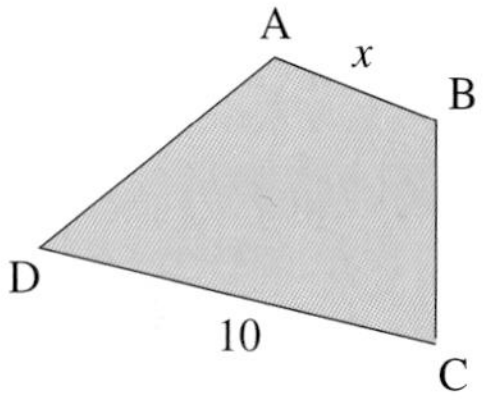

10 The sum of four consecutive whole numbers is 70. Let the first number be x. Write an equation and solve it to find the four numbers.

11 An equilateral triangle has sides of length $(3x + 1)$, $(4x - 5)$ and 19. Find x.

12 The width of a rectangle is $(x + 4)$ and its perimeter is $(8x + 12)$.

(a) Find the length of the rectangle (in terms of x).

(b) Find x if the length of the rectangle is 20 cm.

13 The total distance from P to T is 181 km. The distance from Q to R is twice the distance from S to T.
R is mid-way between Q and S.
The distance from P to Q is 5 km less than the distance from S to T. Find the distance from S to T.

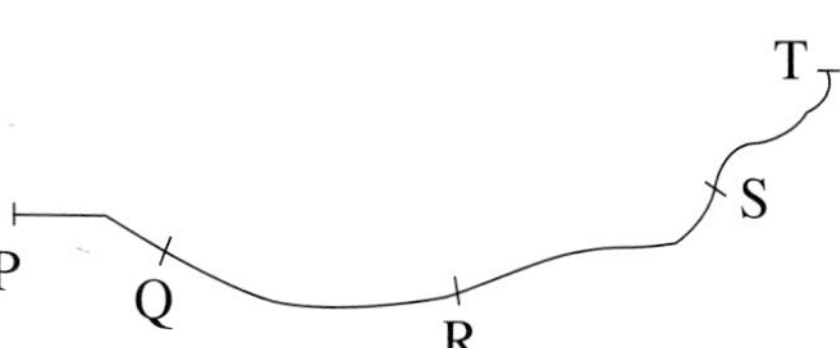

14 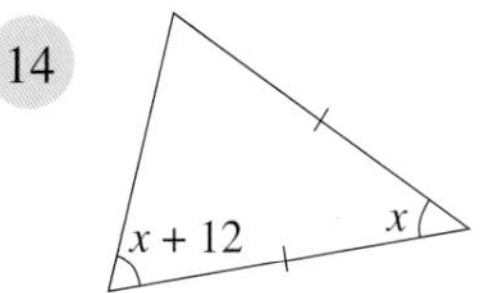

The diagram shows two angles in an isosceles triangle. Find the angles in the triangle.

15 A parallelogram has angles of $n°$ and $(n + 6)°$. Find the angles of the parallelogram.

Multiply out single brackets

$6(4 + 3) \;=\; 6(7) \;=\; 6 \times 7 \;=\; 42$

We also get the correct answer if the number outside the brackets multiplies each number inside the brackets.

$6(4 + 3) \;=\; 6 \times 4 + 6 \times 3 \;=\; 24 + 18 \;=\; 42$

(a) Multiply out 3(a + b)

$3(a + b) = 3 \times a + 3 \times b$
$= 3a + 3b$

(b) Multiply out $6\,(n - 3)$

$6(n - 3) = 6 \times n - 6 \times 3$
$= 6n - 18$

Exercise 6M

Multiply out

1 $2(x + 3)$
2 $6(x + 4)$
3 $3(x + 9)$
4 $5(x + 8)$
5 $4(x - 7)$
6 $2(x - 8)$
7 $9(x - 4)$
8 $6(x - 8)$
9 $4(x + y)$
10 $7(a + b)$
11 $3(m - n)$
12 $5(2x + 3)$
13 $6(4x - 7)$
14 $4(2a + b)$
15 $9(m + 2n)$
16 $4(x + 3y)$
17 $2(4m + n)$
18 $7(5x - 3)$
19 $8(3 - x)$
20 $6(4 - 2x)$
21 $5(3a + 5b)$

'Expand' means 'multiply out'.

(a) Expand $m(n + y)$

$m\,(n + y) \;=\; m \times n + m \times y$
$= mn + my$

(b) Expand $w(w - 3)$

$w\,(w - 3) \;= w \times w - 3 \times w$
$= w^2 - 3w$

Expand

22 $p(q + r)$
23 $m(n - \mathrm{p})$
24 $a(b + c)$
25 $a(b - e)$
26 $x(y + 3)$
27 $m(n - 6)$

28 $x(y - 9)$

29 $p(q - 5)$

30 $a(c + 7)$

31 $d(e + 8)$

32 $a(a + 4)$

33 $m(m - 6)$

34 $p(p - 2)$

35 $x(x + 9)$

36 $a(7 - a)$

37 $x(2 + y)$

38 $5(2a + 3)$

39 $9(3m - 2)$

40 $6(4x - 1)$

41 $4(8n + 7)$

42 $b(4 - b)$

Exercise 6E

Remove the brackets and simplify

1 $3(x + 2) + 2(x + 4)$

2 $5(x + 3) + 2(x + 3)$

3 $5(x + 2) + 2(x + 1)$

4 $7(x + 2) + 4(x + 5)$

5 $3(2x + 3) + 4(x + 6)$

6 $2(5x + 2) + 3(x + 4)$

7 $4(3x + 5) + 5(2 + 5x)$

8 $6(x + 2) + 4(x - 3)$

9 $6(3 + x) + 2(4x + 1)$

10 $5(2x + 3) + (3x - 7)$

11 $8(2 + 3x) + 5x$

12 $3x + 4(2x + 6)$

13 $3(5x + 2) - 9x$

14 $8 + 7\ (3x - 1)$

15 $10x + 4(3x + 2)$

16 $4(7x + 4) + 2(3x - 5)$

17 $6(1 + 3x) - 4$

18 $8\ (2x - 1) + 5(3x + 2)$

19 $7(5x + 3) + x$

20 $4(9x - 6) + 3(4x + 10)$

21

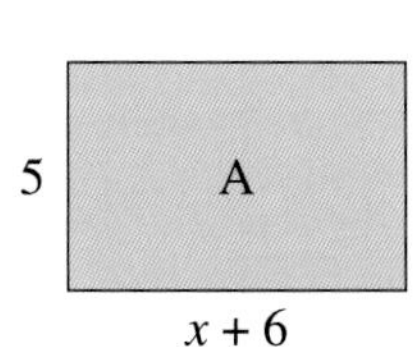

7 B

$x + 4$

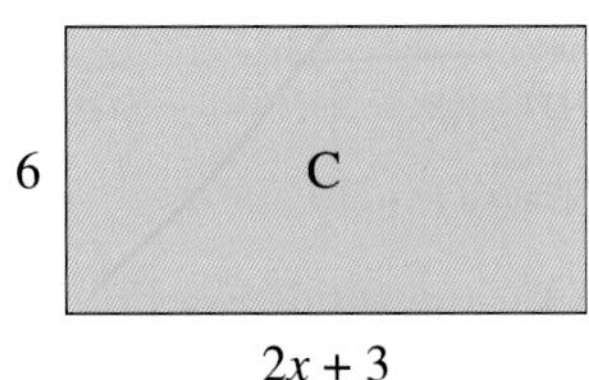

Find an expression for the total area of the rectangles stated below. Simplify each answer.

(a) A and B (b) A and C (c) all three rectangles

CHECK YOURSELF ON SECTIONS 4.5 and 4.6

1 Adding and subtracting negative numbers

Work out

(a) $-6 + 2$ (b) $-3 - 4$ (c) $2 + (-5)$ (d) $-8 - (-6)$

2 Multiplying and dividing negative numbers

Work out

(a) $3 \times (-5)$ (b) $-16 \div (-2)$ (c) $-30 \div 10$ (d) $-8 \times (-4)$

3 Review of section 2 algebra

(a) Simplify $3m + m$

(b) Simplify $ab + a + ba$

(c) Simplify $\frac{6x}{x}$

(d) Simplify $5m \times 3n$

(e) $m = 4(n + 5)$
Find m when $n = 2$.

(f) $y = 3x + 4z$
Find y when $x = 8$ and $z = -5$.

4 Solving equations

Solve

(a) $3n - 7 = 23$ (b) $\frac{m}{6} = 5$

(c) $2n - 3 = 4$ (d) $7 = 6 + 5w$

5 Multiplying out single brackets

Expand (multiply out)

(a) $5(x + 7)$ (b) $n(p - 3)$ (c) $x(x + 8)$

(d) Simplify $3(4x + 2) + 6(x + 1)$

(e) Find an expression for the total area of the rectangles shown.

Simplify your answer.

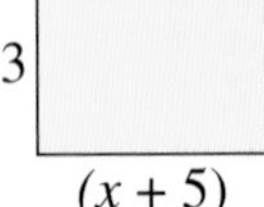

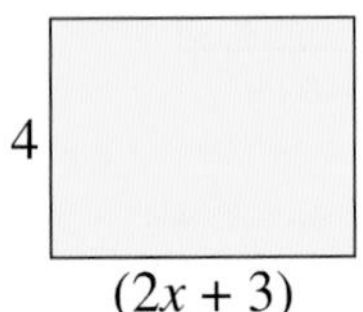

UNIT 4 MIXED REVIEW

Part one

1 The price of a computer game is £40 but it is increased by 5%. What is the new price?

2 Gwen and Tim are given £99 in the ratio 8:3. How much money does Tim get?

3 'Any quadrilateral can be cut into two triangles'. True or false?

4 Use a protractor and ruler to construct this triangle. Measure the side marked x.

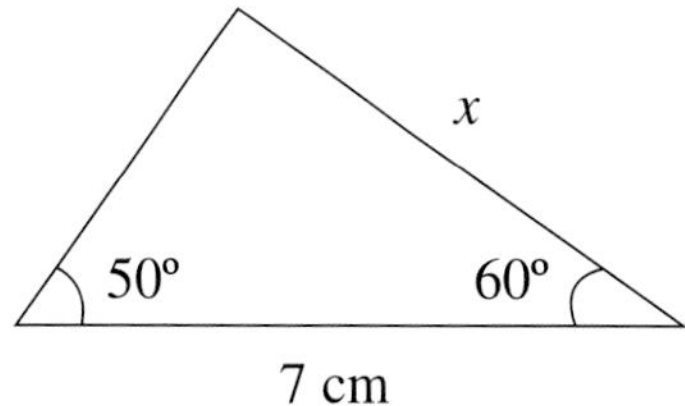

5 Multiply out (a) $5(x - 3)$ (b) $3(2x + 4)$

6 Two fifths of the children in a swimming pool are boys. There are 72 girls in the pool. How many boys are there?

7 Solve (a) $4x - 9 = 11$ (b) $7 = \frac{x}{8}$ (c) $8 = 5 + 4x$

8 

Colin books a holiday to Venice for £670. The holiday firm adds an extra 12% charge when Colin pays for his holiday. How much does Colin have to pay?

9 Which is larger, $\boxed{\frac{7}{25}}$ or $\boxed{27\%}$?

10 Four and a half dozen eggs weigh 2970 g. How much would six dozen eggs weigh?

11 I think of a number. If I add 5 and then multiply the result by 10 the answer is 82. What number was I thinking of?

12 If $y = 3x - c$, find the value of y when $x = 3$ and $c = -8$.

13 Show how the 3 by 8 rectangle can be cut into two identical pieces and joined together to make a 2 by 12 rectangle.

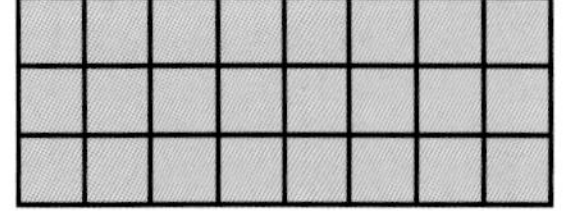

14 Draw a scalene triangle.

15 A train travels 20 km in 8 minutes. How long will it take to travel 25 km at the same speed?

16 Highly trained mosquitoes can be used to find oil. The annual profit in pounds, P, made by the mosquitoes is given by the formula.

$P = 500m - 2$, where m is the number of mosquitoes.

Find the profit when 10000 mosquitoes are employed.

17 A jar of marmalade is made from 50 g fruit, 140 g sugar and 10 g water. How much fruit is needed to make 2 kg of this marmalade?

Part two

1 Without using a calculator, work out 2.5% of £220.

2 Work out $\frac{9}{20} + 0.18$.

3 Write down an expression for the area of this rectangle. Expand your answer.

4 Solve (a) $12 = 5 + 8x$ (b) $3x - 4 = 50$ (c) $2x + \frac{1}{3} = 3\frac{1}{3}$

5 A rectangular window frame in a church measures 24.3 cm by 35.7 cm. 80% of the window is filled with stained glass. What is the area of stained glass in the window?

6 Use a ruler and compasses to construct this diagram. Use a protractor to measure angles x and y.

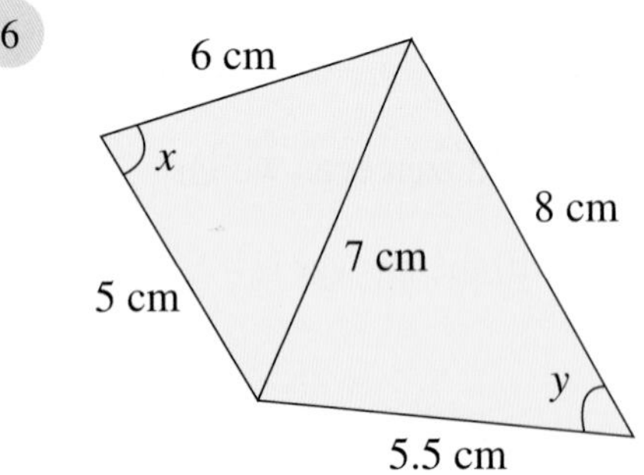

7 A boat sails 2.4 km in 30 minutes. How long will it take to sail one km?

8 Simplify $5(3x + 6) + 4(x - 3)$

9 Joe got 27 out of 40 in a Geography test. What was his mark as a percentage?

10 The diagram shows a rectangle. The perimeter of the rectangle is 42 cm. Work out x.

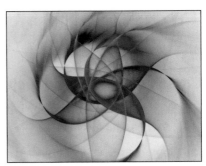

6 cm

$8x - 5$

11 Work out the total cost of:
15 kg of sand at 67p per kg
3 tape measures at £4.80 each
3000 screws at 80p per hundred
Add VAT at 17.5%.

12 Draw a quadrilateral which has two lines of symmetry *only*.

13 Matt and Heather share out some pencils in the ratio 7:13. If Matt gets 21 pencils, how many pencils does Heather get?

14 The price of a TV costing £650 was decreased by 20%.
Three months later the price was increased by 20%. Calculate the final price of the TV.

15 Which calculation below gives the *larger* answer and by how much?

A $-3 + (-4) - (-2) + 1$ or B $-7 + 8 - 3 - 5 - (-2)$

16 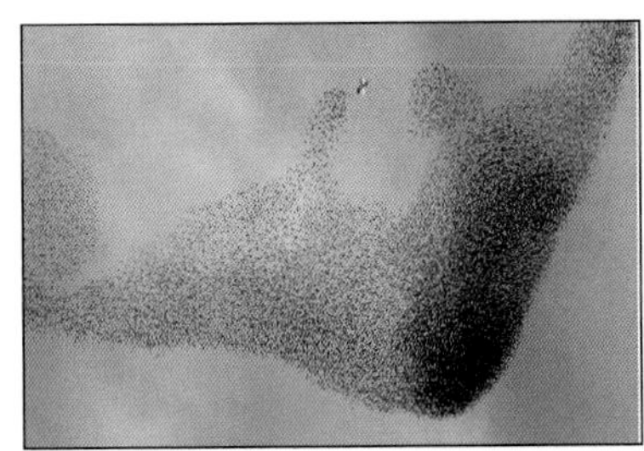

At noon there are 324 600 starlings in a flock.
Two hours later the number has increased by 7.5%.
How many starlings are in the flock at 2.00 p.m?

17 By noon one day $\frac{1}{4}$ of the eggs in a crocodile's nest have hatched. By midnight a further 5 baby crocodiles are walking around, leaving only $\frac{1}{3}$ of the eggs still to hatch.
How many eggs were in the nest originally?

18 In a 'magic square' the sum of the numbers in each row, column and main diagonal is the same. Copy and complete these magic squares.

(a)

–3		
	0	–2
		3

(b)

7	–1	–9
–7		

(c)

	0		–9
–10	–3	1	2
–7			
4			–8

Puzzles and Problems 4

Cross numbers without clues

Here are cross number puzzles with a difference. There are no clues, only answers, and you have to find where the answers go.

(a) Copy out the cross number pattern.
(b) Fit all the given numbers into the correct spaces. Work logically and tick off the numbers from lists as you write them in the squares.

1 Ask your teacher if you do not know how to start.

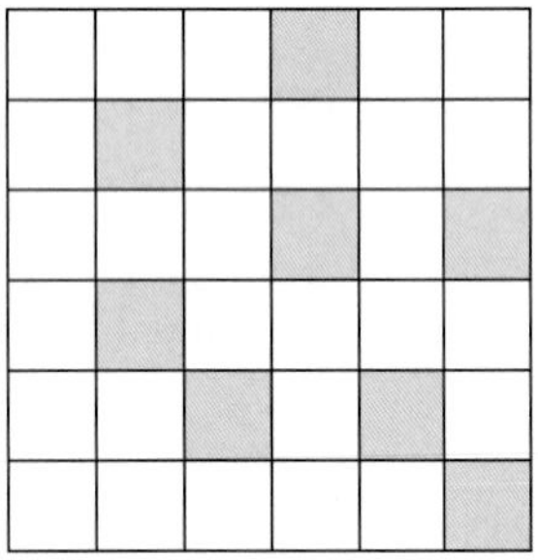

2 digits	*3 digits*	*4 digits*	*5 digits*	*6 digits*
18	375	1274	37 125	308 513
37	692	1625		
53	828	3742		
74		5181		
87				

2

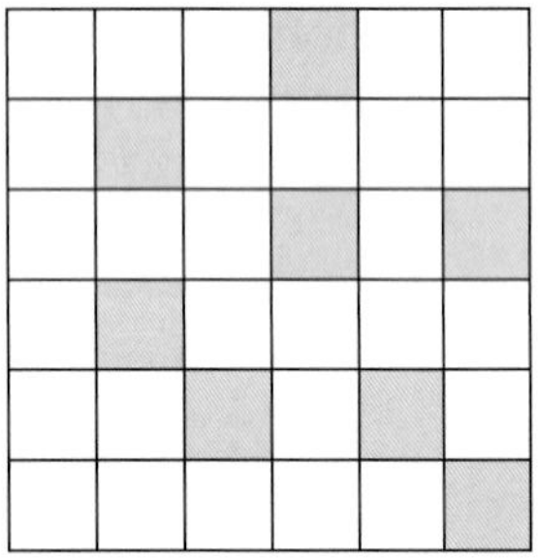

2 digits	*3 digits*	*4 digits*	*5 digits*	*6 digits*
13	382	2630	12 785	375 041
21	582	2725		
45	178	5104		
47		7963		
72				

3

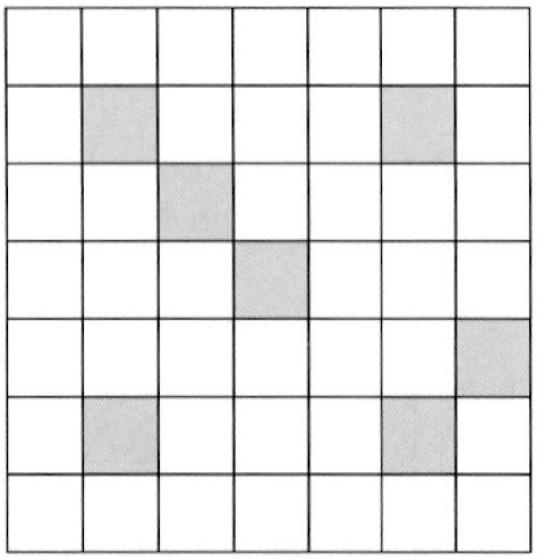

2 digits	*3 digits*	*4 digits*	*6 digits*	*7 digits*
53	182	4483	375 615	3 745 124
63	324	4488		4 253 464
64	327	6515		8 253 364
	337			8 764 364
	436			
	573			
	683			
	875			

4

2 digits	*3 digits*	*4 digits*	*5 digits*	*6 digits*
27	161	1127	34 462	455 185
36	285	2024	74 562	
54	297	3473	81 072	
63	311	5304	84 762	
64	412	5360		
69	483	5370		
	535	5380		
	536			
	636			
	714			

5 *This one is more difficult.*

2 digits	*3 digits*	*4 digits*	*5 digits*	*6 digits*
16	288	2831	47 185	321 802
37	322	2846	52 314	
56	607	2856	56 324	
69	627	2873	56 337	
72	761	4359		
98	762	5647		
	768	7441		
	769			
	902			
	952			

6 *This one is more difficult.*

2 digits	*3 digits*	*4 digits*	*5 digits*	*6 digits*
21	121	1349	24 561	215 613
22	136	2457	24 681	246 391
22	146	2458	34 581	246 813
23	165	3864		
36	216	4351		
53	217	4462		
55	285	5321		
56	335	5351		
58	473	5557		
61	563	8241		
82	917	8251		
83		9512		
91				

A long time ago! 4

The Königsberg Problem

In the 18th century, the city of Königsberg (in Prussia) was split into parts by the river Pregel. There were seven bridges. The people of Königsberg tried to walk across all seven bridges without crossing the same bridge twice.

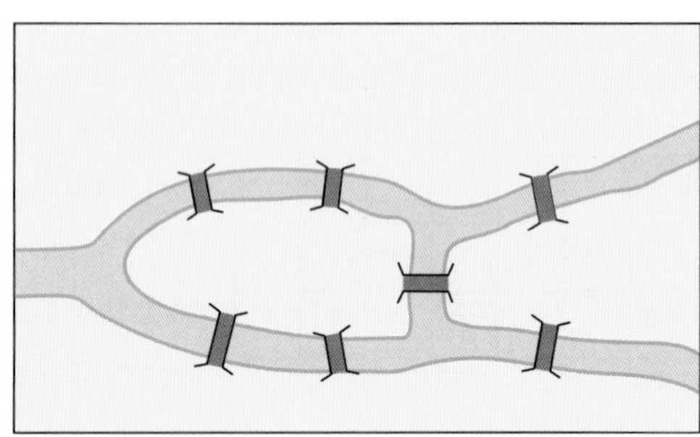

Exercise

1 Sketch the diagram above to show the river and the bridges. Use a pencil to show how you could walk across each bridge without crossing the same bridge twice.
If you make a mistake, rub out the pencil and try again.
If you find a way, show somebody else then show your teacher.

2 Make up a map of a city which has more than seven bridges. Get somebody else to copy your map and try to show you how to walk across each bridge without crossing the same bridge twice.

3 **RESEARCH:**

A famous mathematician, Leonhard Euler, examined the Königsberg problem.

(a) Find out when Euler lived.
(b) Find out what Euler said about the Königsberg problem.
(c) Königsberg is now called Kaliningrad and is in Russia. Find out how many of the seven bridges still exist.
(d) Discuss as a class your main findings about the Königsberg problem.

Mental Arithmetic Practice 4

There are two sets of mental arithmetic questions in this section. Ideally a teacher will read out each question twice, with pupils' books closed. Each test should take about 20 minutes.

Test 1

1. Write down a factor of 35 greater than one.
2. How many more than 17 is 80?
3. Find the change from a £10 note if you spend £2.30.
4. The perimeter of a square is 20 cm. What is the area of the square?
5. What is two point nought one multiplied by one thousand?
6. How many fifteens are there in three hundred?
7. What is the difference between 1.7 and 8?
8. What is the remainder when 50 is divided by 7?
9. What is the cost of 3 magazines at £2.99 each?
10. Subtract the sum of 11 and 12 from 50.
11. I have one 20p, three 10p and one 50p coin. How much money do I have?
12. What four coins make 67p?
13. A saucepan costs £17.95 new. I get a discount of £6. How much do I pay?
14. A film starts at 7.45 and ends at 9.10. How long is the film?
15. Work out 200 times 400.
16. Write the number 'one and a half billion' in figures.
17. What number is exactly mid-way between 4 and 4.1?
18. Work out two squared plus two cubed.
19. A length of 210 mm is cut from a rod of length one metre. What is the length of the remaining rod?
20. How many edges does a square based pyramid have?
21. How many lines of symmetry does a regular hexagon have?
22. An ant walks 20 cm in 5 seconds. How far will it walk in one minute?
23. Find the new price of a £50 scanner after a 10 per cent increase.
24. I think of a number and add 5. The result is equal to 6 times 7. What is the number?
25. What number is next in the sequence 4, 8, 16, 32?

Test 2

1. What is one million pence in pounds?
2. A triangle has a base of 8 cm and a height of 6 cm. What is its area?
3. True or false: 1 yard is equal to 4 feet?
4. A wire of length 590 cm is cut in half. How long is each half?

5 An aircraft begins a 45 minute flight at 10 minutes to six. When does it land?

6 What is a quarter of four hundred and twenty?

7 If the 10th of November is a Monday, what day of the week is the 20th?

8 What percentage of the numbers from 1 to 10 are prime numbers?

9 What four coins make 65 pence? Do this in two ways.

10 A lottery prize of eighteen million pounds is shared between ten winners. How much does each person receive?

11 What is the total of 55 and 66?

12 Two angles of a triangle are 45° and 30°. What is the third angle?

13 What is a half of a quarter of 100?

14 An egg box holds six eggs. How many boxes are needed for 40 eggs?

15 Add together £3.25 and £6.15.

16 Fifty people took their driving test one day and thirty-two passed. What percentage passed?

17 A regular hexagon has sides of length 15 cm. What is the perimeter of the hexagon?

18 Find the difference, in millimetres, between half a metre and one millimetre.

19 How many 20p coins do I need to make £50?

20 A clock shows five past nine but it is fifteen minutes slow. What is the correct time?

21 What is three quarters of £88?

22 What is the smaller angle between the hands of a clock at four o'clock?

23 How many centimetres are there in one kilometre?

24 How many minutes are there in $1\frac{2}{3}$ hours?

25 Add twelve to six times nine.

UNIT 5

5.1 Rotation

In section 5.1 you will learn about:

- rotating shapes
- rotational symmetry

In these diagrams the blue shape has been rotated onto the yellow shape.
In the first diagram the blue shape is rotated 90° (1 right angle) anti-clockwise around point A.
In the second diagram the blue shape is rotated 180° (2 right angles) around point B.
Notice that for a 180° rotation it makes no difference whether you turn clockwise or anti-clockwise.

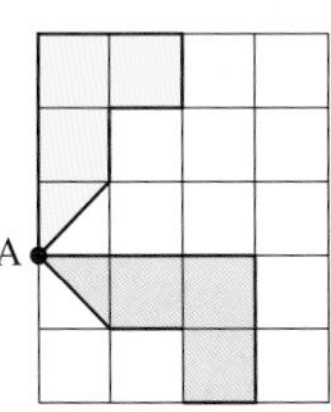

B

Exercise 1M

1 These pictures have been hung incorrectly. Give instructions to turn them the right way round. Remember to give both the angle and the direction.

(a)

(b)

(c)

(d)

(e)

(f)

In questions 2 to 10 copy each diagram and then draw its new position after it has been turned. You can use tracing paper if you wish.

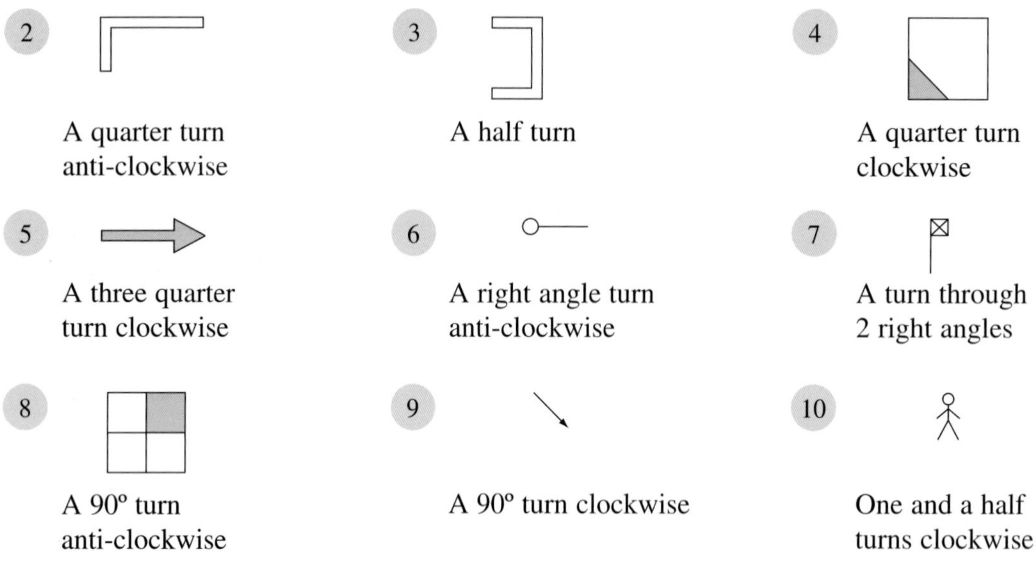

In questions 11 to 16 describe the rotation. Give the angle and the direction.

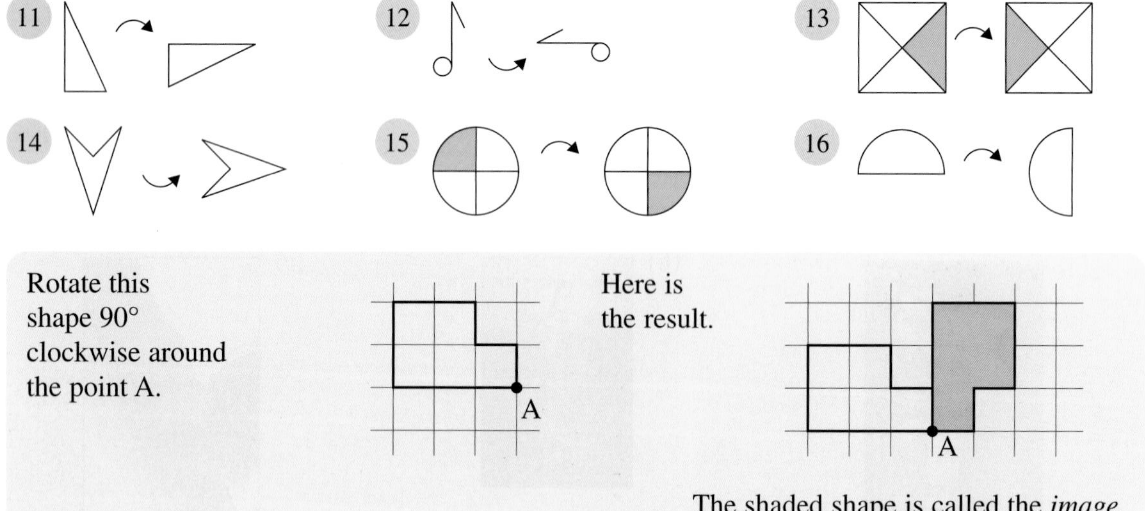

Rotate this shape 90° clockwise around the point A.

Here is the result.

The shaded shape is called the *image*.

Exercise 1E (Use tracing paper if you wish)

1

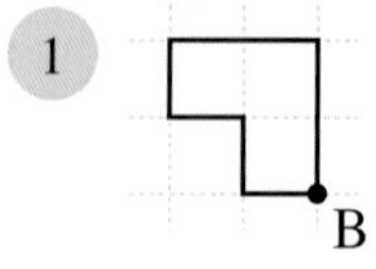

(a) Copy this shape on squared paper

(b) Draw the image of the shape after a quarter turn clockwise around the point B.

In questions 2 to 4 copy the shape on squared paper and then draw and shade its new position.

2 Half turn around the point C

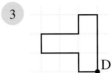

3 Quarter turn clockwise around the point D

4 Turn 90° anti-clockwise around the point E

5 The diagram shows shapes which have been rotated about the points A, B, C, D and E.

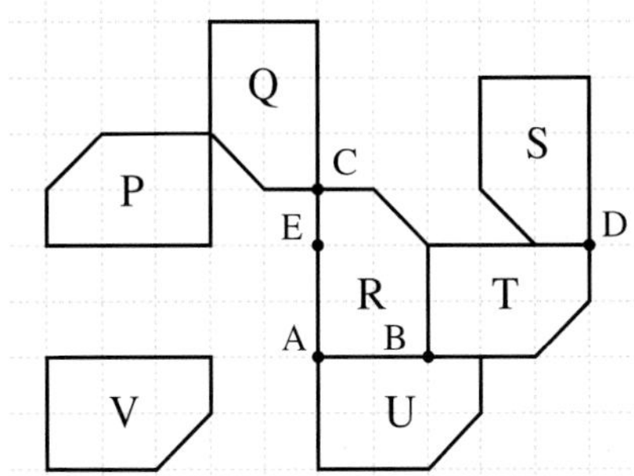

Which shape do you get when you:

(a) rotate shape R 90° clockwise about A
(b) rotate shape R 90° clockwise about B
(c) rotate shape Q 180° about C
(d) rotate shape S 90° anti-clockwise about D
(e) rotate shape P 180° about E

6

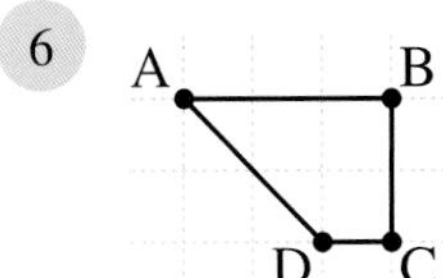

Draw this shape on squared paper.
Draw the image of the shape

(a) after a 90° rotation clockwise about A
(b) after a 180° rotation about B
(c) after a 90° rotation anti-clockwise about C
(d) after a 45° rotation clockwise about A

Rotational symmetry

The shape B fits onto itself three times when rotated through a complete turn. It has *rotational symmetry of order three.*

The shape C fits onto itself six times when rotated through a complete turn. It has rotational symmetry of order six.

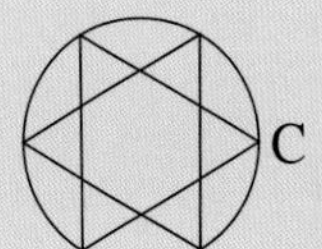

Exercise 2M

For each diagram decide whether or not the shape has rotational symmetry. For those diagrams that do have rotational symmetry state the order.

1

2

3

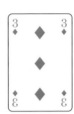

4

5

6

7

8

9

10 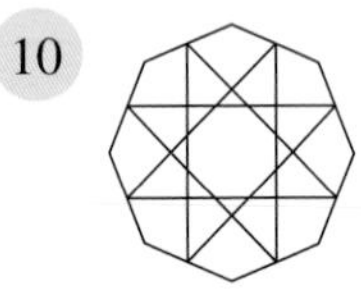

11 

12 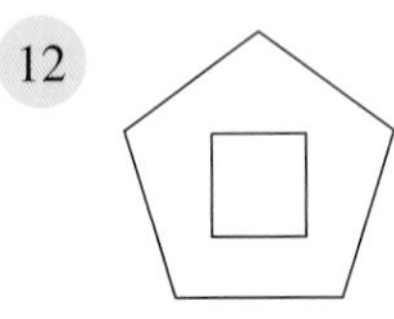

13 

14 

15 

16 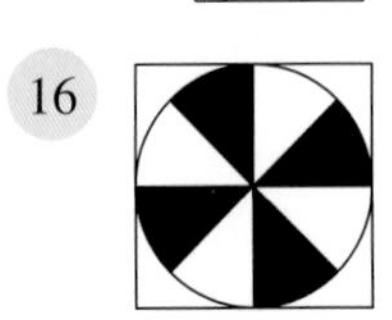

Exercise 2E

1 (a) If this umbrella was viewed from above would it have rotational symmetry?
(b) If so what is the order of rotational symmetry?

In questions 2 to 7 copy each diagram and complete it so that the final design has rotational symmetry of the order stated.

2

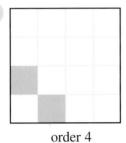

order 4

3 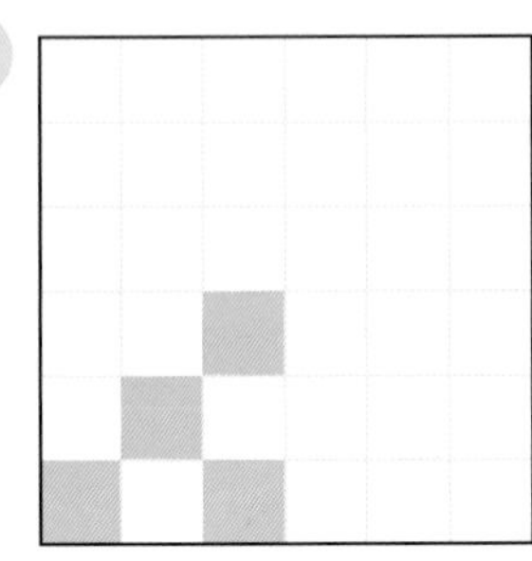

order 4

4

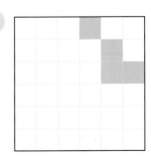

order 4

5 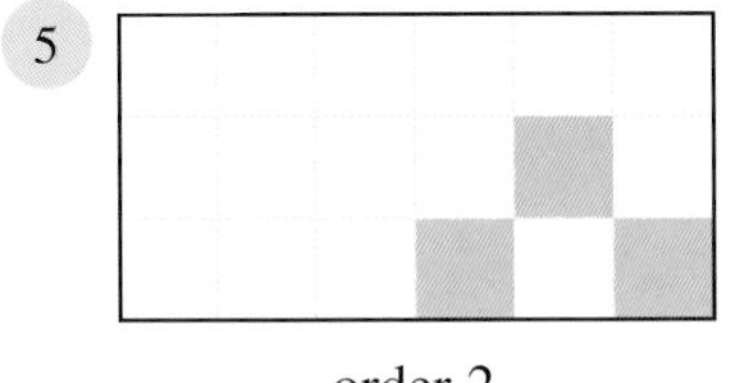

order 2

6 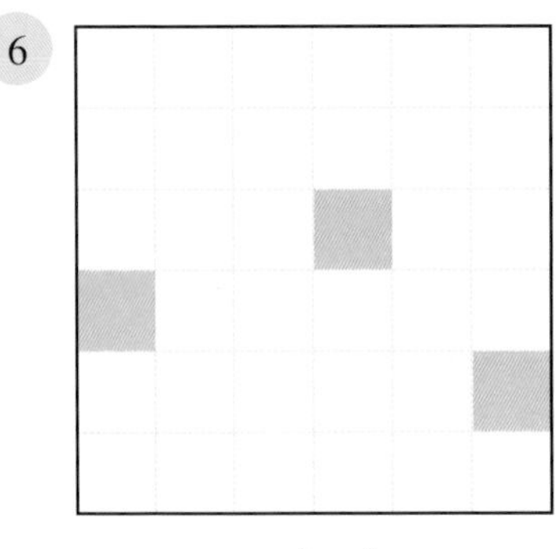

order 4

7 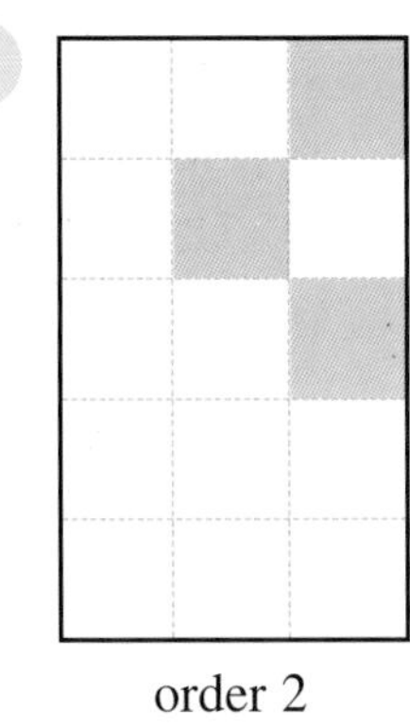

order 2

8 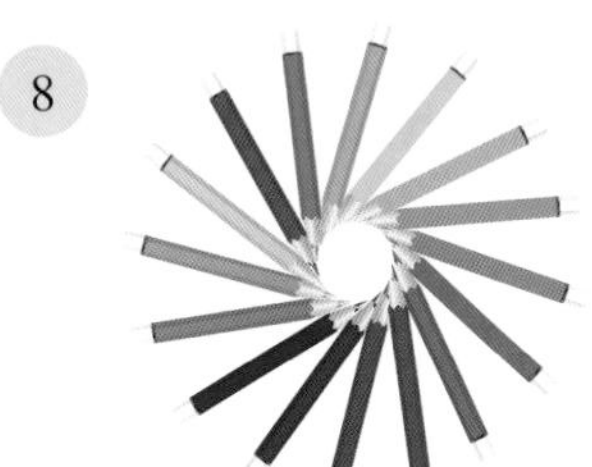

This shape is made using coloured pencils.

If you ignore the different colours, what is the order of rotational symmetry of the shape?

5.2 Line Symmetry

In section 5.2 you will learn about:

- line symmetry
- reflections

Paper folding activities

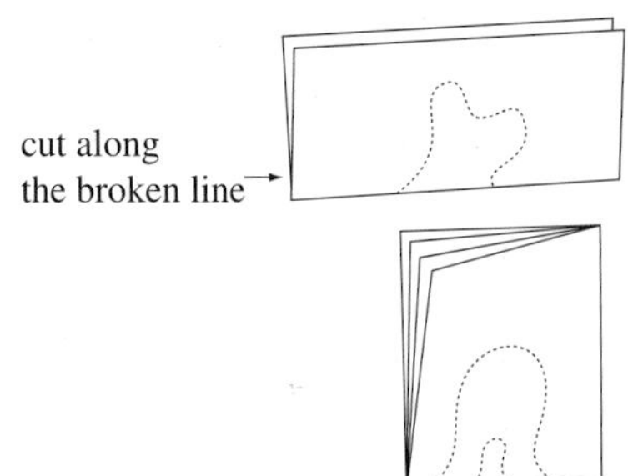
cut along
the broken line

1 Take a piece of paper, fold it once and then cut out a shape across the fold. This will produce a shape with one line of symmetry, which is a mirror line.

2 Fold another piece of paper twice so that the second fold is at right angles to the first fold. Again cut along the fold to see what shapes you can make.

This will produce a shape with two lines of symmetry. [i.e. two mirror lines]

3 Fold the paper three times and cut.

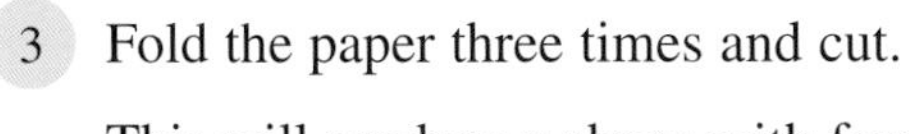

This will produce a shape with four lines of symmetry.

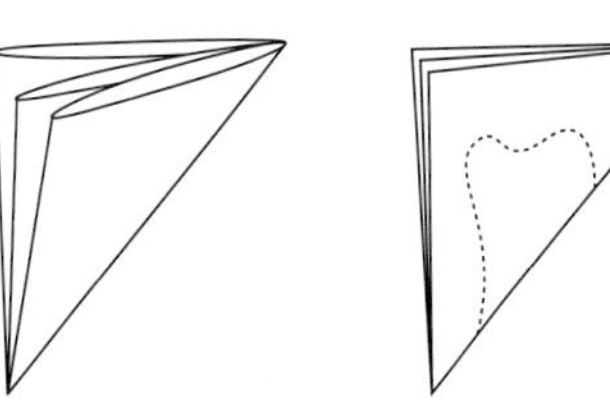

On the next page there are three shapes obtained by folding and cutting as above. Try to make similar shapes yourself. Stick the best shapes into your exercise book.

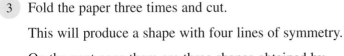

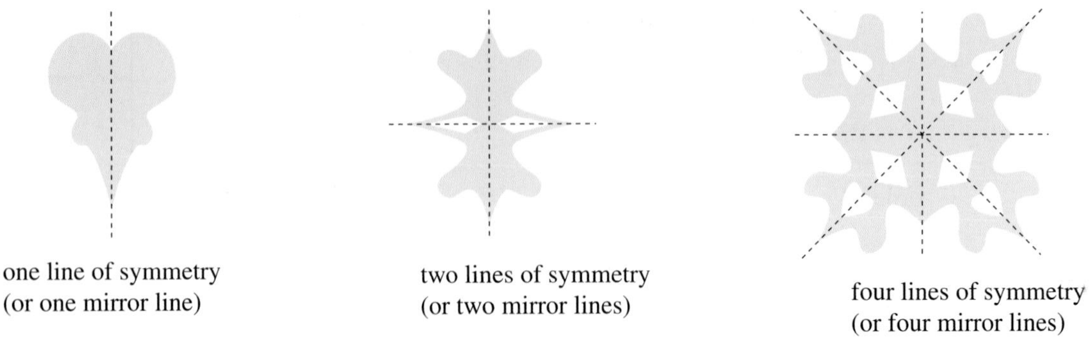

one line of symmetry (or one mirror line)

two lines of symmetry (or two mirror lines)

four lines of symmetry (or four mirror lines)

Exercise 1M

Copy each of the following shapes and mark on the diagram all lines of symmetry.

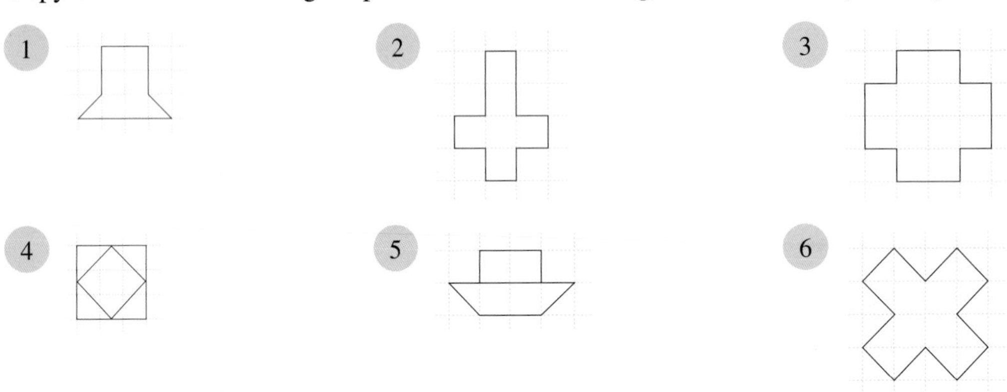

7 Copy these shapes on square 'dotty' paper (or ordinary squared paper). Complete the shapes with the lines of symmetry shown.

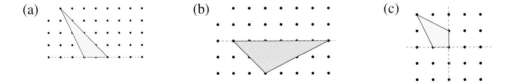

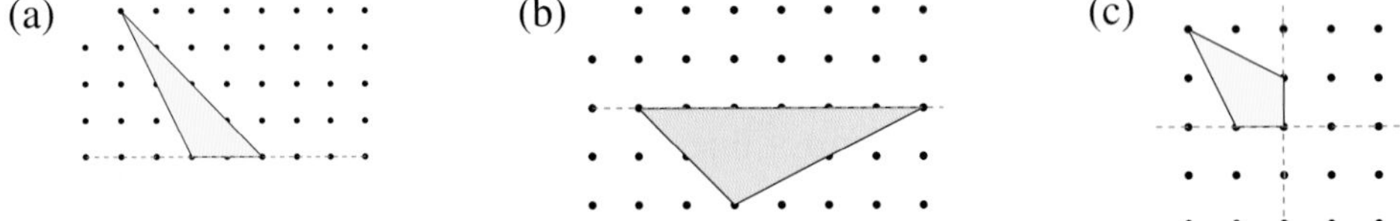

8 **N Z E H T**

(a) Which of these letters have 1 or more lines of symmetry?

(b) Which letters have rotational symmetry?

(c) Do any of these letters have both line symmetry and rotational symmetry?

9

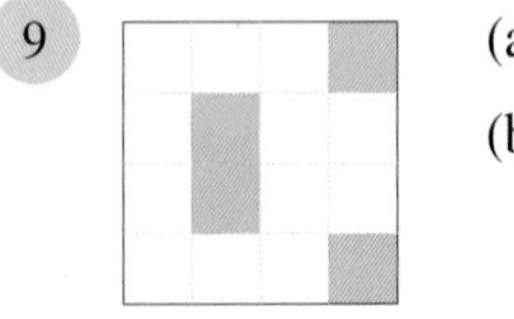

(a) Does this shape have rotational symmetry?

(b) Does this shape have line symmetry?

10 Draw a 4 × 4 grid like the one above. Shade four squares to make a pattern with rotational symmetry but no line symmetry.

11 Draw a 3 × 3 grid. Shade three squares to make a pattern with line symmetry but not rotational symmetry.

12 Draw a 4 × 4 grid and shade four squares to make a pattern with no line symmetry and no rotational symmetry.

Exercise 1E

In the diagram three vertices of a rectangle are given. Find the coordinates of the fourth vertex and write down the equations of any lines of symmetry.

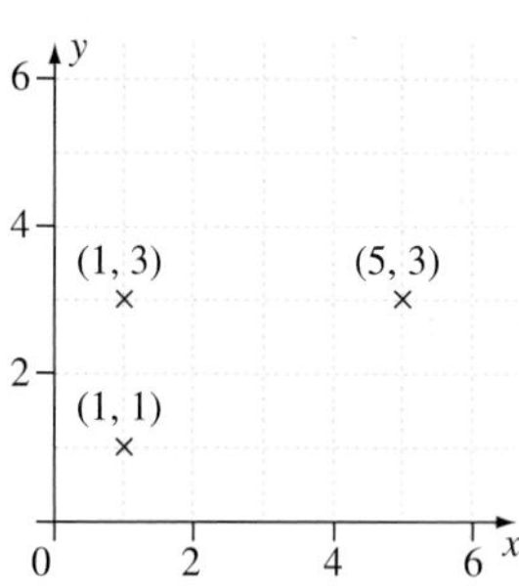

Put the answers in a table :

Shape	Vertices given	Other vertex	Lines of symmetry
Rectangle	(1, 1), (1, 3), (5, 3)	(5,1)	$x = 3$, $y = 2$

Draw axes with values of x and y from – 10 to +10.
Draw the shapes given and hence copy and complete the table.

	Shape	Vertices given	Other vertex	Lines of symmetry
1.	Rectangle	(1, 6), (1, 10), (3, 6)	?	? , ?
2.	Rectangle	(4, 3), (4, – 1), (10, 3)	?	? , ?
3.	Rectangle	(5, –2), (10, –2), (5, –3)	?	? , ?
4.	Isosceles triangle	(5, –10), (10, –8)	?	$y = -8$ only
5.	Isosceles triangle	(2, –4), (0, –8)	?	$x = 2$ only
6.	Rhombus	(–6, 4), (–8, 7), (–6, 10)	?	? , ?
7.	Square	(3, 3), (3, –3), (–3, –3)	?	Give four lines.
8.	Trapezium	(–8, –2), (–7, 1), (–5, 1)	?	$x = -6$ only
9.	Parallelogram	(–8, –5), (–4, –5), (–5, –8)	Give three possibilities	none
10.	Parallelogram	(–3, 4), (–2, 6), (–1, 6)	Give three possibilities	none
11.	Square	(6, 6), (6, 9)	Give two points	$y = x$ is one line. Find three more.

Reflection

A reflection is a transformation in which points are mapped to images by folding along a mirror line.

Exercise 2M

Copy each diagram and, using a different colour, shade in as many squares as necessary so that the final pattern has mirror lines shown by the broken lines. For each question write down how many new squares were shaded in.

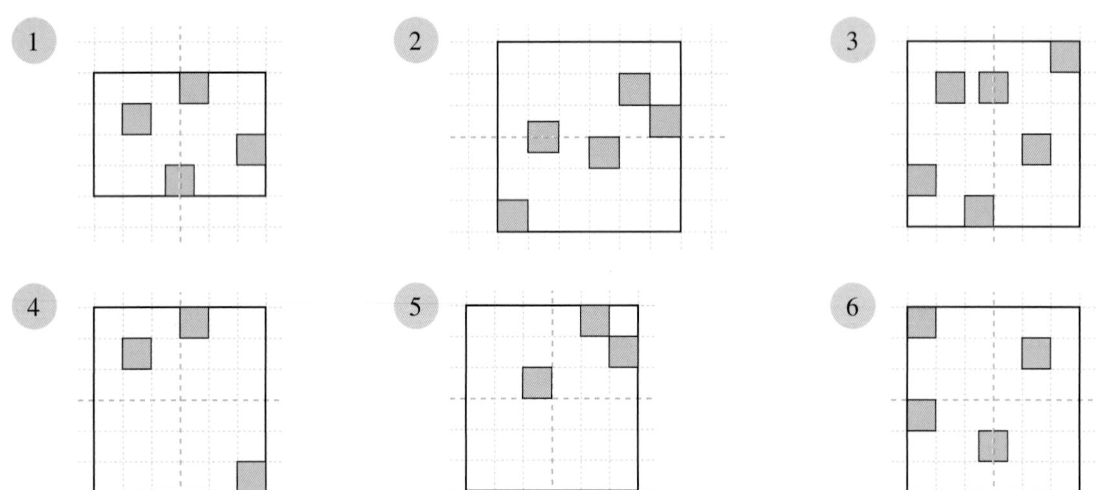

Exercise 2E

Part one

Copy each diagram and, using a different colour, shade in as many squares as necessary so that the final pattern has mirror lines shown by the broken lines. For each question write down how many new squares were shaded in.

Be careful when the mirror line is a diagonal line. You can check your diagram by folding along the mirror line.

1 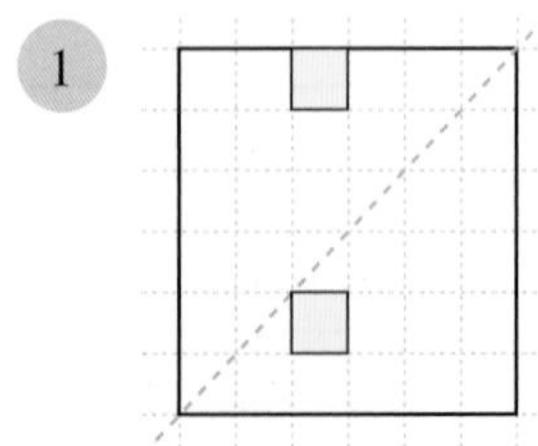

2 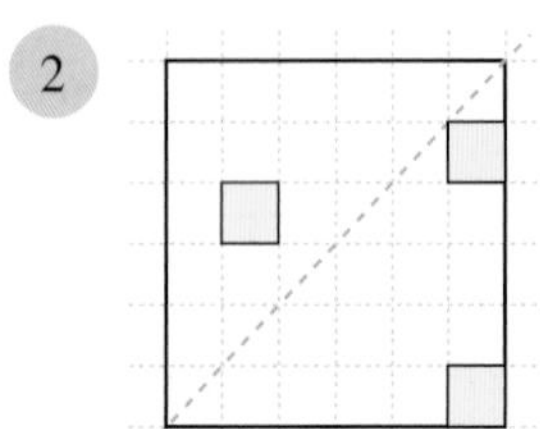

3 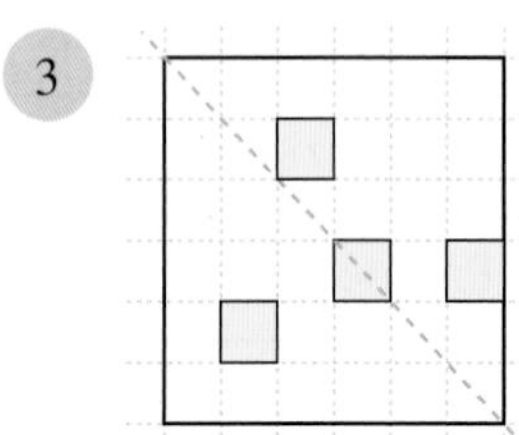

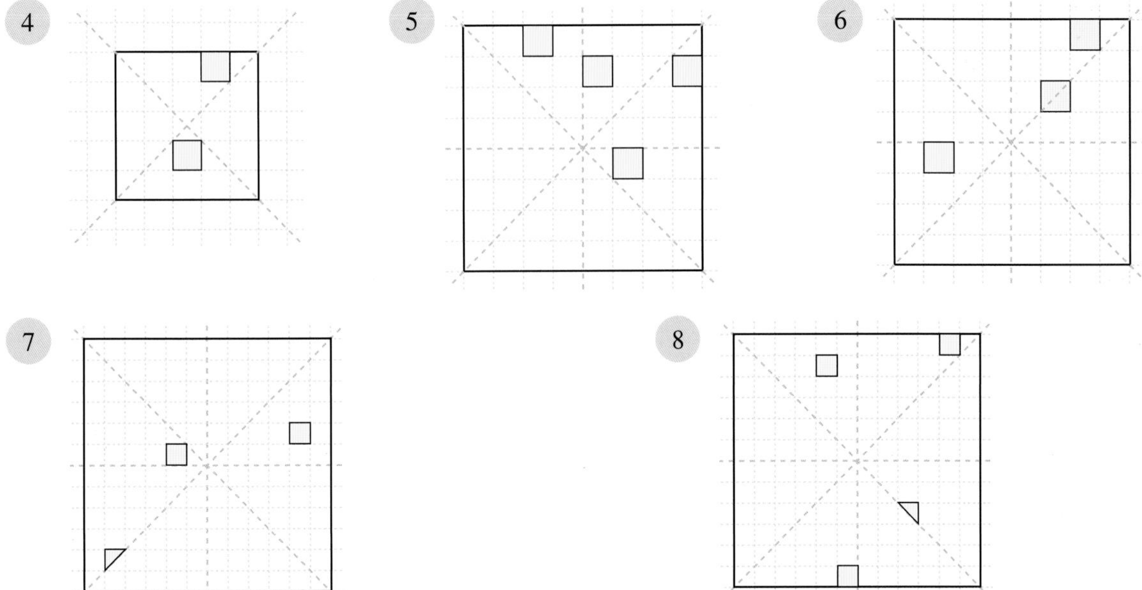

Exercise 3M

1 You have 3 square pink tiles and 2 square white tiles, which can be joined together along whole sides.

So this [pink | white] is allowed but this [offset tiles] is *not* allowed.

Draw as many diagrams as possible with the 5 tiles joined together so that the diagram has line symmetry.

For example fig. 1 and fig. 2 have line symmetry but fig. 3 does not have line symmetry so fig. 3 is not acceptable.

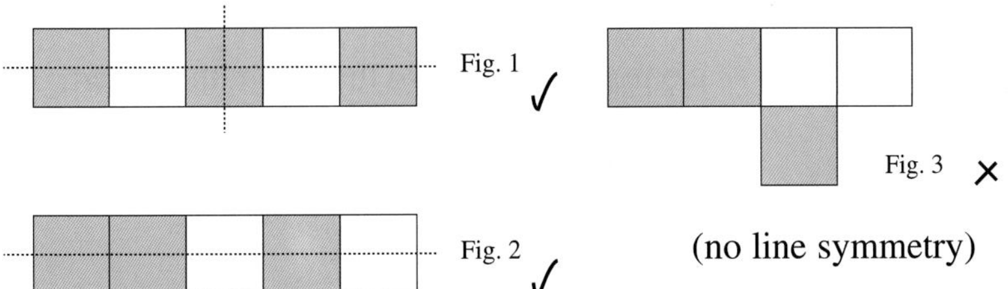

2 Now you have 2 pink tiles and 2 white tiles. Draw as many diagrams as possible with these tiles joined together so that the diagram has line symmetry.

3 Finally with 3 pink tiles and 3 white tiles draw as many diagrams as possible which have line symmetry.

Here is one diagram which has line symmetry

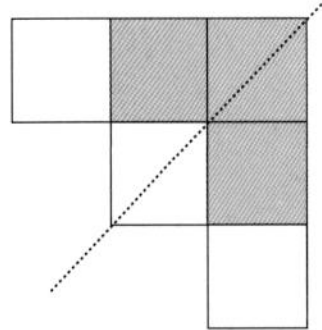

4 Shape A is a single square. A

Shape B consists of four squares. 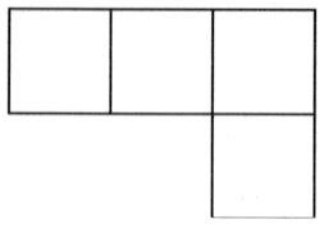 B

Draw three diagrams in which shapes A and B are joined together along a whole edge so that the final shape has line symmetry.

5 Shape C is a single square. C

Shape D consists of five squares. 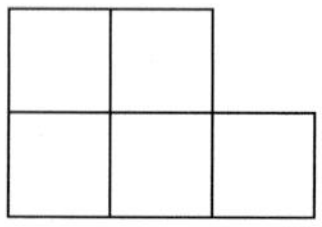 D

Draw four diagrams in which shapes C and D are joined together along a whole edge so that the final shape has line symmetry.

Exercise 3E

1 On a 3 × 3 grid you have to shade in three squares so that the pattern obtained has just *one* line of symmetry.

A ✓

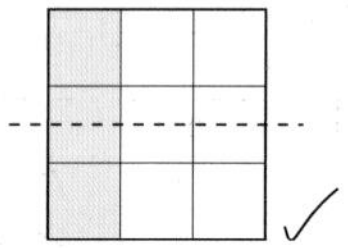

A is accepted because it has just one line of symmetry

B ×

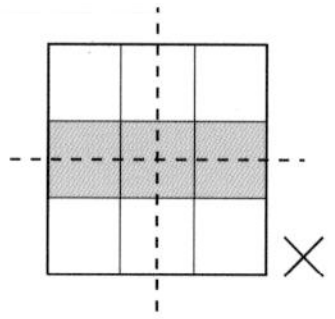

B is not accepted because there are two lines of symmetry

C ×

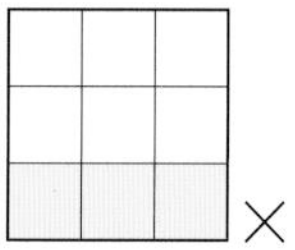

C is the same as A. The square can be cut out and placed exactly over another square.

Copy A above and then draw as many different patterns as you can. Draw the line of symmetry on each pattern. Check that you have not *repeated* any of your designs.

2 On a 4 × 4 grid you have to shade in four squares so that again the pattern obtained has one line of symmetry only.

D ✓

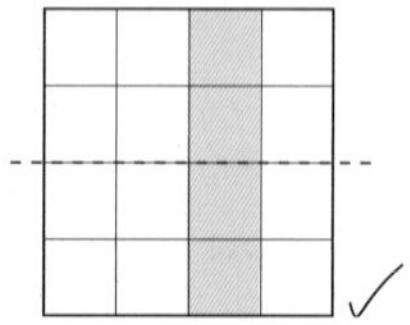

D is accepted

E ×

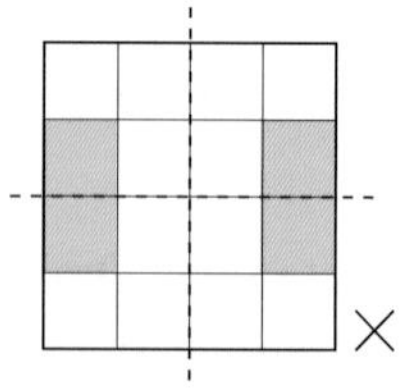

E is not accepted because the pattern has two lines of symmetry.

Draw as many different patterns as you can.

3 Now you decide how you are going to continue.

- Shade five squares in a 5 × 5 grid ? … or 4 squares …. or 3 squares
- Shade three squares in a 4 × 4 grid?

Write down and discuss anything that you notice.

The tile factory: an activity

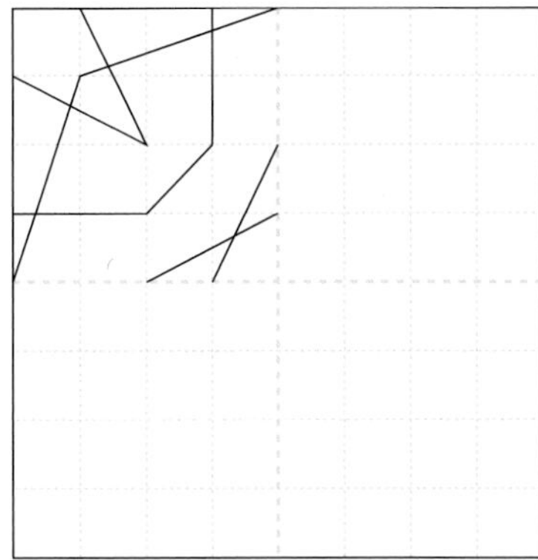

1 Copy this square and pattern onto the top left hand corner of a piece of A4 centimetre squared paper.

2 Lightly mark the reflection lines on the diagram as shown.

3 Use these lines to help you reflect the pattern across ... ... and then down.

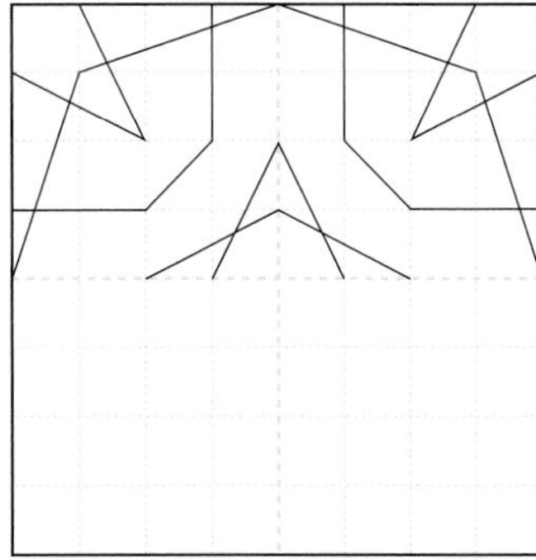

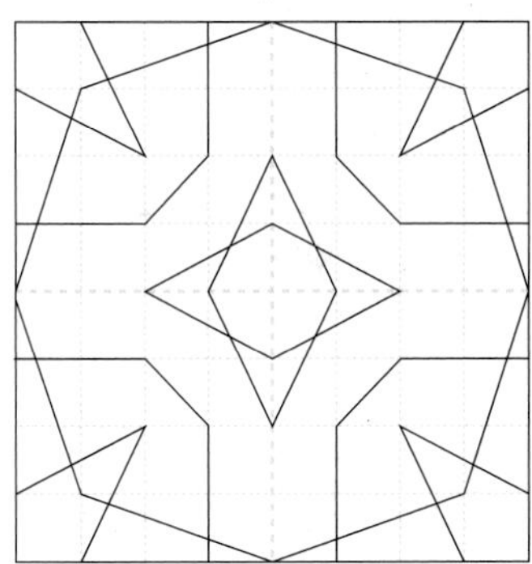

4 Repeat the process with the same tile so that your tile neatly covers the piece of paper as shown on the right.

5 Now colour or shade in your work as neatly and symmetrically as you can.

5.3 Translation

In section 5.3 you will learn about:

- translations

A translation is a transformation in which every point of the object moves the same distance in a parallel direction.

A translation can be described by two instructions, the move parallel to the *x*-axis and the move parallel to the *y*-axis.

In the example shown, the translation is 5 units to the right and 1 unit up.

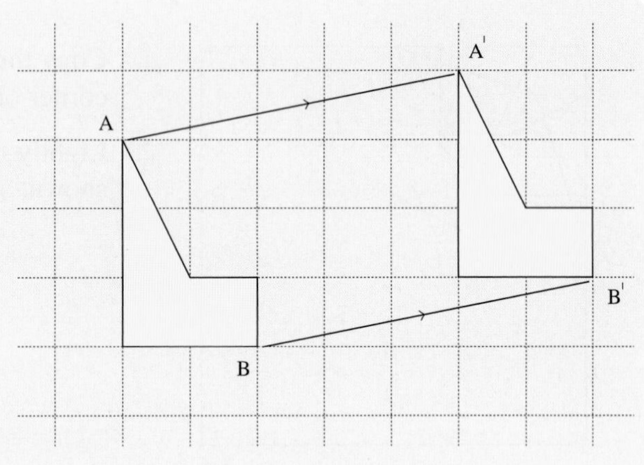

Exercise 1M Use squared paper

1 (a) Draw the object triangle A on squared paper.
(b) Draw the image of A after a translation of 4 units to the right and 1 unit up. Label the image B.
(c) Draw the image of A after a translation of 2 units to the right and 2 units down. Label the image C.

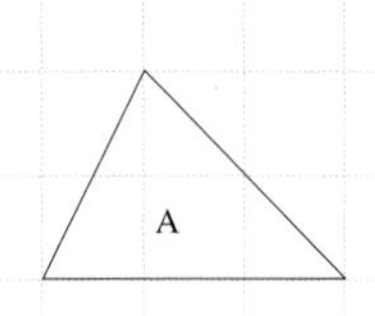

2

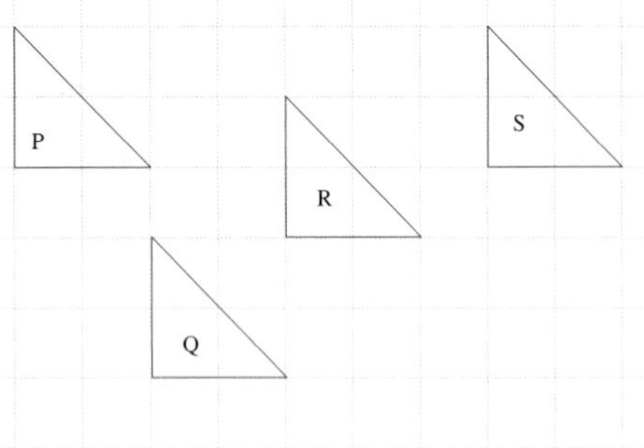

Describe the following translations.
(a) $P \rightarrow Q$
(b) $Q \rightarrow S$
(c) $R \rightarrow P$
(d) $S \rightarrow P$

3 (a) Draw shape A as shown.
(b) Translate shape A 5 units right and label the image B.
(c) Translate shape B 3 units down and label the image C.
(d) Translate shape C 3 units left and 1 unit down and label the image D.
(e) What is the single translation which would move shape A onto shape D?

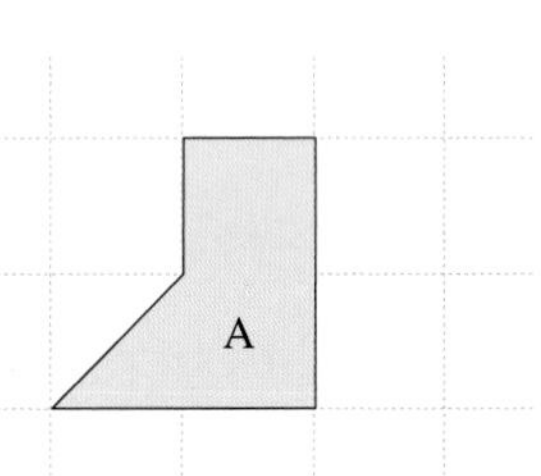

Exercise 1E

1 What shape do you move to when you:

(a) translate shape A 2 units left, 1 unit down
(b) translate shape E 5 units right, 3 units up
(c) translate shape D 3 units right, 2 units down
(d) translate shape B 5 units left

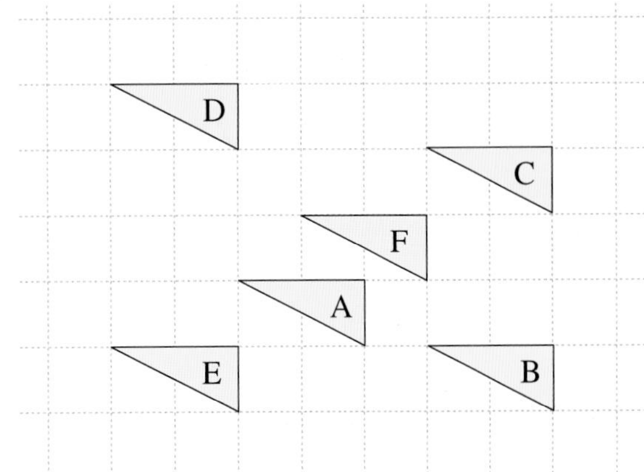

2

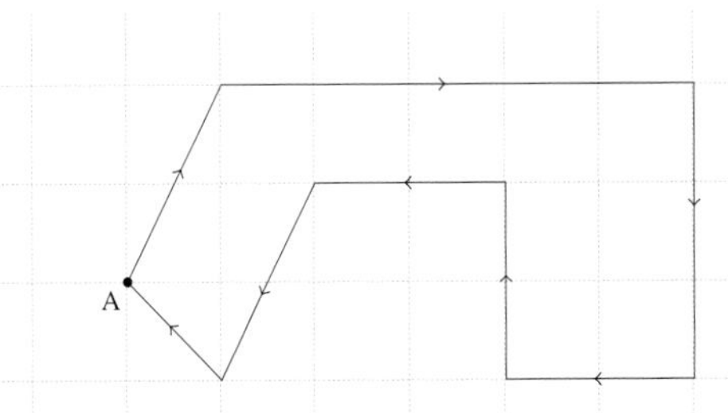

A computer controls a pen which starts at A. Describe the 8 translations required to draw the shape given.

3 Square ABCD can be moved onto square BCEF by either a translation, a rotation or a reflection.
(a) Describe the translation
(b) What is the mirror line for the reflection?
(c) Describe *two* possible rotations which achieve the result given.

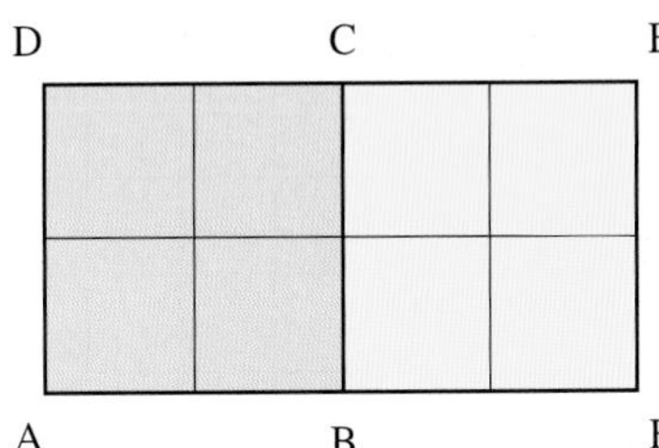

TEST YOURSELF ON UNITS 5.1, 5.2 and 5.3

1 Rotating shapes

Draw the shape on squared paper.

(a) Draw the new position after it is turned clockwise through one right angle around the point A.
(b) Draw the new position after it is turned anticlockwise through one right angle about the point B.

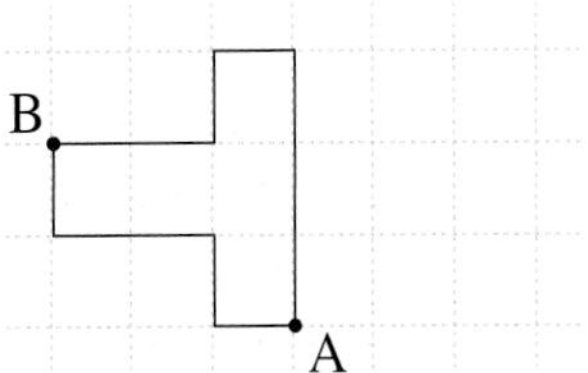

2 Rotational symmetry

State the order of rotational symmetry of each shape

(a) 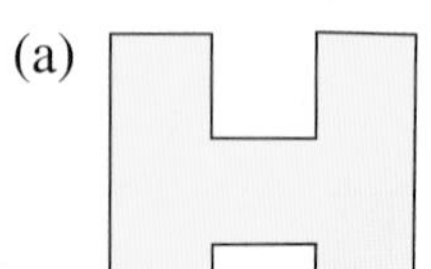 (b) 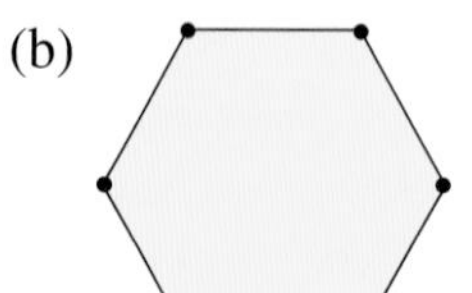 (c) 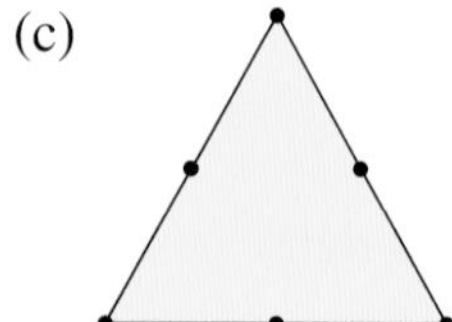 (d) 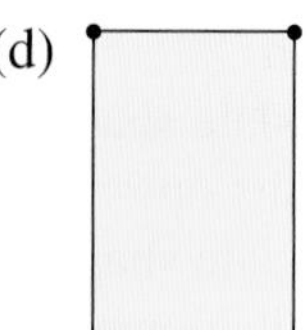

(e) Draw the two patterns on the right and shade in more squares so that the final patterns have rotational symmetry of order 2.

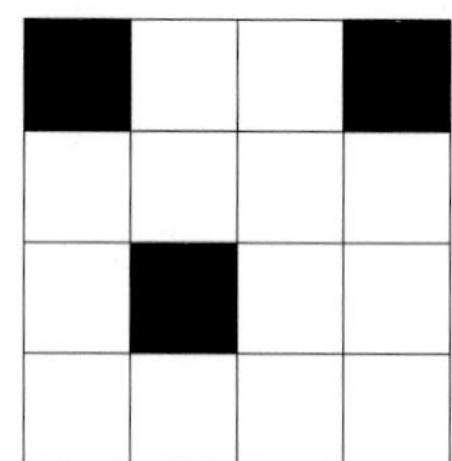 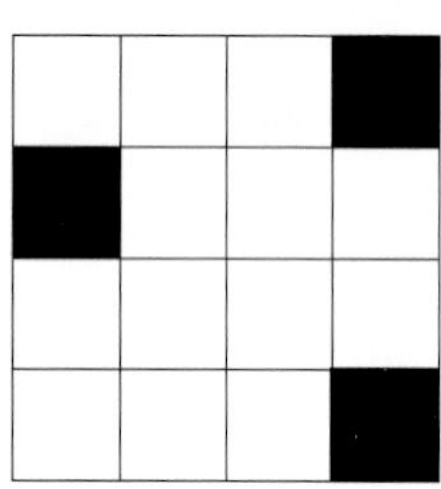

3 Line symmetry

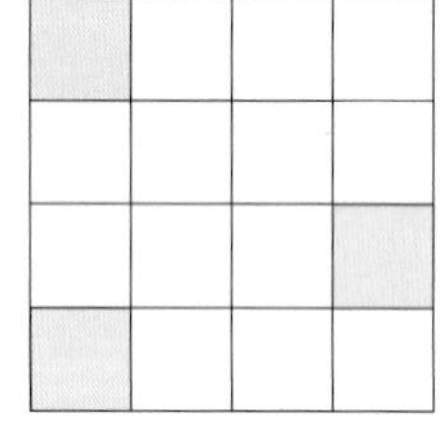 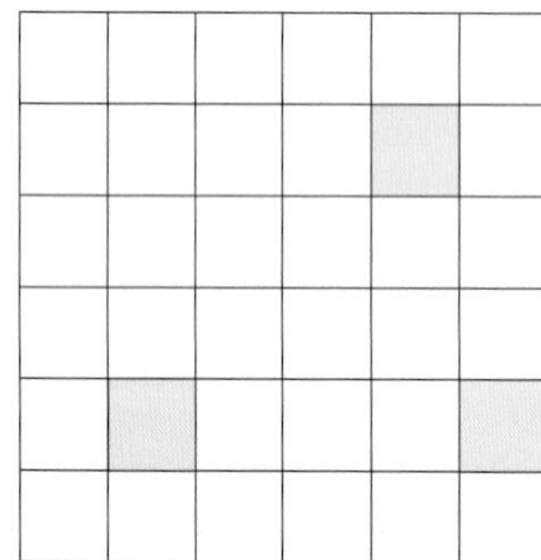

Draw the two patterns on the left and shade in the least number of squares so that the final patterns have line symmetry.

4 Reflections

In each of the following diagrams, mirror lines are shown as broken lines. Copy each diagram and complete the reflections.

(a) (b)

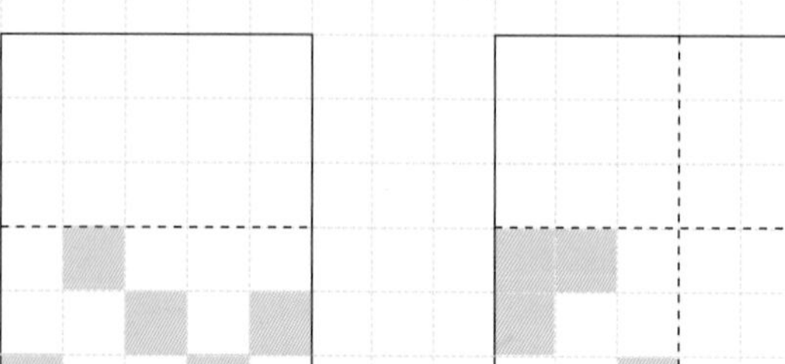

(c)

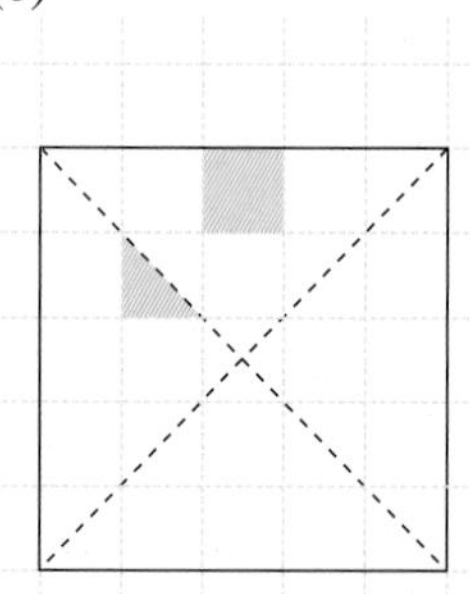

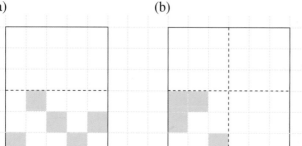

5 Translation

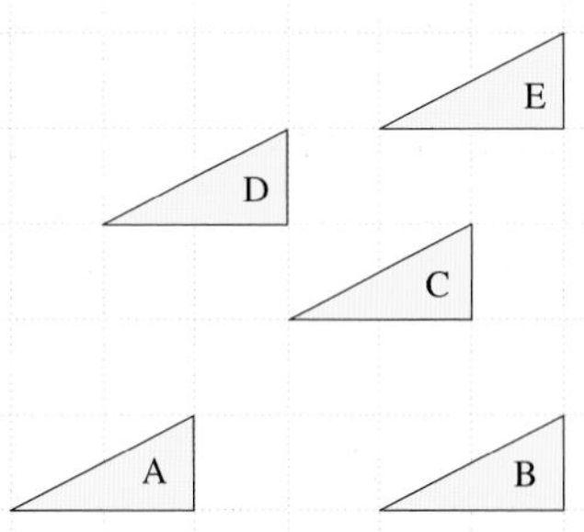

(a) Copy the diagram shown.

(b) Describe the translation.

(i) A → C (ii) C → D (iii) B → E

(c) Draw the new position of shape A after the translation 4 units right and 3 units up.

5.4 Number review

In section 5.4 you will review:

- multiples, factors, prime numbers, HCF and LCM
- fractions, decimals and percentages
- long multiplication and division
- adding, subtracting, multiplying and dividing decimals
- finding a 'fraction of' or a 'percentage of' a quantity.

Multiples, factors and prime numbers

The first six *multiples* of 5 are 5, 10, 15, 20, 25, 30

The factors of 8 are 1, 2, 4, 8

The first five prime numbers are 2, 3, 5, 7, 11

Exercise 1M

1 Continue the list below to write down the first seven multiples of 4

4, 8, 12, ☐, ☐, ☐, ☐

2 Write down the first five multiples of

(a) 3 (b) 7 (c) 2 (d) 10

3 Write down the factors of

(a) 6 (b) 15 (c) 36 (d) 100

4 Write down the odd one out.

(a) Factors of 24: 2, 3, 8, 24, 48
(b) Factors of 50: 2, 5, 10, 20, 25
(c) Multiples of 11: 22, 66, 88, 111
(d) Multiples of 15: 1, 15, 30, 45

5 Write down the first eight prime numbers in order of size.

6 11 21 31 51 71 81

Which of the numbers above are prime numbers?

7 Write down two prime numbers whose sum is a prime number.

8 Write down the 1-digit numbers that have three factors.

9 What is the smallest number with two factors?

10 Find three numbers that are multiples of both 2 and 3

11 Find three numbers that are multiples of both 3 and 5

12 (a) Write down the first six multiples of 4

(b) Write down the first six multiples of 5

(c) Write down the lowest common multiple (L.C.M.) of 4 and 5

Reminder:
The L.C.M. is the lowest number which is in both lists.

13 (a) Write down the first seven multiples of 3

(b) Write down the first seven multiples of 7

(c) Write down the L.C.M. of 3 and 7

14 The table shows the factors and common factors of 12 and 18

number	factors	common factors
12	1, 2, 3, 4, 6, 12	1, 2, 3, 6
18	1, 2, 3, 6, 9, 18	

The H.C.F. is the highest number which is in both lists.

Write down the highest common factor (H.C.F.) of 12 and 18.

15 Find the H.C.F. of

(a) 9 and 12 (b) 24 and 36 (c) 12 and 16

Fractions, decimals, percentages

Exercise 2M

1 Find the missing number to make these fractions equivalent.

(a) $\frac{3}{4} = \frac{\square}{12}$ (b) $\frac{4}{7} = \frac{\square}{35}$ (c) $\frac{6}{10} = \frac{\square}{5}$ (d) $\frac{3}{8} = \frac{\square}{24}$

(e) $\frac{3}{8} = \frac{9}{\square}$ (f) $\frac{4}{5} = \frac{12}{\square}$ (g) $\frac{8}{9} = \frac{16}{\square}$ (h) $\frac{1}{3} = \frac{5}{\square}$

2 Work out

(a) $\frac{1}{5} + \frac{2}{5}$ (b) $\frac{3}{5} - \frac{1}{2}$ (c) $\frac{5}{9} - \frac{2}{9}$ (d) $\frac{5}{8} + \frac{1}{4}$

(e) $\frac{2}{5} + \frac{1}{4}$ (f) $\frac{1}{5} + \frac{1}{3}$ (g) $\frac{5}{6} - \frac{1}{2}$ (h) $\frac{2}{5} + \frac{1}{7}$

3 Convert these fractions into decimals

(a) $\frac{3}{10}$ (b) $\frac{1}{4}$ (c) $\frac{32}{40}$ (d) $\frac{24}{200}$ (e) $\frac{9}{100}$

4 Copy and complete

(a) $\frac{1}{5} = \frac{20}{100} = \square\%$ (b) $\frac{3}{20} = \frac{15}{100} = \square\%$ (c) $\frac{1}{25} = \frac{4}{100} = \square\%$

(d) $\frac{9}{20} = \frac{\square}{100} = \square\%$ (e) $\frac{11}{50} = \frac{\square}{100} = \square\%$ (f) $\frac{11}{25} = \frac{\square}{100} = \square\%$

5 Change these decimals into fractions (cancel down when possible).

(a) 0.2 (b) 0.9 (c) 0.03 (d) 0.11 (e) 0.43

(f) 0.03 (g) 0.15 (h) 0.85 (i) 0.24 (j) 0.05

6 Write down each fraction with its equivalent percentage.

(a) $\frac{1}{3}$ (b) $\frac{2}{5}$ (c) $\frac{3}{4}$ (d) $\frac{3}{100}$ (e) $\frac{2}{3}$ (f) $\frac{1}{1000}$

7 Copy and complete the table

	fraction	decimal	percentage
(a)			40%
(b)		0.15	
(c)	$\frac{3}{25}$		
(d)			16%
		0.04	

8 Write the following in order of size, smallest first

(a) $\frac{3}{4}$, 60%, 0.7 (b) 5%, $\frac{1}{50}$, 0.03 (c) $\frac{3}{9}$, 0.3, 23%

9 Copy and complete

(a) $\frac{7}{35} = \square\%$ (b) $0.55 = \frac{\square}{20}$ (c) $0.08 = \square\%$ (d) $24\% = \frac{\square}{\square}$

Long multiplication and division

Exercise 3M

Work out

1 23 × 14

2 35 × 17

3 27 × 23

4 52 × 24

5 56 × 35

6 72 × 41

7 125 × 19

8 214 × 36

9 Copy and complete.

(a) □ ÷ 25 = 15 (b) □ ÷ 33 = 17 (c) □ ÷ 27 = 42

10 Work out

(a) 784 ÷ 14 (b) 544 ÷ 32 (c) 806 ÷ 31 (d) 1035 ÷ 23

11 There are 47 seats on a coach. How many coaches will be needed to transport 206 people to a concert?

12 There are 23 seats in each row at a football stadium. How many seats are there in 35 rows?

13 Find the remainder when 276 is divided by 11.

14 There are twenty-two balls in a set of snooker balls. Each ball weighs 154 grams. Calculate the total weight of the set of snooker balls.

15 Chocolates are packed eighteen to a box. How many boxes are needed for 648 chocolates?

Calculations involving decimals

Exercise 4M

1 Work out

(a) 4 + 5.2 (b) 6.1 + 18.7 (c) 9.54 – 7 (d) 0.74 + 3.4
(e) 0.65 + 0.888 (f) 11 – 3.2 (g) 4.2 + 7.4 + 6 (h) 32.7 – 19

2 Copy and complete

(a)
```
   6 . □ 4
 + □ . 7 □
 ---------
   8 . 2 7
```

(b)
```
   4 . 7 □
 + 4 . □ 5
 ---------
   □ . 1 0
```

(c)
```
   6 . □ 7 2
 + □ . 2 □ 9
 -----------
   8 . 0 9 □
```

3 A CD costs £5.99, a book costs £4.75 and a calculator costs £7.50. Work out the total cost of the three items.

4 I started with 0.756 and then added a number. The answer was 0.777. What number did I add?

5 What five different coins make £1.77?

6 Copy and complete

(a)
```
   6 . □ 9
 - □ . 3 □
 ---------
   5 . 5 7
```

(b)
```
   □ . 7 □
 - 3 . □ 6
 ---------
   5 . 4 7
```

(c)
```
   7 . 4 8
 - 6 . □ □
 ---------
   □ . 7 0
```

7 Copy and complete the cross number.

Clues across
- **1.** $5.7 \div 3$
- **3.** 0.8×3
- **5.** $6^2 \times 0.5$
- **6.** $44.8 \div 8$
- **7.** $9^2 \div 10 + 0.3$
- **8.** $(10\% \text{ of } 23) \times 3$
- **10.** $8^2 + 5^2 + (0.1^2 \times 100)$
- **11.** $46.4 + 47.6$

Clues down
- **1.** $0.017 \times 1000 + 10^2$
- **2.** $1078 \div 11$
- **3.** 50.8×5
- **4.** $4^3 - 4^2 - (4 \div 2)$
- **7.** $44.5 \div 5$
- **8.** $3 \times 2 \times 5 \times 2$
- **9.** 11×0.4

1	2	■	3	4
5		■	6	
	■	7		■
■	8		■	9
10		■	11	

8 Work out

(a) 3.26×10 (b) 11.4×10 (c) 0.415×100 (d) 1.2×100
(e) $17.6 \div 10$ (f) $427 \div 100$ (g) $16.53 \div 10$ (h) $0.42 \div 10$

9 Copy and complete

(a) $0.72 \times \square = 7.2$ (b) $\square \times 100 = 170$ (c) $10 \times \square = 16$
(d) $100 \times \square = 85.4$ (e) $3.2 \times \square = 3.2$ (f) $\square \times 100 = 2$

10 What number when multiplied by 7 gives an answer of 16.8?

11 Work out

(a) 8.23×4 (b) $3.12 \div 4$ (c) $6.2 \div 5$ (d) 0.85×4
(e) $31.8 \div 6$ (f) 7×1.23 (g) $9.94 \div 7$ (h) 6×8.02

12 Five people share the cost of a meal which costs £42.
How much does each person pay?

Fraction or percentage of a number

Exercise 5M

1 Work out

(a) $\frac{2}{3}$ of 69 (b) $\frac{3}{4}$ of 64 (c) $\frac{4}{5}$ of 80 (d) $\frac{3}{10}$ of 750

2 Copy and complete

(a) $\frac{1}{\square}$ of 35 = 5 (b) $\frac{1}{\square}$ of 121 = 11 (c) $\frac{1}{\square}$ of 74 = 37

(d) $\frac{2}{5}$ of 45 = $\square$ (e) $\frac{2}{\square}$ of 12 = 8 (f) $\frac{7}{\square}$ of 3000 = 210

3 There are four hundred and fifty mushrooms in a garden and $\frac{3}{50}$ of them are poisonous. How many of the mushrooms are poisonous?

4 In one week 400 people took their driving test and three fifths of them passed. How many people passed the test that week?

5 Work out

(a) 10% of £800 (b) 25% of £60 (c) 20% of £55.30 (d) 1% of 200 kg

(e) 75% of 2632 (f) 5% of 1300 (g) 2% of 900 g (h) 25% of 85.6 cm

6 Copy and complete

(a) $\frac{1}{4} = \square\%$ (b) $\frac{2}{5} = \square\%$ (c) $\frac{1}{3} = \square\%$ (d) $\frac{1}{50} = \square\%$

7 Work out

(a) 3% of £250 (b) 7% of 400 km (c) 3.5% of £720

(d) 8.4% of £2400 (e) 0.7% of 2500 kg (f) $33\frac{1}{3}\%$ of 660 miles

8 A factory produces forty-five thousand clocks every week and, when tested, two per cent of them are not accurate.
How many inaccurate clocks are made each week?

9 Write in order of size, smallest first.

(a) 22%, $\frac{1}{4}$, 0.15, $\frac{1}{5}$ (b) $\frac{3}{5}$, 52%, 0.05, $\frac{1}{8}$ (c) 0.7, $\frac{2}{3}$, 66%, 0.17

10 Which is greater: 5% of 800 or 18% of 300?

11 Work out 22% of $\frac{2}{3}$ of 480.

12 Work out (5% of £30) + (4% of £200) + (11% of £1200)

5.5 Probability 2

In section 5.5 you will learn to:

- find the probability of an event

Equally likely outcomes

(a) When you roll a fair dice there are six *equally likely outcomes*.
You can get a 1, 2, 3, 4, 5 or 6
The probability of rolling a 4 is $\frac{1}{6}$

(b) On this spinner there are five equal sections and two of these are blue.
The probability of spinning blue is $\frac{2}{5}$

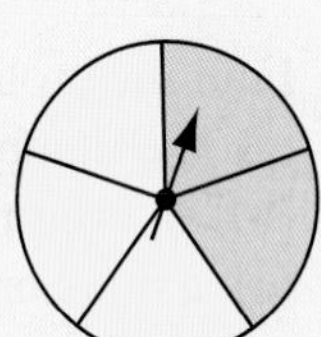

Exercise 1M

1 What is the probability of spinning green on this spinner?

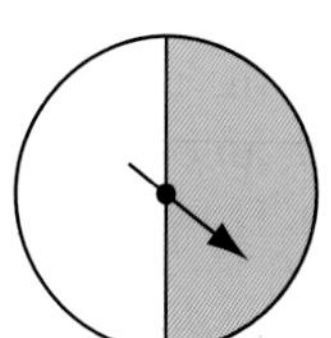

2 What is the probability of spinning green on each of these spinners?

(a) 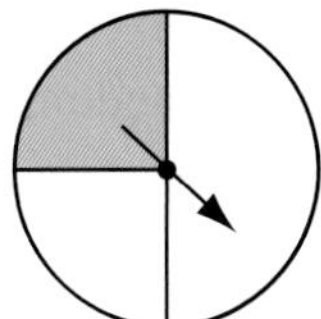 (b) 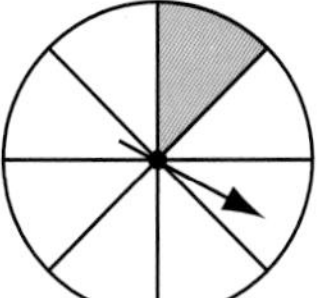 (c) 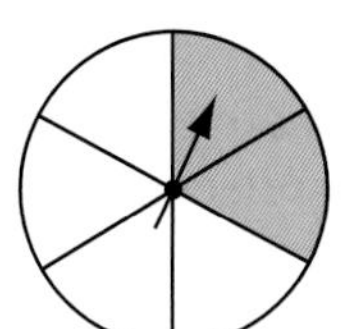 (d) 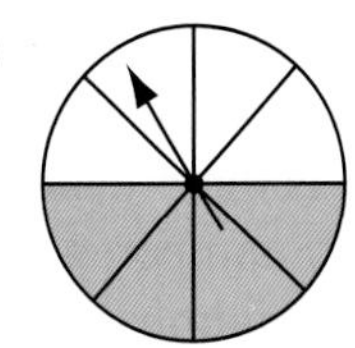

3 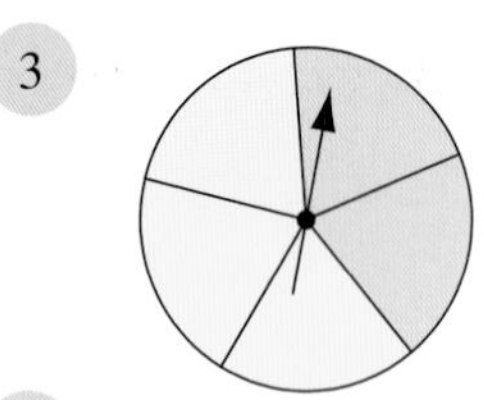

This spinner has five equal sections with 3 yellow and 2 green.
What is the probability of spinning?
(a) yellow (b) green

4 A hat contains 1 red ball, 1 blue ball and 1 orange ball. One ball is selected at random.
What is the probability of selecting?
(a) a blue ball (b) an orange ball.

5 Cards with the letters of the word O C T O P U S are placed in a bag. One letter is selected at random.

Find the probability of selecting
(a) a T, (b) an O

6 Bags A and B contain red and yellow balls as shown. Gary wants to get a yellow ball.
From which bag does he have the better chance of selecting a yellow ball?

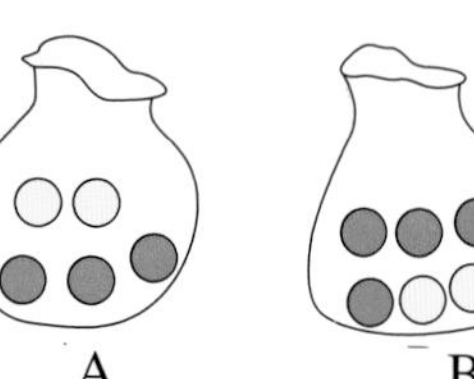

7 The cards below are placed in a bag and then one card is selected at random.

1 2 3 4 5 6 7 8 9

Find the probability of selecting
(a) the number 4,
(b) an even number,
(c) a number less than 5

Exercise 1E

1 Children in France count up to five using their fingers and thumb as shown.
Michele displays one number at random.
Find the probability that she shows
(a) the number three,
(b) an even number.
(c) How do *you* count from 1 to 5 using your fingers?

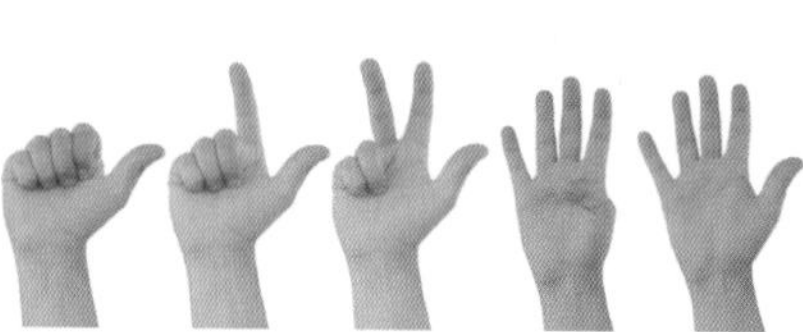

2 A fair dice is rolled. What is the probability of rolling
(a) a 5,
(b) an even number,
(c) a number greater than 7?

3 Four cards numbered 1, 2, 3, 4 are placed face down. One card is chosen at random.
(a) What is the probability of selecting an even number?
(b) A card numbered 5 is added to the cards above. What is now the probability of selecting an even number?

4 

These balls are placed in a bag and then one ball is selected at random.
What is the probability of selecting
(a) a green ball,
(b) a green ball or a red ball?

5 These cards are shuffled and turned over. One card is picked at random.
What is the probability of picking
(a) the number 6,
(b) the number 4,
(c) the number 8?

2	5	6	8	8

6 A raffle has tickets numbered from 1 to 150. Maggie has ticket number 37.
What is the probability that Maggie wins the raffle?

7 There are 16 pens in a box. All of them are black. Steve chooses one of the pens at random.
What is the probability that the pen is

(a) black, (b) red?

8 

There are 54 white cubes and 1 red cube in the pile shown.
The cubes are jumbled up in a box and then one cube is selected at random.

What is the probability of selecting the red cube?

A pack of playing cards, without Jokers, contains 52 cards.
There is Ace, King, Queen, Jack, 10, 9, 8, 7, 6, 5, 4, 3, 2 of four suits.
The suits are…

spades

hearts

diamonds

clubs

A pack of cards is shuffled and then one card is chosen at random.

(a) The probability that it is a King of hearts is $\frac{1}{52}$

(b) The probability that it is an ace is $\frac{4}{52}\left(=\frac{1}{13}\right)$

(c) The probability that it is a spade is $\frac{13}{52}\left(=\frac{1}{4}\right)$

Exercise 2M

1 One card is picked at random from a pack of 52.
Find the probability that it is
(a) a Queen
(b) the King of diamonds
(c) a spade

2 One card is selected at random from a full pack of 52 playing cards.
Find the probability of selecting
(a) a heart (b) a red card (c) a '2'
(d) any King, Queen or Jack (e) the ace of spades

3 A small pack of twenty cards consists of the Ace, King, Queen, Jack and 10 of spades, hearts, diamonds and clubs. One card is selected at random. Find the probability of selecting
(a) the ace of hearts (b) a King (c) a '10'
(d) a black card (e) a heart

4 One card is selected at random from the cards shown.
What is the probability of selecting
(a) a red card,
(b) a 5,
(c) a card of the 'club' suit?

5 A bag contains 3 black balls, 2 green balls, 1 white ball and 5 orange balls.
Find the probability of selecting
(a) a black ball
(b) an orange ball
(c) a white ball

6 A bag contains the balls shown. One ball is taken out at random.
Find the probability that it is
(a) yellow (b) blue (c) red
One more blue ball and one more red ball are added to the bag.

(d) Find the new probability of selecting a yellow ball from the bag.

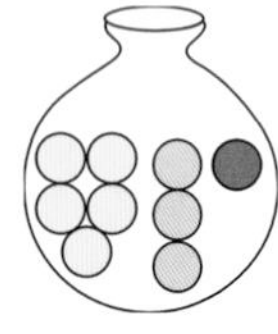

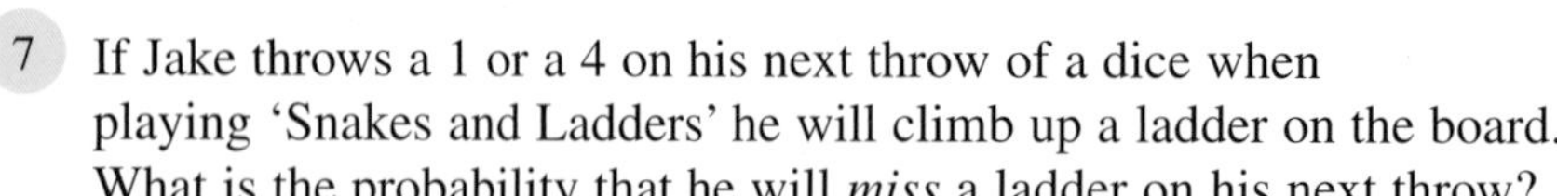
7 If Jake throws a 1 or a 4 on his next throw of a dice when playing 'Snakes and Ladders' he will climb up a ladder on the board.
What is the probability that he will *miss* a ladder on his next throw?

8 A box contains 11 balls: 3 green, 2 white, 4 red and 2 blue
(a) Find the probability of selecting
(i) a blue ball (ii) a green ball
(b) The 3 green balls are replaced by 3 blue balls. Find the probability of selecting
(i) a blue ball (ii) a white ball.

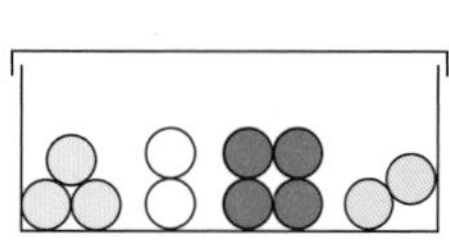

9 Here are two spinners. Say whether the following statements are true or false. Explain why in each case.

(a) 'Sarah is more likely to spin a 6 than Ben'.

(b) 'Sarah and Ben are equally likely to spin an even number.'

(c) 'If Sarah spins her spinner six times, she is bound to get at least one 6.'

Sarah's spinner

Ben's spinner

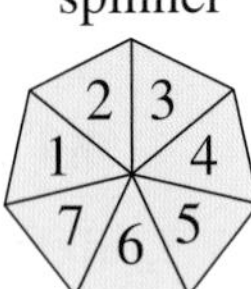

Exercise 2E

In questions 1 to 4 a bag contains a certain number of red balls and a certain number of white balls. The tally charts show the number of times a ball was selected from the bag and then replaced. Look at the results and say what you think was in the bag each time.

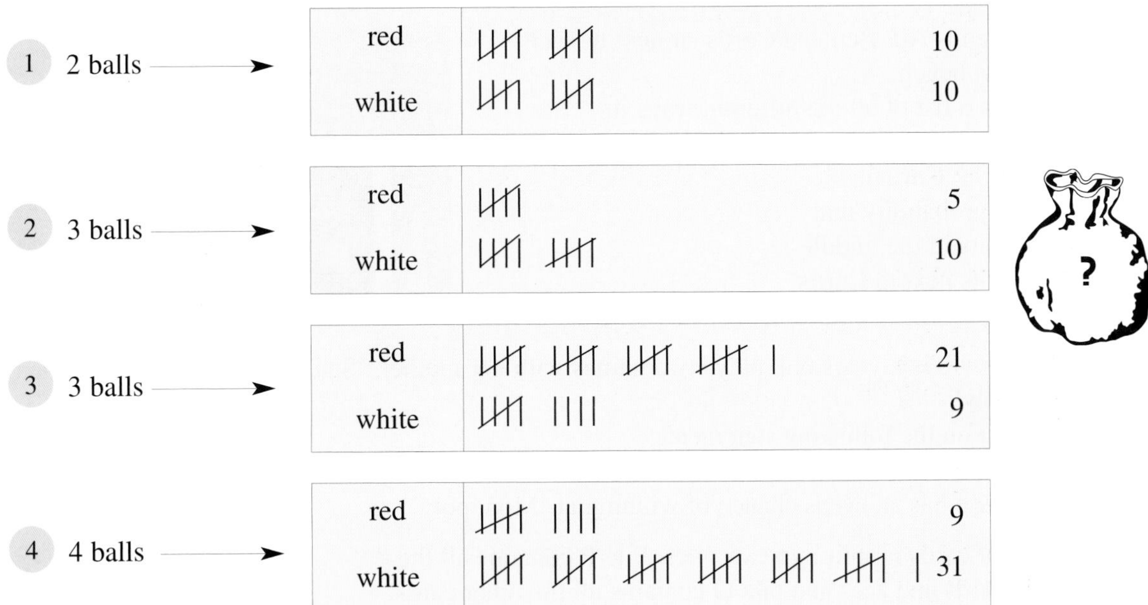

1 2 balls
red 10
white 10
2 3 balls
red 5
white 10
3 3 balls
red 21
white 9
4 4 balls
red 9
white 31
?

5 A bag contains 9 balls, all of which are black or white. Jane selects a ball and then replaces it. She repeats this several times. Here are her results (B = black, W = white):

B W B W B B B W B B W B B W B

B B W W B B B B W B W B B W B

How many balls of each colour do you think there were in the bag?

6 Cards with numbers 1, 2, 3, 4, 5, 6, 7, 8, 9, 10 are shuffled and then placed face down in a line. The cards are then turned over one at a time from the left. In this example the first card is a '4'.

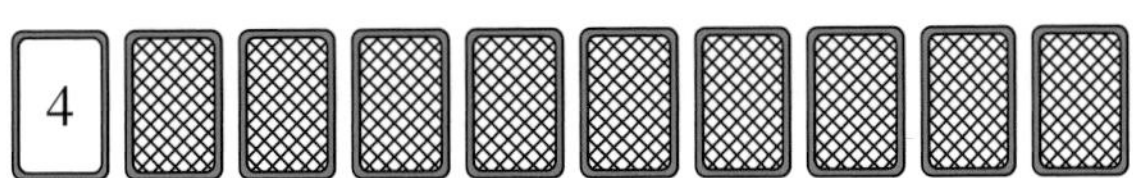

Find the probability that the next card turned over will be

(a) 7 (b) a number higher than 4.

7 Suppose the second card is a 1

Find the probability that the next card will be

(a) the 6 (b) an even number (c) higher than 1.

8 Suppose the first three cards are  ...

Find the probability that the next card will be
(a) less than 8
(b) the 4
(c) an odd number.

9 Three friends Alf, Ben and Curtis sit next to each other on a bench.

(a) Make a list of all the different ways in which they can sit. (Use A = Alf, B = Ben and C = Curtis).

Find the probability that
(b) Alf sits in the middle.
(c) Alf sits next to Curtis.
(d) Ben sits at one end of the bench.

10 Melissa, who is 8 years old, plays two games with her mother, 'Snakes and Ladders' and then 'Monopoly'.
Comment on the following statements:
(a) Melissa has an evens chance of winning at 'Snakes and Ladders'.
(b) Melissa has an evens chance of winning at 'Monopoly'.

11 A pack of cards is split into two piles. Pile P contains all the picture cards and aces and pile O contains all the other cards.
(a) Find the probability of selecting
   (i) the Jack of hearts from pile P
   (ii) a seven from pile O
(b) All the diamonds are now removed from both piles.
   Find the probability of selecting
   (i) the King of clubs from pile P
   (ii) A red card from pile O.

P

O

12 Each letter in the words of the sentence below is written on a separate card.

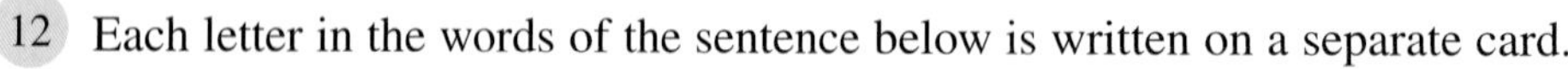
'I have told you a million times, don't exaggerate!'

The cards are placed in a bag and one card is selected at random. Find the probability of selecting
(a) an 'a'
(b) a 't'
(c) a 'b'

13 Helen played a game of cards with Michelle. The cards were dealt so that both players received two cards. Helen's cards were a seven and a four. Michelle's first card was a 10.

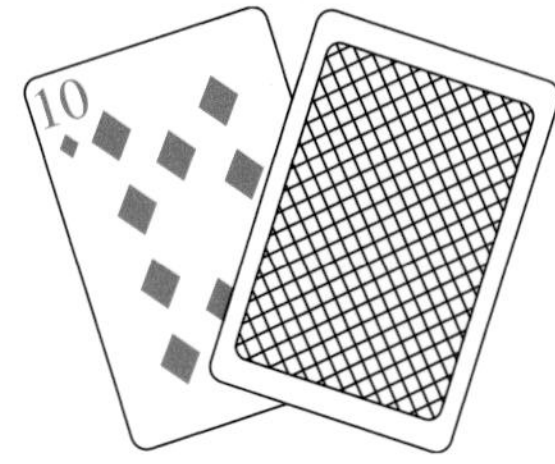

Find the probability that Michelle's second card was
(a) a picture card [a King, Queen or Jack]
(b) a seven.

14 One person is selected at random from the crowd of 14 750 watching a tennis match at Wimbledon. What is the probability that the person chosen will have his or her birthday that year on a Sunday?

15 One ball is selected at random from a bag containing x red balls and y white balls. What is the probability of selecting a red ball?

16 One ball is selected at random from a bag containing w white balls, g green balls and p pink balls. Find the probability of selecting
(a) a white ball, (b) a pink ball,
(c) a ball which is not white.

17 Sana, Liz and Carmel were asked to toss a fair coin 16 times. Here are the results they wrote down.

Sana	H T H T H T H T H T H T H T H T
Liz	H H T H T T H T T T H H T H H T
Carmel	H H H H H H H H T T T T T T T T

One of the three did the experiment properly while the other two just made up results. Explain what you think each person did.

Dice Pontoon

This is a game for two players using a dice.

Version 1

- Player A throws a dice as many times as he likes and keeps a running total for his 'score'.
  So if he throws 2, 3, 5, 1 his score is 11.
- If he throws the same number twice consecutively his score returns to zero and his turn is finished.
  So if he throws 2, 3, 5, 1, 1 his score is 0.

- He can decide to stop throwing the dice at any time to avoid the risk of losing his score.
- Player B then has his turn and throws the dice following the rules above.
- The winner is the player with the higher score.

Version 2

- The players take turns to throw the dice.
- If a player throws the same number that his opponent has just thrown then his score goes to zero.

  For example a game could go like this:

  A3 A5 A3

  B4 B1 B3

  Now B automatically loses because his score is zero.
- A player can decide to stop throwing at any time. If he does stop, his opponent may continue throwing on his own until someone wins.
  Here is another example of a game:

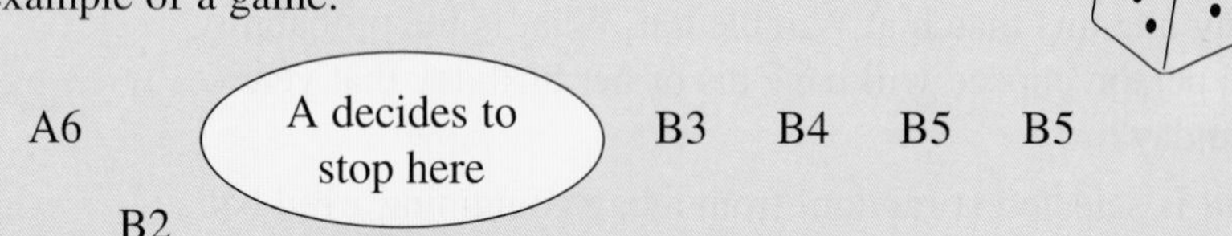

So A is the winner because B's score is zero after throwing two consecutive fives.
Notice that B would have won if he had thrown any number apart from 5 on his last throw.
Think about the rules of the two versions of the game and decide which version you *think* will give both players the most even chance of winning.

Which version do you think involves more skill?
It is not easy to decide which version will give both players the most even chance of winning.
One way to find out is to do an experiment.
Play each version of the game several times and make a tally chart, recording which player (first or second) won. Work out the experimental probability of each player winning for each version.
For example, if you played the game 14 times and the first player won 9 times, the experimental probability of the first player winning would be $\frac{9}{14}$.

Winner	
First player	Second player
卌 ||||	卌

Write a couple of sentences to say what the results of the experiments showed.
Try to think of any further changes to the rules which would make the game more fair or perhaps more interesting. Play the game using your changes and decide if it really does give a better game.

5.6 Interpreting graphs

In section 5.6 you will learn to:

- read information from line graphs
- draw line graphs in real life situations
- interpret and draw travel graphs

Exercise 1M

1 This graph converts miles into kilometres.

(a) Convert 20 miles into km

(b) Convert 64 km into miles

(c) Sharon's journey to work is 10 miles. How far is that in kilometres?

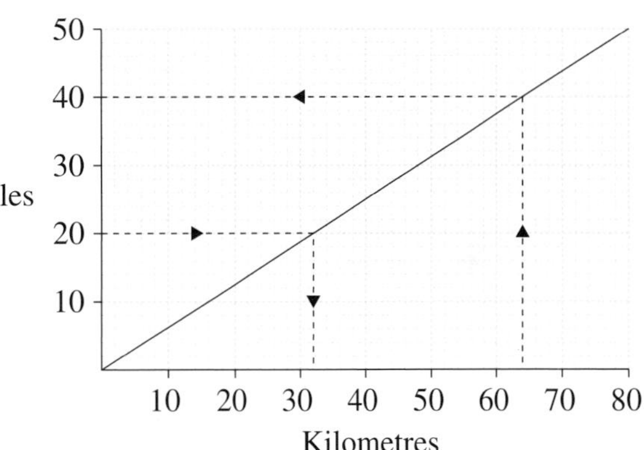

2 This graph converts rupees into pounds. The rupee is the currency in India

(a) Convert into pounds

(i) 280 rupees	(ii) 110 rupees
(iii) 250 rupees	(iv) 360 rupees

(b) Convert into rupees

(i) £5.00	(ii) £2.40
(iii) £4.20	(iv) £0.80

(c) On holiday in India, Jason bought fish and chips for 300 rupees. How much did the meal cost in pounds?

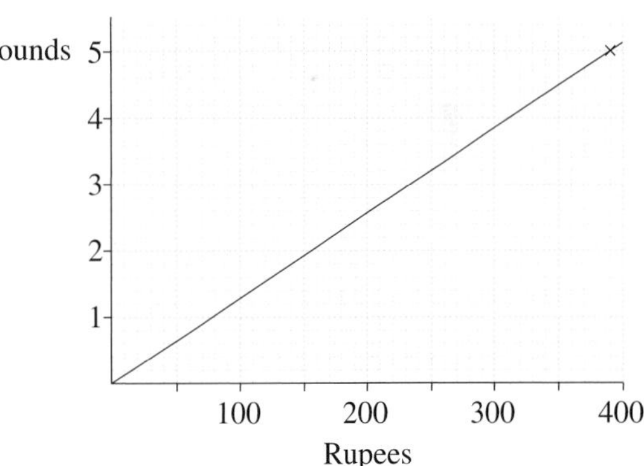

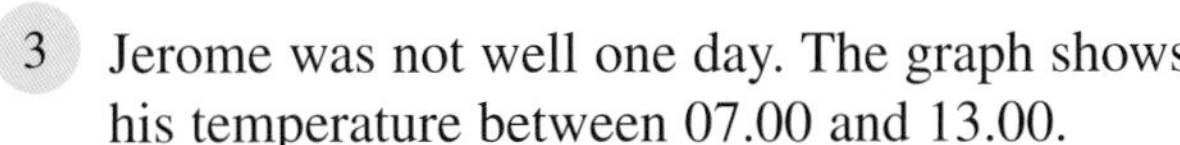

3 Jerome was not well one day. The graph shows his temperature between 07.00 and 13.00.

(a) What was his temperature at 10.30?

(b) At what time was his temperature highest?

(c) At what two times was his temperature 38.5°C?

(d) Between which two times did his temperature rise most quickly?

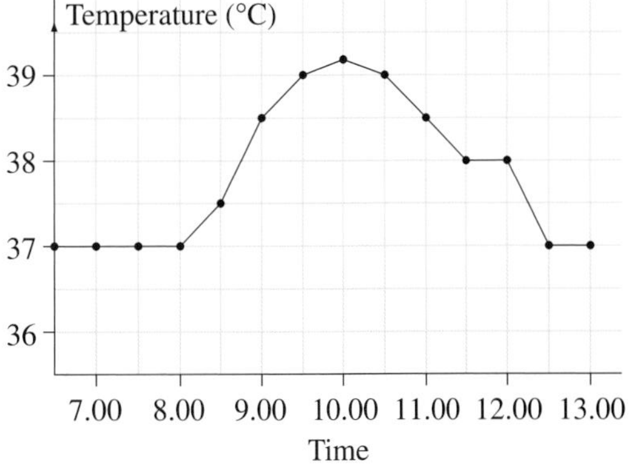

4 A man climbing a mountain measures his height above sea level after every 30 minutes; the results are shown on the graph.

(a) At what height was he at 10.00?
(b) At what height was he at 13.30?
(c) Estimate his height above sea level at 09.45.
(d) At what two times was he 2200 m above sea level?
(e) How high was the mountain? (He got to the top!)
(f) How long did he rest at the summit?
(g) How long did he take to reach the summit?

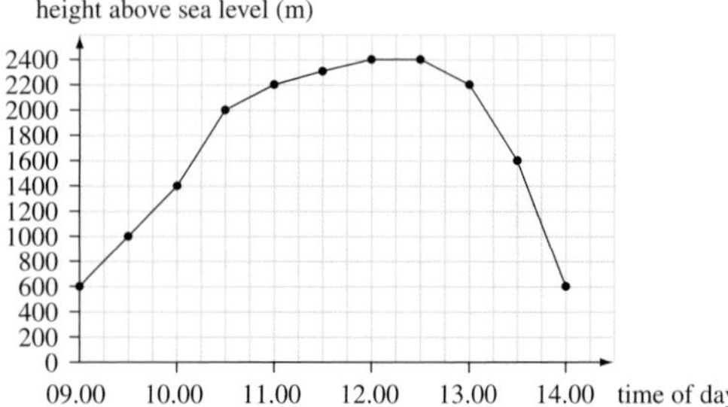

Exercise 1E

1 The cost of hiring a tank for filming depends on the duration of the hire.

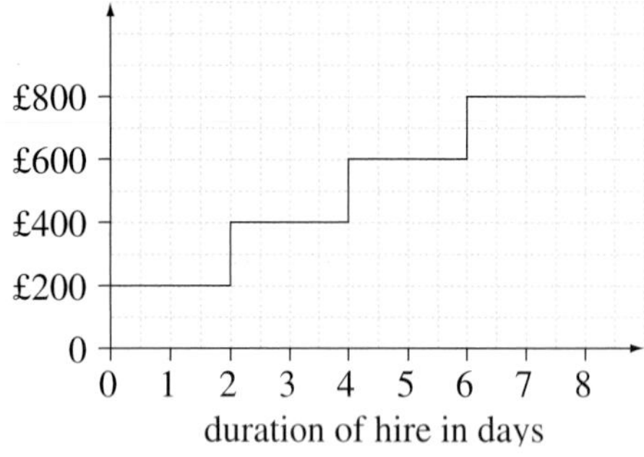

(a) How much does it cost to hire the tank for

(i) 1 day, (ii) $5\frac{1}{2}$ days, (iii) 3 days?

(b) What is the minimum hire charge?

2 The graph shows the cost of making calls to two directory enquiry numbers.

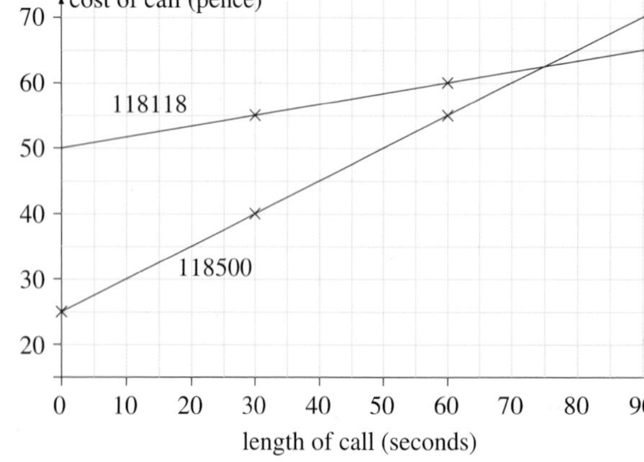

(a) How much does it cost for a 50 seconds call to 118500?

(b) Using 118118, for how long can you call for 55p?

(c) At what length of call do both numbers cost the same?

(d) What would be the cost of a two minute call to 118500?

3 The graph shows the minimum distance between cars at different speeds in good or bad weather.

(a) Think carefully and decide which line is for good weather and which line is for bad weather.
(b) A car is travelling at 50 m.p.h in good weather. What is the minimum distance between cars?
(c) In bad weather John is driving 60 metres behind another car. What is the maximum speed at which John should drive?

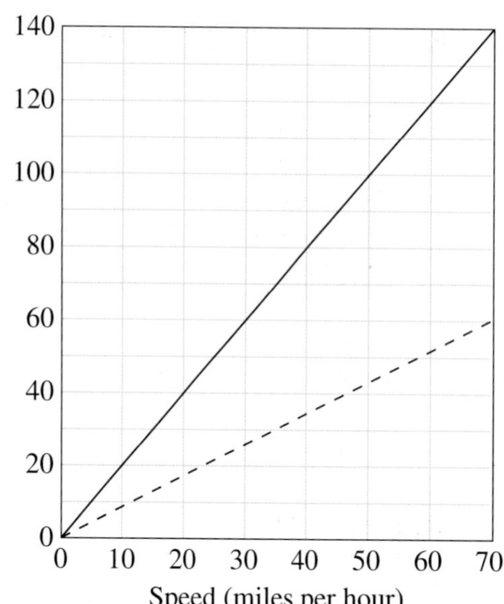

Exercise 2M

1 Draw a graph to convert kilograms into pounds. Draw a line through the point where 3 kg is equivalent to 6.6 pounds. Use a scale of 1 cm to 1 pound across the page and 2 cm to 1 kg up the page.

Use your graph to convert
(a) 1.2 kg into pounds
(b) 2 pounds into kg

2
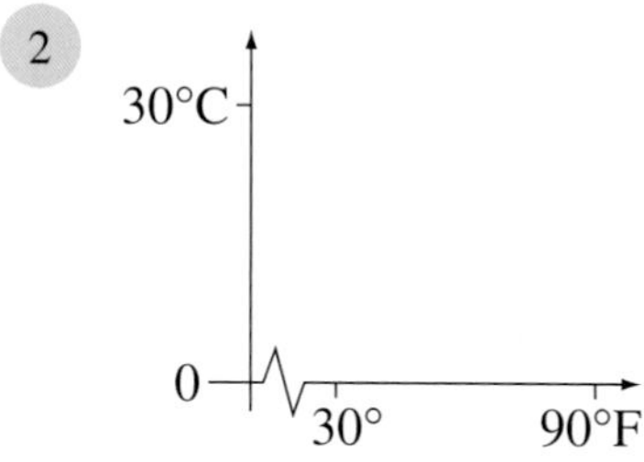

Draw a graph to convert temperatures from °F to °C.
Draw a line through the points 50°F = 10°C.
and 86°F = 30°C.

Use the graph to convert:
(a) 77°F into °C (b) 15°C into °F

3 A mobile phone company charges £10 a month rental plus 20p per minute for calls.

minutes of calls	0	20	40	60	80
cost in £	10	14	18	22	26

(a) Draw a graph to show this information.
(b) Use your graph to find the total cost of making 65 minutes of calls.

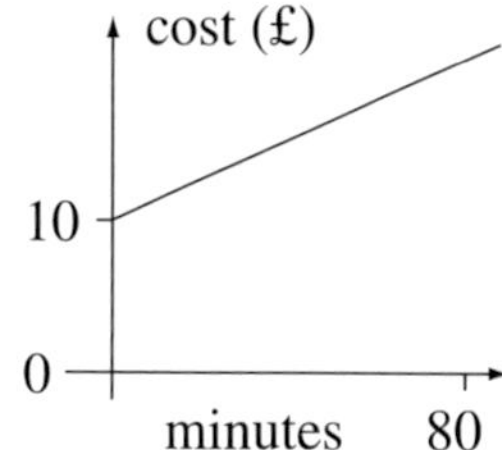

Travel graphs

- This graph shows the details of a cycle ride that Jim took starting from his home.

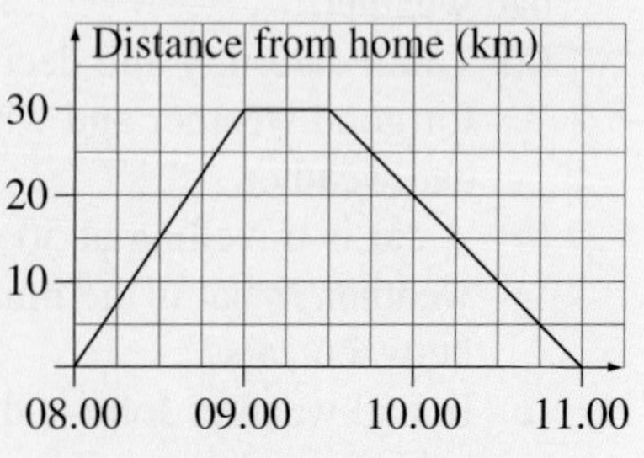

(a) In the first hour Jim went 30 km so his speed was 30 km/h.

(b) He stopped for $\frac{1}{2}$ hour at a place 30 km from his home.

(c) From 09:30 until 11:00 he cycled back home. We know that he cycled back home because the distance from his home at 11:00 is 0 km.

(d) The speed at which he cycled home was 20 km/h.

Exercise 2E

1 The graph shows a car journey from A to C via B.

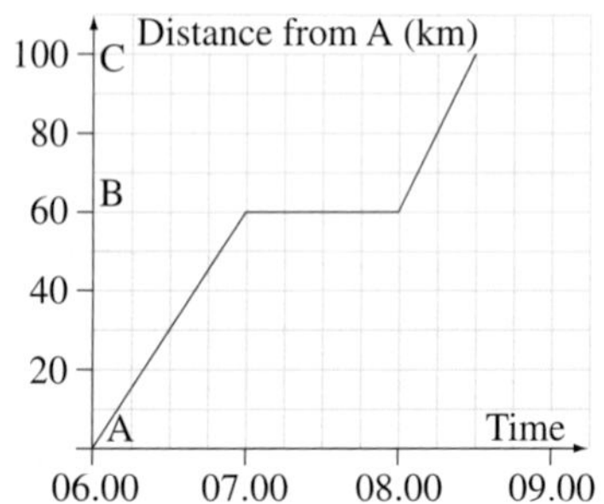

(a) How far is it from A to C?
(b) For how long does the car stop at B?
(c) When is the car half way between B and C?
(d) What is the speed of the car
  (i) between A and B?
  (ii) between B and C?

2 The graph shows the motion of a train as it accelerates away from Troon.

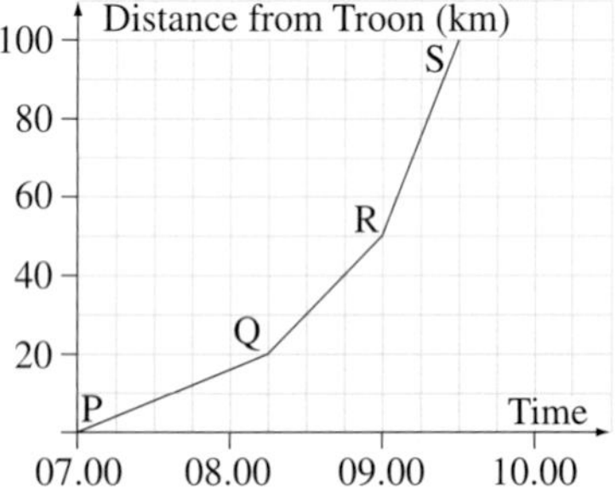

(a) How far from Troon is the train at 08.45?
(b) When is the train half way between R and S?
(c) Find the speed of the train
  (i) from R to S
  (ii) from Q to R
  (iii) (harder) from P to Q
(d) How long does it take the train to travel 100 km?

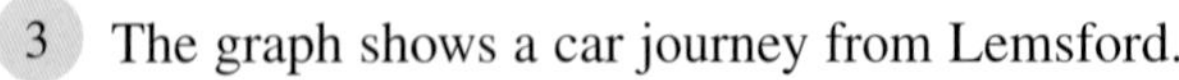

3 The graph shows a car journey from Lemsford.

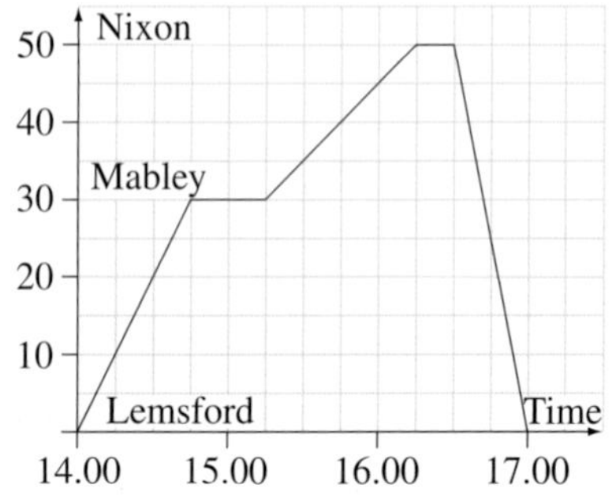

(a) For how long did the car stop at Mabley?
(b) When did the car arrive back at Lemsford?
(c) When did the car leave Mabley after stopping?
(d) Find the speed of the car
  (i) from Mabley to Nixon
  (ii) from Nixon back to Lemsford.

4 The graph shows the journey of a coach and a lorry along the same road between Newcastle and Carlisle.

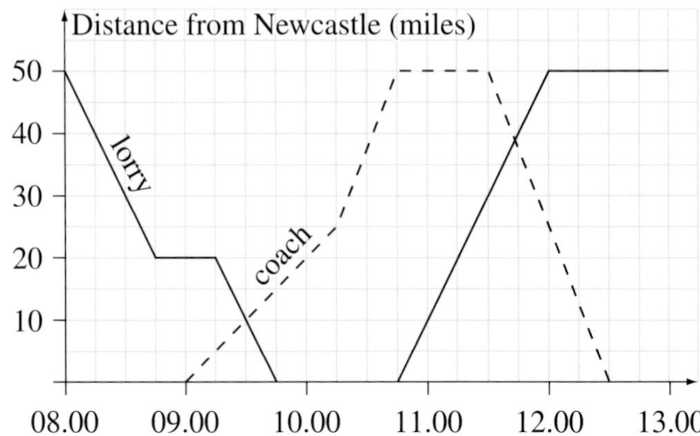

(a) How far apart were the two vehicles at 0915?
(b) At what time did the vehicles meet for the first time?
(c) At what speed did the coach return to Newcastle?
(d) What was the highest speed of the lorry during its journey?

5 The diagram shows the travel graphs of five objects. Which graph shows:

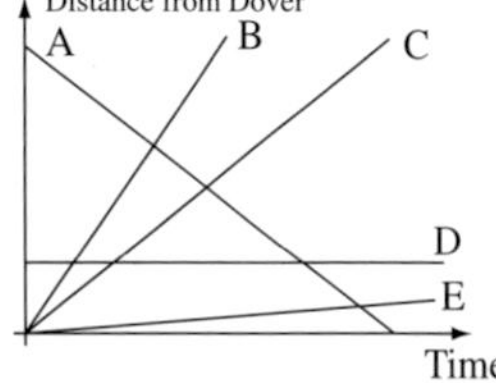

(a) A car ferry from Dover to Calais
(b) A hovercraft from Dover to Calais
(c) A car ferry from Calais to Dover
(d) A buoy outside Dover harbour
(e) A cross channel swimmer from Dover?

In questions 6 to 11 use the same scales as in question 4 of this exercise.

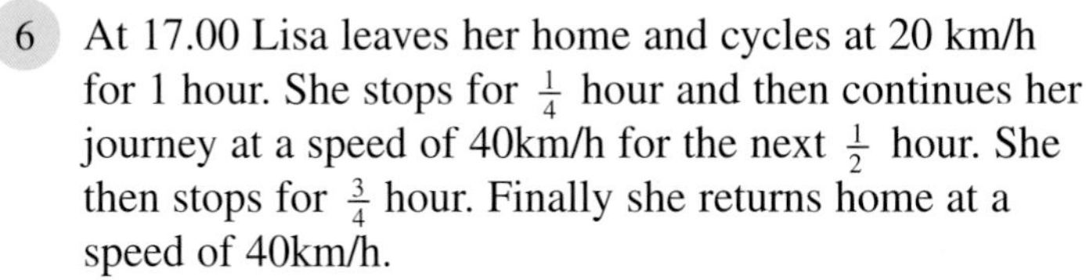

6 At 17.00 Lisa leaves her home and cycles at 20 km/h for 1 hour. She stops for $\frac{1}{4}$ hour and then continues her journey at a speed of 40km/h for the next $\frac{1}{2}$ hour. She then stops for $\frac{3}{4}$ hour. Finally she returns home at a speed of 40km/h.
Draw a travel graph to show Lisa's journey. When did she arrive home?

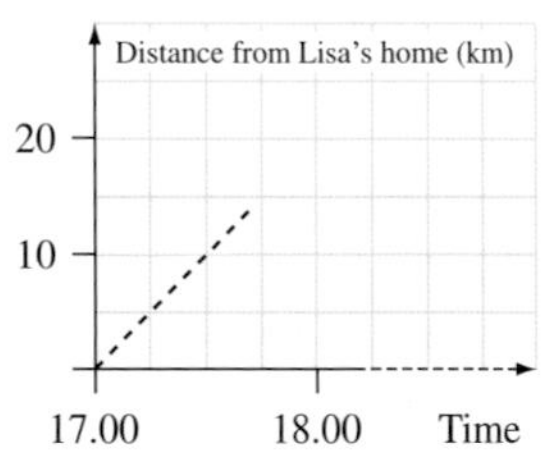

7 Declan leaves home at 13.00 on his horse and rides at a speed of 20 km/h for one hour. Declan and his horse then rest for 45 minutes and afterwards continue their journey at a speed of 15 km/h for another one hour. At what time do they finish the journey?

8 As Mrs. Sadler leaves home in her car at 13.00 she encounters heavy traffic and travels at only 20 km/h for the first $\frac{1}{2}$ hour. In the second half hour she increases her speed to 30 km/h and after that she

travels along the main road at 40 km/h for $\frac{3}{4}$h. She stops at her destination for $\frac{1}{2}$ hour and then returns home at a steady speed of 40 km/h.
Draw a graph to find when she returns home.

9 At 12 00 Amar leaves home and drives at a speed of 30 km/h. At 12 30 he increases his speed to 50 km/h and continues to his destination which is 65 km from home. He stops for $\frac{1}{2}$ hour and then returns home at a speed of 65 km/h.

Use a graph to find the time at which he arrives home.

10 At 08 00 Chew Ling leaves home and cycles towards a railway station which is 65 km away. She cycles at a speed of 30 km/h until 09 30 at which time she stops to rest for $\frac{1}{2}$ hour. She then completes the journey at a speed of 20 km/h.
At 09 45 Chew Ling's father leaves their home in his car and drives towards the station at 60 km/h.
(a) At what time does Chew Ling arrive at the station?
(b) When is Chew Ling overtaken by her father?

11 Kate lives 80 km from Kevin. One day at 12 00 Kate cycles towards Kevin's home at 25 km/h. At the same time Kevin cycles at 30 km/h towards Kate's home

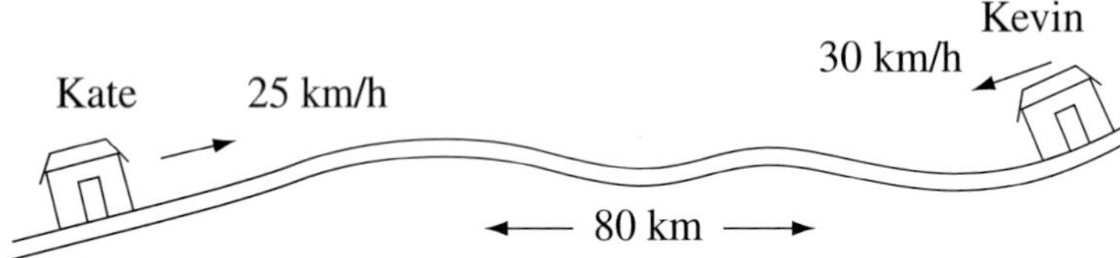

Draw a travel graph with 'Distance from Kate's home' on the vertical axis.
Approximately when and where do they meet?

In questions 12 and 13 use a scale of 2 squares to 15 minutes across the page and 1 square to 10 km up the page.

12 At 01 00 a bank robber leaves a bank as the alarm sounds and sets off along a motorway at 80 km/h towards his hideout which is 150 km from the bank.

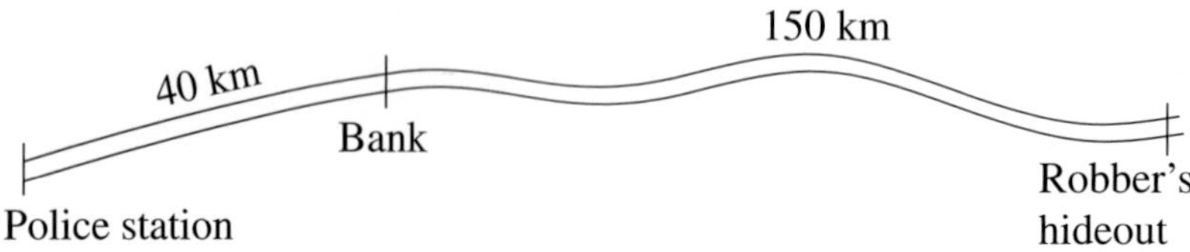

As soon as the alarm goes off a police car leaves the police station, which is 40 km from the bank, and drives at 80 km/h to the bank. After stopping at the bank for 15 minutes, the police car chases after the robber at a speed of 160 km/h.

Draw a travel graph with 'Distance from police station' on the vertical axis.

(a) Find out if the police caught the robber before the robber reached his hideout.
(b) If the robber was caught, say when. If he was not caught say how far behind him the police were when he reached his hideout.

13 The diagram shows three towns A, B and C. The distance from A to B is 50 km and the distance from B to C is 110 km. At the same moment 3 cars leave A, B and C at the speeds shown and in the directions shown.

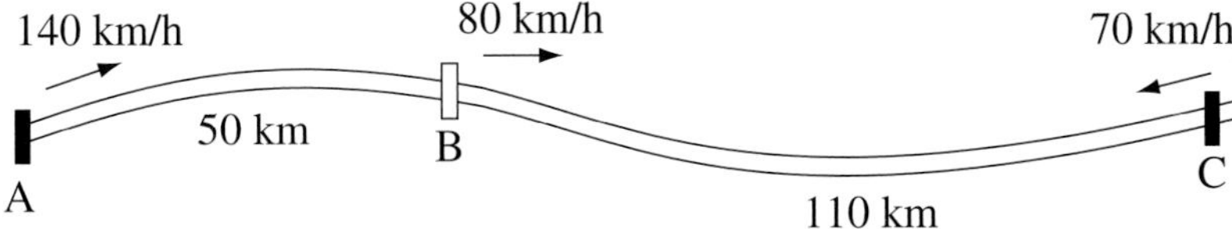

The cars from A and C are trying to intercept the car from B as quickly as possible.
(a) Which car intercepts the car from B first?
(b) After how many minutes does the car from A catch the car from B?

TEST YOURSELF ON UNITS 5.5 and 5.6

1 Finding the probability of an event

(a) One ball is selected at random from the bag shown. Write down the probability of selecting
   (i) a red ball
   (ii) a green ball

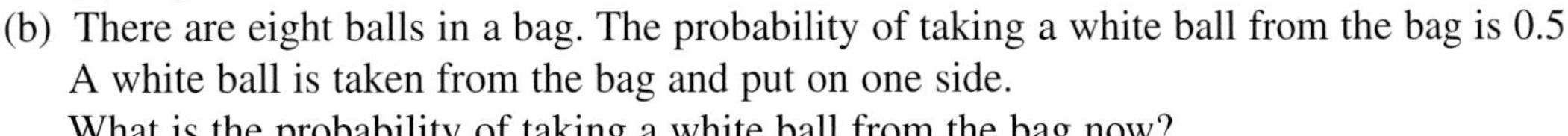

(b) There are eight balls in a bag. The probability of taking a white ball from the bag is 0.5. A white ball is taken from the bag and put on one side. What is the probability of taking a white ball from the bag now?

2 Reading information from line graphs

This line graph shows the average daily temperature in Sweden.

(a) What was the temperature in June?
(b) In which month was the temperature 7ºC?
(c) In which two months was the temperature 3ºC?
(d) Between which two months was there the largest increase in temperature?
(e) What was the range of temperature over the year?

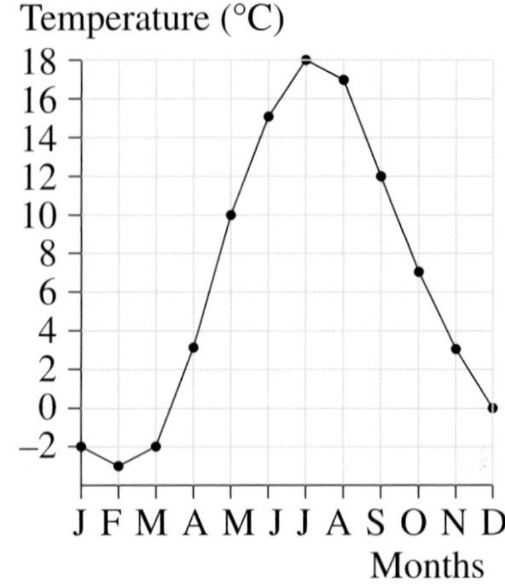

3 Drawing line graphs in real life situations

Draw a graph to convert kilometres into miles. Draw a line through the point where 80 km is equivalent to 50 miles. Use a scale of 1 cm to 10 units.
Use the graph to convert:
(a) 60 km into miles (b) 20 miles into km.

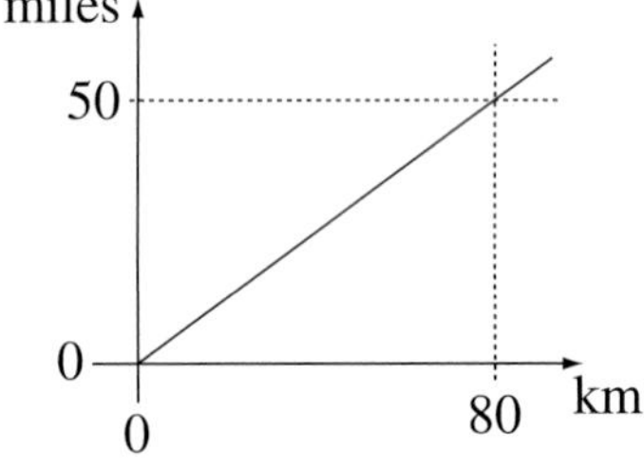

4 Interpreting and drawing travel graphs

A car leaves London at 09 00 and travels at a speed of 10 km /h for 1 hour. It then travels at a speed of 60 km/h for half an hour. The car then stops for one hour before returning to London at a speed of 40 km/h. Draw a travel graph for this journey. At what time did the car return to London?

[Use a scale of 4 squares to 1 hour and 2 squares for 10 km.]

5.7 Rounding numbers

In section 5.7 you will learn how to:

- round numbers
- calculate using estimates

Here are cuttings from two newspapers

A. '360 mm of rain makes summer 2007 the wettest ever'

B. '358.4 mm of rain fell from June to August 2007 to make the summer of 2007 the wettest on record'

In A the figure 360 has been rounded off because the reporter thinks that his readers are not interested in the exact amount of rainfall.

Rounding to the nearest whole number

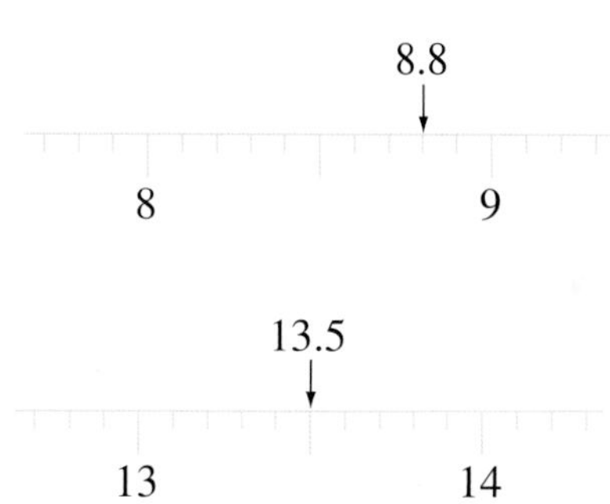

- The arrow points at 8.8 on the scale. 8.8 is nearer to 9 than to 8. So 8.8 is rounded to 9 to the *nearest whole number.*
- This arrow points at 13.5 which is half way between 13 and 14. We have to decide whether to round up or down. The rule is:

  If the first digit after the decimal point is *5 or more* round *up*.
  Otherwise round down.

  57.3 → 57
  89.8 → 90
  5.5 → 6

Rounding to the nearest ten, hundred, thousand

- Rounding to the nearest ten.
  If the digit in the units column is 5 or more round up.
  Otherwise round down.

  27 → 30
  42 → 40
  265 → 270

- Rounding to the nearest hundred.
  If the digit in the tens column is 5 or more round up.
  Otherwise round down.

  593 → 600
  247 → 200
  2643 → 2600

- Rounding to the nearest thousand.
  If the digit in the hundreds column is 5 or more round up.
  Otherwise round down.

  1394 → 1000
  502 → 1000
  11 764 → 12 000

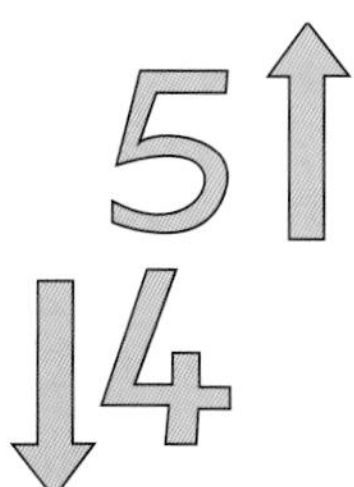

Exercise 1M

1. Round these numbers to the nearest whole number.
(a) 8.2 (b) 9.7 (c) 11.4 (d) 8.5 (e) 11.8
(f) 57.4 (g) 20.8 (h) 108.2 (i) 0.7 (j) 16.5

2. Answer 'true' or 'false' when the numbers are rounded to the nearest whole number.
(a) $7.7 \rightarrow 8$ (b) $3.4 \rightarrow 3$ (c) $11.5 \rightarrow 12$ (d) $9.6 \rightarrow 9$
(e) $11.1 \rightarrow 11$ (f) $6.5 \rightarrow 6$ (g) $0.7 \rightarrow 1$ (h) $27.5 \rightarrow 28$

3. Write these numbers to the nearest ten.
(a) 73 (b) 88 (c) 227 (d) 364 (e) 77
(f) 1283 (g) 253 (h) 1888 (i) 295 (j) 187

4. 1680 1690 1700 1710 1720

Use the scale to round these numbers to the nearest ten.
(a) 1682 (b) 1718 (c) 1694 (d) 1704 (e) 1722

5. Round off these numbers to the nearest hundred.
(a) 584 (b) 293 (c) 6074 (d) 914 (e) 706.5
(f) 2857 (g) 65542 (h) 222 (i) 1486 (j) 28374

6. Round off these numbers to the nearest thousand.
(a) 4555 (b) 757 (c) 8507 (d) 22514 (e) 6511
(f) 614 (g) 2874 (h) 25712 (i) 13568 (j) 294888

7. Work out the following using a calculator and then round the answer to the *nearest hundred*.
(a) 67.5×841 (b) 173×11.4 (c) $25000 \div 241$
(d) $6781.4 + 374$ (e) $784 \div 0.92$ (f) $9801 - 416.2$
(g) 18.6×18.7 (h) $501000 \div 6751$ (i) $\sqrt{623000}$

8. Work out these answers on a calculator and then round off the answer to the *nearest whole number*.
(a) $235 \div 7$ (b) $4714 \div 58$ (c) $2375 \div 11$ (d) $999 \div 17$
(e) 5.62×7.04 (f) 19.3×1.19 (g) 53.2×2.3 (h) 12.6×0.93
(i) $119.6 \div 5.1$ (j) $109 \div 0.7$ (k) $63.4 \div 11$ (l) $1.92 \div 0.09$

9. How long is this rod to:
(a) the nearest cm (b) the nearest 10 cm (c) the nearest metre

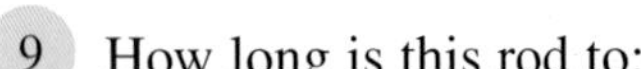

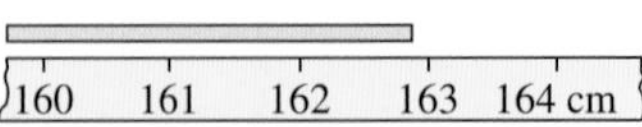

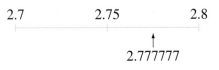

Round to one decimal place

- Using a calculator to work out $25 \div 9$, the answer is 2.777777.

  On a number line we can see that the answer is nearer to 2.8 than to 2.7. We will *round off* the answer to 2.8 correct to 1 *decimal place*.

2.7 2.75 2.8

2.777777

- Using a calculator to work out 11% of 21.23, the answer is 2.3353.

2.3 2.35 2.4

↑ 2.3353

On a number line we can see that the answer is nearer to 2.3 than to 2.4. So the answer is 2.3, correct to 1 decimal place (1 d.p. for short).

- Suppose the calculator shows 1.75. This number is exactly half way between 1.7 and 1.8. Do we round up or not? The rule for rounding off to 1 decimal place is:

> If the figure in the 2nd decimal place is 5 or more, round up. Otherwise do not.

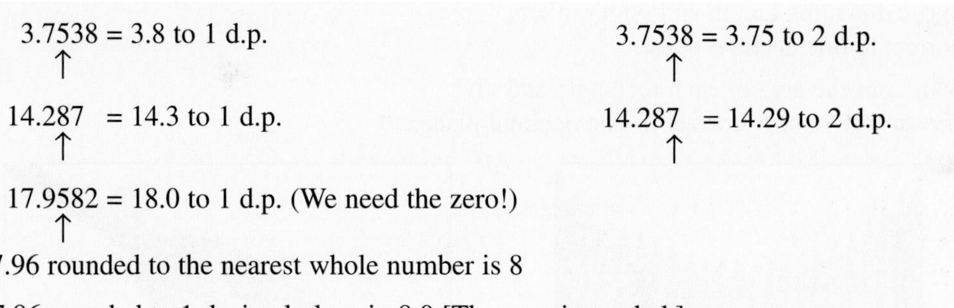

3.7538 = 3.8 to 1 d.p.

14.287 = 14.3 to 1 d.p.

17.9582 = 18.0 to 1 d.p. (We need the zero!)

3.7538 = 3.75 to 2 d.p.

14.287 = 14.29 to 2 d.p.

7.96 rounded to the nearest whole number is 8

7.96 rounded to 1 decimal place in 8.0 [The zero is needed.]

Exercise 1E

1. Round these numbers to 1 decimal place.

(a) 2.41 (b) 8.94 (c) 4.65 (d) 12.47 (e) 16.35

2. Round these numbers to 2 decimal places.

(a) 1.924 (b) 4.065 (c) 9.997 (d) 65.374 (e) 14.043

3. Write the following numbers correct to 1 decimal place.

(a) 18.7864 (b) 3.55 (c) 17.0946 (d) 0.7624
(e) 5.421 (f) 11.27 (g) 10.252 (h) 7.084

4. Write the following numbers correct to 2 decimal places.

(a) 3.75821 (b) 11.64412 (c) 0.38214 (d) 138.2972
(e) 11.444 (f) 7.058 (g) 6.5781 (h) 5.3092

5. Work out these answers on a calculator and then round the answer to one decimal place.

(a) $65 \div 7$ (b) 85×0.7 (c) $8.64 \div 11.014$ (d) 8×16.22
(e) 1.4×0.97 (f) $82 \div 7$ (g) $113 \div 5$ (h) $0.6 \div 0.022$

6 Work out the following on a calculator and write the answers correct to 2 decimal places.

(a) $11 \div 7$ (b) $213 \div 11$ (c) $1.4 \div 6$ (d) $29 \div 13$
(e) 1.3×0.95 (f) 1.23×3.71 (g) $97 \div 1.3$ (h) 0.95×8.3

7 Measure the lines below and give the lengths in cm correct to one decimal place.

(a) ____________________________________

(b) __________

(c) ____

(d) ________________________

(e) ____

8 Measure the dimensions of the rectangles below.

(a) Write down the length and width in cm, correct to one decimal place.

(b) Work out the area of each rectangle and give the answer in cm^2, correct to one decimal place.

(i)

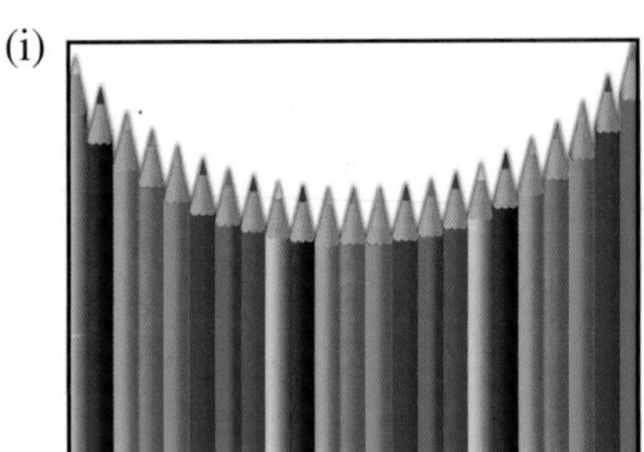

(ii)

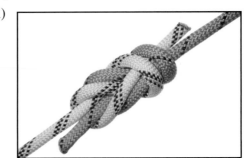

Calculating with estimates, checking results

- Hazim worked out 38.2×10.78 and wrote down 41.1796. He can check his answer by working with estimates.
  Instead of 38.2 use 40, instead of 10.78 use 10.

  So $40 \times 10 = 400$.

  Clearly Hazim's answer is wrong. He put the decimal point in the wrong place.

- Here are three more calculations with estimates.

(a) 27.2×51.7
$\approx 30 \times 50$
≈ 1500

(b) $78.9 \div 1.923$
$\approx 80 \div 2$
≈ 40

(c) 12% of £411.55
≈ 10% of £400
≈ £40

Exercise 2M

Do not use a calculator. Decide, by estimating, which of the three answers is closest to the exact answer. Write the calculation and the approximate answer for each question (use ≈).

	Calculation	A	B	C
1.	102.6 × 9.7	90	500	1000
2.	7.14 × 11.21	30	70	300
3.	1.07 × 59.2	6	60	200
4.	2.21 × 97.8	200	90	20
5.	8.95 × 42.1	200	400	4000
6.	4.87 × 6.18	15	10	30
7.	789 × 12.3	8000	4000	800
8.	978 × 9.83	1 million	100 000	10 000
9.	1.11 × 28.7	20	30	60
10.	9.8 × 82463	8 million	1 million	800 000
11.	307.4 ÷ 1.97	50	100	150
12.	81.2 ÷ 0.99	8	0.8	80
13.	6121 ÷ 102.4	60	300	600
14.	59.71 ÷ 3.14	10	20	180
15.	1072 ÷ 987.2	0.2	1	10
16.	614 – 297.4	300	100	3000
17.	0.104 + 0.511	0.06	0.1	0.6
18.	8216.1 + 1.44	800	4000	8000
19.	51% of £8018.95	£40	£400	£4000
20.	9% of £205.49	£10	£20	£200

Exercise 2E

1 A ‘Pritt Stick’ costs £1.99.

(a) Without a calculator, estimate the cost of twelve Pritt Sticks.
(b) Find the exact cost of twelve Pritt Sticks.

2 A box of drawing pins costs £3.85.

Estimate the cost of 20 boxes of drawing pins.

3 A painting measures 12.2 cm by 9.7 cm.

(a) Without a calculator, estimate the area of the painting.
(b) Use a calculator to work out the exact area of the painting.

4 A new band's first demo CD was sold at £2.95 per copy. Estimate the total cost of 47 copies.

5 Desmond has to pay £208.50 per month for 2 years towards the cost of his car. Estimate the total cost of his payments.

6 Two hundred and six people share the cost of hiring a train. Roughly how much does each person pay if the total cost was £61 990?

In questions 7 and 8 there are six calculations and six answers.

Write down each calculation and insert the correct answer from the list given. Use estimation.

7 (a) 6.9×7.1 (b) $9.8 \div 5$ (c) 21×10.2
(d) $0.13 \div 15.2$ (e) $3114 \div 30$ (f) 4.03×1.9

Answers: 1.96 15.33 48.99 103.8 7.657 214.2

8 (a) $103.2 \div 5$ (b) 7.2×7.3 (c) 4.1×49
(d) $3.57 \div 3$ (e) $36.52 \div 4$ (f) $1.4 \div 10$

Answers: 52.56 1.19 9.13 200.9 20.64 0.14

9

Insult may leave man speechless

CAIRO A Sinai man who insulted a shepherdess was ordered by a tribal court to give her 40 camels and either have his tongue cut out or give five more camels. *(AFP)*

In this area of Egypt an average camel costs 5100 Egyptian pounds (EGP).

(a) Estimate the value in pounds of 40 camels.

(b) Estimate the value in pounds of the extra camels needed to save the man's tongue.

[£100 = 1160 EGP]

10 A footballer is paid £94 800 per week. Estimate how much he is paid in a year.

5.8 Circles

In section 5.8 you will learn how to:

- find the circumference of a circle
- find the area of a circle

Radius, diameter and circumference

Look at the following diagrams.

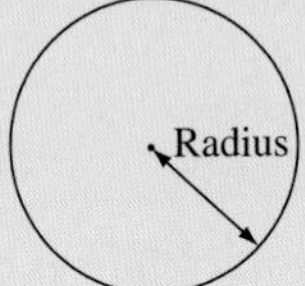

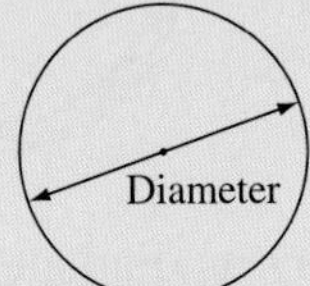

- The radius is half the diameter.
- The diameter is twice the radius.
- The length of the perimeter of a circle is called its *circumference*.

Exercise 1M (Oral or written exercise)

For each of the circles shown below, write down

(a) the radius (b) the diameter

Remember to give the units in your answers!

1
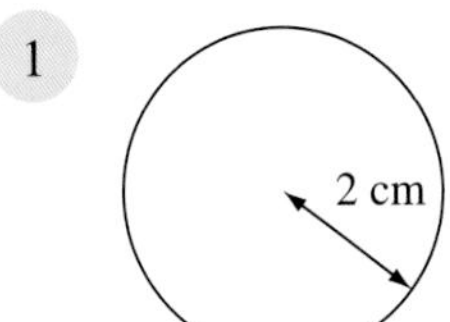

2 3 m

3
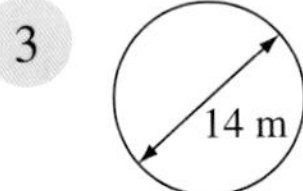

4
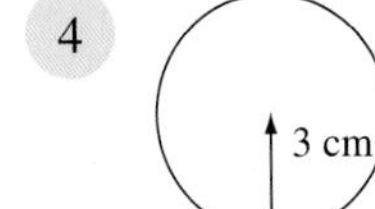

5
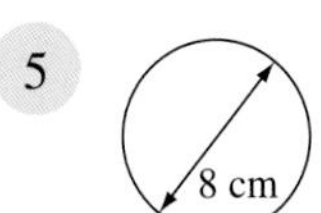

6 16 cm

7
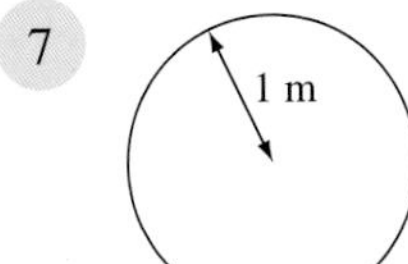

8
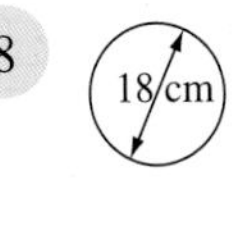

Activity

Find 8 circular objects (tins, plates, buckets, wheels etc.) For each object, measure the diameter and the circumference and write the results in a table. Use a flexible tape measure for the circumference or wrap a piece of string around the object and then measure the string with a ruler. For each pair of readings, work out the ratio (*circumference* ÷ *diameter*).

You should find that the number in the $\frac{c}{d}$ column is about the same each time. Work out the mean value of the 8 numbers in the $\frac{c}{d}$ column.

Object	Circumference c	diameter d	$\frac{c}{d}$
Tin of tuna	28.6 cm	8.8 cm	3.25
...			
...			

A piece of string 22 cm long will make:

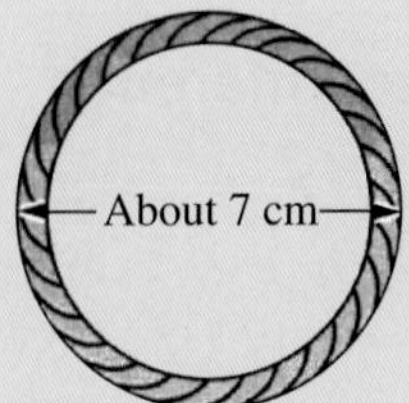

A circle whose diameter is just over 7 cm.

If you divide the circumference of a circle by its diameter the number you obtain is always just over three.

which means $\frac{\text{circumference}}{\text{diameter}} \approx 3$

Circumference ≈ 3 × diameter

This provides a fairly good *estimate* for the circumference of any circle.

Pi

For any circle, the exact value of the ratio $\left(\frac{\text{circumference}}{\text{diameter}}\right)$ is a number denoted by the Greek letter π.

Since $\frac{\text{circumference}}{\text{diameter}} = \pi$ we can write

circumference = π × diameter Learn this formula.

Most calculators have a $\boxed{\pi}$ button, which will give the value of π correct to at least 7 significant figures: 3.141593.

Find the circumference of the circle.

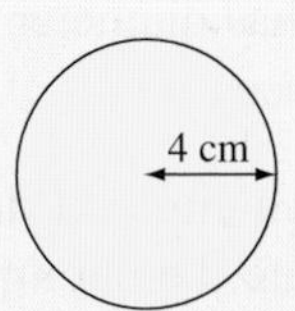

Radius = 4 cm, so diameter = 8 cm

Circumference = $\pi \times 8$

$= 25.13274123....$ cm

$= 25.1$ cm correct to one decimal place

Exercise 1E

Make a table and complete it for questions 1 to 12. Make sure you write the correct units. For the calculated circumference give answers correct to one decimal place.

Number	Radius r	Diameter d	Estimated circumference	Calculated circumference
1	2 cm			
2				

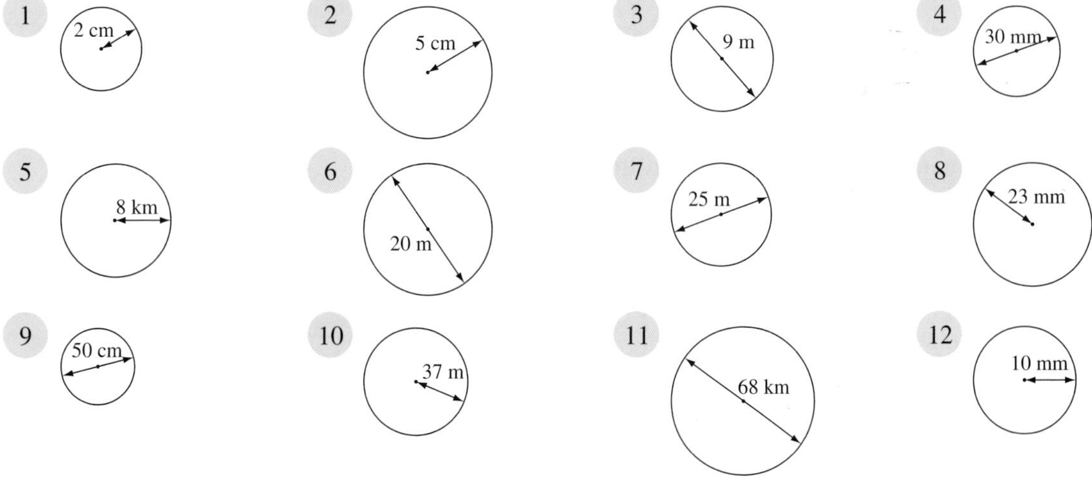

13

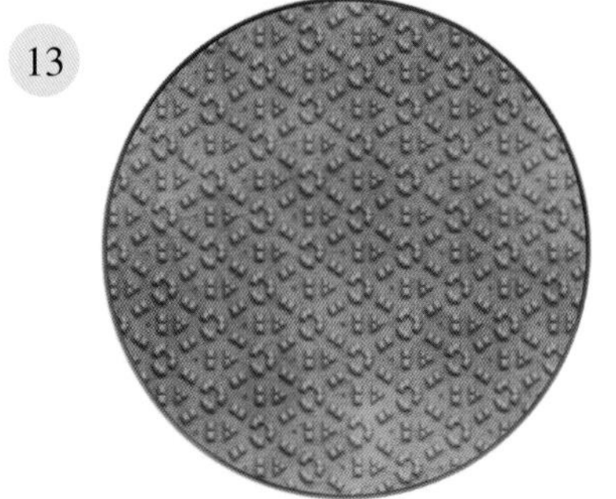

The radius of the man hole cover is 36 cm. Calculate its circumference and give your answer correct to the nearest cm.

14 A circular mirror has diameter 50 cm. Work out its circumference, correct to one decimal place.

15 On an army range a circle of diameter 6 km is 'out of bounds' to all personnel. Calculate the circumference of this circle.

16 The head of a drawing pin is circular with radius 3.5 mm. Find its circumference.

17 In the North Sea a circle of diameter 3 km is prohibited to all shipping because of sandbanks. Calculate the circumference of this circle.

Area of a circle

(a) The circle below is divided into 12 equal sectors

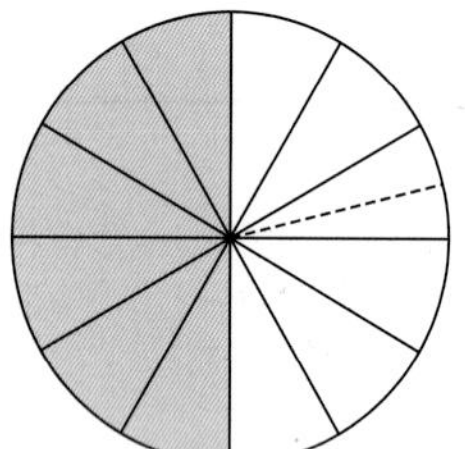

(b) The sectors are cut and arranged to make a shape which is nearly a rectangle. (one sector is cut in half).

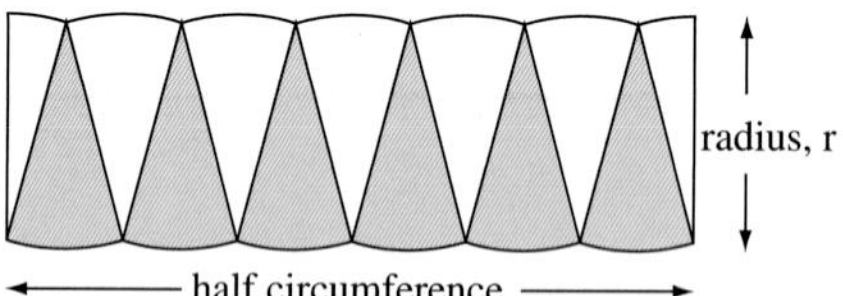

(c) The approximate area can be found as follows:
length of rectangle ≈ half circumference of circle

$$\approx \frac{\pi \times 2r}{2}$$

$$\approx \pi r$$

width of rectangle $\approx r$

$\therefore$ area of rectangle $\approx \pi r \times r$

$$\approx \pi r^2$$

If larger and larger numbers of sectors were used, this approximation would become more and more accurate.

This is a demonstration of an important result.

Area of a circle $= \pi r^2$ *Learn* this formula.

Note: πr^2 means $\pi(r^2)$. i.e. π multiplied by r^2

Find the area of each shape.

(a)

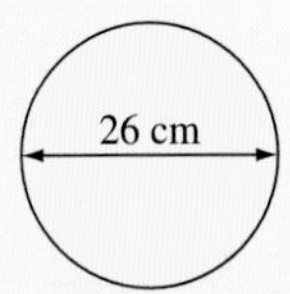

radius = 13 cm

area $= \pi r^2$

$= 530.9 \text{ cm}^2$ (1 d.p.)

On a calculator, press:

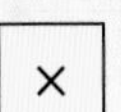

(b)

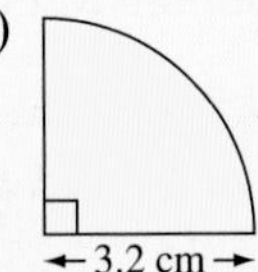

The shape is a quarter circle

area $= \dfrac{\pi(3.2)^2}{4}$

$= 8.0 \text{ cm}^2$ (1 d.p.)

On a calculator, press:

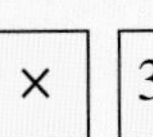

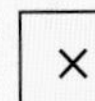

Exercise 2M

Calculate the area of each circle and give your answer correct to one decimal place.

1 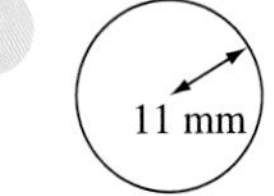

2 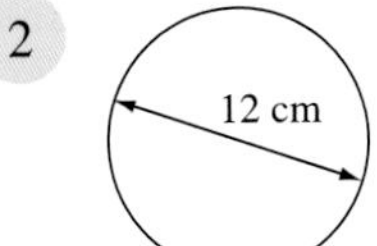

3 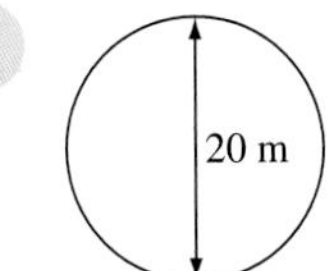

4 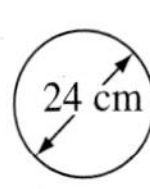

5 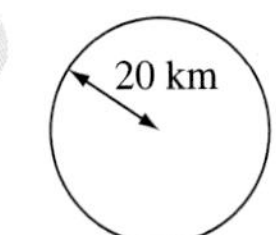

6 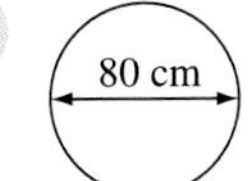

7 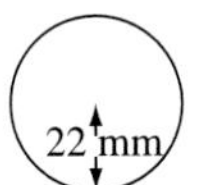

8 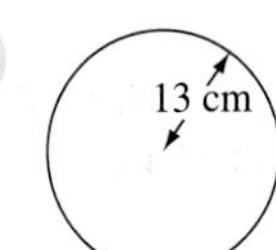

9 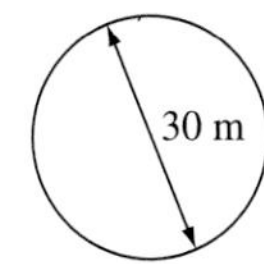

10 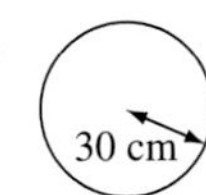

11 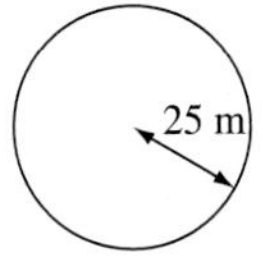

12 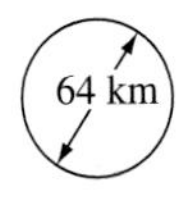

13 The dart board shown has a diameter of 53 cm.
Calculate the area of the dart board.

14 Work out the area of a circular lawn which has a radius of 4.2 m.

15 The top of a mixing bowl is a circle with diameter 33 cm.
Find the area of this circle.

Exercise 2E

Work out the area of each shape and give your answers correct to one decimal place.

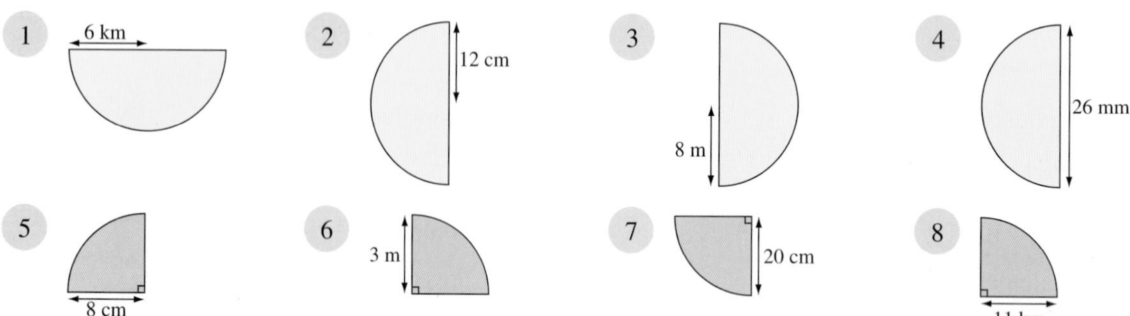

9 A top of a can has a diameter of 6.8 cm. Calculate the circumference and area of the can top.

10 The centre island of a roundabout has radius 32 m. Find the circumference and area of the island.

11 A water-lily leaf is almost circular with diameter 12 cm. Calculate its circumference and area by assuming that it is perfectly circular.

12 An artist paints a circular picture. If its radius is 20 cm, what is its circumference and area?

13 The tyre of a bicycle has a piece of gum stuck to it. The diameter of the tyre is 75 cm. How far does the piece of gum move when the tyre makes one complete revolution?

TEST YOURSELF ON UNITS 5.7 and 5.8

1 Rounding numbers

Round these numbers to the nearest ten.

(a) 561 (b) 2045 (c) 68.5

Round these numbers to one decimal place.

(d) 5.673 (e) 9.15 (f) 0.774 (g) 5.4072

2 Calculating using estimates

Decide, by estimating, which of the three answers is closest to the exact answer.

(a) 81.5×2.24 [1500 150 40]
(b) 0.97×38.4 [40 4 0.4]
(c) $98.1 \div 11.7$ [1 1000 10]
(d) A tin of blackcurrants cost 95p. Estimate the cost of 63 tins.

3 Finding the circumference and area of a circle

(a) Find the circumference of each circle, correct to 1 decimal place.
(b) Find the area of each circle, correct to 1 decimal place.

(i)
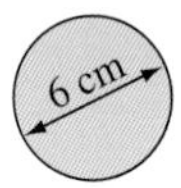

(ii)
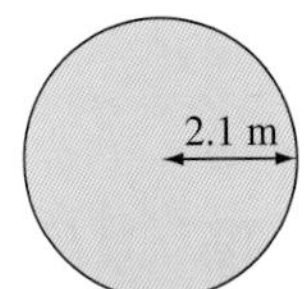

(iii)
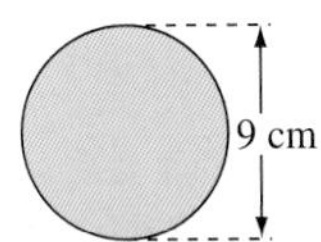

UNIT 5 MIXED REVIEW

Part one

Use a calculator when necessary

1 A cake recipe calls for 500 g of flour to mix with 200 g of sugar. How much sugar should be used if you have only 300 g of flour?

2 Find the total cost:
5 bags of cement at £3.95 per bag
13 m of wire at 40p per m.
8 sockets at 65p each.

Add V.A.T. at $17\frac{1}{2}\%$.

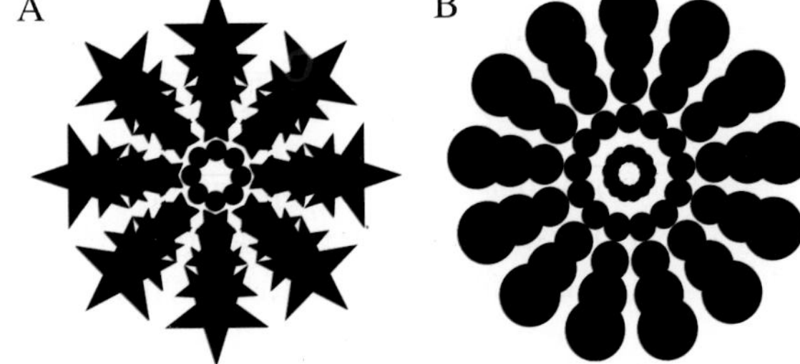

3 (a) How many lines of symmetry has (i) shape A, (ii) shape B?
(b) Describe the rotational symmetry (if any) of (i) shape A
(ii) shape B.

4 How many 5p coins can I exchange for £2.40?

5 Copy and complete by filling in the boxes. You can use any of the numbers 1, 2, 3, 4, 5 but you cannot use a number more than once.

(a) $\square + \square - \square = 7$
(b) $(\square + \square) \div \square = 3$
(c) $(\square + \square) \div (\square - \square) = 1\frac{1}{2}$
(d) $(\square + \square + \square) \times \square = 33$

6 What fraction of the whole figure is shaded green in this diagram?

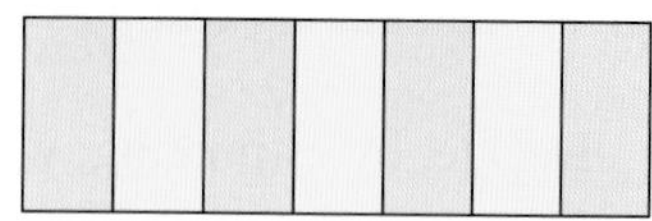

7 Look at this group of numbers...

10, 19, 25, 30, 21

(a) Which of the numbers is a multiple of both 3 and 5?
(b) Which of the numbers is a prime number?
(c) Which of the numbers is a square number?
(d) Which number is a factor of another number in the group?

8 In how many ways can you join the square X to shape Y so that the final shape has line symmetry?

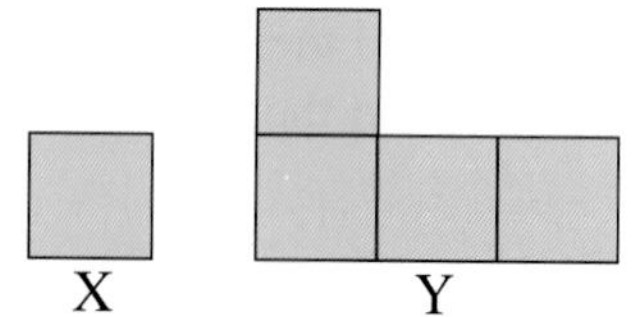

9 On a coordinate grid, plot the points A(1, 4) B(2, 1) C(5, 2).
What are the coordinates of D if ABCD is a square?

10 Two books cost £13.50 in total. One book is one-and-a-half times the price of the other.
How much does each book cost?

11 The temperature in a centrally heated house is recorded every hour from 12.00 till 24.00; the results are shown below.

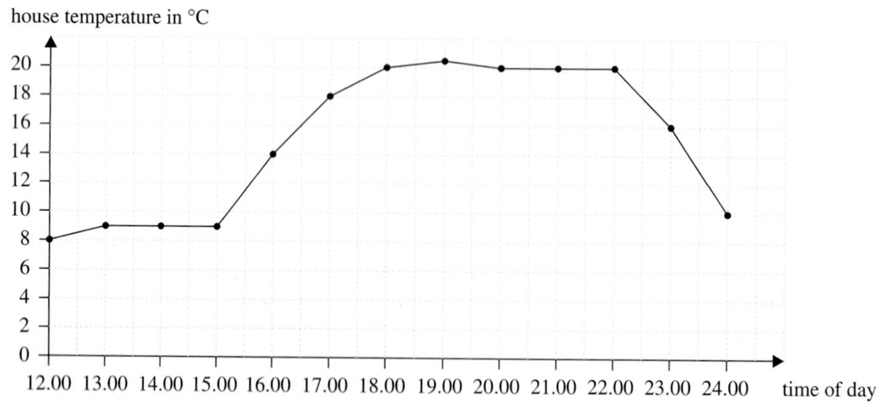

(a) What was the temperature at 20.00?
(b) Estimate the temperature at 16.30.
(c) Estimate the two times when the temperature was 18°C.
(d) When do you think the central heating was switched on?
(e) When do you think the central heating was switched off?

12 Draw a pair of axes with values from 0 to 8.
Plot two corners of a square at (2, 4) and (6, 4).
Find the coordinates of the six possible positions for the other corners of the square.

13

Crash dummies do have feelings! Just before being 'tested' a dummy's heart rate increased from 60 beats per minute by 75%. What is the raised heart rate?

14 Write down these calculations and find the missing digits.

(a)
$$\begin{array}{r} 5\cdot\square\,5 \\ +\;3\cdot7\,\square \\ \hline 9\cdot0\,9 \end{array}$$

(b)
$$\begin{array}{r} 7\cdot\square\,8 \\ -\;3\cdot8\,\square \\ \hline \square\cdot1\,5 \end{array}$$

(c)
$$\begin{array}{r} \square\,3\cdot\square \\ +\;2\,\square\cdot3 \\ \hline 7\,0\cdot0 \end{array}$$

15 (a) Copy the diagram.

(b) Rotate triangle A 90° clockwise around the point (0, 0). Label the image ΔB.

(c) Rotate triangle A 90° anti-clockwise around the point (4, 3). Label the image ΔC.

(d) Translate triangle A 2 units right and 1 unit up. Label the image ΔD.

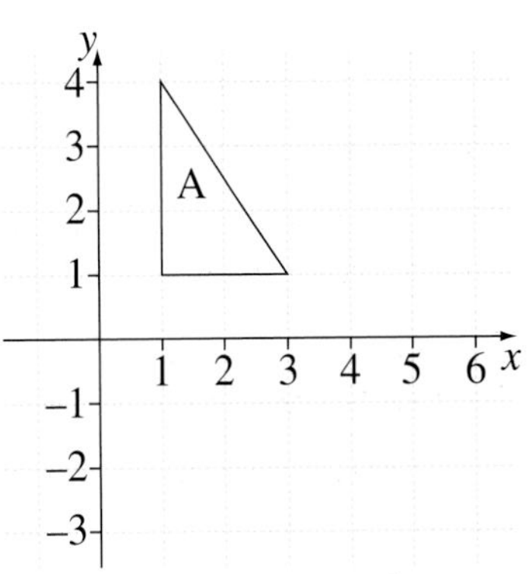

Part two

1 (a) Draw a pair of axes with values from –5 to 5.

(b) Draw and label the following lines

line A: $x = 4$

line B: $y = -2$

line C: $y = x$

(c) Write down the coordinates of the point where

(i) line A meets line B

(ii) line A meets line C

(iii) line B meets line C

(iv) line B cuts the y axis.

2 The price of a dress costing £45 was decreased by 10%. Six months later the price was increased by 10%. Calculate the final price of the dress.

3 An opinion poll was conducted to find out which party people intended to vote for at the next election. The results were.

Conservative	768
Labour	840
Lib Dem	612
Don't know	180

Work out the angles on a pie chart and draw the chart to display the results of the poll.

4 A worker takes 8 minutes to make 12 items.
How long would it take to make 15 items?

5 An advert for toothpaste used a photo of a model's teeth. Sales of the toothpaste rose from 25800 per week by 4%. How many extra tubes were sold?

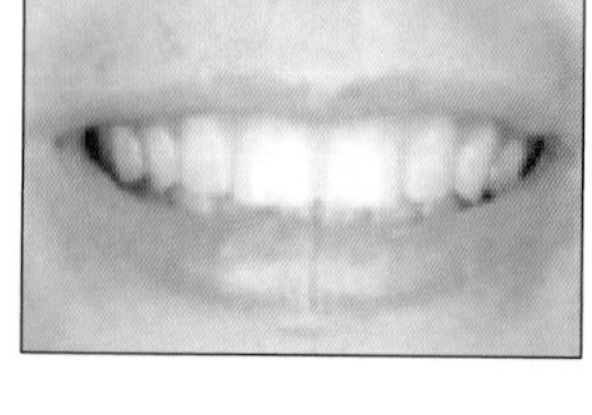

6 A map has a scale of 1 cm to 5 km. A lake appears 3.2 cm long on the map. How long is the actual lake in km?

7 A bag contains 6 coloured balls. One ball is selected at random and then replaced in the bag. This procedure is repeated until 50 selections have been made. Here are the results:
[B = Blue, G = Green, Y = Yellow]

B Y B Y B Y B Y B G B Y B
G B B B B Y G B Y B G B Y
Y B Y Y B B B G B B Y B
B Y B Y G B Y B Y B G B

What do you think were the colours of the balls in the bag?

8 The star shape is made from four triangles like the one shown.

8 10
6

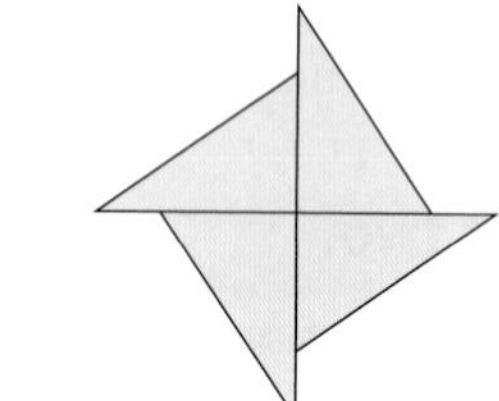

(a) Calculate the area of the star shape.
(b) Calculate the perimeter of the star shape.
(c) Describe the symmetry of the star shape.

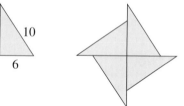

9 The same operations are in each chain of number machines.

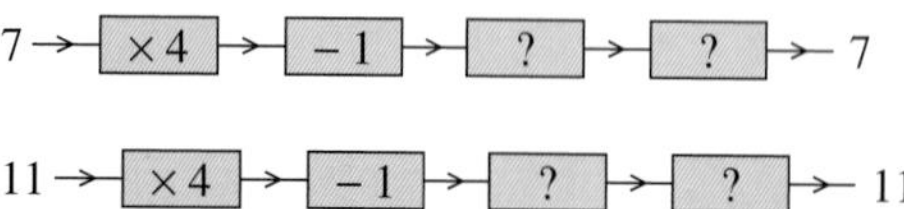

Find the missing operations.

10 (a) Suppose the '5' button on your calculator does not work. Show how you can make your calculator show the number 345.
(b) Suppose none of the numbers 1, 3, 5, 7, 9 work. Show how you can make your calculator show the number 115.

11 In the box is a formula for working out heights. Lindsey's mother is 162 cm tall and her father is 180 cm tall. What is the greatest height to which Lindsey is likely to grow?

> Add the height of each parent.
> Divide by 2
> Add 6 cm to the result.
>
> A girl is likely to be this height plus or minus 7 cm.

12 Use a calculator to work out the following and give your answers correct to 1 decimal place.

(a) $8.62 - \dfrac{1.71}{0.55}$ (b) $\dfrac{8.02 - 6.3}{1.3 + 4.6}$ (c) $\dfrac{5.6}{1.71} - 1.08$

13 Here are some number cards. 6 3 8 2 7

(a) Use two cards to make a fraction which is equal to $\frac{1}{3}$. $\frac{\square}{\square}$

(b) Use three of the cards to make the smallest possible fraction . $\frac{\square}{\square\square}$

14 Mr Gibson the famous balloonist was at a height of 3.2 km when a fault developed and he started to descend at a speed of 10 m/s. How long does Mr Gibson have to fix the problem?

15 Which fraction is closer to one: $\frac{9}{10}$ or $\frac{10}{11}$? Show your working.

16 (a) Calculate the circumference of circle A.
(b) Calculate the area of semi-circle B.

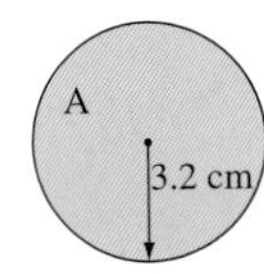

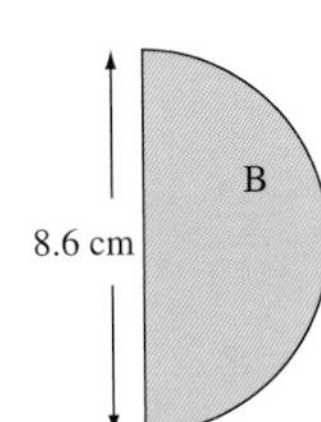

Puzzles and Problems 5

Break the codes

1 The symbols γ, ↑, !, ⊖, ⊥ each stand for one of the digits 1, 2, 3, 5 or 9 but not in that order. Use the clues below to work out what number each symbol stands for.

(a) ↑ × ↑ = ⊥   (b) ⊖ × ↑ = ↑

(c) ⊖ + ⊖ = γ   (d) γ + ↑ = !

2 The ten symbols below each stand for one of the digits 0, 1, 2, 3, 4, 5, 6, 7, 8 or 9 but not that order.

∂ 𝕎 □ ⊙ ↑ ✻ ⧄ △ Φ ⊠

Use the clues below to work out what number each symbol stands for.

(a) ∂ + ∂ + ∂ + ∂ + ∂ = 𝕎
(b) 𝕎 + ⊠ = 𝕎
(c) 𝕎 + ∂ = ⊙
(d) Φ + Φ + Φ + Φ = ↑
(e) ✻ × ✻ = ⧄
(f) ⊙ − Φ = △
(g) ✻ + △ = □

3 The ten symbols used in part 2 are used again but with different values.

(a) ⊠ × ⊙ = ⊙
(b) ⊠ + ⊠ + ⊠ = ✻
(c) ✻ − ⊠ = △
(d) △ × △ × △ = ⊙
(e) ⊙ − ⊠ = ↑
(f) ✻ + 𝕎 = ✻
(g) ⊙ ÷ △ = Φ
(h) ✻ + △ = □
(i) ↑ − ⊠ = ⧄
(j) ∂ − △ = ↑

4 These clues are more difficult to work out.

(a) □ + ↑ = □
(b) ∂ × □ = ∂
(c) ⧄ × ⧄ × ⧄ = ∂
(d) ∂ − ⧄ = Φ
(e) Φ − ⧄ = △
(f) Φ − □ = ⊠
(g) ⊠ + ⧄ = ⊙
(h) 𝕎 + 𝕎 = ✻

Curves from straight lines

- On a sheet of unlined paper draw a circle of radius 8.5 cm and mark 36 equally spaced points on the circle. Use a protractor inside the circle and move around 10° for each point.
- Mark an extra 36 points in between the orininal 36 so that finally you have 72 points equally spaced around the circle.
- Number the points 0, 1, 2, 3,.......72 and after one circuit continue from 73 to 144.
- You can obtain three different patterns as follows:

A (i) Join 0 → 10, 1 → 11, 2 → 12 etc

(ii) Join 0 → 20, 1 → 21, 2 → 22 etc

(iii) Join 0 → 30, 1 → 31, 2 → 32 etc.

B Join each number to double that number.
ie. 1 → 2, 2 → 4, 3 → 6,........

C Join each number to treble that number.
ie. 1 → 3, 2 → 6, 3 → 9,........
For **C** you need to continue numbering points around the circle from 145 to 216.

Mental Arithmetic Practice 5

There are two sets of mental arithmetic questions in this section. Ideally a teacher will read out each question twice, with pupils' books closed. Each test should take about 20 minutes.

Test 1

1. Write 0.07 as a fraction.
2. Jack has £336 and spends £279. How much money does he have left?
3. A triangle has three equal sides. What is its special name?
4. Subtract 0.3 from 5.
5. Write down three factors of 6.
6. What is three-fifths of 40?
7. What is the mean average of 9, 6 and 15?
8. A rectangle of length 6 cm has an area of 21 cm^2. What is the width of the rectangle?
9. Is the difference between 264° and 173° an acute angle or an obtuse angle?
10. Write down a prime number between 24 and 30.
11. How many sixths make up $3\frac{1}{3}$?
12. Sarah is given a bonus of 5% of £440. How much is the bonus?
13. What is the probability of getting a square number if you throw one dice?
14. Donna scores 15 out of 25 in a test. What percentage score is this?
15. What do the angles in a quadrilateral add up to?
16. What is the perimeter of a square whose area is 49 cm^2?
17. Cakes cost 30p each. How many cakes can be bought with £5?
18. If $n = 3$, which is larger: $3n$ or n^2?
19. How many twenty-fours are there in seven hundred and twenty?
20. What is $6 + 4 \times \frac{1}{2}$?
21. What is five per cent of £200 000?
22. A hose of length 170 m is cut in half. How long is each piece?
23. A car travels 50 m in 10 seconds. How far will it go in 10 minutes?
24. Three angles of a quadrilateral are 80°, 90° and 100°. What is the fourth angle?
25. Add together two cubed and three cubed.

Test 2

1. Find 25% of 880.
2. Work out 301–102.
3. What number is eleven less than two thousand?
4. Write 20% as a fraction.
5. 4 apples cost 96p. What is the cost of 6 apples?
6. What is the difference between six squared and two squared?
7. A triangle has two angles of 38° and 67°. What is the size of the third angle?
8. What is $-3 - (-4)$?
9. How many lines of symmetry does a parallelogram have?
10. What is the median of 1, 2, 3 and 4?

11 There are 12 beads in a bag. Seven of the beads are red. I take out one bead from the bag. What is the probability that the bead is *not* red?

12 Don buys a book for £5.35 and a drink costing 57p. How much change does he get from a £10 note?

13 What is 600 divided by 25?

14 How many fifty pence coins make £103.50?

15 What is the product of 3, 4 and 5?

16 A car travels 4 miles in 5 minutes. How far will it travel in one hour?

17 Find five-sevenths of 42.

18 What number is next in the pattern 1, 3, 6, 10, …?

19 How many seconds are there in one hour?

20 I treble a number and add 6. The answer is equal to half of 84. What was the number?

21 True or false '8 miles is about 5 km'.

22 Write down the sum of the numbers from one to five.

23 If apples cost 55p for 200g, how much will 2 kg cost?

24 What is a quarter of six hundred and forty?

25 What is ten cubed take away one cubed?

A long time ago! 5

Roman numerals

Many clock faces still use roman numerals like IV and XI. At the end of a film, the year in which the film was made is often given using roman numerals.
MCMLXXX means 1980.

I	one	XI	eleven
II	two	XII	twelve
III	three	XX	twenty
IV	four (one before five)	XXX	thirty
V	five	XL	forty (ten before fifty)
VI	six	L	fifty
VII	seven	LX	sixty
VIII	eight	C	hundred
IX	nine (one before ten)	CM	nine hundred
X	ten	M	thousand

Note

When we reach 10 before 50, we write XL not XXXX. Your teacher may explain this more fully.

Exercise

1 Write down the value of each of the numbers written below in roman numerals.

(a) VII (b) XIII (c) XVI (d) XXVII

(e) XVIII (f) XIX (g) XLV (h) LXXII

(i) CCCXXVII (j) XCIV (k) MMVI (l) CMXLIX

2 Write these numbers in roman numerals.

(a) 8 (b) 17 (c) 22

(d) 58 (e) 39 (f) 84

(g) 78 (h) 123 (i) 339

(j) 1265 (k) 1066 (l) 3194

3 Write this year in roman numerals.

4 Work out the questions below, giving your answers in roman numerals.

(a) VI + III (b) IX + VIII (c) XIII + XVII

(d) XL – VI (e) LIII – XVIII (f) C – XLVII

(g) LXXV + CCXXXVI (h) V × II (i) IV × IX

(j) CCCXII – CLXXIX (k) VII × VI (l) VII × XII

(m) XXIV ÷ III (n) L ÷ X (o) CXX ÷ XX

(p) XXXVI ÷ IX (q) MCC ÷ XXX (r) MCCV + CCXXVIII – XCIV

5 **RESEARCH:**

(a) In the ancient Greek number system, Δ was the symbol for 10. Find out the ancient Greek symbol for (i) 100 and (ii) 50.

(b) Find the ancient Egyptian symbols for (i) 10 (ii) 100 and (iii) 1000.

(c) Find out three more ancient Egyptian symbols and sketch them as carefully as you can.

(d) Can you find out why particular letters are used for certain roman numerals?
For example, why is C used for 100?

UNIT 6

6.1 More equations

In section 6.1 you will:

- review equations covered in section 4.6

Remember with equations:

You may do the same thing to both sides

Exercise 1M

1 Solve the equations below.

(a) $n - 7 = 9$ (b) $4x = 28$ (c) $8y = 40$

(d) $\frac{w}{3} = 12$ (e) $\frac{m}{9} = 9$ (f) $3n = 1$

2 Now solve these equations:

(a) $2w + 8 = 24$ (b) $7y - 5 = 9$ (c) $6x - 8 = 16$

(d) $5m + 12 = 62$ (e) $5n - 3 = 1$ (f) $7p + 4 = 6$

3 I think of a number, multiply it by 9 and add 14. The answer is 68. Write down an equation then solve it to find the number.

4 Solve these equations:

(a) $7y - 2 = 2$ (b) $13n + 10 = 12$ (c) $6m - 15 = 33$

(d) $5w - 2 = 1$ (e) $9n + 8 = 71$ (f) $7x + 5 = 8$

5 Solve

(a) $5 = 6x + 4$ (b) $10 = 7 + 8m$ (c) $6 = 5 + 2w$

(d) $13 = 10n + 6$ (e) $6 = 12m - 1$ (f) $2 = 8x - 5$

6 Lois thinks of a number. She multiplies it by 7 and subtracts 3. The answer is 5.

Write down an equation then solve it to find the number.

7 Solve

(a) $3w + 20 = 95$ (b) $\frac{1}{4}x = 9$ (c) $2p + \frac{1}{2} = 1$

(d) $5m + 8 = 8$ (e) $5y - 75 = 425$ (f) $10n = \frac{1}{2}$

(a) Any answers with fractions must be cancelled if possible.

Solve $6x + 7 = 11$

(−7) (−7)

$6x = 4$

(÷6) (÷6)

$x = \frac{4}{6}$

cancel down

$x = \frac{2}{3}$

(b) Multiply out any brackets first.

Solve $3(2x - 4) = 18$

$6x - 12 = 18$

(+12) (+12)

$6x = 30$

(÷6) (÷6)

$x = 5$

Exercise 1E

1 Solve these equations:

(a) $8n + 3 = 9$ (b) $10w - 5 = 3$ (c) $4y - 7 = 7$

(d) $20x - 13 = 57$ (e) $11 = 9 + 6m$ (f) $3 = 8p - 9$

2 Solve

(a) $5(x + 2) = 25$ (b) $7(2x - 1) = 21$ (c) $4(3x - 2) = 28$

(d) $2(4x + 5) = 50$ (e) $10(x - 4) = 50$ (f) $6(2x + 7) = 78$

3 [Rectangle with width n and length $2n + 7$]

n

$2n + 7$

The perimeter of this rectangle is 44 cm. Write down an equation involving n then solve it to find the actual length and width of this rectangle.

4 Solve these equations:

(a) $15 = 7 + 10m$ (b) $4(2x + 3) = 16$ (c) $5(4x - 3) = 15$

(d) $40 = 8(n - 2)$ (e) $4y - 7 = 15$ (f) $3(6p + 5) = 21$

5 Abbie is 8 years older than her sister. Her sister is 3 years older than her brother. The sum of their ages is 50. Let Abbie's age be x. Write down an equation involving x then solve it to find Abbie's age.

6 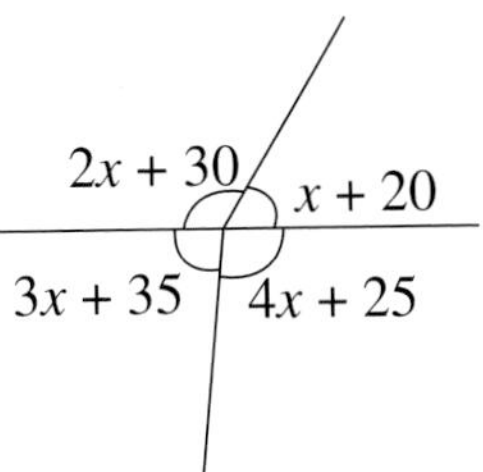

Write down an equation involving x then solve it to find the value of each angle.

7 Solve

(a) $52 = 3 + 7p$ (b) $4 = 9w - 3$ (c) $2n + 6 = 11$
(d) $6d - 3 = 8$ (e) $0 = 3(2x - 8)$ (f) $5(4m + 1) = 20$
(g) $1 = 8n - 9$ (h) $2(6y - 5) = 20$ (i) $7 = 3 + 16q$

6.2 Sequence rules

In section 6.2 you will learn how to:

- find rules for sequences

- Here is a sequence of shapes made from sticks

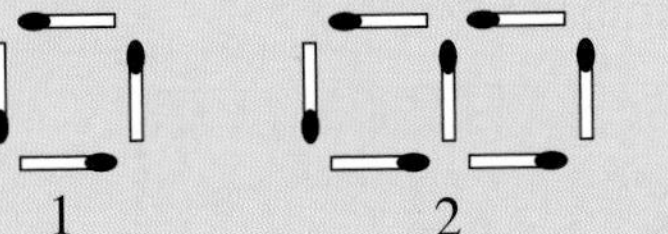
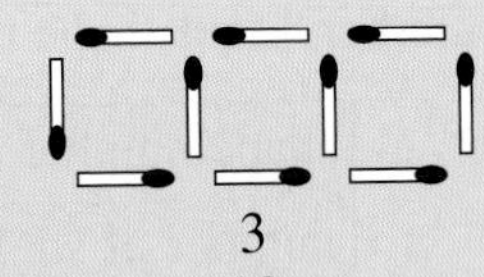

Shape number:	1	2	3
Number of sticks:	4	7	10

- There is a *rule* or *formula* which we can use to calculate the number of sticks for any shape number.
  '*The number of sticks is three times the shape number add one*'.
  Check that this rule works for all the shapes above and also for shape number 4 which you can draw.
- We could also write the rule using symbols. Let n stand for the diagram number and let s stand for the number of sticks.
  The rule (or formula) is '$s = 3n + 1$'.

Exercise 1M

1 Here is a sequence of triangles made from sticks.

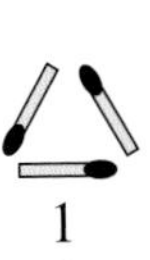

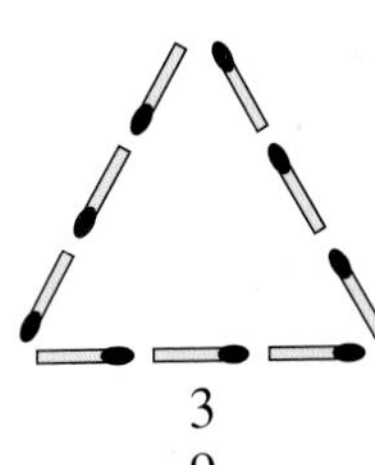

Shape number:	1	2	3
Number of sticks:	3	6	9

(a) Draw shape number 4 and count the number of sticks.
(b) Write down and complete the rule for the number of sticks in a shape:
'The number of sticks is ____ times the shape number'.

2 Here is a sequence of 'steps' made from sticks

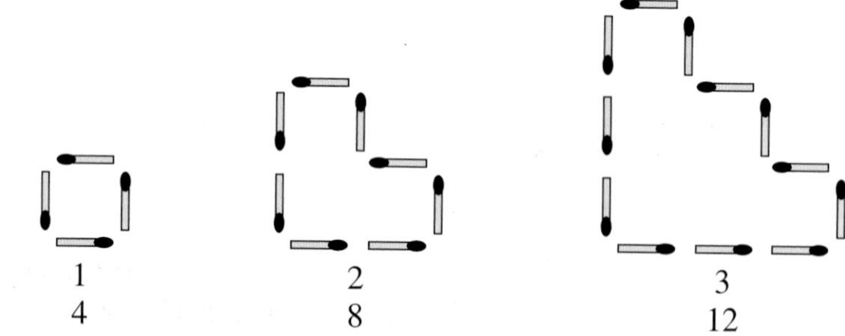

Shape number:	1	2	3
Number of sticks:	4	8	12

(a) Draw shape number 4 and count the number of sticks.
(b) Write down the rule for the number of sticks in a shape. 'The number of sticks is ____ times the shape number'.

3 Louise makes a pattern of triangles from sticks.

Shape number:	1	2	3
Number of sticks:	3	5	7

(a) Draw shape number 4 and shape number 5
(b) Make a table:

shape number	1	2	3	4	5
number of sticks	3	5	7		

(c) Write down the rule for the number of sticks in a shape.
'The number of sticks is ____ times the shape number and then add ____.'

4 Crosses are drawn on 'dotty' paper to make a sequence.

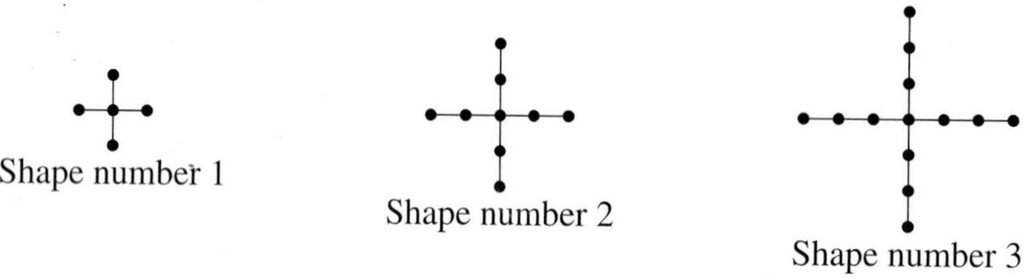

(a) Draw shape number 4
(b) Make a table:

shape number	1	2	3	4
number of dots	5	9	13	

(c) Write down the rule.

'The number of dots is _____ times the shape number and then add _____.'

5 In these diagrams black squares are surrounded on three sides by yellow squares. Let the number of black squares be b and let the number of yellow squares be y.

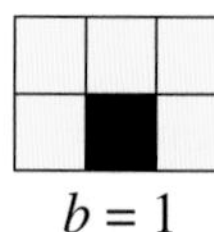
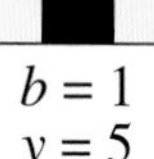
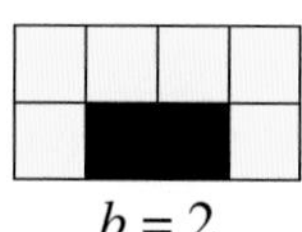
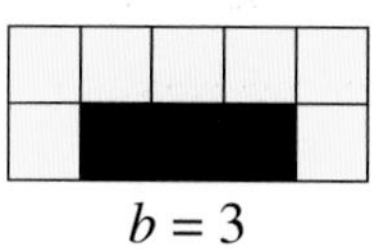

$b = 1$ $y = 5$ $b = 2$ $y = 6$ $b = 3$ $y = 7$

(a) Draw the next diagram which has 4 black squares.
(b) Write down the rule.
'The number of yellow squares is ....'

6 Look again at questions 1, 2, 3, and 4. Use n for the shape number and s for the number of sticks or dots. For each question write the rule connecting n and s without using words. In each question write '$s =$.'

- Here is a sequence 4, 8, 12, 16, ...

The first term is	4×1
The second term is	4×2
The third term is	4×3
⋮	⋮
The 30th term is	4×30

Consider a term n. We call this the nth term.
The nth term is $4 \times n$ in this sequence.

n^{th} term $= 4n$

This formula can be used to find any term in the sequence

eg. 15th term $= 4n = 4 \times 15 = 60$
100th term $= 4n = 4 \times 100 = 400$

- In another sequence the nth term is $3n + 2$

1st term $= 3 \times 1 + 2$ ($n = 1$) $= 5$
2nd term $= 3 \times 2 + 2$ ($n = 2$) $= 8$
3rd term $= 3 \times 3 + 2$ ($n = 3$) $= 11$

Exercise 2M

1 The nth term of a sequence is $6n$. What is the value of:

(a) the first term (use $n = 1$)
(b) the second term (use $n = 2$)
(c) the tenth term (use $n = 10$)

2 The nth term of a sequence is $2n + 5$. What is the value of:

(a) the first term (use $n = 1$)
(b) the fifth term (use $n = 5$)
(c) the one hundredth term (use $n = 100$)

3 Write down the first four terms of each sequence using the nth term given.

(a) $7n$ (b) $n + 3$ (c) $3n + 1$ (d) $25 - n$ (e) $4n + 7$

4 Match up each sequence and the correct formula for the nth term from the list given.

(a) 10, 20, 30, 40, …
(b) 3, 6, 9, 12, …
(c) 5, 9, 13, 17, …
(d) 50, 100, 150, 200, …
(e) $1^2, 2^2, 3^2, 4^2$, …
(f) 8, 10, 12, 14, …
(g) 11, 14, 17, 20, …
(h) 12, 24, 36, 48, …

$3n$

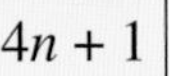

$50n$

$10n$

$12n$ $2n + 6$

n^2 $3n + 8$

5

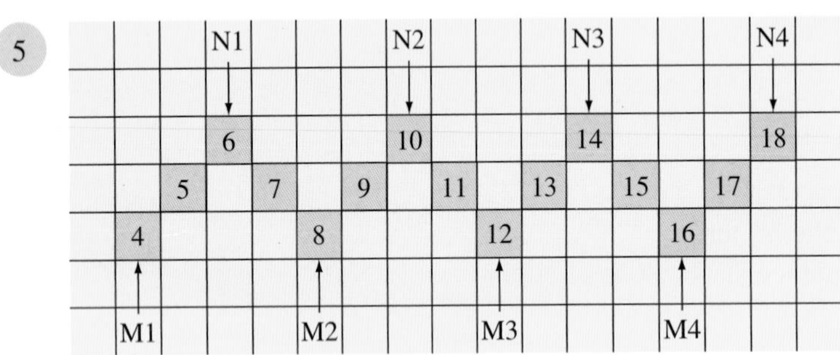

The numbers N1, N2, N3, N4 and M1, M2, M3, M4 form two sequences.

(a) Find M5, M6, N5, N6.
(b) Think of rules and use them to find M15 and N20.

6 Here is a sequence of touching squares.
Copy and complete the table.

Square number	Coordinates of centre
1	(2, 2)
2	(4, 4)
3	
5	
40	
45	

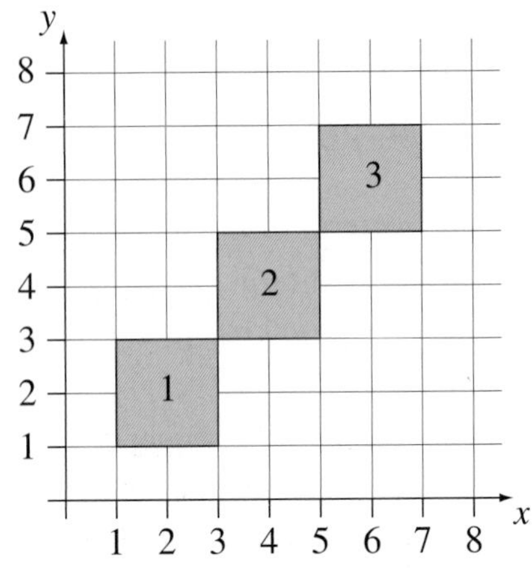

7 Here is a sequence of touching triangles.
Find the coordinates of:

(a) the top of triangle 5
(b) the top of triangle 50
(c) the bottom right corner of triangle 50
(d) the bottom right corner of triangle 100.

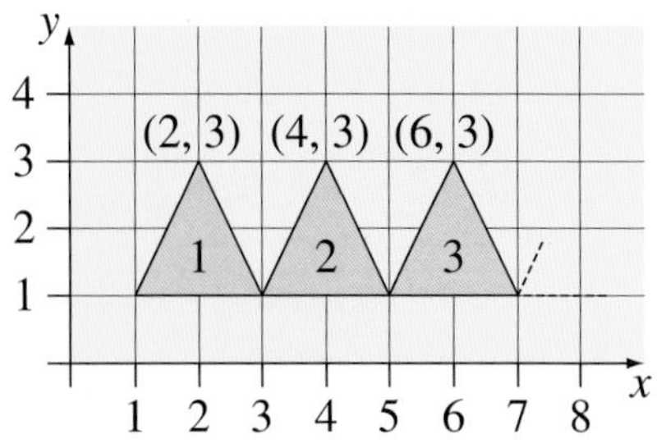

8 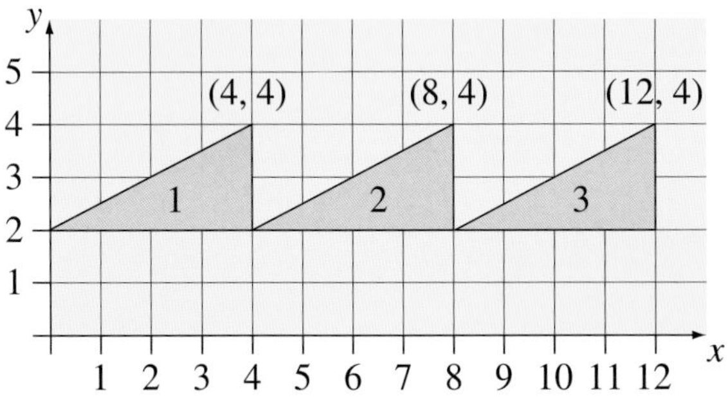 Find the coordinates of the top vertex of:

(a) triangle 4
(b) triangle 20
(c) triangle 2000.

9 Write down the coordinates of the centres of squares 1, 2 and 3.
Find the coordinates of:

(a) the centre of square 4
(b) the centre of square 10
(c) the top vertex of square 70.

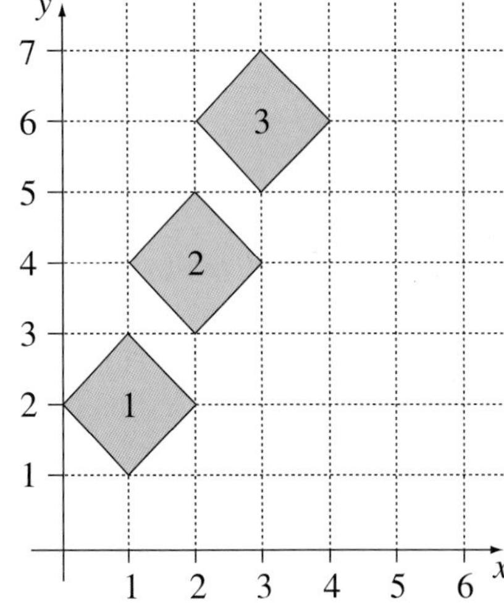

10 Write down the coordinates of the centres of the first six squares shown on the diagram at the top of the next page.

Find the coordinates of:

(a) the centre of square 60
(b) the centre of square 73
(c) the top left corner of square 90
(d) the top left corner of square 101.

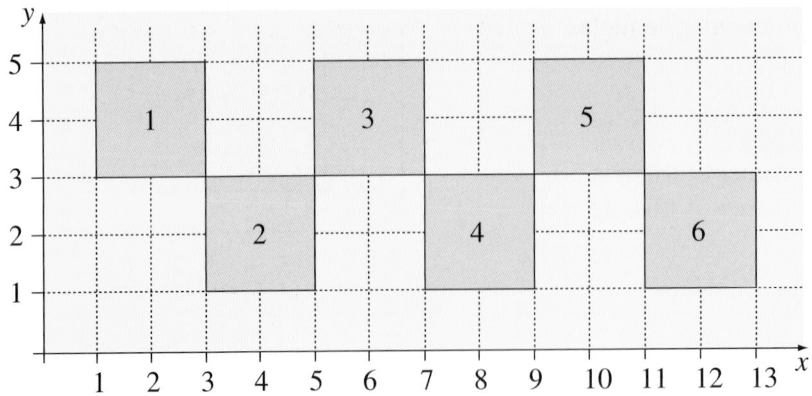

11 Now design some patterns of your own.

Investigation – count the crossovers

Two straight lines have a maximum of one crossover

Three straight lines have a maximum of three crossovers.

Notice that you can have less than three crossovers if the lines all go through one point. Or the lines could be parallel.
In this work we are interested only in the *maximum* number of crossovers.

Four lines have a maximum of six crossovers.

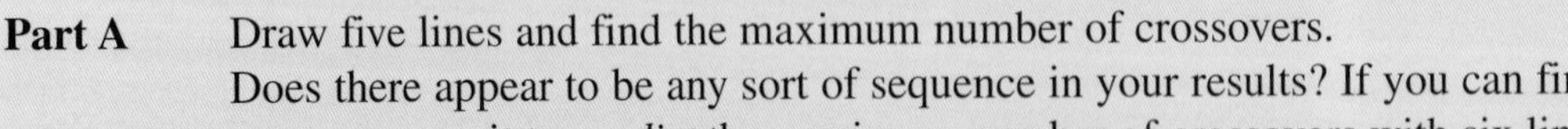

Part A Draw five lines and find the maximum number of crossovers.
Does there appear to be any sort of sequence in your results? If you can find a sequence, use it to *predict* the maximum number of crossovers with six lines.

Part B Now draw six lines and count the crossovers to see if your prediction was correct (remember not to draw three lines through one point).

Part C Predict the number of crossovers for seven lines and then check if your prediction is correct by drawing a diagram.

Part D Write your results in a table:

Number of lines	Number of crossovers
2	1
3	3
4	6
5	
6	

Predict the number of crossovers for 20 lines.

Part E Predict the number of crossovers for 2000 lines (you will need to work out a formula).

CHECK YOURSELF ON SECTIONS 6.1 and 6.2

1 Review of equations covered in section 4.6

Solve the equations below.

(a) $5n - 17 = 28$ (b) $\frac{m}{7} = 8$ (c) $15 = 7y + 10$

(d) $4 = 6w - 1$ (e) $3(2x - 5) = 39$ (f) $54 = 2(4p + 3)$

2 Finding rules for sequences

In these diagrams blue squares are surrounded by green squares.

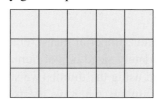

(a) Draw the next diagram which has 4 blue squares.

(b) Make a table. Fill in the missing values.

number of blue squares	1	2	3	4
number of green squares	8	10		

(c) Complete the rule:
'The number of green squares is ____ times the number of blue squares and then add ____.'

(d) Using g for the number of green squares and b for the number of blue squares, write down a formula for g in terms of b.

(e) The nth term of a different sequence is $4n + 3$. What is the value of the tenth term of this sequence?

6.3 Metric and imperial units

In section 6.3 you will learn how to:

- convert metric units
- convert imperial units
- convert between metric and imperial units
- change units for some problems

Metric units

Length	Mass	Volume
1 cm = 10 mm	1 g = 1000 mg	1 millilitre (ml) = 1 cm^3
1 m = 100 cm	1 kg = 1000 g	1 litre = 1000 ml
1 km = 1000 m	1 tonne = 1000 kg	

Exercise 1M

Copy and complete

1. 5.9 m = ☐ cm
2. 9.13 kg = ☐ g
3. 700 g = ☐ kg
4. 3.5 km = ☐ m
5. 43 mm = ☐ cm
6. 70 cm = ☐ m
7. 4 litres = ☐ ml
8. 2500 kg = ☐ t
9. 2.4 kg = ☐ g
10. 300 mm = ☐ m
11. 509 g = ☐ kg
12. 0.2 m = ☐ cm
13. 7.4 litres = ☐ ml
14. 60 g = ☐ kg
15. 62 litres = ☐ ml
16. 3.7 m = ☐ mm
17. 9.5 g = ☐ mg
18. 3 g = ☐ kg
19. 4 litres = ☐ cm^3
20. 5.02 kg = ☐ g

Imperial units

We still use imperial units. Imperial measurements were made by using appropriately sized bits of human being. The inch was measured using the thumb (we still sometimes say 'rule of thumb' when we mean rough measurement), the foot by using the foot.

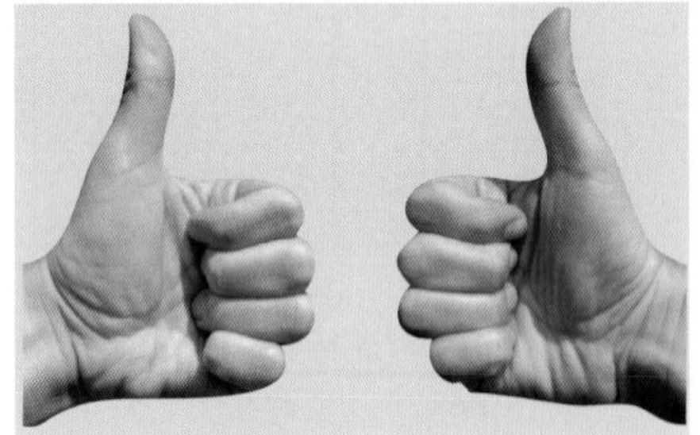

Imperial units

Length	Mass	Volume
1 foot = 12 inches	1 pound = 16 ounces	1 gallon = 8 pints
1 yard = 3 feet	1 stone = 14 pounds	
1 mile = 1760 yards	1 ton = 2240 pounds	

Exercise 1E

Copy and complete

1. 4 feet = ☐ inches
2. 6 yards = ☐ feet
3. 8 stones = ☐ pounds
4. 5 pounds = ☐ ounces
5. 60 inches = ☐ feet
6. $\frac{1}{4}$ pound = ☐ ounces
7. 3 feet 2 inches = ☐ inches
8. 7 stones 9 pounds = ☐ pounds
9. 4 tons = ☐ pounds
10. 6 feet 5 inches = ☐ inches
11. 5 miles = ☐ yards
12. 8 yards 2 feet = ☐ feet
13. 4 stones 6 pounds = ☐ pounds
14. $1\frac{1}{2}$ gallons = ☐ pints

15 1 mile = □ feet

16 1 ton = □ ounces

17 28 pints = □ gallons

18 5 stones 7 pounds = □ pounds

19 $5\frac{1}{2}$ tons = □ pounds

20 3 yards 2 feet 8 inches = □ inches

Converting between metric and imperial units

1 inch ≈ 2.5 cm	1 kg ≈ 2.2 pounds
1 foot ≈ 30 cm	30 g ≈ 1 ounce
8 km ≈ 5 miles	1 gallon ≈ 4.5 litres

'≈' means 'is approximately equal to'

Divide or multiply by the appropriate number shown above.

(a) 3 feet ≈ 90 cm (× 30)

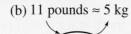

(b) 11 pounds ≈ 5 kg (÷ 2.2)

(c) 3 gallons ≈ 13.5 litres (× 4.5)

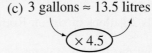

Exercise 2M

1 

Danny puts 8 gallons of petrol into his car. *Roughly* how many litres of petrol did Danny put into his car?

Copy and complete questions 2 to 10

2 4 kg ≈ □ pounds

3 10 gallons ≈ □ litres

4 16 km ≈ □ miles

5 8 inches ≈ □ cm

6 44 pounds ≈ □ kg

7 3 m ≈ □ feet

8 30 miles ≈ □ km

9 90 g ≈ □ ounces

10 5 feet 4 inches ≈ □ cm

11 Copy each sentence and choose the number which is the best estimate.

(a) The Prime Minister is about [1 m, 6 feet, 8 feet] tall.
(b) A can of coke contains about [350 ml, 2 litres, 10 ml].
(c) The perimeter of a classroom is about [30 m, 6 m, $\frac{1}{10}$ mile].
(d) The width of one of my fingers is about [1 mm, 5 mm, 10 mm].
(e) A bag of crisps weighs about [25 g, 500 g, 1 pound].

12 Suppose you have just won a prize which is one million grams of gold! Which of the following would you need to take away your prize?

(a) A large suitcase (b) A van (c) A very large delivery lorry

13 The maximum height limit for children on a bouncy castle is four feet 6 inches. Julie is 132 cm tall. Is Julie inside the limit?

14 Phil has cycled 24 km from his house. His total journey will be 19 miles. How many *more* miles does he have to cycle?

15 Rosa needs 2 gallons of petrol. Roughly how much will it cost if petrol costs £1.04 per litre?

16 A restaurant needs 9 kg of potatoes for one evening. It has 20 pounds of potatoes. Will the restaurant have enough potatoes?

17 A boxer must weigh no more than 10 stones just before his fight. With two days to go he weighs 65 kg. Roughly how much weight in pounds does he have to lose to get down to the 10 stone limit?

18 A carpenter requires a 12 mm drill for a certain job but he has only the imperial sizes $\frac{1}{4}, \frac{1}{2}$ and $\frac{3}{4}$ inch. Which of these drills is the closest in size to 12 mm?

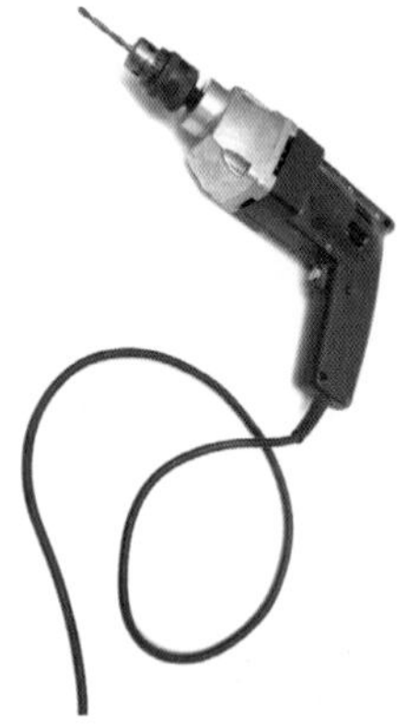

19 Put these amounts in order starting with the largest.

(a) 0.55 m, 7 inches, 16 cm, 2 feet, 50 cm
(b) 0.4 kg, 1.1 pound, 0.48 kg, 9 ounces, 450 g

20 Grass seed should be sown at the rate of $\frac{2}{3}$ of an ounce per square yard. One packet of seed contains 3 pounds (lb) of seed. How many packets of seed are needed for a rectangular garden measuring 54 feet by 30 feet? [3 feet = 1 yard, 16 ounces = 1 pound (lb)]

Changing units

When a problem has quantities measured in different units the first thing you must do is change some of the units so that all quantities are in the same units.

1.5 m 80 cm

(a) Find the area of the rectangular table top shown.
Write 80 cm as 0.8 m.
Area of table = 1.5×0.8.
= 1.2 m^2.

(b) A piece of metal weighing 3 kg is melted down and cast into small cubes each weighing 40 g.
How many cubes can be made?
Write 3 kg as 3000 g.
Number of cubes = $3000 \div 40$
= 75.

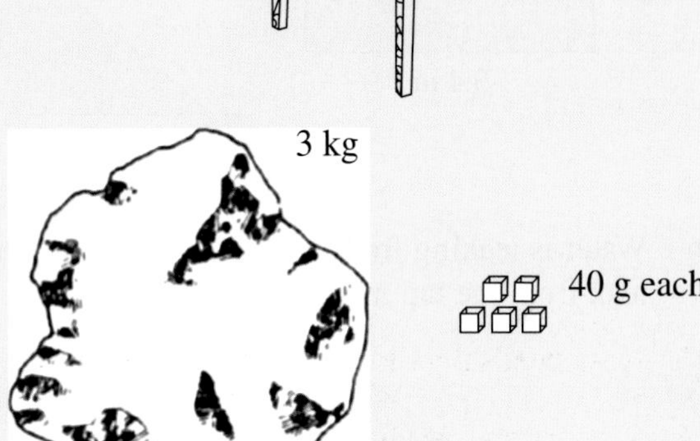

A *very* common error occurs where the units of an area are changed.

Here is a square of side 1 m.

Area = 1 m^2 (1 m by 1 m)

The same square has sides of 100 cm.

Area = 10000 cm^2 (100 cm by 100 cm)

We see that 1 m^2 = 10000 cm^2 [NOT 100 cm^2!]

Exercise 2E

You may use a calculator in this exercise.

1. A piece of gold weighing 0.9 kg is melted down and cast into tiny coins each weighing 180 mg. How many coins can be made?

2. An urn containing 45 litres of water is used to fill cups of capacity 150 ml. How many cups can be filled?

3 A large lump of 'playdoh' weighing 2.1 kg is cut up into 300 identical pieces. Find the weight of each piece in grams.

4 Polly buys 3 bags of sugar weighing 0.6 kg each, a tube of toothpaste weighing 225 g and 12 packets of crisps each weighing 25 g. Find the total weight of these items in kg.

5 Find the area of each shape in m^2.

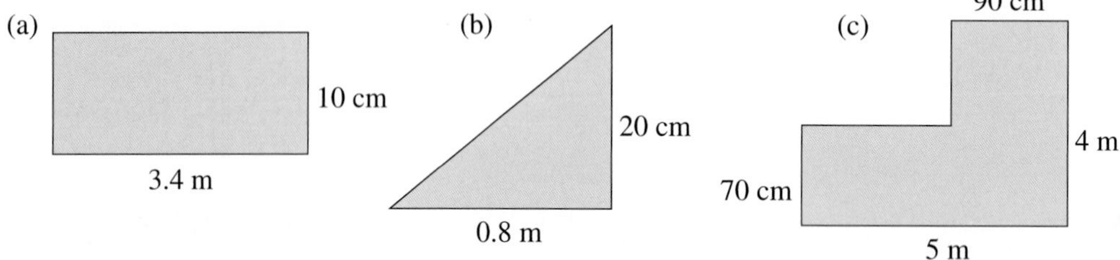

6 Water is leaking from a tap at a rate of 1.3 cm^3 per second. How many litres of water will leak from the tap in one day?

7

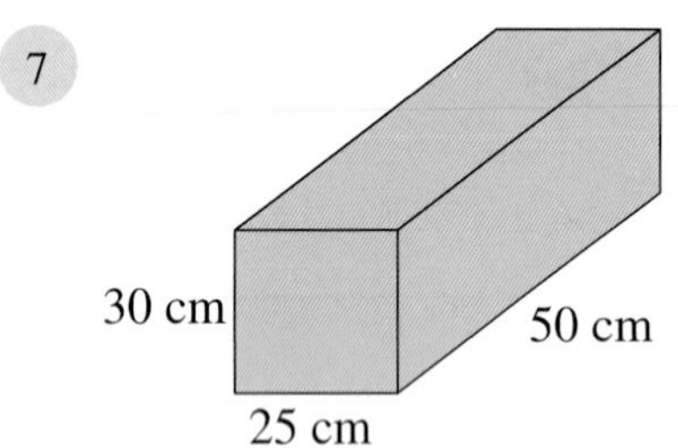

Every face of the rectangular block shown is painted. The tin of paint used contains enough paint to cover an area of 10 m^2. How many blocks can be painted completely?

8 Calculate the area of each shape in cm^2.

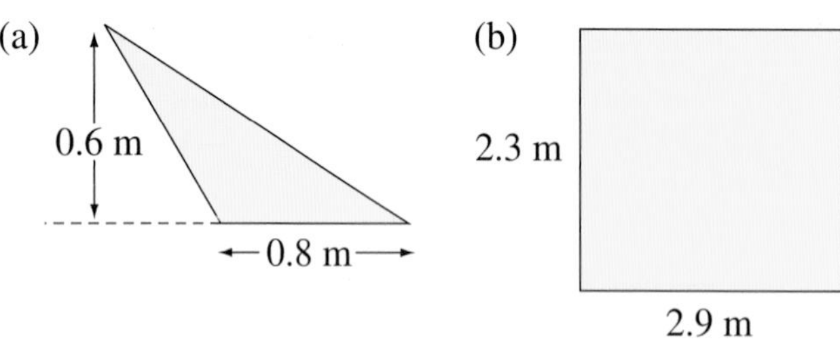

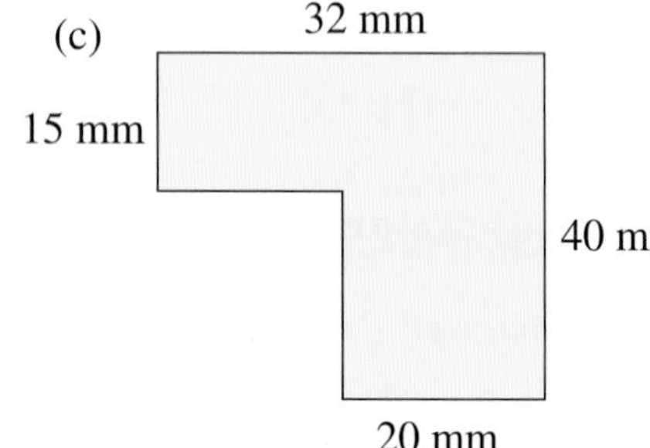

9 The diagram shows the outline of a strip of farmland.

(a) Calculate the area of the field in hectares
[1 hectare = 10 000 m^2]

(b) The field is sprayed with a pesticide and it takes 3 seconds to spray 100 m^2. How many hours will it take to spray the entire field?

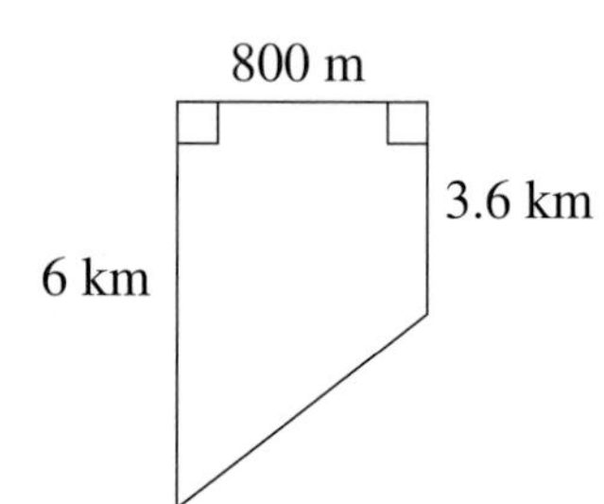

10 The waterfall with the greatest flow of water in the world is the 'Guaira' between Brazil and Paraguay. Its estimated average flow is 13 000 m^3 per second. The dome of St Paul's Cathedral has a capacity of 7800 m^3. How long would it take the waterfall to fill the dome?

CHECK YOURSELF ON SECTION 6.3

1 Converting metric units

Copy and complete:

(a) 7.65 km = ☐ m

(b) 0.4 m = ☐ cm

(c) 7500 ml = ☐ litres

2 Converting imperial units

Copy and complete:

(a) $\frac{1}{2}$ pound = ☐ ounces

(b) $2\frac{3}{4}$ gallons = ☐ pints

(c) 72 inches = ☐ feet

3 Converting between metric and imperial units

(a) Ed is 6 feet tall. Mo is 1.75 m tall. Roughly how many cm is Ed taller than Mo?
(b) Jade fills her car with 12 gallons of petrol, costing her £57.24. How much per litre did the petrol cost?

4 Changing units for some problems

(a) Which rectangle has the larger area and by how much?

Rectangle P: 70 cm by 0.9 m

Rectangle Q: 30 cm by 2 m

(b) In a forest a young tree grows at a constant rate of 18 cm per day. How much in mm does it grow in one minute?

6.4 Angles and constructions

In section 6.4 you will:

- review angle work from unit 2
- construct bisectors of lines and angles

Review of angle work

Exercise 1M

1

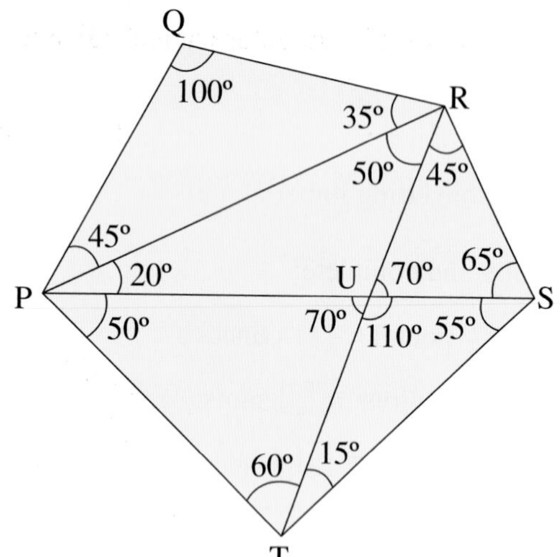

Write down the value of each angle listed below:

(a) $P\hat{R}Q$

(b) $T\hat{S}U$

(c) $R\hat{P}T$

(d) $R\hat{T}S$

(e) $R\hat{S}T$

2 Use a protractor to draw the following angles accurately:

(a) 65° (b) 110° (c) 170° (d) 300° (e) 73° (f) 285°

3 Which angles in question 2 are *reflex*?

4 Find the angles marked with letters.

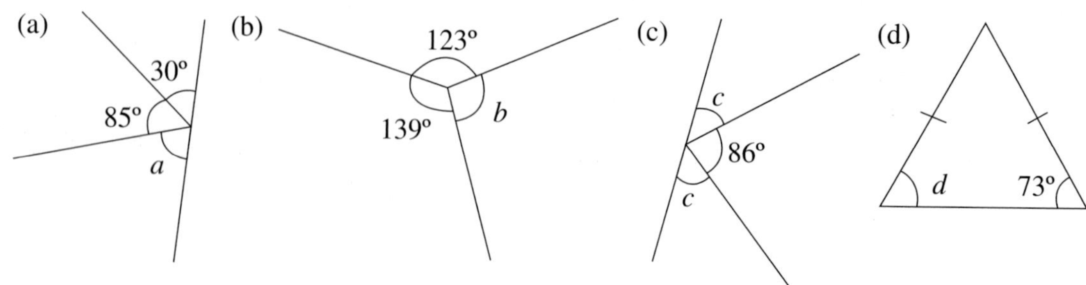

5 Find the angles marked with letters.

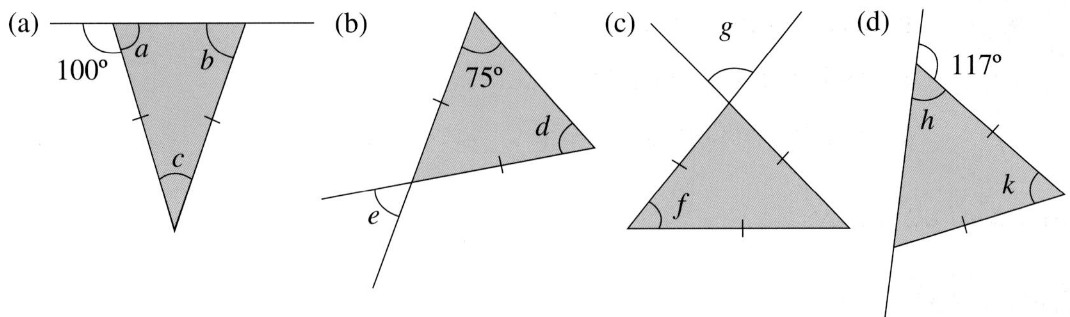

6 If you add together two acute angles, will the answer always be an obtuse angle? Give a reason for your answer.

7 If you add together two obtuse angles, will the answer always be a reflex angle. Explain your answer.

8

9

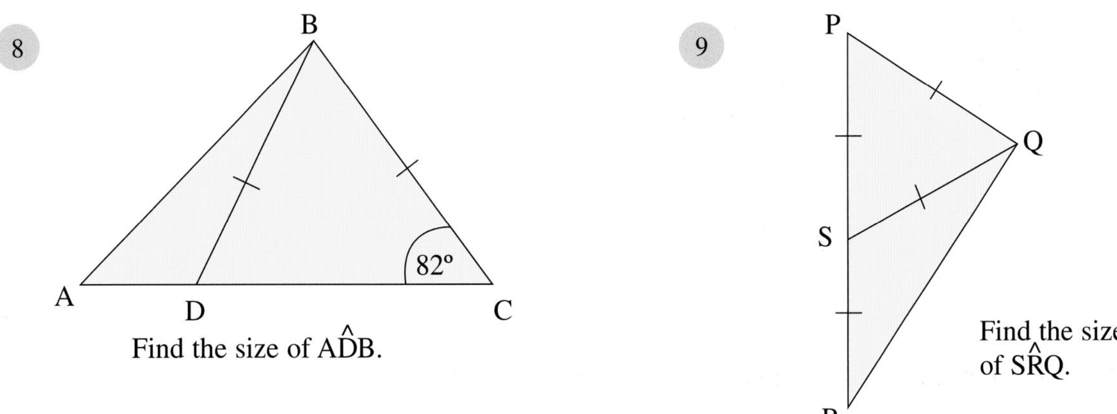

Exercise 1E

Find the angles marked with letters.

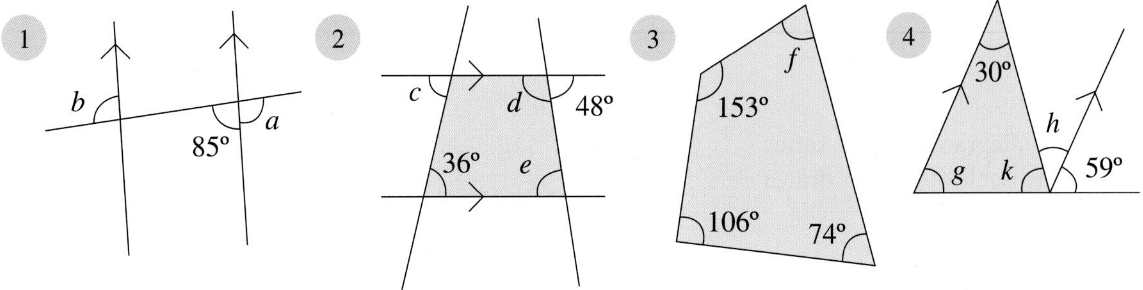

5

6

7

8

9

Find the size of $E\hat{B}F$.

10

Find the size of $Q\hat{P}S$.

11 In the diagram KL is parallel to NM and LJ = LM.
Calculate the size of angle JLM.

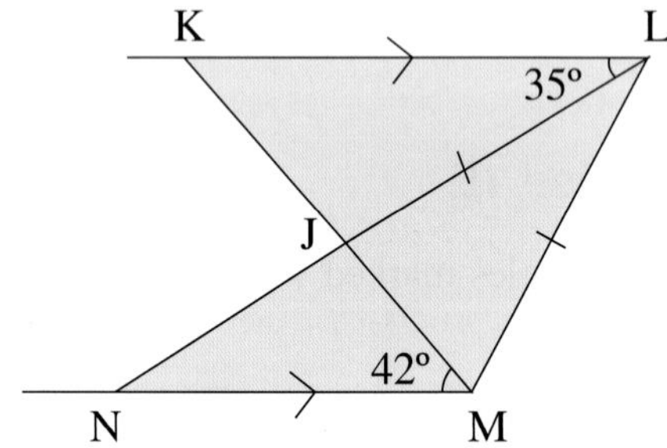

12 The diagram shows a series of isosceles triangles drawn between two lines.
Find the value of x.

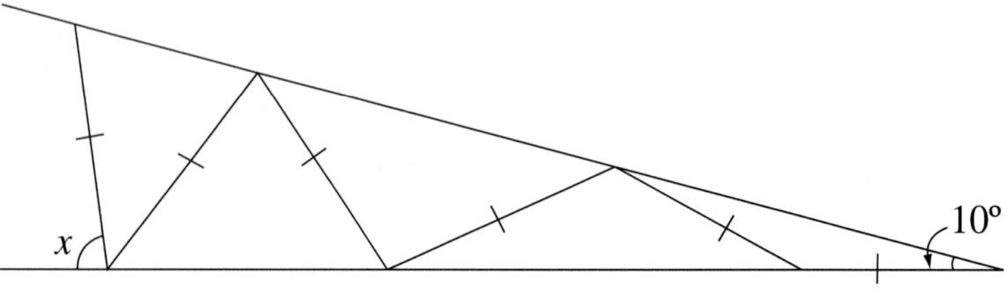

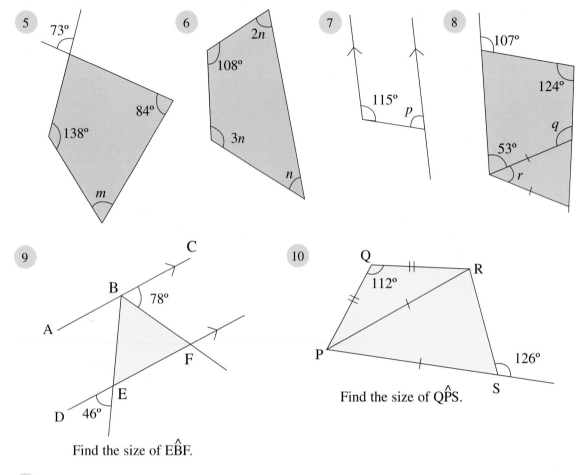

Constructing bisectors

Perpendicular bisector

Draw a line AB 8 cm long.

Set the pair of compasses to more than 4 cm (half the line AB). Put the compass point on A and draw an arc as shown.

Put the compass point on B (DO NOT LET THE COMPASSES SLIP). Draw another arc as shown.

Draw a broken line as shown.

This broken line cuts line AB in half (bisects) and is at right angles to line AB (perpendicular).

The broken line is called the perpendicular bisector of line AB.

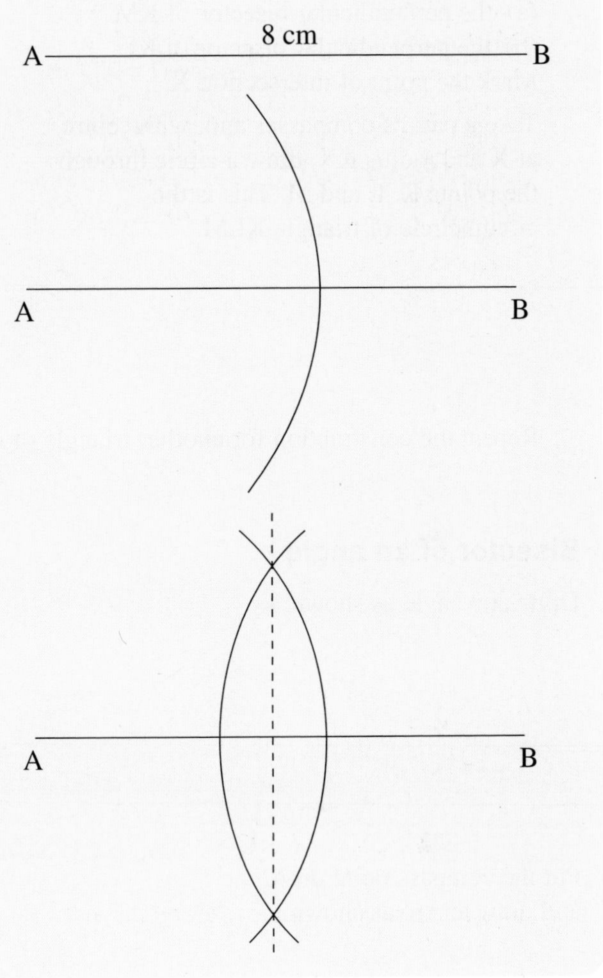

Exercise 2M

1 Draw a horizontal line AB of length 8 cm. Construct the perpendicular bisector of AB.

2 Draw a vertical line CD of length 6 cm. Construct the perpendicular bisector of CD.

3 Draw a vertical line EF of length 5 cm. Construct the perpendicular bisector of EF.

4 (a) Use a pencil, ruler and a pair of compasses only to construct the triangle ABC shown opposite.
(b) Construct the perpendicular bisector of line AB.
(c) Construct the perpendicular bisector of line AC.

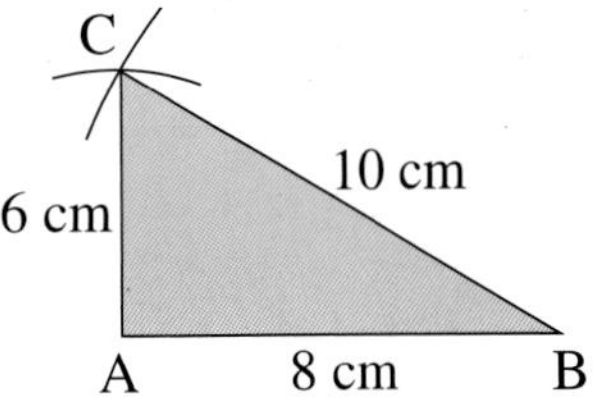

If done accurately, your two lines from (b) and (c) should cross exactly on the line BC.

5 Draw any triangle KLM and construct
(a) the perpendicular bisector of KM
(b) the perpendicular bisector of KL.
Mark the point of intersection X.

Take a pair of compasses and, with centre at X and radius KX, draw a circle through the points K, L and M. This is the circumcircle of triangle KLM.

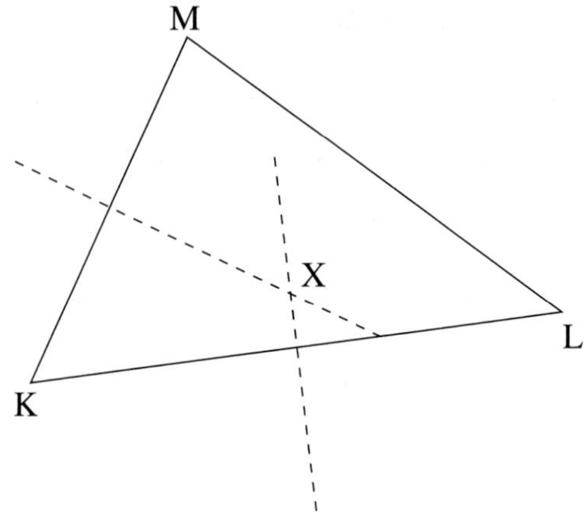

Repeat the construction for another triangle of different shape.

Bisector of an angle

Draw any angle as shown.

Put the compass point on A and draw an arc as shown.

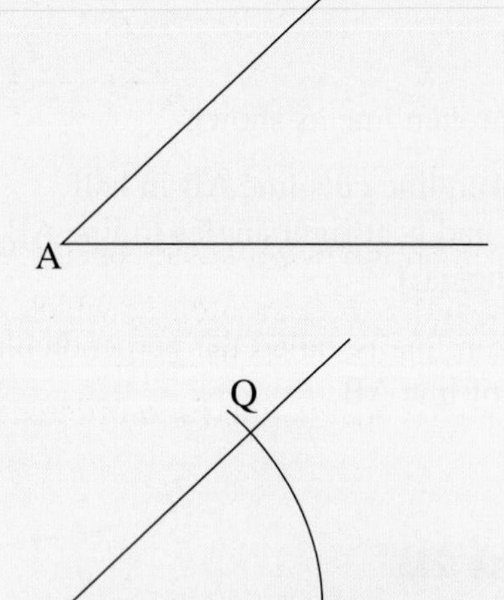

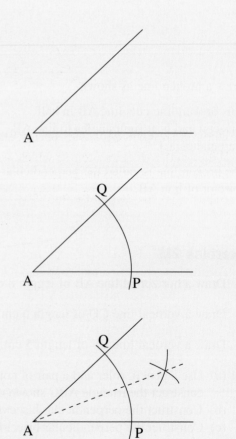

Put the compass point on P and draw an arc as shown.
Put the compass point on Q and draw an arc as shown.

Draw a broken line as shown.

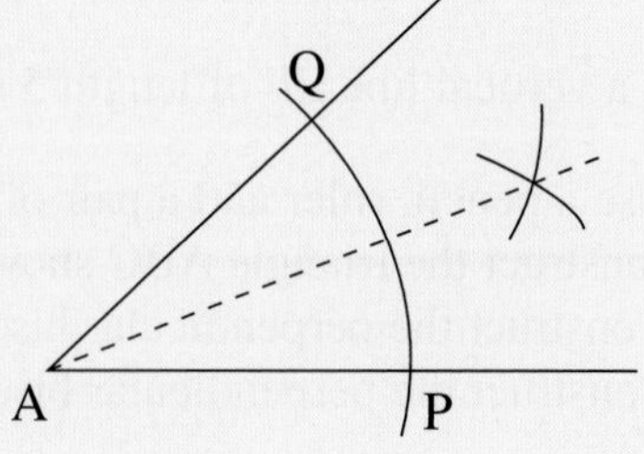

This broken line cuts the angle in half (bisects).

This broken line is called the angle bisector.

Exercise 3M

1 Draw an angle of 60°. Construct the bisector of the angle (use a protractor to measure the angles to check that you have drawn the angle bisector accurately).

2 Draw an angle of 40°. Construct the bisector of the angle.

3 Draw an angle of 130°. Construct the bisector of the angle.

4 Draw an angle of 50°. Construct the bisector of the angle.

5 Draw any triangle ABC and then construct the bisectors of angles A, B and C. If done accurately the three bisectors should all pass through one point.

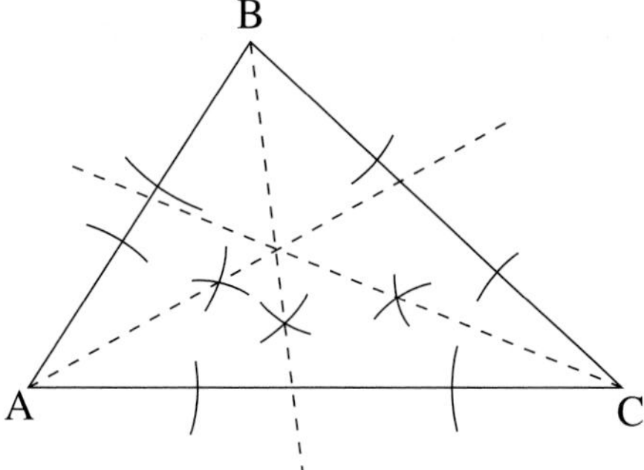

6 Draw any triangle ABC and construct the bisectors of angles B and C to meet at point Y. With centre at Y draw a circle which just touches the sides of the triangle. This is the inscribed circle of the triangle.

Repeat the construction for a different triangle.

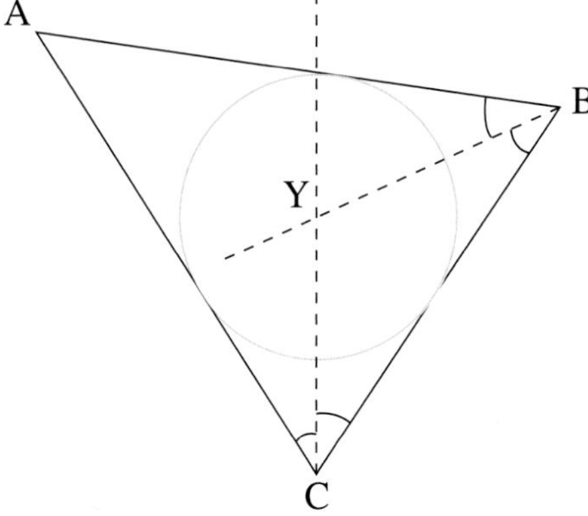

6.5 Three dimensional objects

In section 6.5 you will learn how to:

- count faces, edges and vertices
- make shapes with nets

Faces, edges and vertices

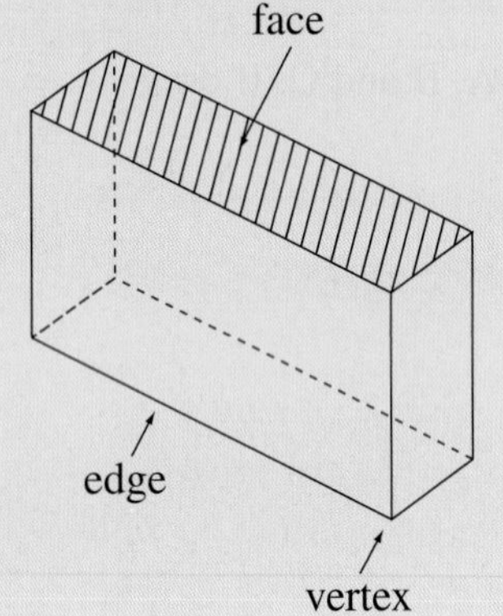

Many three-dimensional shapes have faces, edges and vertices.

'vertices' is the plural of 'vertex'.

The *faces* of the cuboid are the flat surfaces on the shape. A cuboid has 6 faces.

The *edges* of the cuboid are the lines where the faces meet. A cuboid has 12 edges.

The *vertices* are where the edges meet at a point. A cuboid has 8 vertices (corners).

Exercise 1M

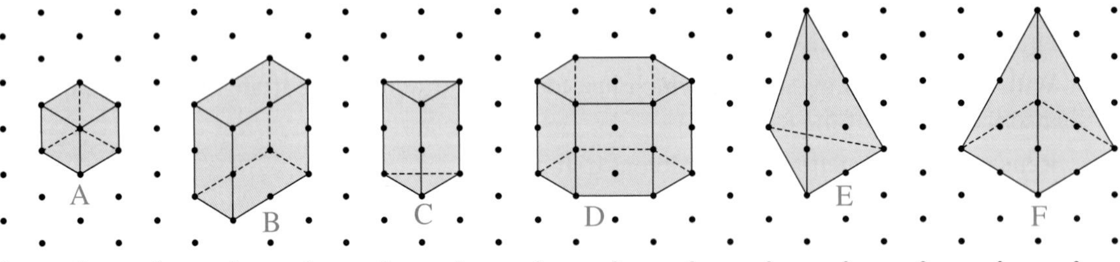

1 (a) For objects A to F, state the number of faces, edges and vertices. Write your answers in a table with columns for 'shape', 'faces', 'edges' and 'vertices'.
(b) Try to find a connection between the number of faces, edges and vertices which applies to all the objects A to F.

2 Imagine a large cube which is cut in half along the dotted lines.
Describe the two new solids formed.
How many faces, edges and vertices does each solid have?

3 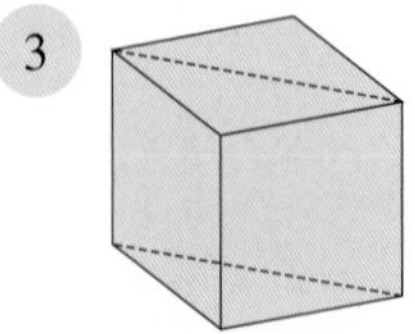

Suppose the same large cube is now cut in half along a different dotted line.
Describe the two new solids formed.
How many faces, edges and vertices does each solid have?

4 Suppose you cut off one corner from a cube. How many faces, edges and vertices has the remaining shape? How about the piece cut off?

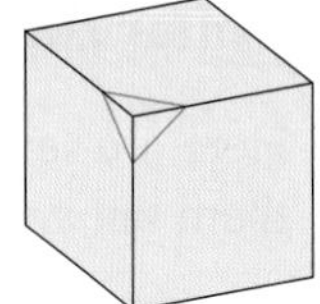

5 These diagrams show different solids when viewed from directly above. Describe what each solid could be. [There may be more than one correct response but you only have to give one.]

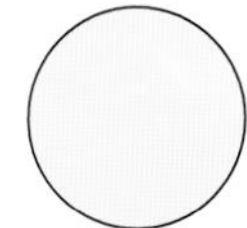
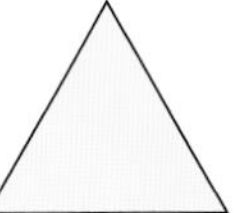
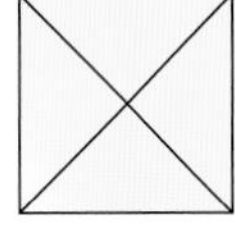
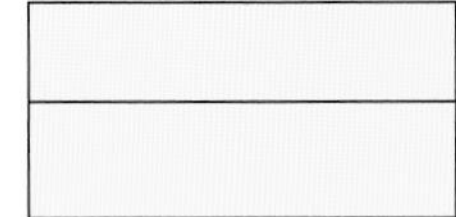

6 Describe two different ways in which you could cut a cylinder into two identical pieces. Describe and/or sketch the solids you would obtain in each case.

7 Here is an object made from four cubes.
(a) Copy the drawing on isometric paper. (Make sure you have the paper the right way round.)
(b) Make as many *different* objects as you can using four cubes. Draw each object on isometric paper.

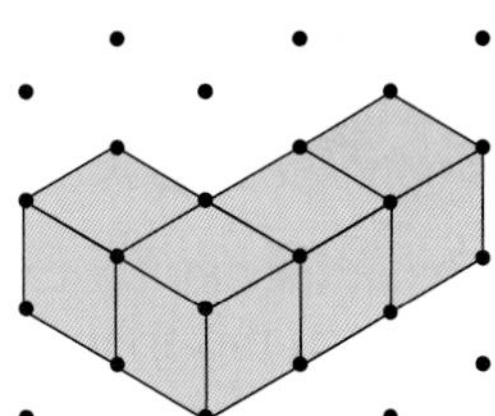

Nets for making shapes

- If the cube shown was made of cardboard, and you cut along some of the edges and laid it out flat, you would have a net of the cube. There is more than one net of a cube as you will see in the exercise below.

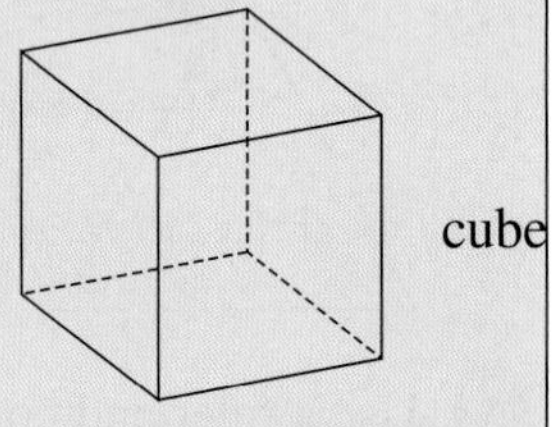

- To make a cube from card you need to produce the net shown below complete with the added 'tabs' for glueing purposes.

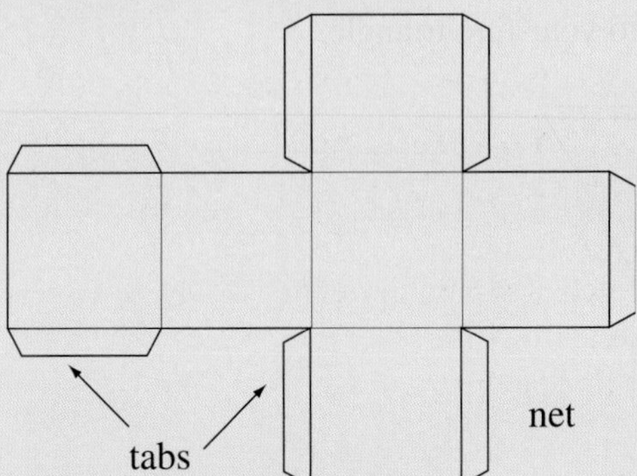

- In this section you will make several interesting 3D objects. You will need a pencil, ruler, scissors and either glue (Pritt Stick) or Sellotape.

Exercise 2M

1 Here are several nets which may or may not make cubes. Draw the nets on squared paper, cut them out and fold them to see which ones do make cubes.

(a)

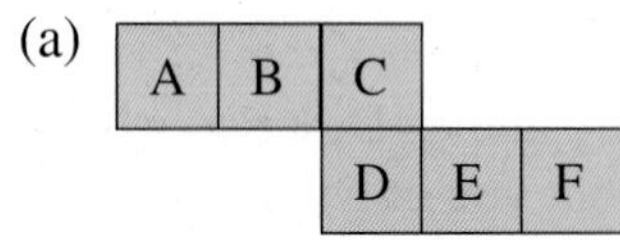

(b)

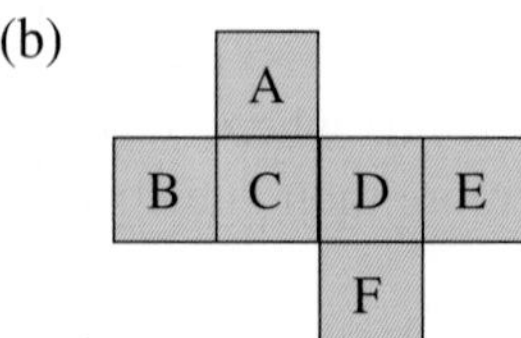

(c)

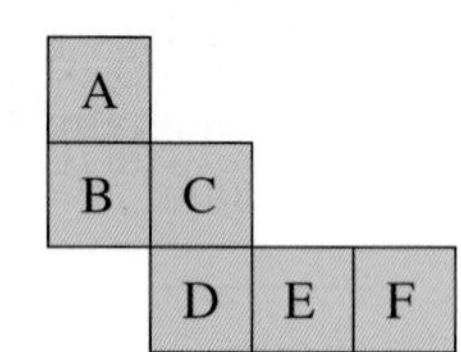

(d)

A B
C D
E F

(e)

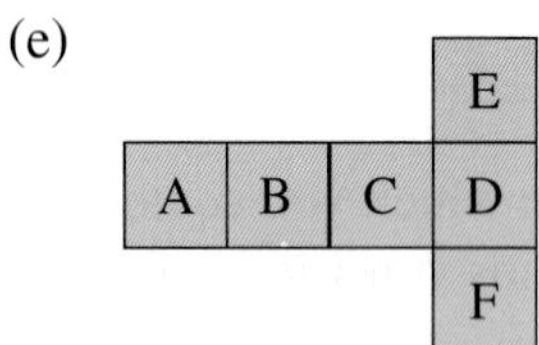

2 For the nets, which *did* make cubes in question 1, state which of the faces B, C, D, E or F was opposite face A on the cube.

3 Ask your teacher for cardboard. Use a ruler and compasses to construct this triangle in the middle of the cardboard. All lengths are in cm.

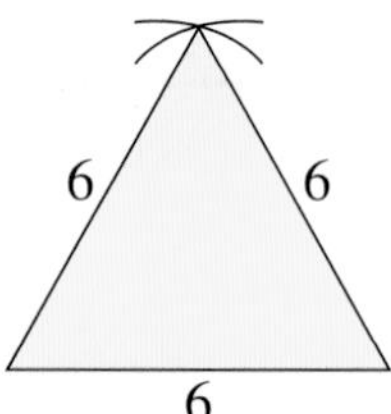

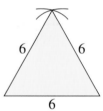

4

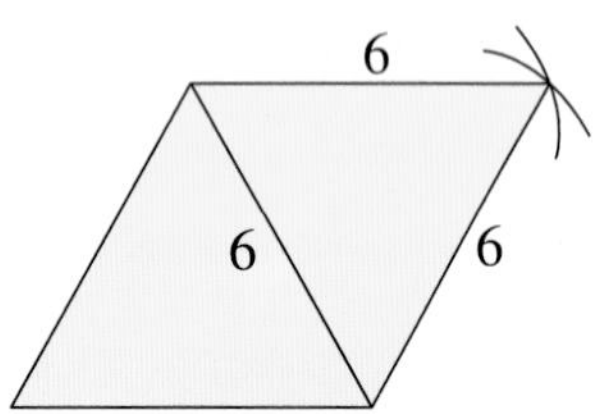

Use a ruler and compasses to construct this triangle joined to the first triangle.

5 Use a ruler and compasses to draw 2 more triangles joined to your first triangle.

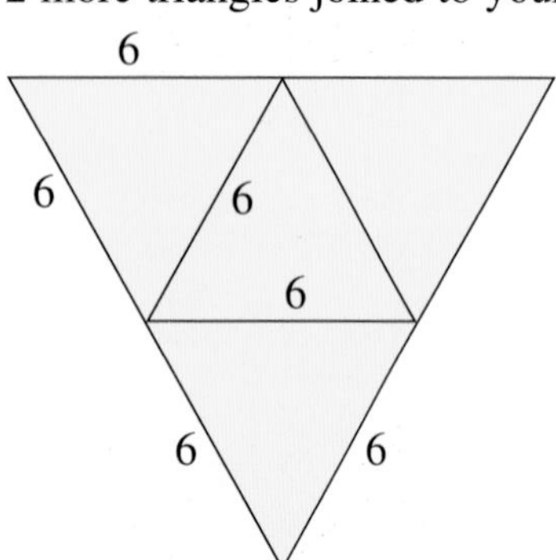

6 Draw on some flaps like this:

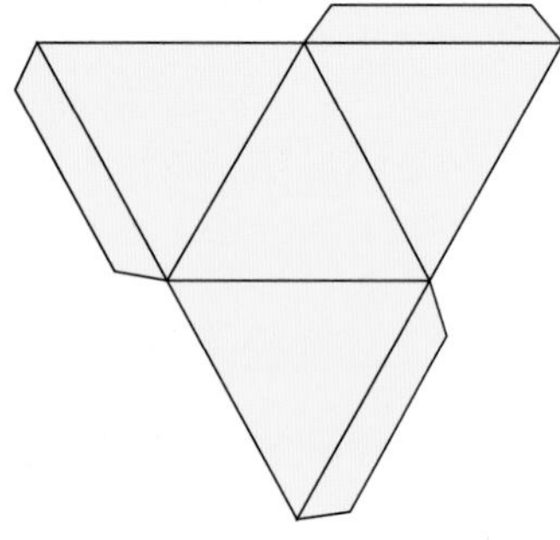

7 *Score* all the lines then cut out the net. Fold and glue to make a triangular pyramid (called a *tetrahedron*).

8 Draw accurately the nets for these three dimensional objects:

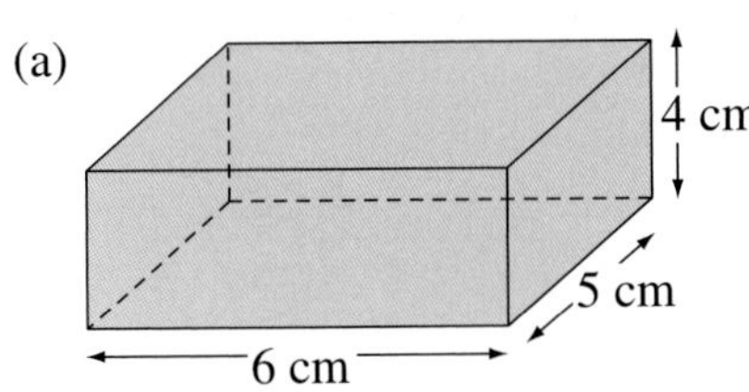

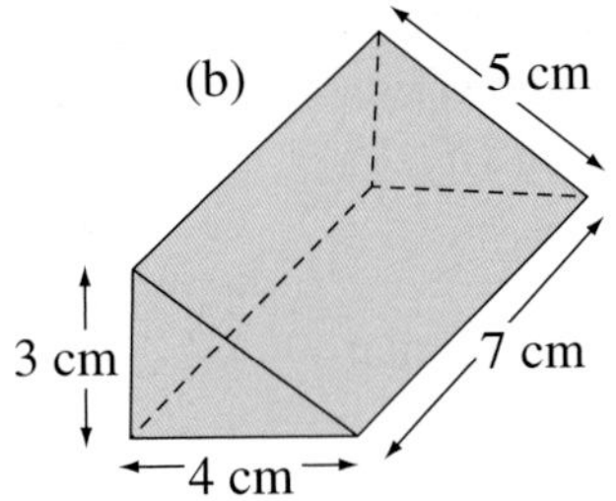

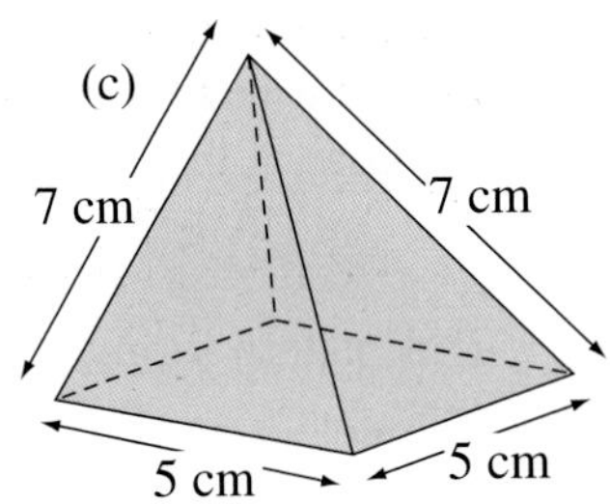

Exercise 2E

1 Use triangle dotty paper. Draw each net then make the solid shown.

(a) Octahedron (octa: eight; hedron: faces)

(b) Icosahedron (an object with 20 faces)

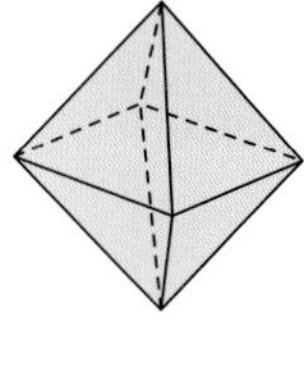
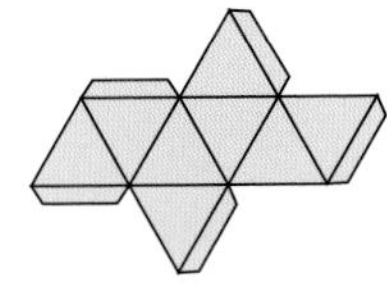
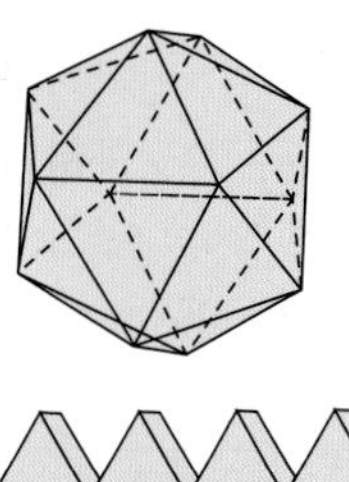
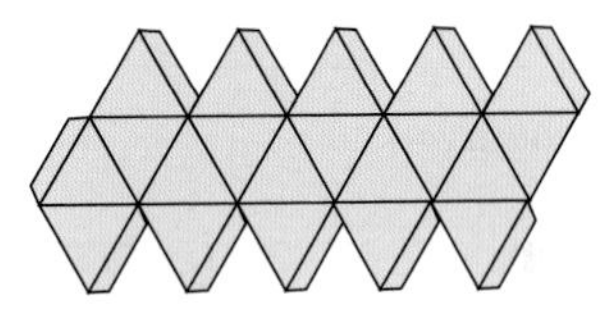

2 (More difficult) Here you are going to construct the net for a dodecahedron (12 faces). Take extra care with this one!

(a) Draw a circle of radius 10 cm and construct a large pentagon using the 72° angles as shown. Draw the lines OA, OB, OC, OD, OE very faintly because it is best to rub them out as soon as we have found the positions for A, B, C, D, E.

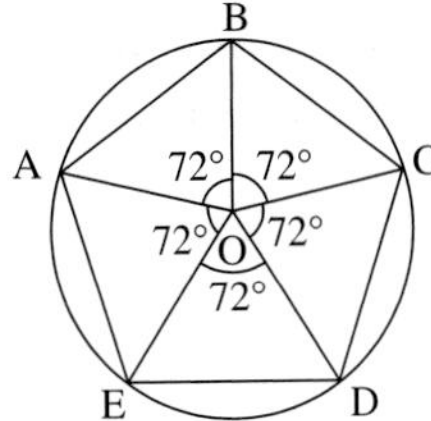

(b) Join A to C and A to D. Join B to E and B to D. Join C to E. Mark the points V, W, X, Y, Z.

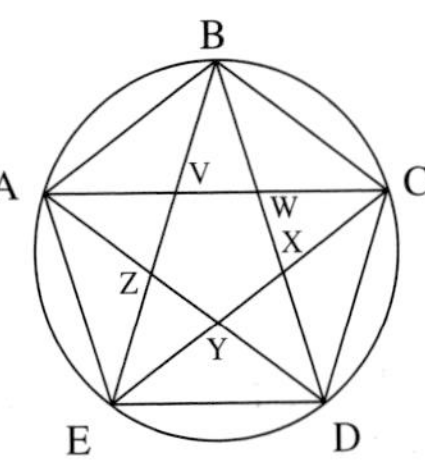

(c) Draw a line through Z and W.
Draw a line through V and X.
Draw a line through W and Y.
Draw a line through Z and X.
Draw a line through V and Y.

This pattern forms a series of regular pentagons.

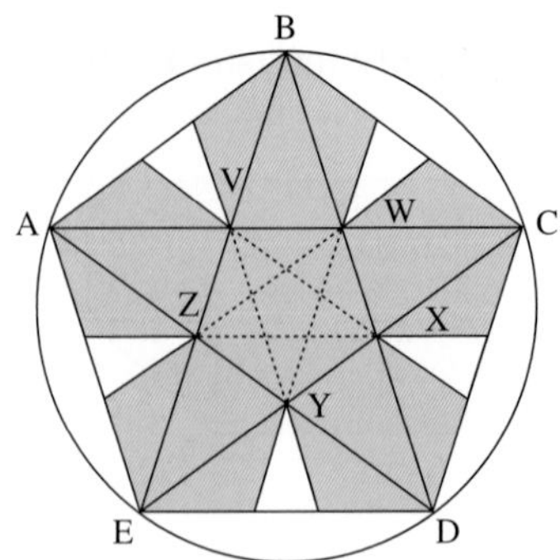

Draw the pattern of regular pentagons twice. *Remember to draw tabs before cutting out the net.* Join the two patterns of pentagons along the line PQ as shown.

net:

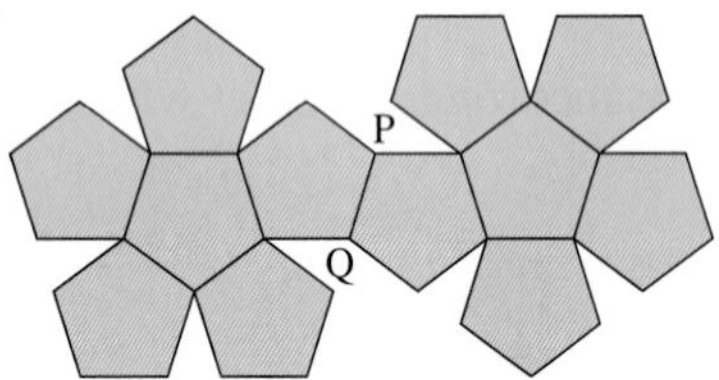

dodecahedron:

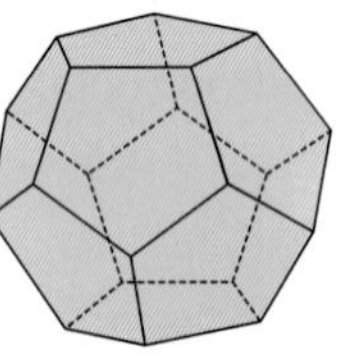

Try drawing accurately the nets shown in questions 3 and 4 if you feel up to the challenge! Draw on tabs and make the solids.

3 Cuboctahedron

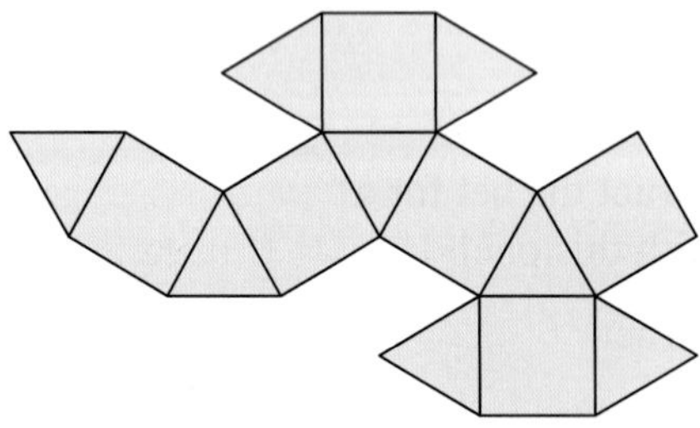

4 Truncated octahedron

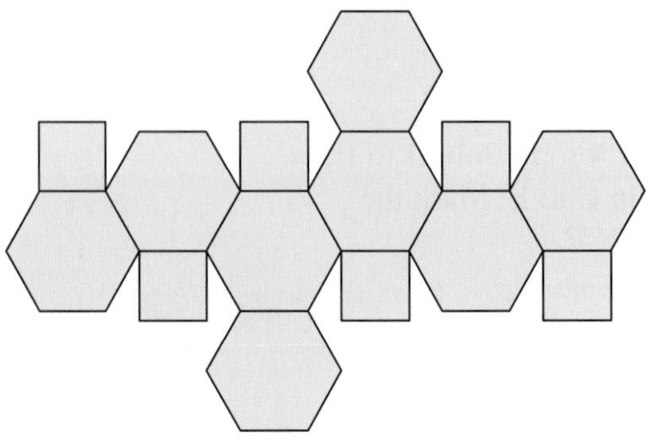

CHECK YOURSELF ON SECTIONS 6.4 and 6.5

1 Review of angle work from unit 2

Find the angles marked with letters.

(a)

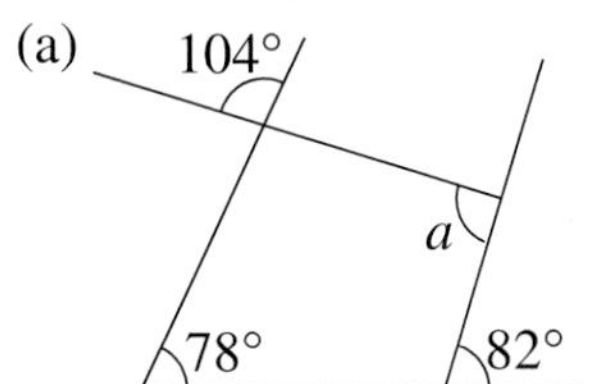

(b)

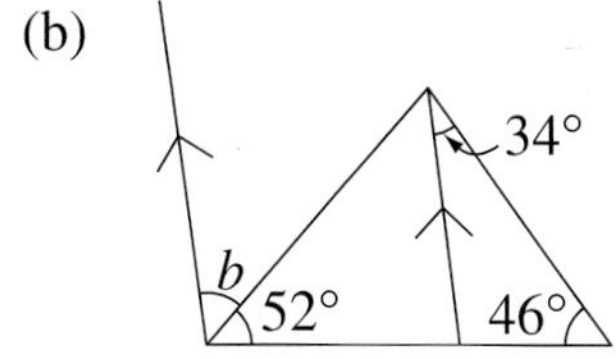

(c)

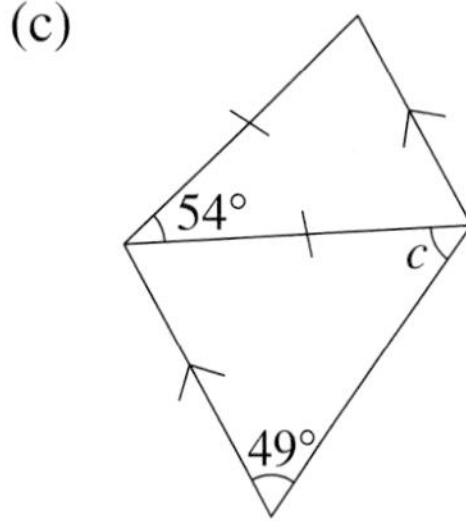

2 Constructing bisectors

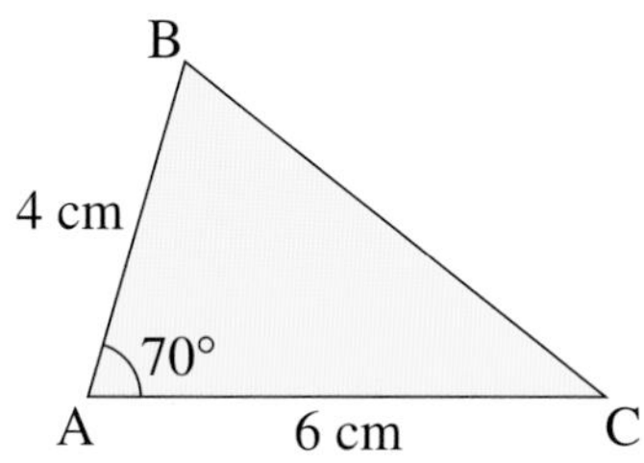

Use a ruler and protractor to draw this triangle accurately. Construct the perpendicular bisector of AC and the angle bisector of angle A. Mark with a P the point where the two bisectors meet. Measure and write down the length of AP.

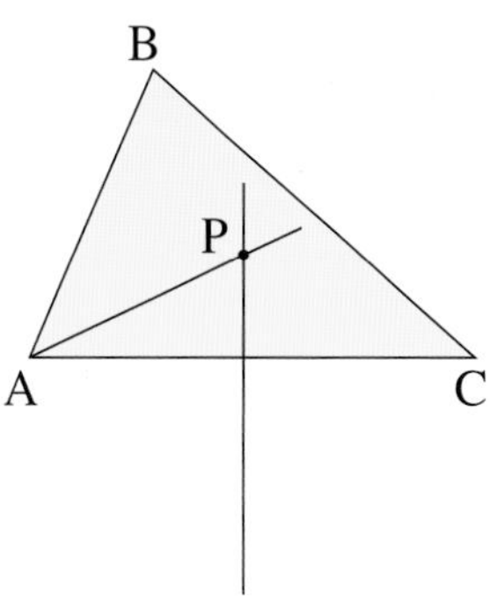

3 Counting faces, edges and vertices

For each solid below, write down how many faces, edges and vertices there are.

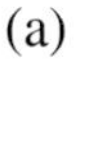

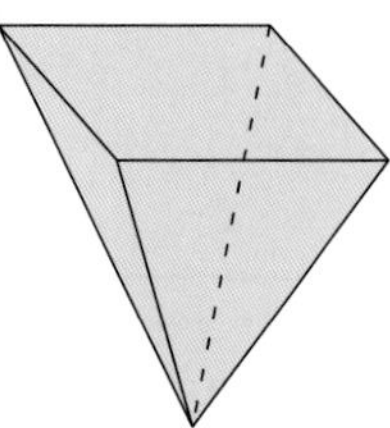

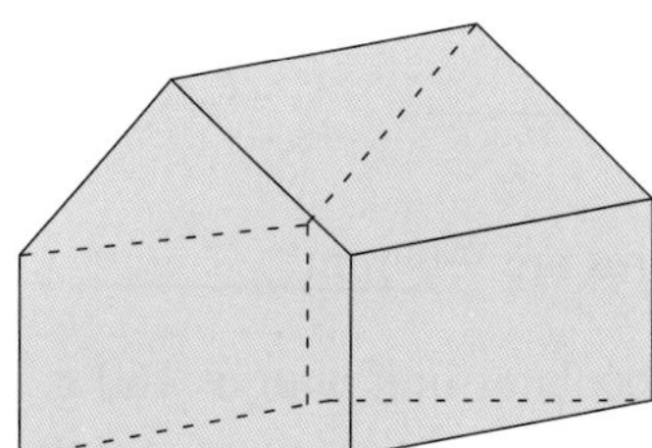

4 Making shapes with nets

(a) Draw a net for a triangular prism.

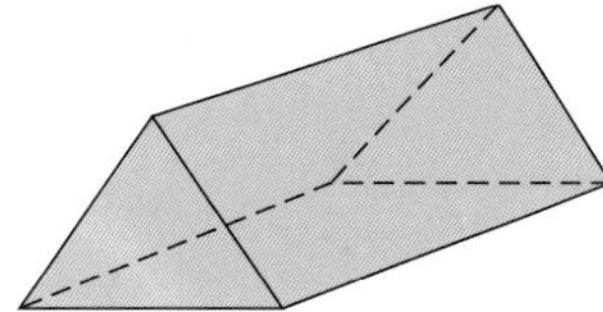

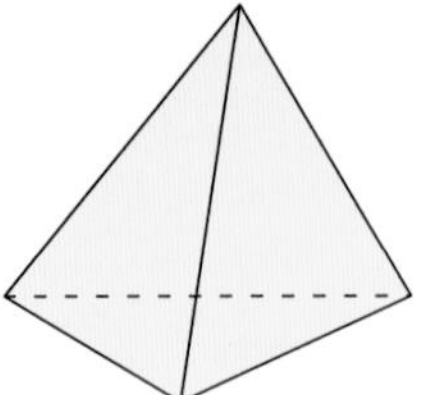

This is a tetrahedron(a triangular pyramid)

Which of these nets will make a tetrahedron?

(b) 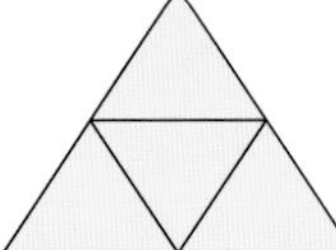

(c) 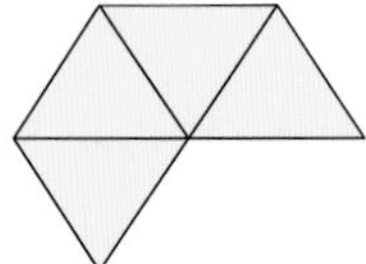

(d) 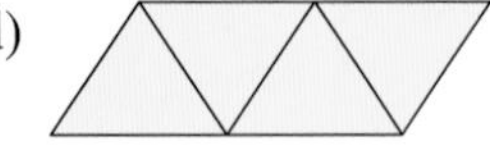

UNIT 6 MIXED REVIEW

Part one

1 What is the next number in the sequence

6, 13, 27, 55?

2 Here is the net for a cube.

(a) When the net is folded up, which edge will be stuck to the edge JI?

(b) Which edge will be stuck to the edge AB?

(c) Which corner will meet corner D?

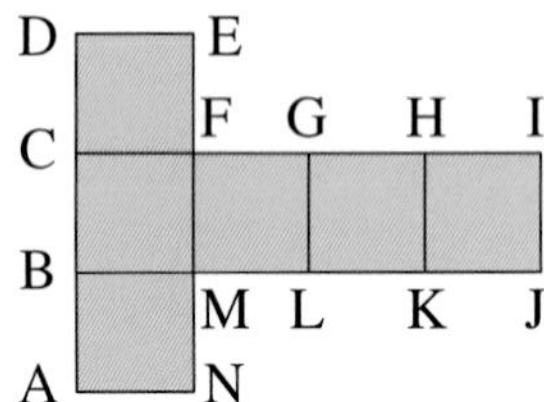

3 What is the mathematical name for a snooker ball that has been cut in half.

4 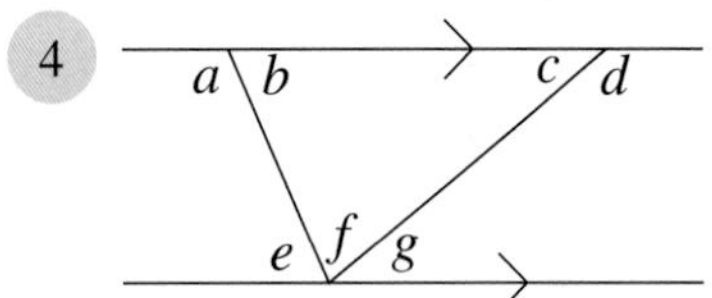

Which statement below is correct?

A $a = g$ B $b = d$

C $c = f$ D $b = e$

5 How many metres are 999 mm?

6 A jar with 8 chocolates in it weighs 160 g. The same jar with 20 chocolates in it weighs 304 g. How much does the jar weigh on its own?

7 P ——— 7 cm ——— Q Draw a line PQ of length 7 cm. *Construct* the perpendicular bisector of PQ.

8 Solve the equations.

(a) $\frac{n}{7} = 6$ (b) $6y - 3 = 45$ (c) $8x + 7 = 12$

(d) $3 = 5w - 1$ (e) $4p = \frac{1}{2}$ (f) $75 = 4a - 17$

9 Here is a sequence of diagrams showing an arrangement of counters ...

Diagram 1 Diagram 2 Diagram 3

(a) Draw diagram number 4.

(b) Copy and complete this table for the diagrams so far.

Diagram Number	Counters used
1	7
2	
3	
4	

(c) Without drawing, how many counters will be needed for diagram number 5?

(d) Write in words how you found your answer without drawing.

10 How many wine glasses of capacity 30 ml can be filled from a barrel containing 210 litres?

11

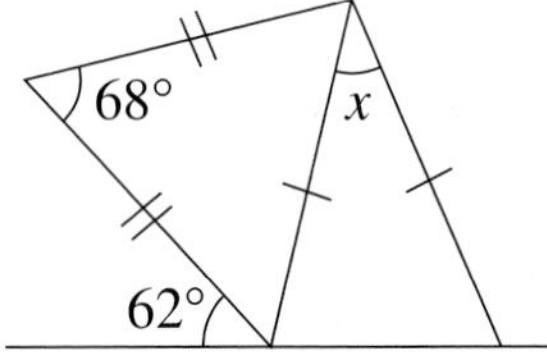

Find the size of angle x.

12 Unifix cubes can be joined together to make different sized cuboids.

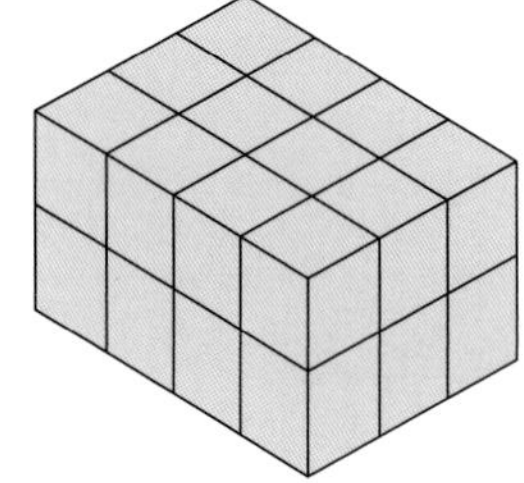

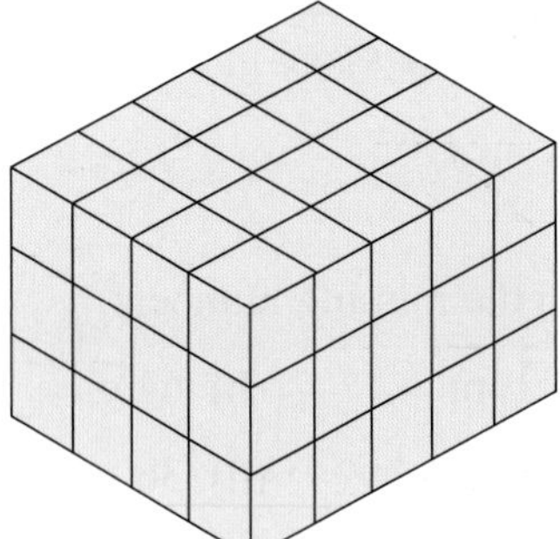

If the smaller cuboid weighs 96 g, how much does the large cuboid weigh?

13 A pile of 250 cards is 1 m deep. How thick is each card?

14 *Construct* this triangle with a ruler and compasses only. Use a protractor to measure the size of $A\hat{B}C$.

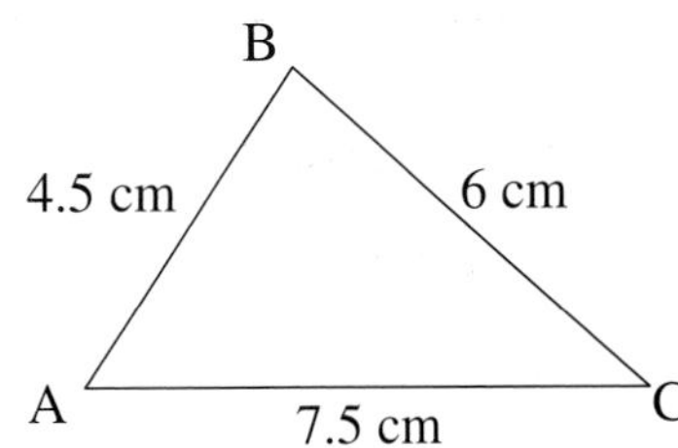

15 In a code the 25 letters from A to Y are obtained from the square using a 2 digit grid reference similar to coordinates. So letter 'U'is 42 and 'L' is 54.
The missing letter 'Z' has code 10.

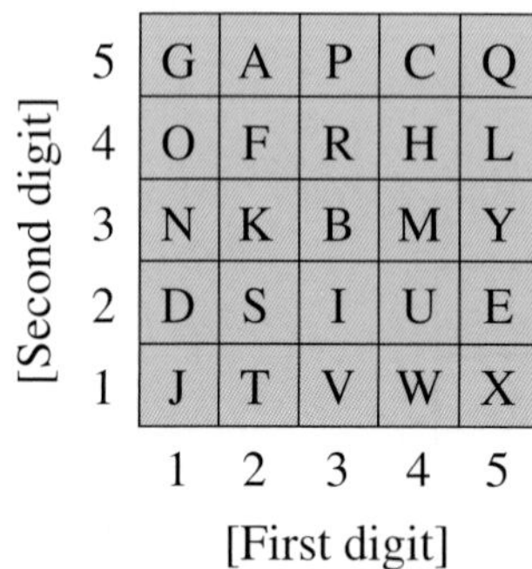

[Second digit]
5 G A P C Q
4 O F R H L
3 N K B M Y
2 D S I U E
1 J T V W X
1 2 3 4 5
[First digit]

Decode the following messages:

(a) 41, 52
13, 52, 52, 12
43, 14, 34, 52
22, 42, 43, 22

(b) 44, 25, 31, 52
25
13, 32, 45, 52
12, 25, 53

(c) 22, 35, 42, 34, 22
25, 34, 52
34, 42, 33, 33, 32, 22, 44

In part (d) each pair of brackets gives one letter

(d) $\left(\frac{1}{4} \text{ of } 140\right)$, $(7^2 + 5)$, $(7 \times 8 - 4)$, $(4^2 + 3^2)$, $\left(\frac{1}{5} \text{ of } 110\right)$, $\left(26 \div \frac{1}{2}\right)$
$(3 \times 7+1)$, $(83 - 31)$, $(2 \times 2 \times 2 \times 2 + 5)$
$(100 - 57)$, $(4^2 - 2)$, (17×2), $(151 - 99)$
$(2 \times 2 \times 2 \times 5 + 1)$, $\left(\frac{1}{4} \text{ of } 56\right)$, $(2 \times 3 \times 2 \times 3 - 2)$, $(5^2 - 2)$.

(e) Write your own message in code and ask a friend to decode it.

Part two

1 Copy and fill in the missing numbers

(a) 4.7 m = ☐ cm
(b) 63 g = ☐ kg
(c) 4 feet = ☐ inches
(d) 360 m = ☐ km
(e) 8 litres = ☐ ml
(f) 2 pounds = ☐ ounces
(g) 45 mm = ☐ cm
(h) 5 yards = ☐ feet
(i) 7.6 kg = ☐ g

2 The tenth number in the sequence 1, 4, 16, 64 ...... is 262 144.
What is (a) the ninth number,
(b) the twelfth number?

3 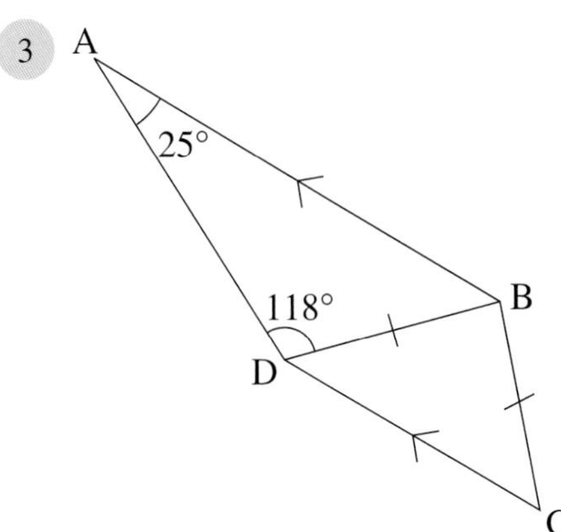

Find the size of $B\hat{C}D$.

4 A car travels 10 miles on a litre of petrol and petrol costs 98p per litre. In six months the car is driven a total of 6500 miles. Find the cost of the petrol to the nearest pound.

5 Solve the equations.
(a) $3y - 5 = 9$ (b) $4(2x + 3) = 52$ (c) $35 = 7(x - 4)$

6 These nets form cubical dice. Opposite faces of a dice always add up to 7.
Write down the value of *a*, *b*, *c*, *d*, *e*, and *f* so that opposite faces add up to 7.

		c	
a	b	1	3
		2	

2			
d	e	1	3
			f

7 A metal ingot weighing 58 kg is made into 20000 buttons. What is the weight in grams of one button?

8 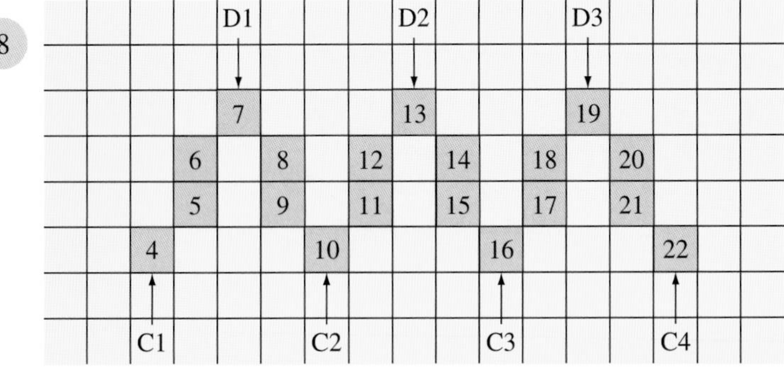

The numbers C1, C2, C3, ... and D1, D2, D3, ... form two sequences.
(a) Find C5 and D5. (b) Use a rule to find C10 and D30.

9 Lana is 5 feet 3 inches tall. Her sister Beth is 157 cm tall.
Which sister is taller and by how much?

10 (a) Use a ruler and compasses only to construct an equilateral triangle.
(b) Construct the angle bisector of one of the angles.
(c) Use a protractor to check that the angle bisector has made two angles each of 30°.

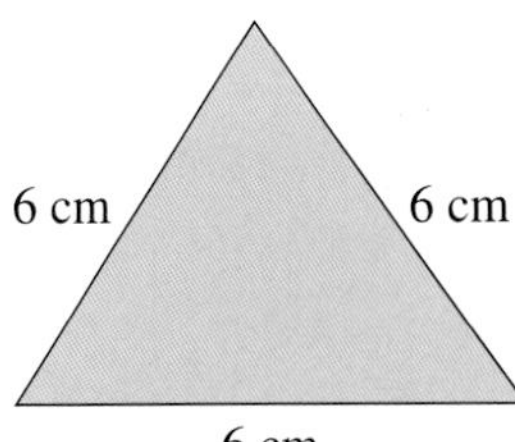

11 A book has pages numbered 1 to 300 and the thickness of the book, without the covers, is 15 mm. How thick is each page? [Hint: Most people get this question wrong!]

12 The numbers 1 to 12 are arranged on the star so that the sum of the numbers along each line is the same.

Copy and complete the star.

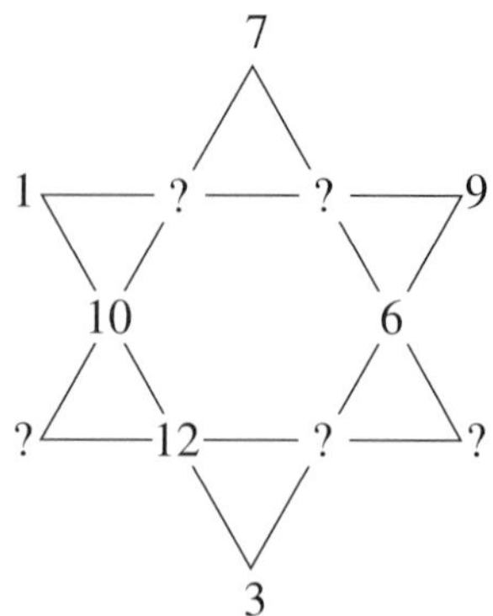

13 Don has £5 more than Annie. Janine has £41 more than Annie. Janine has three times as much money as Don. Let Annie's money be x. Write down an equation involving x then solve it to find out how much money Annie has.

14 Draw a net for a cuboid 2 cm × 3 cm × 4 cm.

15 Find the size of angle x in each of the diagrams below.

(a)

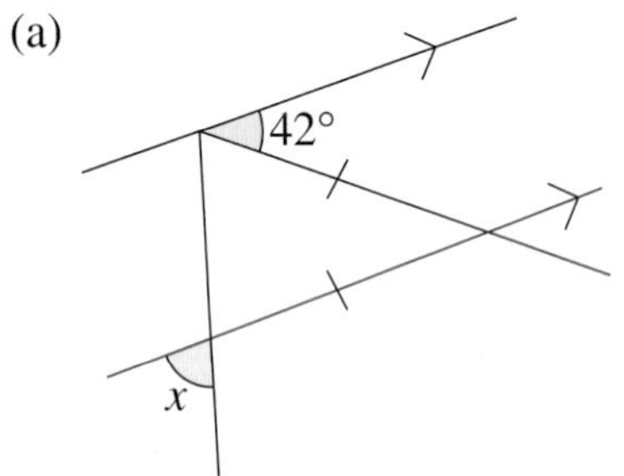

(b)

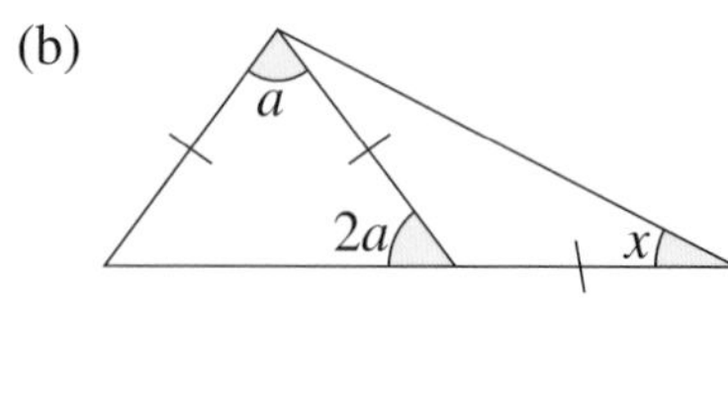

Answers to Check Yourself Sections

Page 17 Sections 1.1 and 1.2

1. (a) 6500000 (b) 406012 (c) (i) 6407 (ii) 3036 (iii) 5600

2. (a) 6457 (b) 502351 (c) 4368 (d) 13000 (e) 4688

3. (a) 354 (b) 807 (c) 56r3 (d) 348r8 (e) 439

4. (a) 62 (b) 75 **5.** (a) 1104 (b) 2331 (c) 29375

6. (a) 45 (b) 249 **7.** (a) 3306 (b) 26 each, 2 left over

Page 44 Sections 1.3 and 1.4

1. (a) (i) 0.0065, 0.007, 0.08, 0.081

(ii) 0.022, 0.2, 0.202, 0.221

(b) (i) 7.172 (ii) 3.7182 (iii) 0.603

2. (a) 1.642 (b) 51.8 (c) 0.91 (d) 0.322

3. (a) 22.68 (b) 3.54 (c) 0.2 (d) 0.16 (e) 0.0401

4. (a) 2 (b) 19 (c) 7

(d) 120 (e) 3 (f) 45

5. (a) 89.7 (b) 0.808 (c) 6.05 (d) 3.6

6. (a) 11.05 (b) 13.5 (c) 5.44 (d) 3.95

Page 61 Section 1.6

1. (a) 62 cm (b) 7 m

2. (a) 92 cm^2 (b) 153 m^2 (c) 248 cm^2 (d) 7 m

3. (a) 84 cm^2 (b) 115 cm^2 (c) 12 cm (d) $10\frac{1}{2}$ u^2

Page 80 Section 2.1

1. (a) 9 (b) 8.5 (c) 8

2. 37 **3.** Warriors : mean = 23.8, range = 14

Sabers : mean = 22.7, range = 12

4. (a) 3 (b) 2.6125

Page 95 Sections 2.2 and 2.3

1. (a) 7 (b) 36 (c) 3 (d) $\frac{49}{36}$, $\frac{63}{72}$

2. (a) 20 (b) 42 (c) 49

3. (a) $\frac{29}{35}$ (b) $\frac{1}{12}$ (c) $2\frac{13}{40}$ (d) $3\frac{11}{12}$

4. $\frac{1}{20}$, 0.05, 5%; $\frac{9}{20}$, 0.45, 45%; $\frac{3}{4}$, 0.75, 75%; $\frac{2}{5}$, 0.4, 40%

Page 107 Section 2.4

1. (a) 85° (b) 30° (c) 100°

2. (a) 62° (b) 115°

3. (a) 65° (b) 125° (c) $X\hat{W}Y$ = 100°, $V\hat{W}X$ = 80°

4. (a) 28° (b) 102° (c) 121°

5. (a) $B\hat{E}F$ = 78°, $F\hat{E}H$ = 102° (b) 61°

6. (a) 103° (b) 85°

Page 122 Section 2.5

1. (a) $n - 6$ (b) $5x - 8$ (c) $2w + 24$

2. (a) $2m + 9n$ (b) $7y$ (c) $4p + 6$ (d) $4xy + 4y$

3. (a) $28mn$ (b) $32pqr$ (c) C and D

4. (a) 345 (b) 6 (c) 3

5. (a) 8 (b) square = 12, circle = 3

Page 158 Sections 3.1, 3.2, 3.3 and 3.4

1. (a) (5,3) (b) (7,5) (c) (4,3)

2. (a) 945 (b) 17658 (c) 45 (d) 11

3. (a) 12.24, 13, 2.6 (b) £11.75 (c) 7 cm

4. (a) (i) 3, 31 (ii) 3, 51 (iii) 4, 8

(b) 3 + 97, 11 + 89 (+ others)

5. (a) 24 (b) 15 (c) 108

(d) (i) 9 (ii) 189 (iii) 10 (e) 3, 4, 5

Page 187 Sections 3.5, 3.6 and 3.7

1. (a) (1,4) (b) $x = 1$ (c) $y = 2$ (d) (3,3)

2. (a) $y = x–2$ (b) (i) $y = x + 3$

(ii) $y = 2x$ (c) P,R (d) 1, 3, 5

3. (b) AB no rain, no use; BC rainfall; CD no use; DE water used; EF no use; FG rainfall; GH no use

4. (a) 175 (b) 300 (c) 200

5. (a) (i) $\frac{1}{4}$ (ii) $\frac{5}{8}$ (iii) $\frac{3}{8}$ (iv) $\frac{1}{3}$

(b) (i) $\frac{1}{52}$ (ii) $\frac{1}{13}$ (iii) $\frac{1}{2}$

6. (a) white (b) (i) $\frac{7}{11}$ (ii) $\frac{3}{11}$ (iii) 0 (iv) $\frac{1}{11}$

Page 215 Sections 4.1 and 4.2

1. (a) 70° (b) 40° **2.** (a) 41°→43° (b) 48°→50°

3. (a) trapezium (b) square (c) rhombus (d) kite

(e) parallelogram (f) parallelogram with four equal sides

4. (a) P and R (b) 10 (c) regular octagon

5. (a) 2 (b) 1 (c) diagonals are not correct

Page 230 Sections 4.3 and 4.4

1. (a) $\frac{2}{25}$, 8% (b) 0.8, 80% (c) $\frac{9}{10}$, 90%

(d) $\frac{8}{25}$, 0.32 (e) 0.72, 72%

2. (a) 40% (b) maths(70.6%)

3. (a) £18 (b) £285 (c) £96 (d) £0.72

4. (a) $\frac{13}{22}$ (b) £61.32

5. (a) 3:8 (b) 9 (c) £80

Page 246 Sections 4.5 and 4.6

1. (a) –4 (b) –7 (c) –3 (d) –2

2. (a) –15 (b) 8 (c) –3 (d) 32

3. (a) $4m$ (b) $2ab + a$ (c) 6
(d) $15mn$ (e) 28 (f) 4

4. (a) 10 (b) 30 (c) $3\frac{1}{2}$ (d) $\frac{1}{5}$

5. (a) $5x + 35$ (b) $np - 3n$ (c) $x^2 + 8x$
(d) $18x + 12$ (e) $11x + 27$

Page 267 Units 5.1, 5.2 and 5.3

2. (a) 2 (b) 6 (c) 3 (d) 2

(e) 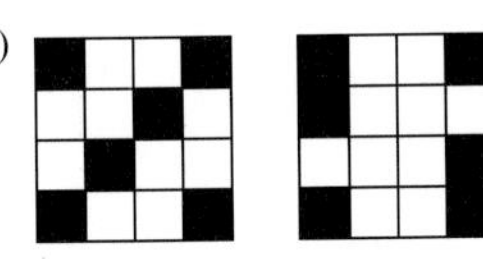

3. 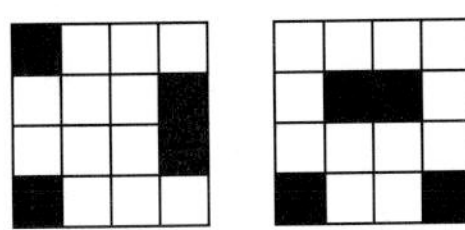

5. (b) (i) 3 units right and 2 units up
(ii) 2 units left and 1 unit up (iii) 4 units up

Page 289 Units 5.5 and 5.6

1. (a) (i) $\frac{3}{7}$ (ii) $\frac{2}{7}$ (b) $\frac{3}{7}$

2. (a) 15°C (b) October (c) April and November
(d) April, May (e) 21°C

3. (a) 37.5 miles (b) 32 km **4.** 12.30

Page 302 Units 5.7 and 5.8

1. (a) (i) 560 (ii) 2050 (iii) 70
(b) (i) 5.7 (ii) 9.2 (iii) 0.8 (iv) 5.4

2. (a) 150 (b) 40 (c) 10 (d) £60

3. (a) (i) 18.8 cm (ii) 13.2 m (iii) 28.3 cm
(b) (i) 28.3 cm^2 (ii) 13.9 m^2 (iii) 63.6 cm^2

Page 321 Sections 6.1 and 6.2

1. (a) 9 (b) 56 (c) $\frac{5}{7}$ (d) $\frac{5}{6}$ (e) 9 (f) 6

2. (b) 12, 14 (c) 'two times', 'then add six'
(d) $g = 2b + 6$ (e) 43

Page 327 Section 6.3

1. (a) 7650 m (b) 40 cm (c) 7.5 litres

2. (a) 8 ounces (b) 22 pints (c) 6 feet

3. (a) 5 cm (b) £1.06

4. (a) P is larger by 300 cm^2 (b) 0.125 mm

Page 339 Sections 6.4 and 6.5

1. (a) 108° (b) 48° (c) 68° **2.** AP $\approx$ 5.2 cm

3. (a) 5 faces, 8 edges, 5 vertices
(b) 7 faces, 15 edges, 10 vertices

4. (b) and (d) make a tetrahedron

INDEX